ELECTROCHEMICAL INTERFACES:

MODERN TECHNIQUES FOR IN-SITU INTERFACE CHARACTERIZATION

Edited by:

Héctor D. Abruña

Department of Chemistry
Cornel University
Ithaca, New York

.4311589

Héctor D. Abruña
Department of Chemistry
Baker Laboratory
Cornell University
Ithaca, New York
14853-1301

Library of Congress Cataloging-in-Publication Data

Abruna, Hector D.
  Electrochemical interfaces: modern techniques for in-situ interface characterization/ edited by Hector D. Abruna
      p.   cm.
  Includes bibliographical references and index
  ISBN 0-89573-715-9
  1. Electrochemistry. 2. Surface chemistry I. Abruna, Hector D.
QD553.E33   1991
541.3'7–dc20   91-18599

British Library Cataloguing in Publication Data

Electrochemical interfaces.
  1. Electrochemistry
  I. Abruna, Hector
  530.417
ISBN   0-89573-715-9

ISBN   0-89573-715-9 VCH Publishers
ISBN   3-527-27840-0 VCH Verlagsgesellschaft

Printing History:
10   9   8   7   6   5   4   3   2   1

Published jointly by:

VCH Publishers, Inc.	VCH Verlagsgesselschaft mbH	VCH Publishers (UK) Ltd.
220 East 23rd Street	P.O. Box 10 11 61	8 Wellington Court
Suite 909	D-6940 Weinheim	Cambridge CB1 1HW
New York, New York 10010	Federal Republic of Germany	United Kingdom

TABLE OF CONTENTS

Héctor D. Abruña
Department of Chemistry
Baker Laboratory
Cornell University
Ithaca, N.Y. 14853-1301

Chapter 2:   Surface X-Ray Scattering

Michael F. Toney and Owen R. Melroy
IBM Research Division
Almaden Research Center
San Jose, CA 95120-6099

Chapter 3: Elucidation of Structural Aspects of Electrode/Electrolyte Interfaes with X-Ray Standing Waves

James H. White
Department of Chemistry
Baker Laboratory
Cornell University
Ithaca, N.Y. 14853-1301

Chapter 4:   Measurement of Surface Forces

Christopher P. Smith, Shelly R. Snyder, and
Henry S. White
Department of Chemical Engineering and Materials Science
University of Minnesota
Minneapolis, MN 55455

Chapter 5:   Surface Enhanced Raman Scattering

Jeanne E. Pemberton
Department of Chemistry
University of Arizona
Tucson, AZ 85721-0001

**Chapter 6:   Investigations of Electrochemical Interfaces by
Nonlinear Optical Methods**

Geraldine L. Richmond
Department of Chemistry
University of Oregon
Eugene, OR 97403-1253

Chapter 7:　Infrared Spectroelectrochemistry: A Probe of the Molecular Architecture of the Electrochemical Interface

Scott M. Stole, Darwin D. Popenoe, and
Marc D. Porter
Ames Laboratory - USDOE and Department of Chemistry
Iowa State University
Ames, Iowa 50011-3020

Chapter 8:   Mossbauer Spectroscopy

Daniel A. Scherson
Case Center for Electrochemical Sciences
and The Department of Chemistry
Case Western Reserve University
Cleveland, OH 44106

Chapter 9: Radioactive Labeling: Toward Characterization of Well-Defined Electrodes

Piotr Zelenay
Department of Chemistry
Warsaw University
02-089 Warsaw, Poland

Andrzej Wieckowski
Department of Chemistry
University of Illinois
Urbana, IL 61801

Chapter 10: The Quartz Crystal Microbalance as an In Situ Tool in Electrochemistry

Daniel A. Buttry
Department of Chemistry
University of Wyoming
Laramie, WY 82071-3838

INTRODUCTION

The in situ study of the electrode/solution interface (or more generally the solid/liquid interface) represents a problem of great relevance to electrochemistry and other interfacial disciplines. These studies, however, had, until recently, proved very elusive to direct experimental interrogation.

Traditionally, electrochemists have relied on the measurement of potential, current, and charge, which provides links to thermodynamic parameters, rate, and extent of reaction. These traditional techniques, although exquisitely sensitive, have severe limitations with regards to atomic and molecular specificity and structure. It is these measurements, however, coupled with theoretical models, that account for a large fraction of our electrochemical data base. The use of other techniques is crucial if we are to understand the thermodynamic structural, mechanistic, and dynamic aspects of these interfacial reactions.

In the recent past, there has been an emergence of new technologies applicable to the in situ study of electrochemical interfaces. These include the scanning tunneling microscope, surface EXAFS (extended X-ray absorption fine structure), surface diffraction, second harmonic generation, the quartz crystal microbalance, and others. In addition, developments in traditional techniques such as infrared, Raman (Surface Enhanced Raman Spectroscopy: SERS) and Mossbauer spectroscopy, and others have made them amenable to the study of electrochemical interfaces. It is clear that the application of these and other techniques to the study of electrochemical interfaces will result in a more detailed understanding and control of interfacial reactivity.

The scientific and economic importance of such studies have been recently underscored by two reports from the National Materials Advisory

Board entitled *New Horizons in Electrochemical Science and Technology* (NMAB 438-1) and *In Situ Characterization of Electrochemical Processes* (NMAB 438-3).

The intent of this volume is to provide an up-to-date account of various techniques available for the in situ study of electrochemical interfaces or solid/liquid interfaces in general. The purpose is not to provide an exhaustive sampling of techniques, but rather to focus on emerging new technologies and novel advances in more established techniques.

The book is written with a general audience in mind, including individuals involved in the broad areas of surface chemistry, surface physics, chemical engineering, and materials science.

Each chapter is designed to provide sufficient background material so that the nonspecialist and the specialist alike will be able to follow the presentation. Specific examples are discussed in some detail so as to highlight both advantages and shortcomings of a particular technique.

All of the contributors to this volume were deliberately chosen to be active young researchers. I felt that they would best convey both the flavor and excitement of a particular field, and I believe that they have all succeeded.

The first three chapters deal with the use of X rays as a tool for probing interfacial structure in electrochemical systems. Because of their short wavelength and significant penetration, X rays represent unique tools with which to probe electrochemical interfacial structure in situ. Although the principles of X-ray absorption spectroscopy, X-ray standing waves, and X-ray diffraction have been known for quite some time, only in the very recent past have they been applied to electrochemical systems, and this has been due to the development of synchrotron sources that provide high intensity X rays.

In the first chapter, entitled "X-ray Absorption Spectroscopy in the Study of Electrochemical Interfaces," I begin with a brief description of X rays, with emphasis on synchrotron radiation sources. This is followed by a detailed description of X-ray absorption spectroscopy, with emphasis on EXAFS (extended X-ray absorption fine structure) spectroscopy and how it can be employed in the study of electrochemical systems. After a description of data analysis and experimental problems, I discuss some of the areas of electrochemical interest to which surface EXAFS has been applied. These include corrosion and oxide films, batteries and fuel cells, underpotentially deposited monolayers, spectroelectrochemistry, and adsorption. Of particular note is the development of dispersive arrangements which can provide access to time-resolved studies, at least in the millisecond time regime.

Drs. M. Toney and O. Melroy discuss surface X-ray scattering and its applicability to the study of electrochemical systems. They begin with a description of diffraction in three dimensions and use this as a point of departure for describing scattering from surfaces, these being either an isolated monolayer or a truncated lattice. The derivations in the appendix are especially well presented and give an in-depth analysis of the theory. This is followed by a very comprehensive discussion of the various parameters that need to be addressed, with emphasis on scattering geometry and signal to noise ratio considerations. They then discuss, in great detail, some of their work on underpotentially deposited metal monolayers. These studies are not only exquisitely done, but in addition, serve as very illustrative examples. Because of the general familiarity of X-ray diffraction (although not at surfaces), I believe that this area will see a very rapid growth in the near future.

In the third chapter, Dr. James White discusses the use of X-ray standing waves (XSW) in the study of electrochemical systems. This technique is a relative newcomer to the field, and as a result, only a limited number of systems have been studied. However, it is an extremely powerful tool, particularly with regard to the study of potential dependent distributional charges of species within the diffuse double layer, since the probing depth can be as large as 1,000Å. Dr. White begins with a brief description of the basic theoretical aspects of XSW. The main point is that its description requires a dynamical rather than a kinematic treatment and is thus a bit more involved. This is followed by a description of data analysis and experimental aspects. He then discusses, in depth, the various reported studies of electrochemical systems employing the XSW technique. In addition to the conventional (near grazing incidence) geometry, a back reflection geometry may allow for the use of single crystals and for the precise study of the compact double layer.

Professor H. White discusses the use of the surface forces apparatus for electrochemical studies. This instrument is unique in that it allows the experimenter to bring two surfaces from distances as far as a few microns to as close as a few angstroms and measure the forces between them. In addition, if the surfaces are electrodes (typically metal films on mica), one can measure forces between electrodes at very close distances as a function of electrode potential. Dr. White discusses the use of this instrument in the measurement of surface forces in general and then describes possible electrochemical applications. Of particular interest is the study of electrochemical reactions as a function of distance and applied potential. Rather dramatic effects can arise due to the interpenetration of the double layers.

It should be mentioned that the surface forces apparatus is a close relative of the scanning tunneling microscope (STM). Although of very recent vintage, it has been used in the study of electrochemical interfaces, and this area has been very recently reviewed by Sonnenfeld, Schneir, and Hansma (*Modern Aspects of Electrochemistry,* vol. 21).

The discussion of spectroscopic techniques begins with Professor G. Pemberton's up-to-date account of the use of surface enhanced Raman scattering in electrochemical systems. Since its discovery about 15 years ago, SERS has been the subject of numerous studies. Professor Pemberton begins with a description of the fundamental aspects of SERS, with emphasis on the discussion of the enhancement mechanisms, particularly electromagnetic and chemical. This is followed by a description of experimental aspects, which in turn is followed by an extensive discussion of a number of studies geared to a better understanding of the technique itself as well as to exploiting its great power and versatility.

Although chronologically young, the SERS technique is relatively well established, and this is due, at least in part, to the great excitement that its discovery generated. However, I am certain that new and more elaborate studies will continue to appear.

The use of nonlinear optics in electrochemical systems is also of relatively recent vintage. Of these, second harmonic generation is especially well suited to in situ electrochemical studies because of its inherent sensitivity to surfaces (due to loss of inversion symmetry). The use of second harmonic generation is described by Professor G. Richmond. She begins with a description of the basic phenomena, with emphasis on the origin of second harmonic generation and nonlinear susceptibility tensors. This is followed by a description of the experimental aspects.

She then discusses a variety of studies, with emphasis on her own work. Of particular relevance have been the measurement of the point of zero charge of electrodes by following the potential dependent change in the second harmonic intensity as well as the study of underpotentially deposited metal monolayers. In addition, by making use of selection rules, polarization dependencies, and rotational symmetry, she has been able to follow the reconstruction of electrochemically roughened surfaces. These studies should provide a wealth of information on the thermodynamics and kinetics of roughening, reconstruction, and annealing of electrochemical surfaces.

Analogous to SERS, the use of infrared methods in the study of electrochemical systems is becoming a well-established and widely applied technique. Professor Marc Porter describes the use of infrared spectroelectrochemistry as a probe of the molecular architecture of electrochemical interfaces. He begins with a description of the fundamental aspects, with emphasis on surface selection rules, polarization dependences, and reflectivity characteristics. This is followed by a description of experimental aspects, with emphasis on various modulation techniques and the use of Fourier transform infrared spectrometers. He then presents a variety of studies geared to the characterization of electrodes with modified layers of deliberate architecture. Particular emphasis is placed on the study and characterization of intermediates in the catalytic oxidation of methanol at platinum electrodes, molecular adsorption and double layer studies. The use of spectroscopic techniques in the study of electrochemical interfaces concludes with Professor D. Scherson's discussion on Mossbauer spectroscopy. Although the technique is applicable to a limited number of elements, one of these is iron, an element of great importance. Mossbauer spectroscopy can provide unique insights in the study of corrosion and passive films on iron. Professor Scherson begins his discussion with a description of the Mossbauer effect and the types of information that it can provide, with emphasis on quadrupole splitting and isomer shifts. This is followed by a description of experimental aspects and an in-depth discussion of work geared to an understanding of corrosion phenomena and passivation of steel. Because of its unique sensitivity to iron and the important role that iron plays in numerous applications, Mossbauer spectroscopy will continue to be of great value in the study of dynamic and mechanistic aspects of electrochemical processes of iron.

One of the main difficulties associated with in situ studies of electrochemical interfaces has been the lack of techniques capable of providing element-specific compositional (concentration) information. This specific aspect is addressed by Professor Wieckowski in his chapter on the use of radioactive labeling for characterizing well-defined electrodes. Although the use of radioactive isotopes has been employed for some time in the determination of compositional information at electrode surfaces, the early studies employed porous and/or roughened electrodes, so that the information obtained had limited utility. Recent experimental developments (especially from Professor Wieckowski's laboratory) now allow for the use of smooth polycrystalline as well as single crystal electrodes. This is of great significance, since it allows for the careful and precise determination of electrosorption isotherms in situ and, in some cases, may even provide a glimpse of adsorption/desorption kinetics. Professor Wieckowski discusses in detail some of these results, with emphasis on the determination of adsorption isotherms. An especially interesting finding was the adsorption of sulfate on underpotentially deposited copper on gold electrodes. Because of its ability to provide compositional information in situ and its relatively broad applicability, this technique will provide a great deal of information on the thermodynamics of surface interactions.

The use of the quartz crystal microbalance in electrochemical systems, discussed by Professor D. Buttry, completes this volume. This technique is based on the frequency changes that accompany mass changes on a quartz crystal oscillator. By making the electrode part of the oscillator, changes in mass due to electrochemical process can be monitored. Due to the extraordinary mass sensitivity, the deposition and stripping of metallic monolayers can be easily followed. Its application to the study of polymer modified electrodes has provided new insights into the incorporation/expulsion of solvent and electrolyte ions upon redox transformations. Even differences associated with H/D changes can be monitored. Because of its relatively low cost and general applicability, I am confident that this technique will find widespread use in the study of polymer modified electrodes and in the development of sensors.

This brief introduction is meant to provide an overview of the various techniques discussed. I sincerely hope that the readers will find this volume to be a useful source of information, and that it will provide a glimpse of what future developments to anticipate.

Héctor D. Abruña
Department of Chemistry
Baker Laboratory
Cornell University
Ithaca, New York 14853-1301
January, 1990

CHAPTER 1

X-RAY ABSORPTION SPECTROSCOPY IN THE STUDY OF ELECTROCHEMICAL SYSTEMS

Héctor D. Abruña

Department of Chemistry
Baker Laboratory
Cornell University
Ithaca, N.Y. 14853-1301

CONTENTS

I. X RAYS AND THEIR GENERATION

X rays comprise that portion of the electromagnetic spectrum which lies between ultraviolet and gamma rays. The range of wavelengths is typically from about 0.01 to 100 angstroms. Because of their very short wavelengths, X rays are powerful probes of atomic structure.

X rays have been traditionally produced by impinging an electron beam (at energies from about 20 to 50 keV) onto a target material such as copper, molybdenum, or tungsten. The sudden deceleration of the electron beam by the target material gives rise to a broad spectrum of emission termed bremsstrahlung. The wavelength in angstroms of the emitted X rays is given by

$$\lambda(Å) = hc/E = 12,400/V, \tag{1}$$

where lambda is in angstroms, and V is the accelerating voltage. The minimum wavelength of emission is obtained when all of the electron energy is converted to an X-ray photon. The intensity and wavelength distribution of this bremsstrahlung are both a function of the accelerating voltage, the current, and the target material. As the accelerating voltage is increased or a higher atomic number element is used as a target material, the emission distribution shifts to higher energies.

When the accelerating voltage reaches a threshold value (dependent on the nature of the target material), core electrons from the target material can be ejected, thus giving rise to core level vacancies. These vacancies are quickly filled by electrons in upper levels, resulting in the emission of X-ray photons of characteristic energies that depend on the nature of the target. The energies and intensities of characteristic lines depend on the nature of the core hole generated (e.g. K,L, or M shell vacancy) as well as the level from which the electron that fills the vacancy originates. Figure 1 shows a schematic of some of the more important X-ray emission lines. These characteristic lines are much more intense than the bremsstrahlung emission and are superimposed on the same as very sharp emissions.

The main difficulty with conventional X-ray sources is their low intensity, especially away from characteristic lines. Rotating anode X-ray generators can provide significantly higher intensities and thus have been used in EXAFS experiments. However, such studies require extended periods of data acquisition and are limited to bulk samples.

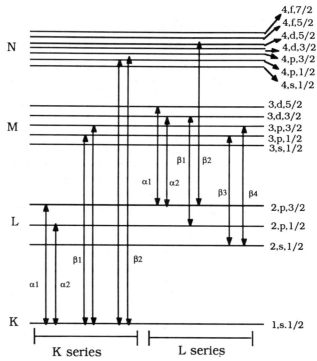

Figure 1. *Energy level diagram depicting part of the K and L series lines.*

An alternative, and the most generally employed source of X-rays for EXAFS experiments, is radiation from synchrotron sources [1] based on electron (or positron) storage rings.

II. SYNCHROTRON RADIATION AND ITS ORIGIN

No single development has influenced the use of X-ray based techniques more than the development of synchrotron radiation sources based on electron (or positron) storage rings [1]. In its simplest form, a synchrotron source consists of a beam of electrons (positrons) orbiting at relativistic speeds in a storage ring [Fig. 2]. The path of the electrons (positrons) is controlled by magnets, and they are maintained in orbit by constantly supplying energy through high power RF (radio frequency) generators. Synchrotron sources provide a

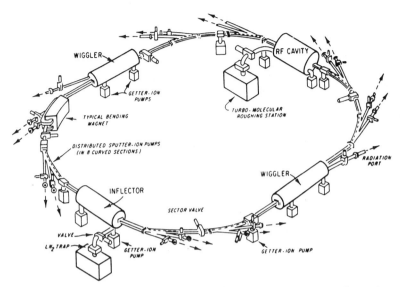

Figure 2. *Schematic of a storage ring for use as a source of synchrotron radiation (Reprinted with permission from Reference 1).*

continuum of photon energies at intensities that can be from 10^3 to 10^6 higher than those obtained with X-ray tubes, thus dramatically decreasing data acquisition times as well as making other experiments feasible.

The most attractive features of synchrotron radiation include [2]:

1. High intensity
2. Broad spectral range
3. High polarization
4. Natural collimation
5. Small source-spot size
6. Stability
7. Pulsed time structure

From Maxwell's equations we know that whenever a charged particle undergoes acceleration, electromagnetic waves are generated. An electron (or positron) in a circular orbit experiences an acceleration towards the center of the orbit and, as a result, emits radiation in an axis perpendicular to the motion. At relativistic speeds the radiation pattern is highly peaked [3], and one can think of an orbiting search light in the shape of a thin slab as a good approximation to the radiation pattern. The cone of emitted radiation is characterized by an emission angle $1/\gamma$, where γ is the electron energy divided by its rest mass. This natural collimation effect gives rise to very high fluxes on small targets.

Since the accelerated electrons are constantly emitting radiation, we need to resupply the energy if they are to remain in orbit. This is typically done with high power RF cavities as mentioned above.

The spectral distribution of synchrotron radiation is continuous and depends on a number of factors, and two that are particularly important are the electron energy, E, (expressed in GeV; 10^9 eV) and the bending radius R (in meters) of the orbit. These are related by the critical energy E_c given by

$$E_c(\text{keV}) = 2.21E^3/R.$$

The critical energy represents the midpoint of the radiated power. That is, half of the radiated power is above and below this energy. In general, useful fluxes are obtained at energies up to four times the critical energy, although in this region the output decreases precipitously. Figure 3 presents some flux curves for the Cornell High Energy Synchrotron Source (CHESS) operated at various electron beam energies.

The fact that the critical energy is inversely proportional to the bending radius is used in so-called insertion devices such as wiggler and undulator magnets and wavelength shifters [4]. These are magnetic structures that make the electron beam undergo sharp serpentine motions, thereby giving rise to a very short radius of curvature. The differences between these various insertion devices lies in the number of periods in the magnetic structure, the angular excursion of the electron beam (relative to $1/\gamma$) and the magnetic field. A wiggler is a magnetic device with a small number of periods in which the angular excursion is considerably greater than $1/\gamma$. The output from a wiggler is, to a good approximation, equal to that from a bending magnet with the same field multiplied by a factor equal to the number of poles. Figure 3 shows the output from the CHESS wiggler at 5.2 GeV. An undulator is a structure with many periods in which the the angular excursion of the electron beam is smaller or of the same order as $1/\gamma$. Because of interference effects, the output from an undulator is highly

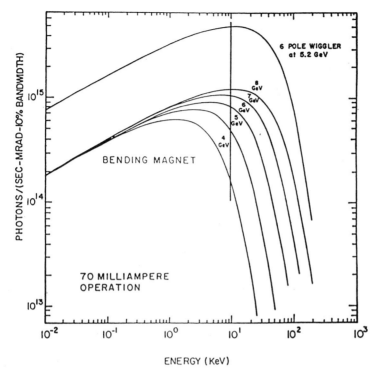

Figure 3. *Photon flux as a function of energy for the Cornell High Energy Synchrotron Source (CHESS) operated at various accelerating voltages. The top-most curve is the radiation profile from the 6 pole wiggler magnet (Figure courtesy of the Laboratory for Nuclear studies at Cornell University).*

peaked rather than continuous, and in the limiting case, the output intensity is proportional to the square of the number of poles, rather than directly proportional as for wigglers. Thus, at the characteristic peaks, undulators are exceedingly intense sources. A wavelength shifter is a device with a few poles but with a very high magnetic field. Its basic purpose is to shift the spectrum to higher energies.

Another very important property of synchrotron radiation is its very high degree of polarization. The radiation is predominantly polarized with the electric field vector parallel to the acceleration vector. Thus, in the plane of the orbit, the radiation is 100% plane polarized. Elliptical polarization can be obtained by going away from the plane; however, intensities also decrease significantly.

Finally, the pulsed time structure, useful for kinetic studies, arises from the fact that in a storage ring the electrons are orbiting in groups or bunches. The specific beam energy, the number of bunches, and the circumference of the storage ring dictate the exact time structure. Although this feature has not been employed in the study of electrochemical systems, it has been employed in other time-resolved studies.

III. INTRODUCTION TO EXAFS AND X-RAY ABSORPTION SPECTROSCOPY

EXAFS, or extended X-ray absorption fine structure, refers to the modulations in the X-ray absorption coefficient beyond an absorption edge [5]. Such modulations can extend up to about 1000eV beyond the edge and have a magnitude of typically less than 15% of the edge jump.

In order to gain a basic grasp of the EXAFS phenomena, I will begin by considering the general features observed in an X-ray absorption spectrum. Analogous to a conventional uv-vis spectrum of a molecule, in an X-ray absorption experiment, one measures the absorbance of a sample (typically expressed as an absorption coefficient μ) as a function of the incident photon energy [Fig. 4]. In general, as the incident photon energy increases, there is a monotonic decrease (proportional to E^3) in the absorption coefficient. However, when the incident X-ray energy is enough to photoionize a core level electron, there is an abrupt increase in the absorption coefficient, and this is termed an absorption edge. There are absorption edges that correspond to the various atomic shells and subshells. For example, a given atom will have one K absorption edge, three L edges, five M edges, and so forth, with the energies decreasing in the expected order K > L > M [Fig. 1].

As the scan continues to higher energies beyond the edge, one can encounter two different situations, depending on whether or not the species that we are investigating has near neighbors (typically at 5Å or closer). If there are no near neighbors, the absorption coefficient will again decrease in a monotonic fashion [dashed line in Fig. 4] until its next absorption edge, or that of another element present in the sample, is encountered.

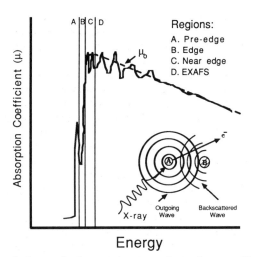

Figure 4. *Depiction of the various regions in an X-ray absorption spectrum. Inset: interference between outgoing (solid line) and backscattered (dashed line) waves.*

In the presence of one or more near neighbors, however, there will be modulations in the absorption coefficient as we scan out to energies about 1000 eV beyond the edge. The modulations present at energies from about 40 eV to 1000 eV beyond the edge are termed EXAFS.

The phenomenon of EXAFS has been known since the 1930s through the work of Kronig [6], who stated that the oscillations are due to the modification of the final state of the photoelectron by near neighbors. The absorption coefficient is a measure of the probability that a given X-ray photon will be absorbed and therefore depends on the initial and final states of the electron. The initial state corresponds to the localized electron in a core level. The final state is represented by the photoionized electron, which can be visualized as an outgoing photoelectron wave that originates at the center of the absorbing atom and that, for an S core level, has spherical symmetry. In the presence of near neighbors, this photoelectron wave can be backscattered [inset in Fig. 4] so that the final state will be given by the sum of the outgoing and backscattered waves. It is the interference between the outgoing and backscattered waves that gives rise to the EXAFS oscillations.

To a good approximation, the frequency of the EXAFS oscillations will depend on the distance between the absorber and its near neighbors, whereas the amplitude of the oscillations will depend on the numbers and type of neighbors as well as their distance from the absorber. From an analysis of the EXAFS, one can obtain information on near neighbor distances, numbers, and types. A further advantage of EXAFS is that it can be applied to all forms of matter: solids, liquids, and gases, and that in the case of solids, single crystals are not required. In addition, one can focus on the environment around a particular element by employing X-ray energies around an absorption edge of the element of interest without interferences from other elements in the sample, except for those with very similar atomic number.

The simple description of EXAFS given above is based on the so-called single electron, single scattering formalism [7]. Here it is assumed that for sufficiently high energies of the photoelectrons, one can make the plane wave approximation, and in addition, only single backscattering events will be important. This is the reason why the EXAFS is typically considered for energies higher than 40 eV beyond the edge, since in this energy region the above approximations hold well.

In addition to the EXAFS region, Figure 4 shows that there are also three other regions: the pre-edge, edge, and near edge. Below or near the edge, there can be absorption peaks due to excitations to bound states, which can be so intense as to dominate the edge region. Because the transitions are to localized states, the pre-edge region is rich in information pertaining to the energetic location of orbitals, site symmetry, and electronic configuration.

The position of the edge contains information concerning the effective charge of the absorbing atom. Thus, its location can be correlated with the oxidation state of the absorber in a way that is analogous to XPS measurements. Such shifts can be very diagnostic in assessing oxidation states and can be especially important in potential dependent studies of electrochemical systems.

Finally, there is the near edge region generally termed XANES (X-ray absorption near edges structure) or NEXAFS (near edge X-ray absorption fine structure) where uv or soft X-rays are employed. In this region of the spectrum, the photoelectron wave has very small momentum, and as a result, the plane-wave as well as the single electron single scattering approximations are no longer valid. Instead, one must consider a spherical photoelectron wave as well as the effects of multiple scattering.

Because of multiple scattering, the photoelectron wave can sample much of the environment around the absorber, making this region of the spectrum very rich in structural information. However, the theoretical modeling is very complex. Increased attention is being given by theorists, and in the not so distant future, much information will be extracted from this region.

IV. THEORY OF EXAFS

I will consider the theoretical description of EXAFS based on the single scattering short range order formalism mentioned previously. The EXAFS can be expressed as the normalized modulation of the absorption coefficient as a function of energy:

$$\chi(E) = [\mu(E) - \mu_0(E)] / \mu_0(E) \qquad (2)$$

Here, $\mu(E)$ is the total absorption coefficient at energy E, and $\mu_0(E)$ is the smooth atomlike absorption coefficient [dashed line in Fig. 4]. In order to be able to extract structural information from the EXAFS, we need to use a wave vector (k) formulation given by

$$k = \sqrt{[2m(h\nu - E_0)]}/h, \qquad (3)$$

where E_0 is defined as the threshold energy, which is typically close, but not necessarily congruent with, the energy at the absorption edge.

In wave vector form, the EXAFS can be expressed as a summation over the various coordination (near neighbor) shells and is given by

$$\chi(k) = \sum_j \frac{1}{kr_j^2} N_j F_j(k) \, S_i(k) \exp^{-2\sigma_j^2 k^2} \exp^{-2r_j/\lambda(k)} \sin(2kr_j + \phi_j(k)), \qquad (4)$$

where k represents the wave vector, r_j is the absorber-backscatterer distance, and N_j is the number of scatterers of type j with backscattering amplitude $F_j(k)$. The product of these last two terms gives the maximum amplitude. There are also amplitude reduction factors. The term $S_i(k)$ takes into account many-body effects such as electron shake-up and shake-off processes, whereas the term $\exp^{-\sigma_j^2 k^2}$ (known as the Debye-Waller factor) accounts for thermal vibration and static disorder. Finally, the term $\exp^{-2r_j/\lambda(k)}$ takes into account inelastic scattering effects where $\lambda(k)$ is the mean free path of the photoelectron.

Equation 4 can be divided into two main terms that correspond to amplitude and frequency, respectively, and which will be discussed below.

A. Amplitude Term

The amplitude term

$$\frac{1}{kr_j^2} \, N_j F_j(k) \, S_i(k) \, \exp^{-2\sigma_j^2 k^2} \exp^{-2r_j/\lambda(k)}$$

can be subdivided into two main components: a maximum amplitude term and an amplitude reduction factor.

For a given shell, the maximum amplitude is given by the product of the number (N_j) of the j type of scatterer atom times its backscattering amplitude $F_j(k)$. This maximum amplitude is then reduced by a series of amplitude reduction factors, which are considered below.

1. Many-Body Effects   The $S_i(k)$ term takes into account amplitude reduction due to many body effects and includes losses in the photoelectron energy due to electron shake up (excitation to upper localized levels of other electrons in the absorber), shake-off (ionization of low binding energy electrons in the absorber), and plasmon excitation processes. Such energy losses change the energy of the outgoing photoelectron wave so that it no longer has the appropriate wave vector for constructive interference, thus resulting in a reduction of the amplitude.

2. Thermal Vibrations and Static Disorder   Photoionization, and therefore EXAFS, takes place on a time scale that is much shorter relative to atomic motions, so the experiment samples an average configuration of the neighbors around the absorber. Thus, one needs to consider the effects of thermal vibration and static disorder, both of which will have the effect of reducing the EXAFS amplitude. These effects are considered in the so-called Debye-Waller factor, which represents the mean square relative displacement along the absorber-backscatterer direction and is given by

$$\exp^{-\sigma_j^2 k^2}.$$

This can be separated into static disorder and thermal vibrational components:

$$\sigma_j^2 = \sigma_{vib}^2 + \sigma_{stat}^2.$$

It is generally assumed that the disorder can be represented by a symmetric Gaussian type pair distribution function, and that the thermal vibration will be harmonic in nature.

Experimentally, one can only measure a total sigma. However, the two contributions can be separated by performing a temperature dependence study of sigma or by having a priori knowledge of σ_{vib} from vibrational spectroscopy. Whereas there is little that one can do to overcome the effects of static disorder, the effects of thermal vibration can be significantly decreased by performing experiments at low temperatures, and in fact, many solid samples are typically run at liquid nitrogen temperatures in order to minimize such effects. In general, failure to consider the effects of thermal vibration and static disorder can result in large errors in the determination of coordination numbers (number of neighbors) and interatomic distances [8,9].

3. Inelastic Losses   Photoelectrons that experience inelastic losses will not have the appropriate wave vector to contribute to the interference process. Such losses are taken into account by an exponential damping factor

$$\exp^{-2r_j / \lambda(k)},$$

where r is the interatomic distance between the absorber and backscatterer, and $\lambda(k)$ is the electron mean free path. This damping term limits the range of photoelectrons in the energy region of interest, and this is in part responsible for the short range description of the EXAFS phenomenon.

In general, it is the product of all of the above-mentioned factors that will give rise to the observed amplitude.

B. Oscillatory Term

The frequency term or oscillatory part of the EXAFS takes into account the relative phases (i.e. phase shifts) between the outgoing and backscattered waves as well as the interatomic distance between absorber and scatterer.   The phase shifts can be understood by considering that the outgoing photoelectron wave will experience the absorbing atom's phase shift $\delta_i(k)$ on its outward trajectory, the near neighbor's phase shift $\alpha_s(k)$ upon scattering, and the absorbing atom's phase shift once again upon returning.   There is, in addition, a $2kr$ term which represents twice the interatomic distance between absorber and scatterer.   Thus, the oscillatory part of the EXAFS is given by

$$\sin\left[2kr + 2\,\delta_i(k) + \alpha_s(k)\right].$$

Since the accuracy of the determination of interatomic distances depends largely on the appropriate determination of the relative phases, a great deal of attention has been given to this aspect. The problem can be simply stated as follows: When the outgoing photoelectron wave is backscattered by near neighbors, it is the neighbor's electron cloud, and not its nucleus, that is largely responsible for the scattering.   As a result, one needs to correct for this effect (through the use of phase shifts), since it is the internuclear distance that is the desired parameter. The correction can be achieved by ab initio calculation of the phases involved, or alternatively, they can be determined experimentally through the use of model compounds. A more thorough discussion of phase correction will be given later.

C. Data Analysis

The purpose behind the analysis of EXAFS data is to be able to extract information related to interatomic distances, numbers, and types of backscattering neighbors.   In order to accomplish this, there are a number of steps involved in the data analysis, and these include:

1. Background subtraction and normalization
2. Conversion to wave vector form
3. k weighing
4. Fourier transforming and filtering
5. Fitting for phase
6. Fitting for amplitude

1. Background Subtraction and Normalization   The first step in the analysis is the background subtraction. That is, separating the modulation in the absorption coefficient from the smooth atomiclike absorption (that is the absorption for an isolated atom). However, since the latter is usually not available, it is generally assumed that the smooth part of $\mu(E)$ at large energies beyond the absorption edge is a good approximation to $\mu_0(E)$.

Background removal routines employ polynomial splines of some order (typically second or third order). These are defined over a series of intervals, with the constraint that the function and a stipulated number of derivatives be continuous at the intersections. In addition, the observed EXAFS oscillations need to be normalized to a single atom value, and this is generally done by normalizing the data to the edge jump intensity.

2. Conversion to Wave Vector Form   In order to extract structural information, the EXAFS must be expressed in terms of wave vector k. However, this requires a value for the threshold energy E_0. The choice is important because of its effect on the phase of the EXAFS oscillations, especially at low k values. The difficulty in determining E_0 arises from the fact that there is no way of identifying an edge feature with E_0. A procedure proposed by Beni and Lee [10] is to have E_0 as an adjustable parameter in the data analysis, and its value is changed until the observed phase shifts are in good agreement with theoretical values. When good model compounds are available (vide-infra), the use of a fixed value for E_0 works well [11]. However, in many cases it is difficult to assess a priori whether a given material is a good model compound. Figure 5A depicts a generic data set after background subtraction, normalization, and conversion to wave vector form.

3. k Weighing   Once the data has been transformed to wave vector form, it is generally multiplied by some power of k; typically k^2 or k^3. Such a factor cancels the $1/k$ factor in Eq. 4 as well as the $1/k^2$ dependence of the backscattering amplitude at large values of k. The weighing is important because it prevents the large amplitude oscillations (typically present at low k) from dominating over the smaller ones (typically at high k). This is critical, since the determination of interatomic distances depends on the frequency, and not the amplitude, of the oscillations. Figure 5B depicts multiplication of the data in Figure 5A by k^3.

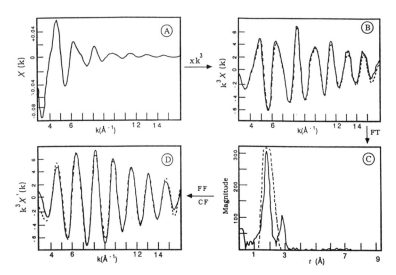

Figure 5. *Data reduction and analysis in EXAFS spectroscopy: (A) EXAFS spectrum $\chi(k)$ vs k after background removal; (B) The solid curve is the weighted EXAFS spectrum $k^3\chi(k)$ vs k (after multiplying $\chi(k)$ by k^3); (C) Fourier transformation (FT) of the weighted EXAFS spectrum in (B); (D) Fourier-filtered EXAFS spectrum of the major peak in (C) after backtransforming into k space. The dashed curve represents an attempted fit to the filtered data (Adapted with permission from Reference 5d).*

4. Fourier Transforming and Filtering   Examination of the EXAFS formulation in wave vector form reveals that it consists of a sum of sinusoids with phase and amplitude.   Sayers, Lytle, and Stern [7a] were the first to recognize the fact that a Fourier transform of the EXAFS from wave vector form yields a function that is qualitatively similar to a radial distribution function and is given by

$$\phi(r) = \frac{1}{\sqrt{2\pi}} \int_{k_{min}}^{k_{max}} k^n \chi(k) \exp^{(2ikr)} dk.$$

Such a function exhibits peaks [Fig. 5C] that correspond to interatomic distances between the central atom and the individual coordination shells, but are shifted to smaller values (recall the distance correction mentioned above).   This finding was a major breakthrough in the analysis of EXAFS data since it allowed ready visualization. However, because of the shift to shorter distances and the effects of truncation, such an approach is generally not employed for accurate distance determination. However, it allows for the use of Fourier filtering techniques, which make possible the isolation of individual coordination shells. For example, the dotted line in Figure 5C represents a Fourier filtering window that isolates the first coordination shell. After Fourier filtering, the data is back-transformed to k space [Fig. 5D] where it is fitted for amplitude and phase. The basic principle behind the curve-fitting analysis is to employ a parametrized function that will model the observed EXAFS, and the various parameters are adjusted until the fit is optimized.

5. Fitting for Phase Accurate distance determinations depend critically on the accurate determination of phase shifts. There are two general approaches to this problem, and these are theoretical and empirical determination. The main approaches to the theoretical calculation of phase shifts are based on the Hartree-Fock (HF) [7e,12] and Hartree-Fock-Slater (HFS) [13,14] methods. The first treatment begins with tabulated atomic wave functions, and the HF equation of the atom plus the external electron is solved by iteration. In the HFS (or local density functional) approach, the atom is replaced by an electron gas of varying density. In general, both of these approaches are too involved for common use. Teo and Lee [15] used the theoretical approach of Lee and Beni [7f] to calculate and tabulate theoretical phase shifts for the majority of elements. Use of these theoretical phase shifts requires the use of an adjustable E_0 in the data analysis (vide-supra). Most recently, McKale and coworkers [16] performed ab initio calculations of amplitude and phase functions using a curved wave formalism for the range of k values $2 \leq k \leq 20$.

The second, and more commonly employed, approach is the empirical one based on the use of model compounds and the concept of phase transferability. This approach consists of employing a compound of known structure (e.g. by X-ray diffraction) and which has the same absorber/backscatterer combination as that of the material of interest. The EXAFS spectrum of the known compound is obtained, and the oscillatory part of the EXAFS is fitted. Since r is known in this case, the phase shift can be determined. Typically the phase shift is parametrized as a quadratic expression. Implicit in this treatment is the applicability of phase transferability which states that, for a given absorber/scatterer combination, the phase shifts can be transferred to any compound with the same absorber/scatterer combination without regard to chemical effects such as ionicity or covalency of the bonds involved. This is based on the idea that, at sufficiently high kinetic energies for the photoelectron (e.g. about 50 eV above threshold), the EXAFS scattering processes are largely dominated by core electrons, and thus, the measured phase shifts are insensitive to chemical effects. Thus, determination of the phase shift for an absorber/scatterer pair in a system of known r allows for the determination of the distance in an unknown having the same atom pair. This was thoroughly demonstrated by Citrin, Eisenberger, and Kincaid [17] on a study of germanium compounds.

With good quality data and appropriately determined phase shifts, distances determined by EXAFS are typically good to ±0.01 angstroms and sometimes better in favorable cases.

6. Fitting for Amplitude   Fitting for amplitude is employed in order to determine the types and numbers of backscattering atoms around a given absorber.   The problem can be divided in two parts: identification of the types of backscatterers, and the determination of their numbers. In the absence of any information as to the probable nature of the backscatterer, identification is difficult, especially among atoms that have similar atomic numbers such as nitrogen and oxygen. This is because the backscattering amplitudes are not a very strong function of atomic number.   For example, Figure 6 shows the backscattering amplitude for various elements as calculated by Teo and Lee [15]. It is clear that for Si and C the differences are small, and so these two elements would be difficult to differentiate. However, for the case of a heavy atom backscatterer, there is typically a resonance in the backscattering amplitude so that differentiation between light and heavy backscatterers can be readily made.   For example, notice in Figure 6 the resonance (minimum) in the backscattering amplitude for Pb at about k equal to 6Å^{-1}.

It should be mentioned that when a peak from a Fourier transform is filtered and back-transformed to k space, the envelope represents the backscattering amplitude for the near neighbor involved.

If the identity of the backscatterer is known, the interest is in determining the number of near neighbors.   In this case,

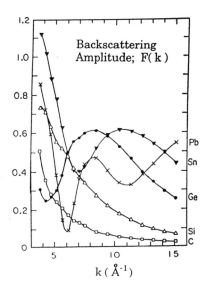

Figure 6. *Backscattering amplitude as a function of wave vector for C, Si, Ge, Sn and Pb (Adapted from Reference 15).*

one needs to compare the amplitude of the EXAFS of the material of interest (unknown) to that for a compound of known coordination number and structure. However, unlike transferability of phase, which is generally regarded as an excellent approximation, the transferability of amplitude is not. This is because there are many factors that affect the amplitude, and except for the case of model compounds with structure very similar to that of the unknown, these will not necessarily (and often will not) be the same. As a result, determination of coordination numbers (near neighbors) is usually not better than ±20%.

V. SURFACE EXAFS AND POLARIZATION STUDIES

EXAFS is fundamentally a bulk technique due to the significant penetration of high energy X rays. In order to make the technique surface sensitive, one can take either of two general approaches. In the first, if one knows a priori that the specific element of interest is present only at the surface, then a conventional EXAFS measurement will necessarily give surface information. Alternatively, one can employ detection techniques or geometries such that the detected signal arises predominantly from the surface or near surface regions [18]. Such techniques include electron detection (e.g. Auger, partial, or total electron yield) and operating at angles of incidence that are below the critical angle of the particular material so that only an evanescent wave penetrates the substrate, thus resulting in a very shallow sampling depth. These aspects will be discussed further in the experimental section, and in addition, there have been a number of reviews of this matter with Citrin's being the most comprehensive [18e].

For studies on single crystals, surface EXAFS offers an additional experimental handle, and this refers to the polarization dependence of the signal [19]. As mentioned, synchrotron radiation is highly polarized, with the plane of polarization lying in the plane of orbit. Since only those bonds whose interatomic vector has a projection on the plane of polarization of the X ray will contribute to the observed EXAFS, polarization dependence studies can provide a wealth of information on the geometric disposition of scatterers. Such studies are also extremely valuable in surface EXAFS studies of adsorbed layers [Fig. 7] since they allow for the determination

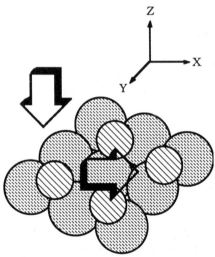

Figure 7. *Depiction of the polarization vector (arrows) of the X-ray beam being either parallel or perpendicular to a surface covered by an ad-layer.*

of the site of adsorption as well as the structure and geometry of the adsorbed layer [20]. This is a significant enhancement over the information content of a conventional EXAFS experiment. Polarization dependent surface EXAFS measurements have provided some of the best defined characterizations of adsorbate structures.

For a near neighbor shell of atoms (N_i) whose interatomic vector with the absorber makes an angle Θ_j relative to the plane of polarization one can relate the effective coordination number (N_i^*) and the true coordination number by [21]

$$N_i^* = 3 \sum_{j}^{N_i} \text{Cos}^2 \Theta_j .$$

VI. EXPERIMENTAL ASPECTS

A. Synchrotron Sources

There are a number of experimental factors to be considered when performing an in situ surface EXAFS experiment on an electrochemical system. First and foremost is having access to a synchrotron source (for the reasons previously mentioned) with significant flux in the hard X ray region. In the United States three such facilities exist presently:

1. Cornell High Energy Synchrotron Source (CHESS)
2. Stanford Synchrotron Radiation Laboratory (SSRL)
3. National Synchrotron Light Source (NSLS at Brookhaven National Laboratory

It should be mentioned that another high energy synchrotron source, the Advanced Photon Source (APS), will be built at the Argonne National Laboratory and should be operational in the mid-1990s.

In addition to having access to a synchrotron, one needs to pay close attention to detection schemes and the design of specialized equipment. Some of these aspects will be discussed below.

B.   Detection

The mode of detection is usually dictated by the concentration of the species of interest, the nature of the sample, and the experiment. All of these aspects have been considered in great detail by Lee et. al. [5e], so only some of the most important aspects will be covered here. In general, the measurement of any parameter that can be related to the absorption coefficient can be employed in a detection scheme, and the most common ones are discussed below.

1.   Transmission   For concentrated or bulk samples, a transmission experiment is both the simplest and most effective. It involves measuring the X-ray intensities incident and transmitted through a thin and uniform film of the material.   Careful analysis of signal to noise ratio considerations indicates that optimal results are obtained when the sample thickness is of the order of 2.5 absorption lengths. Since in transmission experiments Beer's Law applies, the data are usually plotted as ln (I/I_0) vs. E.   The X-ray intensities are typically measured using ionization chambers in conjunction with high gain electrometers. Figure 8 depicts a typical transmission experimental setup.

2. Fluorescence   For dilute samples, where absorption of the X-ray beam by the element of interest would be very low, a transmission geometry cannot be employed. Instead, fluorescence detection is the method of choice [22,23]. Fluorescence can be used for detection because the characteristic X-ray fluorescence intensity depends on the

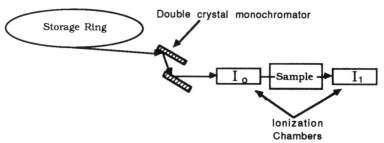

Figure 8. *Schematic diagram of a transmission EXAFS experimental setup. I_0 and I_1 refer to the incident and transmitted intensities, respectively.*

number of core holes generated, which in turn depends on the absorption coefficient. Fluorescence detection is much more sensitive than transmission because one is measuring the signal over an essentially constant background. Typically, the incident and fluorescent beams impinge and leave the surface at 45 degrees, with the sample and the detector being at 90 degrees. The detector can be either an ionization chamber or a solid state detector. The former is much simpler to implement, whereas the latter gives the best resolution. A filter, to minimize the contributions from elastic and compton scattering, and soller slits are typically placed in front of the detector. The filter material is chosen so as to have an absorption edge that falls between the excitation energy employed and the energy of the characteristic X-ray photon emission from the element of interest. Thus, the filter is generally made from the Z-1 or Z-2 element where Z represents the atomic number of the element of interest. For example, for the detection of CuK_α radiation at 8.04 keV, a nickel filter would be employed. In this way, the characteristic fluorescence is only slightly attenuated, whereas both the elastic and compton intensities are greatly reduced. However, there is the problem that often the K_β emission from the filter material is energetically very close to that of the K_α emission from the element of interest and may present some background problems.

A solid state detector, either Si(Li) (lithium drifted silicon) or intrinsic germanium, offers the ability to discriminate on the basis of energy. The resolution can be as good as 150 eV, although it degrades somewhat with increasing detector area. The main drawback with a solid state detector is its limited count rate of approximately 15,000 cps. Since the detector accepts a wide range of photon energies from which the region of interest is chosen (via a single channel analyzer), it can take significant amounts of time to obtain adequate statistics. In addition, the cost of solid state detectors and associated electronics is much higher than that of ion chambers.

3. Reflection When the sample under study is a planar surface, one can take advantage of X-ray optics to enhance surface sensitivity [24]. The most important aspect is specular or mirror reflection, and this is due to the fact that at X-ray energies the index of refraction of matter is slightly less than one and is given by

$$n = 1 - \delta - i\beta$$

$$\delta = \frac{1}{2\pi}(\frac{e^2}{mc^2})(\frac{N_o\rho}{A})\,[Z + \Delta f']\,\lambda^2$$

$$\beta = \frac{\lambda\mu}{4\pi},$$

where $(e^2/(mc^2)$ is the classical electron radius, $(N_o\rho/A)$ is the number of atoms per unit volume, N_o is Avogadro's number, ρ is the density, A is the atomic weight, Z is the atomic number, and λ is the wavelength of the X-ray. The term $[Z + \Delta f']$ is the real part of the scattering factor (including the so-called dispersion term f') and is essentially equal to Z. The imaginary part of the index of refraction β is related to absorption, where μ is the linear absorption coefficient. Considering an X-ray beam incident on a smooth surface and Snell's Law, one finds that the critical angle for total reflection is given by

$$\theta_{crit} = \sqrt{2\delta}.$$

Delta is of the order of 10^{-5} and Θ_{crit} is typically of the order of a few milliradians. Thus, as long as the beam is incident below this critical angle, it is totally reflected, and only an evanescent wave penetrates the substrate. This has two very important consequences. First of all, the penetration depth is of the order of 20Å, and thus, one can significantly discriminate in favor of a surface contained material. Compton and elastic scattering are also minimized. In addition, the reflection enhances the local intensity by as much as a factor of four as well as the effective "path length." All of these factors combined enhance the surface sensitivity of the technique, and when combined with solid state fluorescence detection, submonolayer amounts of material can be detected [23].

Using a reflection geometry one can employ the technique known as REFLEXAFS [25] which consists of measuring the ratio of the reflected and incident intensities as a function of energy. Although an EXAFS spectrum can be obtained from such a measurement, the process is somewhat involved, since the reflectivity is a complex function of the angle of incidence, the refractive index, and energy.

Heald and coworkers [26] have made a careful comparison of reflexafs vs. measurements at grazing incidence with fluorescence detection. They conclude that, in general, the latter offers enhanced sensitivity for studies of monolayers.

However, the reflexafs technique can be applied in a dispersive arrangement (vide-infra) allowing for faster data acquisition and the possibility of performing kinetic studies on the millisecond time scale.

4. Electron yield Electron yield, Auger, partial, or total, can be employed as a means of detection, since again they depend on the generation of core holes. Because of the very small mean free paths of electrons, electron yield detection is very well suited for surface EXAFS measurements. However, for this very same reason, in situ studies of electrochemical interfaces are precluded. Details of electron yield EXAFS have been discussed by a number of authors [18].

5. Dispersive arrangements In all of the experimental techniques described up to this point, spectra were obtained by monitoring one of the above mentioned parameters as the incident energy was scanned using monochromator crystals. This conventional mode of operation suffers from the fact that only a very narrow range of wavelengths is employed at a given time, and thus requires a significant amount of time to obtain a complete spectrum. In addition, it precludes real-time kinetic studies of all but the slowest of reactions. An alternative is to employ a dispersive arrangement [27] [Fig. 9] where, by the use of focusing optics (using a bent crystal), a range of energies can be brought to focus on a small spot. The exact energy spread will depend on the specific optical elements employed but a range of 500 to 600 eV represents a realistic value. Coupling this with a photodiode array [Fig. 9] allows for the simultaneous use of the full range of wavelengths, and thus, a spectrum can be obtained in periods as short as milliseconds rather than minutes. This is of great significance because a number of relevant dynamic processes take place on this time scale. The application of this approach to electrochemical studies will be discussed in a later section.

C. Electrochemical Cells

A number of cell designs have been employed in EXAFS studies of electrochemical systems. Of these, two general types can be identified, depending on whether a transmission or a

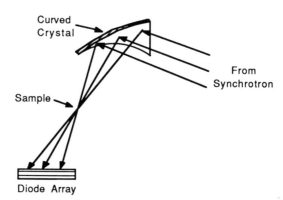

Figure 9. *Schematic depiction of a dispersive EXAFS setup.*

fluorescence mode of detection is employed.   In a transmission mode, cells should be designed to minimize absorption losses due to the window material, electrolyte, and the electrode itself. As a result, the windows are typically made of thin films (25 μm) of low absorbing materials, such as polyethylene and polyimide (Kapton). The electrolyte layer thickness is typically small, and electrodes are generally metal films evaporated on a thin polymer film or small particles dispersed in a low Z matrix. Carbon can be employed in a variety of forms and shapes because of its low absorption.

Figure 10 shows the transmission cell employed by O'Grady and coworkers [28] in the study of the nickel oxide electrode.   Figure 11 shows a cell employed by Heineman and coworkers [29] in X-ray spectroelectrochemical studies.

When fluorescence detection is employed, the most important consideration is to have a very thin window material as well as a thin layer of electrolyte. As a result, very thin films (6 μm) of the materials previously mentioned are typically employed. In addition, the cell configuration is of the thin layer type where a thin layer of electrolyte (10 μm) is trapped between the electrode and the window.   An advantage of this cell configuration is that conventional bulk electrodes can be easily employed, since transparency is not required.   Figures 12, 13, and 14 show three different cells employed in the study of anodic films [30], UPD metal monolayers [31], and chemically modified electrodes [32], respectively.

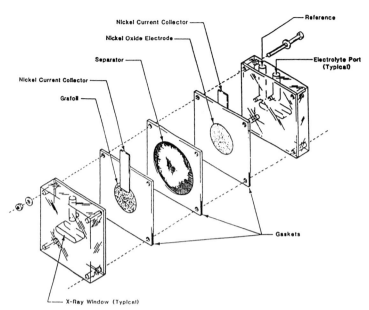

Figure 10. *In situ transmission EXAFS cell for the study of Ni oxide electrodes (Reprinted with permission from Reference 28).*

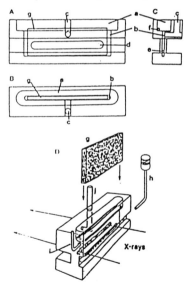

Figure 11. *EXAFS spectroelectrochemical cell employed by Heineman and coworkers (Reprinted with permission from Reference 29).*

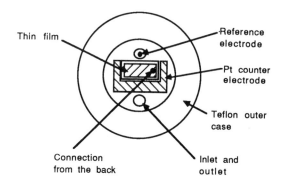

Figure 12. *In situ cell for performing EXAFS studies on passivated iron films (Reprinted with permission from Reference 30).*

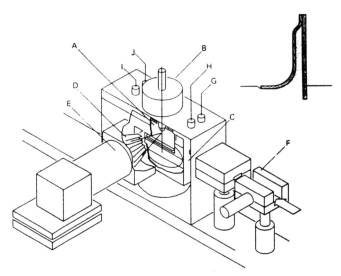

Figure 13. *Cell employed in the study of underpotentially deposited metal monolayers (Reprinted with permission from Reference 31).*

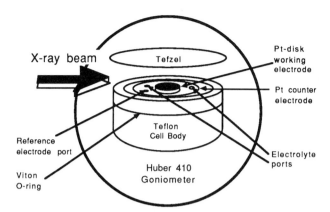

Figure 14. *Cell employed in the study of electropolymerized films on electrodes (Reprinted with permission from Reference 32).*

VII. EXAFS STUDIES OF ELECTROCHEMICAL SYSTEMS

The discussion of EXAFS studies of electrochemical systems will be divided into:

1. Oxide films
2. Batteries and fuel cells
3. Monolayers
4. Spectroelectrochemistry
5. Adsorption

A. Oxide Films

Because of their relevance to corrosion phenomena, the study of passive films on electrode surfaces is an area of great fundamental, technological, and practical relevance. Despite decades of intensive investigations, there still exists a great deal of controversy as to the exact structural nature of passive films, especially when they are formed in the presence or absence of glass forming additives such as chromium.

One of the main sources of controversy arises from the fact that many of the structural studies performed have been on dried films, and, as correctly pointed out by O'Grady [33], the structure of dehydrated films can be significantly different from that of hydrated ones.

The use of surface EXAFS to the study of passive films represents a natural application of the technique, and in fact, the studies by Kruger and coworkers [30,34-36] on the passive film on iron represent the first reported. In their first studies, they employed vacuum deposited iron films on glass slides and subsequently oxidized the films in either nitrite or chromate solution. They obtained the EXAFS spectra for the oxidized films employing a photocathode ionization chamber (detecting the emitted electron current) and compared these with spectra for γ-FeO(OH), γ-Fe$_2$O$_3$ and Fe$_3$O$_4$. Although these studies were not in situ, they did not require evacuation of the samples and therefore represent an intermediate situation between dehydrated films and in situ experiments. The spectra for Fe, Fe$_3$O$_4$, and the nitrite and chromate generated passive films are shown in Figures 15A and B. The near edge region for the nitrite generated film showed evidence of an enhancement, similar to that observed for Fe$_3$O$_4$, indicative of an increase in the density of available final states with p-character. Such an enhancement is absent in the chromate formed films. These results point to a more covalent bonding in the chromate vs. the nitrite passivated films.

Upon Fourier transforming of the data [Fig. 16], two peaks corresponding to Fe-O and Fe-Fe distances were obtained. The peaks in the Fourier transform of the chromate generated film were much less well-resolved than those for the nitrite films, and this was ascribed to the presence of a glassy structure associated with the chromium. From a comparison of the edge jump for Fe and Cr, the authors estimate that the films had about 12% Cr.

They have also employed an in situ cell [Fig. 12] for carrying out these experiments. Again, they studied nitrite and chromate passivated films. The results obtained in this case were significantly different from the ex situ measurements, with the spectral features for both nitrite and chromate passivated films being quite similar. This surprising similarity underscores the importance of in situ measurements.

Most recently [37], they established the presence of Cr(VI) in oxide scales formed in Fe/Cr alloys oxidized at 600°C. In this study, they compared the chromium near edge region of

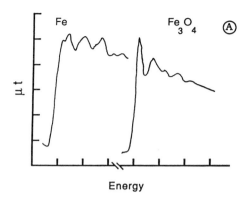

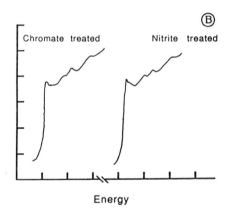

Figure 15. *Absorption spectra of: (A) Fe and Fe₃O₄; (B) Iron films after treatment in chromate and nitrite solutions (Adapted with permission from Reference 35).*

the oxidized film [Fig. 17B] with those of Cr_2O_3, CrO_3, and metallic chromium [Fig. 17A]. The presence of Cr(VI) was clearly established by the appearance of the very characteristic sharp feature at about 6001 eV. Although these studies were ex situ, they demonstrate the utility of using the near edge region (XANES) in the determination of oxidation state.

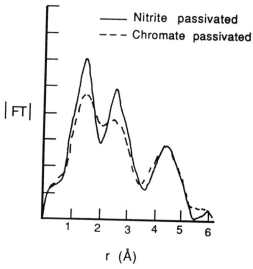

Figure 16. *Fourier transform of the EXAFS for iron films after treatment in chromate and nitrite solutions (Adapted with permission from Reference 35).*

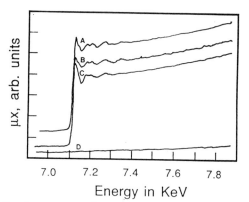

Figure 17. *Cr K edge spectra for: (A) Cr, CrO_3 and Cr_2O_3; (B) Oxide formed on a Fe 25% Cr film by oxidation in oxygen at $600°C$.*

Hoffman and coworkers [38,39] have carried out a series of studies on the passive films on iron, with particular attention being given to cell design. They have employed a so-called bag [38] cell that allows for the in situ passivation and/or cathodic protection of the iron films, which were deposited onto gold films deposited on melinex (a polymer film with excellent adhesive properties). In addition, they employed a set up where the working electrode is partially immersed in solution and continuously rotated. In this way, they could expose the electrode to the X-ray beam with ostensibly only a very thin film of electrolyte. Under these conditions, they were able to obtain spectra [Fig. 18] of the film as prepared, a cathodically

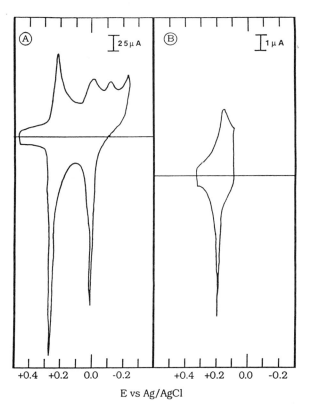

Figure 18. *Fluorescence detected X-ray absorption spectra for a 4 nm iron film in emersion cell. Spectra are for: A) Dry film; B) Cathodically protected film; C) Passivated film; D) Background electrolyte (Adapted with permission from Reference 38).*

protected film as well as a film passivated in borate solution at 1.3 V. From an analysis of their data, they concluded that the passive film had an Fe-O coordination with six near neighbors at a distance of 2.0 ± 0.1Å. The approach followed by these authors appears most appropriate, since they were able to reduce the deposited films to the metallic state and subsequently oxidize them. It would be most interesting to ascertain how the structure of the passive film varies through sequential reduction/passivation cycles.

Forty and coworkers [40] have investigated the passive films formed on iron and iron-chromium alloys upon immersion in sodium nitrite solution. Studies were carried out in a wet environment (which they term in situ) as well as after dehydration. For a FeCr alloy (13% Cr), they find that the structure of the wet film is analogous to that of γ-FeOOH, but with a higher degree of disorder, consistent with the Mössbauer results of O'Grady [33]. Upon dehydration, the structure transforms to one that is closer to that of γ-Fe$_2$O$_3$ but with reduced long-range order. In addition, they looked at the chromium EXAFS and found that the local structure around chromium in the passive films was similar to that of Cr$_2$O$_3$. They concluded that the presence of chromium in alloys stabilized the γ-Fe$_2$O$_3$ layers against dehydration, thus forming a glassy structure which enhances the stability of the passive film. These results are in good agreement with those of Kruger and coworkers mentioned previously.

Froment and coworkers [41-43] have employed reflexafs (vide-supra) for studying passive films on iron and nickel. They report some preliminary data, but do not derive extensive conclusions as their purpose was to demonstrate the applicability of reflexafs to electrochemical systems.

B. Batteries and Fuel Cells

The performance and lifetime of fuel cells and batteries can often be determined by the structural features (and their change) of the various components. Structural studies of these systems are generally very difficult because the materials involved are often noncrystalline, so X-ray diffraction measurements are of very limited use. Because of its ability to provide short range order, EXAFS is ideally suited to the in situ study of such systems, and a number of applications have been reported [44].

Linford and coworkers [45] studied the changes in the structure of the electrolyte in the system

Metal/CuI:sulphonium iodide(5.5:1)/Metal

as a function of discharge, since they had previously observed long induction periods in attaining a steady voltage. They examined the EXAFS around the copper *k* edge and found that the starting electrolyte had a structure that was essentially identical to that of γ-CuI. After 2,000 hours of discharge, the spectrum was significantly changed, and this was ascribed to the incorporation of sulfur from the electrolyte.

O'Grady and McBreen [28] performed an extensive study of the nickel oxide electrode employing the cell shown in Figure 10 in a transmission mode. The study of nickel oxide is complicated by the numerous species present and their interconversion. They find that the as-prepared β-Ni(OH)$_2$ has the same structure within the *x-y* plane as that determined by X-ray diffraction experiments, but with a significant degree of disorder along the *c*-axis. Oxidation to the trivalent state results in contraction of the Ni-O and Ni-Ni distances along the *x-y* plane. Rereduction of this material yields a structure that is similar to that of the freshly prepared Ni(OH)$_2$. Repeated oxidation-reduction cycles resulted in an increased disorder, which is believed to be responsible for facilitating the electrochemical oxidation to the trivalent state.

Boudart and coworkers [46] recently reported on a study where they monitored X-ray absorption spectra around the Pt L$_{III}$ edge during the electrochemical reduction of oxygen at electrocatalysts containing 1 nm clusters of platinum dispersed on carbon. Changes in the threshold peak area and edge position in the spectra suggest that the oxidation state of the metal decreases linearly with the applied potential in the range from 1010 to 900 mV (vs NHE), which is similar to the behavior of bulk platinum electrodes. However, they also found that the overall oxidation state of the clusters was consistent with a surface stoichiometry that was closer to PtO$_{0.5}$ rather than PtO which is the one proposed for the surface of bulk electrodes.

O'Grady and Koningsberger [47] have studied metal-carbon interactions in carbon supported platinum catalysts in fuel cells. They concluded that there are two types of Pt-C interactions.

Van Wingerden and coworkers [48a] obtained the EXAFS spectra around the Co K edge for 5,10,15,20-tetra-(p-chloro-phenyl) porphyrinatocobalt (III) supported on Norit BRX and heated in nitrogen to various temperatures up to 850°C. This study was geared to an understanding of the enhanced catalytic effect toward oxygen reduction that accompanies heat treatment. They find that upon adsorption or after heating up to $550°C$ (where the catalytic activity is maximal), the cobalt chelate retains its square planar configuration. Further heating causes some decomposition, and at the highest temperatures, metallic cobalt is obtained. Similar results were obtained by O'Grady and coworkers [48b].

C. Monolayers

The study of electrochemically deposited monolayers poses the strictest experimental constraints because of the very low signals involved. However, these studies can provide much detail on interfacial structure as well as the effects of solvent and supporting electrolyte ions.

An especially attractive way of preparing metallic monolayers on electrodes is by a process known as underpotential deposition(UPD) [49]. This refers to the deposition of metallic layers on an electrode of a different material. The first monolayer is deposited at a potential that is less negative (typically by several hundred millivolts) than the expected thermodynamic potential; hence the term underpotential deposition. This occurs over a somewhat narrow range of potentials where the coverage varies from zero to a monolayer (i.e. a layer on atom in thickness). A distinct advantage of this approach is that it allows for the precise control of the surface coverage from a fraction of a monolayer up to a full monolayer. Since subsequent electrodeposition (bulk deposition) will require a significantly different potential, very reproducible monolayer coverages can be routinely obtained. Thus, this represents a unique family of systems with which to probe electrochemical interfacial structure in situ.

We, and others, have been involved in the study of UPD systems including Cu/Au(111) [50], Ag/Au(111) [51], Pb/Ag(111) [31], and Cu/Pt(111)/I [52]. The first three systems involved the use of epitaxially deposited metal films on mica as electrodes, which gives rise to electrodes with well-defined single crystalline structures [53]. In the last case, a bulk platinum single crystal was employed. Because of the single crystalline nature of the electrodes, polarization dependence studies could be used to ascertain surface structure.

In order to minimize background scattering, thin layer cells were employed in all of these studies and although very slow sweep rates had to be employed, well-defined voltammetric responses were obtained. For example, Figures 19A and B show voltammograms for the underpotential deposition of copper on an epitaxial film of gold (111 orientation) on mica and on a bulk Pt(111) single crystal electrode that had been pretreated with a layer of adsorbed iodine. The very well-defined voltammetric features are immediately apparent.

The salient features of the UPD systems studied to date will be considered below.

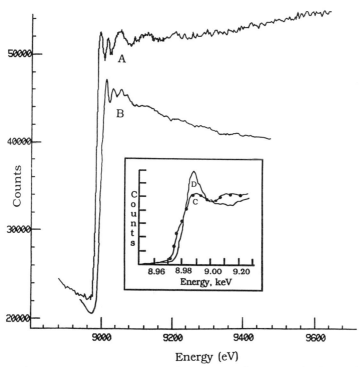

Figure 19. *Voltammetric scans for the underpotential deposition of copper on (A) an epitaxial film of gold (111 orientation) on mica, and on (B) a bulk Pt(111) single crystal electrode coated with a layer of iodine. Experimental conditions: A) 1 M H_2SO_4 containing 5 x 10^{-5} M Cu^{+2}, sweep rate 1 mV/sec. B) 0.1 M H_2SO_4 containing 5 x 10^{-5} M Cu^{+2}, sweep rate 1 mV/sec.*

1. Cu UPD on a Au(111) Electrode   This is one of the best
characterized systems to date.   The experiments were conducted
using a cell similar to that depicted in Figure 13 and spectra
obtained by monitoring the characteristic CuK_α fluorescence
intensity at 8.04 keV. Spectra were obtained with the
polarization of the X-ray beam being either perpendicular [Fig.
20A] or parallel [Fig. 20B] to the plane of the electrode.   In both
cases, a number of well defined oscillations were observed in
addition to a sharply defined edge. From a qualitative
comparison of the spectra for copper foil and $CuAu_3$, it is clear
that spectra for the UPD monolayer resemble the latter to a
much greater extent, pointing to the strong influence exerted
by the gold substrate in the UPD monolayer.
        That the signal arises from the monolayer of copper on
the gold surface can be demonstrated by adjusting the potential
to a value (+0.50 V) where the monolayer is oxidized to Cu^{+2} and
dissolved (stripped) into the thin layer of electrolyte. The
spectrum of the edge region taken under these conditions is
compared to that of the UPD layer in Figures 20 C and D.   There
are two noticeable differences.   First of all, the edge position for
the Cu^{+2} ions in solution (i.e. after oxidation and stripping of
the monolayer) [Fig. 20C] is shifted to higher energy by about

Au (111) Surface
Cu-Au = 2.58 Å
Cu-Cu = 2.92 Å
Cu-O = 2.08 Å

Figure 20. *Fluorescence detected (in situ) x-ray absorption spectrum
for an underpotentially deposited (UPD) monolayer of copper on a gold
(111) electrode with the plane of polarization of the X-ray beam being
perpendicular (A) or parallel (B) to the plane of the electrode; Inset:
Edge region of the X-ray absorption spectrum for a copper UPD monolayer
before (C) and after (D) stripping.*

2 eV relative to the value of the UPD layer [Fig. 20D], and this is consistent with the higher oxidation state of Cu+2. In addition, the presence of the very characteristic "white-line" (very sharp feature near the edge) for Cu+2 and its absence in the spectrum of the UPD layer further corroborates spectral assignments. It should be mentioned that the reason we are able to detect the Cu+2 ions in solution stems from the fact that upon oxidation and stripping, the concentration of Cu+2 within the thin layer volume is of the order of 1×10^{-3} M (as opposed to the bulk solution concentration of 10 μM) and therefore, detectable.

From analysis of the data, a number of salient features can be pointed out. First of all the copper atoms appear to be located at three fold hollow sites (i.e. three gold near neighbors) on the gold (111) surface with copper near neighbors. The Au/Cu and Cu/Cu distances obtained are 2.58 and 2.91 ±0.03Å, respectively. This last number is very similar to the Au/Au distance in the (111) direction, suggesting a commensurate structure. Most surprising, however, was the presence of oxygen as a scatterer at a distance of 2.08 ±0.02Å. From analysis and fitting of the data, we determined that the surface copper atoms are bonded to an oxygen from either water or sulfate anions from the electrolyte. That there might be water or sulfate in contact with the copper layer is not surprising; however, such interactions generally have very large Debye-Waller (very weak interaction) factors, so that typically no EXAFS oscillations (or heavily damped oscillations) are observed. The fact that the presence of oxygen (from water or electrolyte) at a very well-defined distance is observed is indicative of a significant interaction and underscores the importance of in situ studies.

A pictorial representation of this system is shown in Figure 21 where the source of oxygen is presented as water. However, it should be mentioned that from the EXAFS experiment one cannot rule out sulfate anions as the source of oxygen. In fact, experiments by Kolb and coworkers [54] indicate that sulfate may be present, since at the potential for monolayer deposition the electrode is positive of the potential of zero charge, so that sulfate would be present to counterbalance the surface charge.

2. Ag UPD on a Au(111) Electrode Studies of Ag on Au(111) [51] yield very similar results in terms of the structure of the deposited monolayer with the silver atoms being bonded to three surface gold atoms and located at three-fold hollow sites

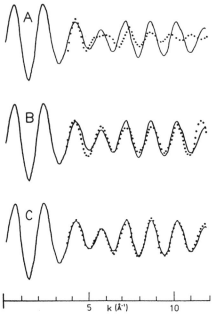

Figure 21. *Structure of a copper UPD monolayer on a gold (111) electrode surface with water as the source of oxygen.*

forming a commensurate layer. Again, strong interaction by oxygen from water or electrolyte (perchlorate) was present.

This is clearly demonstrated by considering the fits to the Fourier filtered data with only gold [Fig. 22A], or oxygen [Fig. 22B], or both [Fig. 22C] as backscatterers. Whereas in the first two cases there were significant deviations in different parts of the spectrum, the fit with both gold and oxygen backscatterers is excellent over the entire range of k values.

3. Pb UPD on a Ag(111) Electrode Melroy and coworkers [31] have obtained the EXAFS spectrum of Pb underpotentially deposited on a silver (111) electrode. In this case no Pb/Ag scattering was observed and this was ascribed to the large Debye-Waller factor for the lead as well as to the presence of an incommensurate layer. However, data analysis as well as comparison of the edge region of spectra for the lead UPD, lead foil, lead acetate, and lead oxide indicated the presence of

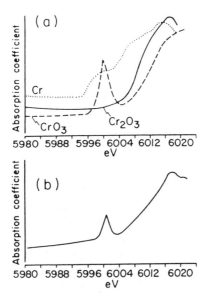

Figure 22. *Fourier filtered EXAFS (solid lines) and fit for a silver UPD monolayer on a gold (111) electrode with only gold (A), or oxygen (B), or both gold and oxygen (C) as backscatterers.*

oxygen from either water or acetate (from electrolyte) as a backscatterer.

They were also able to perform a potential dependence study of the lead oxygen distance. They find that it increases from 2.33 ±0.02 to 2.38 ±0.02Å upon changing the potential from -0.53 to -1.0 V vs. Ag/AgCl. This is consistent with the negatively charged electrode repelling a negatively charged or strongly dipolar adsorbate.

In all of these studies it is clear that scattering from water and/or electrolyte plays a crucial role, once again underscoring the importance of in situ measurements.

4. Cu UPD on a Pt(111)/I Electrode Most recently we [52] have studied the structure of a half-monolayer of copper underpotentially deposited on a platinum (111) bulk single crystal electrode annealed in iodine vapor. The spectrum, shown in Figure 23A, exhibits five well defined oscillations in addition to a sharply defined edge. It should be mentioned that, in this experiment, the plane of polarization of the X-ray beam

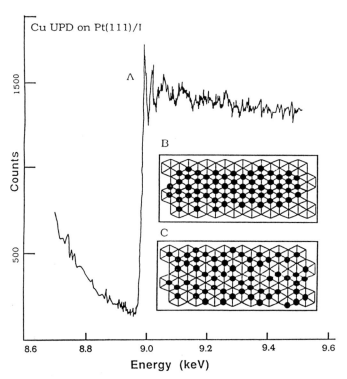

Figure 23. *(A) Fluorescence detected (in situ) X-ray absorption spectrum for an UPD half-monolayer of copper on a Pt (111) single crystal electrode. Inset: Depiction of models involving clustering (B) and random decoration (C).*

was parallel to the electrode surface so that it was most sensitive to in-plane scattering of copper by other copper neighbors. From analysis of the data, we determined a Cu-Cu distance of 2.85 ±0.02Å, which is very close to the Pt-Pt distance in the (111) direction and suggests that the copper atoms are present at three-fold hollow sites and that they form a commensurate layer with the platinum substrate. More important, however, was finding that the average number of Cu near neighbors was six. This strongly suggests that at half-monolayer coverage, the surface is better represented by one that contains large clusters [Fig. 23B] rather than by one that is randomly decorated with copper atoms or covered with a lattice with a large interatomic spacing [Fig. 23C]. This is significant, since it is a direct experimental documentation of a mechanism where monolayer formation involves nucleation and growth rather than random deposition with subsequent coalescence.

We also found that heating of the sample, resulted in the loss of the pronounced features of the fine structure and this seems to indicate that the structure initially formed is a metastable one and that the stability is derived from the clustering.

D. Spectroelectrochemistry

EXAFS and XANES techniques have been applied in the more traditional type of spectroelectrochemical experiments where a thin layer cell configuration is employed. Drawing from extensive experience in the related uv-vis measurements, Heineman in collaboration with Elder were the first to report on an in situ EXAFS spectroelectrochemistry experiment [55,56]. Their first cell design employed gold minigrid electrodes similar to those typically employed in traditional uv-vis experiments. They studied the ferro-ferricyanide couple in each oxidation state by monitoring the region about the iron K edge using fluorescence detection. From analysis of their data, they were able to determine that for Fe(II) there are 7.4 carbon atoms at 1.97 ±0.01Å, whereas for Fe(III) there are 6.8 carbon near neighbors at a distance of 1.94 ±0.01Å. Since, as mentioned previously, coordination number determination is usually not better than 20%, the numbers they find are in agreement with the known value of six. More interesting is the fact that they observed a contraction of the Fe-C bond upon oxidation, a finding that is contrary to results based on crystallographic studies. This points to the importance of in situ measurements, since by the applied potential, one can precisely control the oxidation state of the species being studied. The determination of metal/ligand bond distances in solution and their oxidation state dependence are critical to the application of electron transfer theories, since such changes can contribute significantly to the energy of activation through the so-called inner sphere reorganizational energy term.

Those authors have also developed a cell that employs reticulated vitreous carbon as a working electrode [Fig. 11], and they find that such a design allows for much faster electrolysis. Using such a cell, they have studied the $[Ru(NH_3)_6]^{+3/+2}$ couple, a cobalt(III/II) sepulchrate as well as the Fe-C distance in cytochrome C.   For the case of the cobalt sepulchrate, they were able to obtain spectra at five different applied potentials, and as shown in Figure 24, very well defined isosbestic points were obtained.

Most recently they have developed a cell configuration for the study of modified electrodes [57] that employs, as a working electrode, colloidal graphite deposited onto kapton tape (typical window material).   Such an arrangement minimizes attenuation due to the electrolyte solution.   They coated the working electrode with a thin film of Nafion (a perfluoro sulfonate ionomer from E.I. DuPont de Nemours, Inc.) and incorporated [Cu(2,9-dimethy-1,10-phenanthroline)$_2$]$^{+1}$ by ion exchange.   They were able to obtain the EXAFS spectra around the copper K edge for the complex in both the Cu(I) and Cu(II) oxidation states.

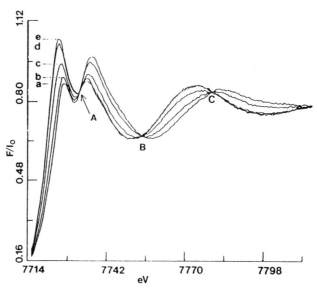

Figure 24. *X-ray absorption spectra of 10 mM cobalt sepulchrate in 1 M sodium acetate at applied potential values of: (a) -0.30 V, (b) -0.58 V, (c) -0.60 (d) -0.62 and (e) -0.80 V vs. Ag/AgCl (Reprinted with permission from Reference 29).*

Antonio, Wainwright, and Murphy [58] have performed an in situ EXAFS spectroelectrochemical study of heteropolytungstate anions and observed differences in the edge position as a function of oxidation state. However, the changes appeared to be excessively large, and the effect responsible for this is at present unclear.

Although the field of chemically modified electrodes has seen a tremendous growth in the recent past, there is very limited information on the structure of these layers. In an effort to bridge this gap, we have performed some in situ EXAFS measurements on chemically modified electrodes [32]. We have studied films of $[M(v\text{-}bpy)_3]^{2+}$ (v-bpy is 4-vinyl,4'methyl-2,2'bipyridine, M=Ru,Os), and $[Os(v\text{-}bpy)_2(phen)]^{+2}$ electropolymerized onto a platinum electrode and in contact with an acetonitrile/0.1M TBAP (tetra n-butyl ammonium perchlorate) solution and under potential control. We have focused on determining the lower limit of detection as well as trying to ascertain any differences in the metal/ligand bond distances for the electropolymerized films as a function of surface coverage when compared to the parent complex. Figures 25C and B show spectra for electrodes modified with one and five equivalent monolayers of the ruthenium complex whereas Figure 25A shows the spectrum for bulk $[Ru(bpy)_3]^{+2}$. In Figure 25C one can ascertain that only the most prominent features of the spectrum of the parent compound [Fig. 25A] are present. (It should be mentioned that a monolayer of $[Ru(v\text{-}bpy)_3]^{+2}$ represents about 5.4×10^{13} molecules/cm^2, which is about 5% of a metal monolayer, since it is the metal centers that give rise to the characteristic fluorescence employed in the detection.) However, at a coverage of five monolayers [Fig. 25B], the spectrum is essentially indistinguishable from that of the bulk material. Upon fitting of the data for phase and amplitude, we obtain a Ru-N distance of 2.01Å and a coordination number of six. This correlates very well with the known values of 2.056Å and six, respectively. In addition, it is also clear that there is little difference between the electrodeposited polymer and the monomeric parent compound in terms of the near edge spectral features, pointing to a similar geometric disposition of scatterers. Furthermore, changes in oxidation state can be monitored by the shift in the position of the edge. For example, upon oxidation of the polymer film (at +1.60 V) from Ru(II) [Fig. 25D] to Ru(III), the edge position shifts to higher energy by about 1.5 eV [Fig. 25E]. Thus, one can

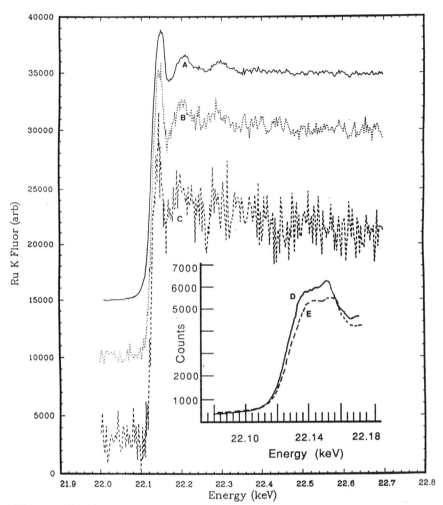

Figure 25. *Fluorescence detected X-ray absorption spectrum for bulk [Ru(bpy)₃]⁺² (A) and for platinum electrodes modified with one (C) and five (B) monolayers of poly-[Ru(v-bpy)₃]⁺². Changes in the edge location for a platinum electrode modified with a polymeric film of [Ru(v-bpy)₃]⁺² as a function of oxidation state. Curves (D) and (E) are for Ru(II) and Ru(III), respectively (Reprinted with permission from Reference 32).*

determine the oxidation state of the metal inside a polymer film on an electrode surface.

Similar results were obtained for the osmium complexes in terms of the local structure around the metal center and changes in the position of the edge as a function of oxidation state. In addition, we were able to correlate changes in the near edge features with the coordination environment around the osmium metal center.

These results indicate that the structure of electroactive polymer films and the oxidation state of the metal center can be obtained at relatively low coverages, and this should have important implications in trying to identify the structure of reactive intermediates in electrocatalytic reactions at chemically modified electrodes.

Tourillon and coworkers [59-67] have also reported on a number of spectroelectrochemical studies, especially of electrodeposition of metals, particularly copper, on electrodes modified with poly 3-methylthiophene. What sets his experiments apart is the use of a dispersive approach [Fig. 9]. As mentioned previously, in such a setup, focusing optics are employed so as to have a range of energies (as wide as 500 eV) come to a tight focal spot at the sample. The beam then impinges a photodiode array so that all energies are monitored at once. The net result is to significantly decrease data acquisition times so that spectra can be obtained in times as short as a few milliseconds. Thus, this opens up tremendous possibilities in terms of kinetic and dynamic studies. One of the more impressive results using this approach is shown in Figure 26, which shows spectra obtained around the copper K edge for a poly 3-methylthiophene film (on a platinum electrode) doped with Cu^{+2} ions. The potential of the electrode is stepped so as to reduce the Cu^{+2} ions to Cu^{+1} and subsequently to Cu^0. The spectra shown in Figure 26 were taken at seven second intervals, and the transitions from Cu^{+2} to Cu^{+1} and then to metallic copper are clearly evident. These authors have also employed this technique for the study of other metallic inclusions into poly 3-methylthiophene films, including Ir, Au, and Pt. Thus, this type of arrangement could open up new exciting possibilities in terms of kinetic studies.

In addition, these same authors have carried out extensive ex-situ studies on the structure of conducting polymers, following the features around the carbon edge [68].

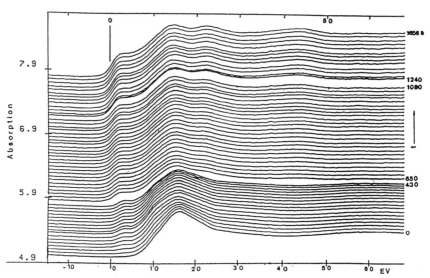

Figure 26. *In situ measurements of the time evolution of the Cu K-edge when a platinum electrode coated with a polymeric film of poly-methylthiophene is cathodically polarized in an aqueous solution containing 50 mM CuCl₂ (Reprinted with permission from Reference 62).*

E. Adsorption

Since the magnitude of the edge jump in an X-ray absorption spectrum is proportional to the number of absorbers, the potential dependence of the edge jump can be employed to measure potential/surface-concentration (electrosorption) isotherms in situ. We have carried out such a study on iodide adsorption on a Pt(111) electrode surface [69]. The resulting isotherm, shown in Figure 27, displayed two plateaus separated by a transition centered at about -0.10 V vs Ag/AgCl. The iodide coverage at the most negative potential studied (-1.0 V) went to an essentially negligible value, while that at the positive potential limit (+0.50 V) increased rapidly, suggesting an interfacial accumulation of absorbers.

The results at the most negative potentials can be interpreted in terms of a model where adsorbed iodine is converted to adsorbed iodide, which subsequently shows the behavior expected for a specifically adsorbed anion. That is, there is a marked dependence of the coverage on potential.

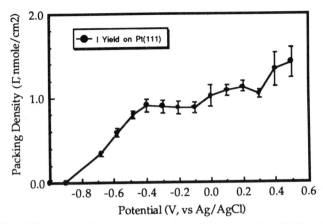

Figure 27. *Electrosorption isotherm of iodine on a Pt (111) electrode.*

The plateau-like features in the isotherm may be explained in thermodynamic terms. For example, we attribute the flatness in the region between -0.50 and -0.10 V to the absence of potential dependence of coverage of a neutral adsorbate (iodine). On the other hand, between -0.1 and +0.3 V, further uptake involves adsorption of iodide. The potential dependence here is due to interaction of the anion with an increasingly positive surface charge. The attainment of a saturation coverage is due to closest packing of iodine species as well as to possible lateral electrostatic interactions. The features in the electrosorption isotherm present at intermediate potentials may also be attributed to the formation of stable structures. Hubbard and coworkers [70] have shown that a transition from a mixed $\sqrt{3} \times \sqrt{3}$ and $\sqrt{7} \times \sqrt{7}$ structure to one that is purely $\sqrt{7} \times \sqrt{7}$ occurs between -0.2 and 0.0 V and is accompanied by a change in coverage from 3/9 to 4/9. A similar transition is observed here and is assumed, because of the similarity in the packing density change over the transition, to be due to the same structural transition. At the most positive potentials, we believe that the increase in the iodine/iodide concentration is produced by faradaic charge flow, followed by association with the adsorbed iodine layer at that potential.

VIII. CONCLUSIONS

The use of X rays is providing a rare glimpse of the in situ structure of electrochemical interfaces of both fundamental and technological importance, and as these experiments become more widespread, a wide range of phenomena will be explored. I am certain that these studies will help provide the basis for a better understanding and control of electrochemical reactivity.

IX. ACKNOWLEDGMENTS

Our work was generously supported by the Materials Chemistry Initiative of the National Science Foundation, the Materials Science Center at Cornell University, the Office of Naval Research, the Army Research Office, the Dow Chemical Company, and Xerox Corporation. Special thanks to Dr. James H. White as well as to Michael Albarelli, Dr. Martin McMillan, and David Acevedo. The work on the copper and silver UPD on gold was in collaboration with Dr. Owen Melroy and Dr. Joseph Gordon (I.B.M., San Jose) and Professor Lesser Blum (University of Puerto Rico).

X. REFERENCES

1. Winick, H., and Doniach, S., eds. *Synchrotron Radiation Research.* New York: Plenum, 1980.
2. Winick, H. *In Synchrotron Radiation Research.* ed. H. Winick and S. Doniach, 11. New York: Plenum, 1980.
3. Tomboulian, D.H., and Hartman, P. *Phys. Rev.* 102 (1956): 1423.
4. For an Introductory discussion see: Winick, H.; Brown, G.; Halbach, K.; and Harris, J. *Physics Today* (May 1981): 50.
5. There have been numerous reviews of EXAFS over the last ten years. A selected number of leading references is listed below.
   a. Stern, E.A. *Sci. Am.* 234 (4) (1976): 96.
   b. Eisenberger, P., and Kincaid, B.M. *Science* 200 (1978): 1441.
   c. Cramer, S.P., and Hodgson, K.O. *Prog. Inorg. Chem.* 25 (1979): 1.
   d. Teo, B.K. *Accts. Chem. Res.* 13 (1980): 412.
   e. Lee, P.A., et al. *Rev. Mod. Phys.* 53 (1981): 769.
   f. Teo, B.K., and Joy, D.C., eds. *EXAFS Spectroscopy; Techniques and Applications.* New York: Plenum, 1981.

g. Bianconi, A.; Inoccia, L.; and Stippich, S., eds. *EXAFS and Near Edge Structure*. Berlin: Springer Verlag, 1983.

h. Hodgson, K.O.; Hedman, B.; and Penner-Hahn, J.E., eds. *EXAFS and Near Edge Structure III*. Berlin: Springer Verlag, 1984.

i. Teo, B.K. *EXAFS: Basic Principles and Data Analysis*. Berlin: Springer Verlag, 1986.

6. Kronig, R. deL. *Z. Phys.* 70 (1931): 317; 75 (1932): 191, 468.

7. a. Sayers, D.E.; Stern, E.A.; and Lytle, F.W. *Phys. Rev. Lett.* 27 (1971): 1204.

b. Stern, E.A. *Phys. Rev. B* 10 (1974): 3027.

c. Stern, E.A.; Sayers, D.E.; and Lytle, F.W. *Phys. Rev. B* 11 (1975): 4836.

d. Ashby, C.A., and Doniach, S. *Phys. Rev. B* 11 (1975): 1279.

e. Lee, P.A., and Pendry, J.B. *Phys. Rev. B* 11 (1975): 2795.

f. Lee, P.A., and Beni, G. *Phys. Rev. B* 15 (1977): 2862.

8. Eisenberger, P., and Brown, G.S. *Solid State Commun.* 29 (1979): 481.

9. a. Hayes, T.M., et al. *Phys. Rev. Lett.* 40 (1978): 1282.

b. Hayes, T.M.; Boyce, J.B.; and Beeby, J.L. *J. Phys. C* 11 (1978): 2931.

10. Lee, P.A., and Beni, G. *Phys. Rev. B* 15 (1977): 2682.

11. a. Hayes, T.M.; Sen, P.N.; and Hunter, S.H. *J. Phys. C* 9 (1976): 4357.

b. Cramer, S.P., et al. *J. Am. Chem. Soc.* 100 (1978): 7282.

c. Cramer, S.P., et al. *J. Am. Chem. Soc.* 100 (1978): 3814.

d. Cramer, S.P., et al. *J. Am. Chem. Soc.* 100 (1978): 2748.

e. Tullius, T.; Frank, P.; and Hodgson, K.O. *Proc. Nat. Acad. Sci. USA* 75 (1978): 4069.

12. Pettifer, R.F., and McMillan, P.W. *Phil. Mag.* 35 (1977): 871.

13. Ashby, C.A., and Doniach, S. *Phys. Rev. B* 11 (1975): 1279.

14. Lagarde, P. *Phys. Rev. B* 13 (1976): 741.

15. Teo, B.K., and Lee, P.A. *J. Am. Chem. Soc.* 101 (1979): 2815.

16. McKale, A.G., et al. *J. Am. Chem. Soc.* 110 (1988): 3763.

17. Citrin, P.H.; Eisenberger, P.; and Kincaid, B.M. *Phys. Rev. Lett.* 36 (1976): 1346.

18. a. Stern, E.A. *J. Vac. Sci. Tech.* 14 (1977): 461.

b. Landman, U., and Adams, D.L. *J. Vac. Sci. Tech.* 14 (1977): 466.

c. Stohr, J. *In Emission and Scattering Techniques Studies of Inorganic Molecules, Solids, and Surfaces*, ed. P. Day. Holland: D. Reidel Publ., 1981.

d. Hasse, J. *Applied Phys.* A 38 (1985): 181.

e. Citrin, P.H. *Jnl. de Phys. Coll. C8* 47 (1986): 437.

19. Beni, G., and Platzman, M. *Phys. Rev. B* 14 (1976): 1514

20. a. Sette, F., et al. *Phys. Rev. Lett.* 59 (1987): 311.

b. Sette, F., et al. *Phys. Rev. Lett.* 61 (1988): 1384.

21. Lee, P.A. *Phys. Rev. B* 13 (1976): 5261.

22. a. Jaklevic, J., et al. *Solid State Commun.* 23 (1977): 679.
    b. Hastings, J.B., et al. *Phys. Rev. Lett.* 43 (1979): 1807.
23. Heald, S.M.; Keller, E.; and Stern, E.A. *Phys. Lett.* 103A (1984): 155.
24. a. James, R.W. *The Optical Principles of the Diffraction of X-rays.* Woodbridge, CT: Oxbow Press, 1982.
    b. see also: Bilderback, D.H. *SPIE Proc.* Vol. 315 (1982): 90.
25. a. Martens, G., and Rabe, P. *Phys. Stat. Solidi A* 58 (1980): 415.
    b. Goulon, J., et al. *J. Phys.* 43 (1982): 539.
    c. Gurman, S.J., and Fox, R. *Phil. Mag. B* 54 (1986): L45.
26. a. Heald, S.M.; Tranquada, J.M.; and Chen, H. *Jnl. de Phys. Coll. C8* 47 (1986): 825.
    b. Stern, E.A., et al. *In EXAFS and Near Edge Structure III.* ed. K.O. Hodgson; B. Hedman; and J.E. Penner-Hahn, 261. Berlin: Springer Verlag, 1984.
27. a. Dartyge, E., et al. *In EXAFS and Near Edge Structure III.* ed. K.O. Hodgson; B. Hedman; and J.E. Penner-Hahn, 472. Berlin: Springer Verlag, 1984.
    b. Flank, A.M., et al. *In EXAFS and Near Edge Structure.* ed. A. Bianconi; L. Inoccia; and S. Stippich, 405. Berlin: Springer Verlag, 1983.
    c. Sayers, D.E., et al. *In EXAFS and Near Edge Structure.* ed. A. Bianconi; L. Inoccia; and S. Stippich, 209. Berlin: Springer Verlag, 1983.
    d. Oyanagi, H., et al. *Jnl. de Phys. Coll. C8* 47 (1986): 139.
    e. Saigo, S., et al. *Jnl. de Phys. Coll. C8* 47 (1986): 555.
    f. Mimault, J., et al. *In EXAFS and Near Edge Structure III.* ed. K.O. Hodgson; B. Hedman; and J.E. Penner-Hahn, 47. Berlin: Springer Verlag, 1984.
28. McBreen, J., et al. *Langmuir* 3 (1986): 428.
29. Dewald, H.D., et al. *Anal. Chem.* 58 (1986): 2968.
30. Long, G.G.; Kruger, J.; and Kuriyama, M. *In Passivity of Metals and Semiconductors.* ed. M. Froment, 139. Amsterdam: Elsevier, 1983.
31. Samant, M.G., et al. *J. Am. Chem. Soc.* 109 (1987): 5970.
32. Albarelli, M.J., et al. *J. Electroanal. Chem.* 248 (1988): 77.
33. O'Grady, W.E. *J. Electrochem. Soc.* 127 (1980): 555.
34. Long, G.G., et al. *J. Electrochem. Soc.* 130 (1983): 240.
35. Long, G.G., et al. *J. Electroanal. Chem.* 150 (1983): 603.
36. a. Kruger, J., et al. *In Passivity of Metals and Semiconductors.* ed. M. Froment, 163. Amsterdam: Elsevier, 1983.
    b. Kruger, J., and Long, G.G. *Proc. Electrochem. Soc.* 86-7 (1986): 210.
37. Long, G.G.; Kruger, J.; and Tanaka, D. *J. Electrochem. Soc.* 134 (1987): 264.
38. Kordesch, M.E., and Hoffman, R.W. *Nucl. Inst. Meth. Phys. Res.* 222 (1984): 347.

39. Hoffman, R.W. *In Passivity of Metals and Semiconductors*. ed. M. Froment, 147. Amsterdam: Elsevier, 1983.

40. Forty, A.J., et al. *Jnl. de Phys. Coll. C8* 47 (1986): 1077.

41. Bosio, L., et al. *In Passivity of Metals and Semiconductors*. ed. M. Froment, 131. Amsterdam: Elsevier, 1983.

42. Bosio, L., et al. *J. Electroanal. Chem.* 180 (1984): 265.

43. Bosio, L.; Cortes, R.; and Froment, M. *In EXAFS and Near Edge Structure III*. ed. K.O. Hodgson; B. Hedman; and J.E. Penner-Hahn, 484. Berlin: Springer Verlag, 1984.

44. McBreen, J.; O'Grady, J.E.; and Pandya, K.I. *J. Power Sources* 22 (1988): 323.

45. Linford, R.G., et al. *Solid State Ionics* 14 (1984): 199.

46. Weber, R.S.; Peuckert, DallaBetta, R.A.; and Boudart, M. *J. Electrochem. Soc.* 135 (1988): 2535.

47. O'Grady, W.E., and Koningsberger, D.C. *J. Chem. Phys.* (to be published).

48. a. Van Wingerden, B.; Van Veen, J.A.R.; and Mensch, C.T.J. *J. Chem. Soc. Farad. Trans.* 84 (1) (1988): 65.
    b. McBreen, J., et al. *Proc. Electrochem. Soc.* 87-12 (1987): 182.

49. Kolb, D.M. *In Advances in Electrochemistry and Electrochemical Engineering*, vol. 11, ed. H. Gerischer, and C. Tobias, 125. New York: Pergamon Press, 1978.

50. a. Blum, L., et al. *J. Chem. Phys.* 85 (1986): 6732.
    b. Melroy, O.R., et al. *Langmuir* 4 (1988): 728.

51. White, J.H., et al. *J. Phys. Chem.* 92 (1988): 4432.

52. White, J.H., and Abruña, H.D. *J. Phys. Chem.* (submitted).

53. a. Pashley, D.W. *Phil.Mag.* 4 (1959): 316.
    b. Grunbaum, E. *Vacuum* 24 (1973): 153.
    c. Reichelt, K., and Lutz, H.O. *J. Cryst. Growth* 10 (1971): 103.

54. Zei, M., et al. *Ber. Bunsenges. Phys. Chem.* 91 (1987): 349.

55. Smith, D.A., et al. *J. Am. Chem. Soc.* 106 (1984): 3053.

56. Smith, D.A.; Elder, R.C.; and Heineman, W.R. *Anal. Chem.* 57 (1985): 2361.

57. Elder, R.C., et al. *J. Electroanal. Chem.* 240 (1988): 361.

58. Antonio, M.R.; Wainwright, J.S.; and Murphy, O.J. (submitted).

59. Tourillon, G., et al. *J. Electroanal. Chem.* 178 (1984): 357.

60. Tourillon, G., et al. *Surf. Sci.* 156 (1985): 536.

61. Dexpert, H.; Lagarde, P.; and Tourillon, G. *In EXAFS and Near Edge Structure III*. ed. K.O. Hodgson; B. Hedman; and J.E. Penner-Hahn, 400. Berlin: Springer Verlag, 1984.

62. Tourillon, G., et al. *Phys. Rev. Lett.* 57 (1986): 603.

63. Dartyge, E., et al. *Jnl. de Phys. Coll. C8* 47 (1986): 607.

64. Dartyge, E., et al. *Nucl. Inst. Meth. Phys. Res.* A246 (1986): 452.

65. Dartyge, E., et al. *Phys. Lett.* 113A (1986): 384.

66. Fontaine, A., et al. *Nucl. Inst. Meth. Phys. Res.* A253 (1987): 519.

67. Tourillon, G.; Dexpert, H.; and Lagarde, P.   *J. Electrochem. Soc.*   134 (1987): 327.

68. a. Tourillon, G.; Dexpert, H.; and Lagarde, P.   *J. Electrochem. Soc.* 134 (1987): 327.

   b. Tourillon, G., et al.   *Surf. Sci.*   184 (1987): L345.

   c. Tourillon, G., et al.   *Jnl. de Phys. Coll. C8*   47 (1986): 579.

   d. Tourillon, G., et al.   *Phys. Rev. B* 36 (1987): 3483.

   e. Tourillon, G., et al.   *Phys. Rev. B* 35 (1987): 9863.

69. White, J.H., and Abruña, H.D.   *J. Phys. Chem.* (in press).

70. Lu, F., et al.   *J. Electroanal. Chem.*   222 (1987): 305.

CHAPTER 2

SURFACE X-RAY SCATTERING

Michael F. Toney and Owen R. Melroy

IBM Research Division
Almaden Research Center
San Jose, CA 95120-6099

CONTENTS

1 INTRODUCTION

The structure of the metal/electrolyte interface and that of atoms or molecules adsorbed at this interface are widely recognized as long standing questions of fundamental importance in electrochemistry. Despite this, a determination of the structure of the electrochemical interface has proved elusive. Surfaces (particularly smooth surfaces) inherently contain very few atoms. Hence, to obtain the required sensitivity, surface science has largely relied on probes that interact very strongly with matter. In addition to the high sensitivity, this approach has the added advantage of providing surface selectivity, since the probe does not penetrate far into the bulk substrate. Unfortunately, the same features which make these techniques so attractive for surface studies preclude their use outside ultrahigh vacuum (UHV), and thus, the techniques are unusable as in situ probes of electrochemical interfaces. To date, most successful in situ studies have relied primarily on ultraviolet, visible, or infrared radiation, since their propagation distances in many solutions are suitably long. Such methods as surface enhanced Raman spectroscopy, surface infrared spectroscopy, surface plasmon spectroscopy, and others have provided valuable information on the type and possible orientation of interfacial species. These techniques, however, only indirectly indicate atomic structure.

X-ray diffraction has long been recognized as the most powerful technique for probing long-range order in solids. The principal advantages of X rays are that they interact weakly with matter (which simplifies data analysis), and their wavelength is comparable to interatomic distances (the commonly used Cu K_α line at 8.04 keV has a wavelength of 1.54Å). Thus, X-ray diffraction is able to directly probe crystal lattice spacings, and crystallographic data analysis can easily be performed using a kinematic approximation. The weak interaction of X rays with matter provides an additional advantage for measurements of structures that are "buried" beneath a condensed phase or thin film, since it results in a large penetration depth. Thus, X rays can be used to probe buried interfaces, unlike many other surface science techniques routinely used in vacuum. The ability to penetrate condensed phases, coupled with unparalleled structure sensitivity, makes X-ray diffraction an exceptionally powerful tool, well-suited for in situ studies of electrochemical systems. Indeed, X-ray diffraction has been successfully applied in both ex-situ and in situ studies of electrodeposited films by a number of investigators. Among the earliest works applying in situ X-ray diffraction to study film growth was Dahn et al. [1], who monitored changes in lattice spacings of intercalation compounds as a function of electrode potential, and Chianelli et al. [2], who measured the lattice parameter of a TiS_2 cathode during discharge.

Despite its formidable powers, X-ray diffraction has received considerably less attention in electrochemistry (and surface science in general) than both the in situ optical techniques and ex-situ techniques such as low-energy electron diffraction (LEED) following transfer into vacuum. This relative lack of attention has been a direct result of the limitations of conventional X-ray sources. Because of the low scattering cross-section of atoms, and since both conventional X-ray tubes and rotating anode sources provide relatively low photon fluxes, probing the structure of ultra thin films or surfaces has required either excessively long acquisition times or detector arrays that have only recently become available. Thus, in the past, X-ray diffraction was limited to studying relatively thick electrodeposited films and was generally considered incapable of probing electrochemical surface structure. However, the construction of the first synchrotron in the 1960s and the general availability of synchrotron radiation in the late 1970s radically altered the perception and limitations of X-ray techniques. Surface studies are now possible, and both surface EXAFS (extended X-ray absorption fine structure) and surface X-ray diffraction are becoming routine surface science tools. Although their application to electrochemical environments, in situ, is still in its infancy, there is little doubt that these techniques will have a significant impact on our understanding of electrode surfaces and adsorbed layers.

The purpose of this chapter is to provide an introduction to surface studies using X-ray diffraction, with an emphasis on in situ applications to electrochemistry. We begin with a review of diffraction from bulk, three dimensional (3D) crystals and introduce the important concept of reciprocal space. A discussion of diffraction from two dimensional solids (Bragg rods), surfaces of bulk crystals (crystal truncation rods), and adsorbed layers follows this. We then discuss the experimental aspects of surface X-ray scattering. These include the properties of synchrotron X-ray radiation, the X-ray beam lines that are required to effectively bring the radiation to the experimenter, four-circle diffractometers, and the phenomenon of total external reflection that is used in the grazing incidence scattering geometry employed for surface X-ray scattering. Although limited, examples of surface reconstruction, adlayer structure, and the initial stages of bulk metal deposition will be presented.

2 DIFFRACTION IN TWO AND THREE DIMENSIONS

In this section, X-ray diffraction from two (2D) and three dimensional (3D) crystals is reviewed. There are two equivalent approaches to this problem: that due to Bragg, which views the crystal lattice as sets of lattice planes, and that of von Laue, which employs the concept of a reciprocal lattice. We review both of these here, and in Appendix A discuss the von Laue formulation in more detail, since it is the most useful for this chapter. Appendix A also includes a brief discussion of diffraction when there is more than one atom per unit cell, and a description of the effect of some types of crystal imperfections on the shapes of diffraction peaks. For the reader who is interested in a complete description, there are several excellent texts on the X-ray diffraction [3-6].

A. DIFFRACTION CONDITIONS

A crystal has long-range translational order and is composed of a periodic array of identical structural units. These repeating units may be single atoms, groups of the same or different atoms, molecules, ions, and so forth and are referred to as unit cells. The periodic array is described in terms of a lattice, and each unit cell occupies a certain site on that lattice. For simplicity we consider a crystal with only one atom per unit cell. Each atomic site is labeled by the integers n, m, and p and the position of an atom at that site is

$$\mathbf{R}_{nmp} = n\,\mathbf{a} + m\,\mathbf{b} + p\,\mathbf{c}, \tag{1}$$

where $\mathbf{a}$, $\mathbf{b}$, and $\mathbf{c}$ are the lattice vectors of the crystal. All the atoms in the crystal fall on sets of parallel lattice planes, and in the Bragg approach, the crystal is imagined as consisting of sets of these planes, which are spaced a distance d apart (the "d-spacing," which depends on $\mathbf{a}$, $\mathbf{b}$, and $\mathbf{c}$). This construction is illustrated in Figure 1. X rays that are incident on the planes with an angle θ have a small fraction ($\sim 10^{-4} - 10^{-2}$) of their incident radiation specularly reflected at the same angle. A peak in the intensity of the scattered radiation will occur when reflections from successive planes interfere constructively. Since the path length difference between planes is $2d \sin \theta$, the condition for constructive interference is

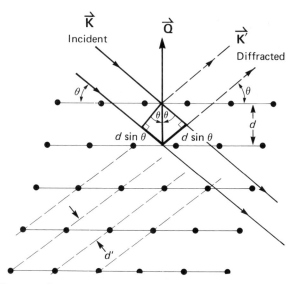

Figure 1. Bragg reflection from lattice planes with spacing d. The wave vector of the incident X rays (shown by the solid lines) is **k** and makes an angle θ with the lattice planes. The small portion of the incident beam that is specularly reflected is shown by the dashed lines and has wave vector **k′**. The scattering vector is $Q = (4\pi/\lambda)\sin\theta = 2\pi/d$. A set of planes with spacing d' is also shown.

$$n\lambda = 2d\sin\theta, \tag{2}$$

where n is an integer and λ is the X-ray wavelength. This is the well-known Bragg's law.

When discussing X-ray diffraction, it is convenient to define the scattering vector

$$\mathbf{Q} = \mathbf{k}' - \mathbf{k}, \tag{3}$$

where **k** and **k′** are, respectively, the incident and scattered wave vectors and are shown in Figure 1. Since X-ray scattering is elastic, they have the same magnitude $k' = k = 2\pi/\lambda$, and thus, the magnitude of **Q** is

$$Q = (4\pi/\lambda)\sin\theta. \tag{4}$$

Using Equation (2) one can see that an alternative formulation of Bragg's law is $Q = 2\pi/d$. In addition, when the diffraction condition is satisfied, **Q** is perpendicular to the lattice planes, as shown in Figure 1. An advantage of using **Q** rather than the Bragg angle θ_B is that the scattering vector $\mathbf{Q}$ that fulfills the Bragg condition is independent of λ, unlike θ_B.

Crystals can be resolved into any of an infinite number of crystallographic planes, each with a different d-spacing, and therefore, a different θ_B, which satisfies Bragg's law. These different sets of crystallographic planes can be uniquely distinguished by their Miller indices hkl. If one hkl plane is drawn through an atom at the origin, then the adjacent plane intercepts the crystallographic axes at a/h, b/k, and c/l. Several examples are shown in Figure 2 for a simple cubic (sc) lattice. The d-spacing between hkl planes is denoted d_{hkl}.

The angles θ_B, where diffraction occurs, are given by Bragg's law, but to calculate the scattering intensity from crystals it is necessary to adopt the von Laue approach and perform a deeper analysis. This approach is outlined in Appendix A and we summarize the results here. It is first convenient to write $\mathbf{Q}$ as

$$\mathbf{Q} = Q_a \mathbf{a}^* + Q_b \mathbf{b}^* + Q_c \mathbf{c}^* \tag{5}$$

where $\mathbf{a}^*$, $\mathbf{b}^*$, and $\mathbf{c}^*$ are the primitive reciprocal lattice vectors of the crystal and are given by Equation (A3). The conditions for diffraction from the crystal are then simply expressed by the three Laue conditions [Appendix A]

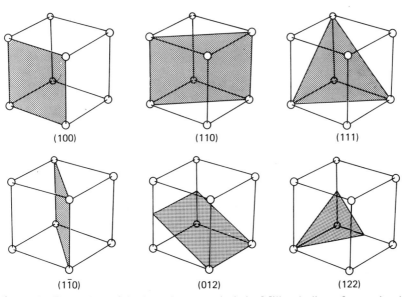

(100) (110) (111)

$(1\bar{1}0)$ (012) (122)

Figure 2. Examples of lattice planes and their Miller indices for a simple cubic (sc) lattice.

$$Q_a = h, \quad Q_b = k, \quad \text{and} \quad Q_c = l, \tag{6}$$

where h, k, and l are integers. An alternative and useful way to describe this is

$$\mathbf{Q} = \mathbf{G}_{hkl} \equiv h\mathbf{a}^* + k\mathbf{b}^* + l\mathbf{c}^*. \tag{7}$$

The vector $\mathbf{G}_{hkl}$ is a reciprocal lattice vector that is perpendicular to the hkl lattice planes and has a magnitude $G_{hkl} = 2\pi/d_{hkl}$. When the Laue conditions are satisfied and diffraction is observed the scattering vector is equal to the reciprocal lattice vector $(\mathbf{Q} = \mathbf{G}_{hkl})$ and thus $Q = 2\pi/d_{hkl}$, which is equivalent to Bragg's law.

B. RECIPROCAL SPACE AND THE EWALD CONSTRUCTION

The concept of "reciprocal space," which is the most common means for describing and visualizing diffraction effects, can now be introduced. Reciprocal space is the "Fourier transform space" of real space and is spanned by the reciprocal lattice vectors of the crystal. The positions in reciprocal space where the Laue conditions are fulfilled and diffraction can occur are referred to as Bragg points. One use of reciprocal space is the Ewald construction, which is a geometric construction that is helpful for understanding diffraction conditions. Figure 3 shows a representation of reciprocal space in two dimensions, with the Bragg points marked by the solid circles. The incident wave vector $\mathbf{k}$ is drawn with its tip at the center of reciprocal space $(\mathbf{G} = 0)$. Its tail defines the origin O of the Ewald sphere, which is a sphere with radius k drawn about O. The possible diffracted wave vectors $\mathbf{k}'$ are vectors between O and the Ewald sphere (since they satisfy energy conservation $k = k'$). Where the Ewald sphere intercepts one of the Bragg points, the diffraction conditions, $\mathbf{G}_{hkl} = \mathbf{k} - \mathbf{k}' = \mathbf{Q}$, are satisfied and a diffraction peak is observed at the wave vector $\mathbf{k}'$.

C. DIFFRACTION FROM TWO-DIMENSIONAL SOLIDS

One of the most exciting aspects of applying X-ray scattering to electrochemical interfaces is the ability to directly probe the structure of adsorbed monolayers and surface reconstructions. Before discussing these applications, it is important to understand the differences between diffraction from 3D crystals and 2D layers or surfaces. It is convenient to first treat the case of diffraction from a free standing, ordered 2D

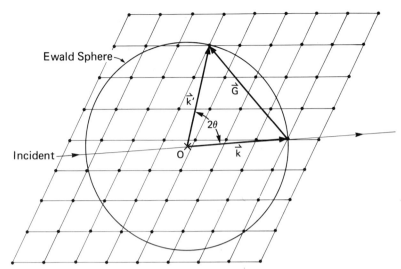

Figure 3. Two dimensional representation of Ewald construction. The Bragg points are shown by the solid circles, and the Laue conditions are represented by the intersection of the Ewald sphere with the Bragg points. For the case shown, there is a diffracted beam that has wave vector $\mathbf{k}'$ and is related to the reciprocal lattice vector $\mathbf{G}$ by $\mathbf{k}' - \mathbf{k} = \mathbf{G}$. The scattering angle 2θ is the angle between $\mathbf{k}'$ and $\mathbf{k}$.

solid. The most pronounced difference between this and a bulk solid is the absence of any diffracting planes normal to the surface (the z-direction). The effect of this on the diffraction is most obvious if one starts with a 3D crystal and then begins to increase the d-spacing along the z-axis. This transformation is illustrated in Figure 4 (top) and a reciprocal space representation of the diffraction is shown below. Only one first order reflection in the $x - y$ plane has been illustrated. Starting with the unperturbed crystal [Fig. 4A], Bragg points are observed at equal spacings corresponding to the multiple order reflections of planes normal to the surface. As the periodicity in the z-direction is dilated [Fig. 4B], the Bragg points move closer together as expected from Bragg's Law. In the limit, as d_z approaches infinity, the Bragg points are no longer discrete points but form a continuous streak of intensity perpendicular to the monolayer. Neglecting Debye-Waller and atomic form factor contributions, the intensity along these lines is constant. By analogy to Bragg points, these streaks of intensity are called Bragg rods.

Alternatively, a free standing monolayer can be considered as a bulk crystal, but consisting of only one layer of atoms. This is equivalent to the von Laue approach in 3D and is described in Appendix A.4. We find that it is necessary to fulfill only the two Laue

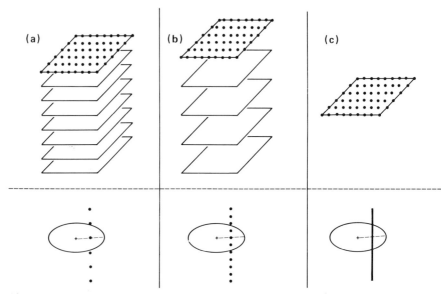

Figure 4. Top: lattice planes with varying spacing in the z-direction. (A) $d_z = d_0$; (B) $d_z = 2d_0$; (C) $d_z = \infty$ (2D solid). Bottom: reciprocal space representation of the diffraction. For simplicity, only one reflection in the $x - y$ plane is illustrated.

conditions in the plane of the monolayer and that no Laue condition must be satisfied for the component of the scattering vector perpendicular to the monolayer. In other words, the diffraction from a monolayer consists of Bragg rods. This result is simply due to the loss of translational symmetry perpendicular to the monolayer, e.g., the monolayer is two dimensional. A more complete discussion of 2D diffraction can be found elsewhere [7].

    A free standing monolayer can be a good approximation to an incommensurate adsorbed monolayer, if the substrate-adsorbate interaction is weak. However, for commensurate adsorbates or strongly interacting incommensurate adsorbates, this is not so, and the substrate influences the diffraction from the adsorbate [8]. Before discussing monolayers adsorbed on substrates (a real occurrence contrary to the idealized situation just discussed), we must discuss the X-ray scattering that results purely from a surface.

D. CRYSTAL TRUNCATION RODS

The termination of a crystal at a sharp boundary, e.g., a surface or interface, causes 2D-like diffraction features [9-12], which have been termed crystal truncation rods [9] (also known as Bragg reflectivity [13], or asymmetric Bragg diffraction [10]). Measurements of crystal truncation rods (CTRs) can provide important information on surface and interface topography (lattice roughness). They have been used to elucidate the nature of thermal roughening transitions of Ag(110) [14] and Cu(110) [13] and the extent of crystalline order into the amorphous regions of amorphous-Si/Si(111) and amorphous-SiO$_2$/Si(111) [12]. Measurements of CTRs can also determine atomic positions on surfaces with relaxations or reconstructions extending several layers into the substrate [10, 15, 16]. Finally, the intensity of CTRs provides a good indication of substrate quality and may be useful for the determination of crystallographic phase information [17].

The scattered intensity from CTRs is considered in detail in Appendix A.5, where we take the c-direction of the crystal as parallel to the surface normal (z-direction). It is shown that an ideally truncated (flat) surface gives rise to streaks of intensity that connect Bragg points along directions normal to the surface and have an intensity that is similar to that from a monolayer. These are the CTRs, and their scattering intensity is not independent of Q_c, as for a 2D layer, but has a ($\sin \pi Q_c$)$^{-2}$ shape. An example of the Q_c dependence of scattering intensity from a CTR is shown in Figure 5.

Figure 6 shows the CTRs for the (001) surface of a body-centered cubic (bcc) crystal. The CTRs run along the (001) direction and connect bulk Bragg points. Figure 6A shows a prospective 3D view of the CTRs. From this, it can be seen that diffraction scans along the CTRs measure the intensity at (hkQ_z), as Q_z varies from zero at the surface through the Bragg points. Figure 6B shows a cut through reciprocal space at the surface plane, $Q_z = 0$. A LEED pattern of this surface is similar to this and it is useful to write the CTRs in the usual surface (LEED) notation. For this surface the conversion takes a very simple form,

$$(hk0)_{bulk} = (hk)_{surface}. \tag{8}$$

In general, however, the conversion is more complicated. Note that although CTRs occur in the same position in reciprocal space as LEED spots, they have very different origins. LEED spots result from the small penetration length of the electrons, while CTRs originate from the

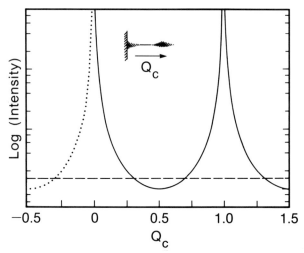

Figure 5. Scattering intensity of a crystal truncation rod. The intensity from an ideally truncated surface [Eq. A18] is plotted vs the perpendicular scattering vector Q_c. The region of negative Q_c is shown by the dotted line and is experimentally inaccessible, since the scattering vector is into the crystal. The dashed line represents the scattering intensity from a free standing monolayer; it is independent of Q_c and has about the same strength as that from the CTR.

incomplete destructive interference of X rays scattered from planes parallel to the surface.

Figure 7 shows CTR scans for W(001) in UHV taken from Robinson [9]. The functional form for a perfectly flat surface [Eq. A18] is plotted by the dashed line and is clearly inadequate. Robinson described the data with a model that allows partially filled layers with fractional occupancy β per layer $(0 < \beta < 1)$. With this surface roughness model, the CTR shape is

$$\frac{(1-\beta)^2}{1+\beta^2-2\beta\cos 2\pi Q_c}\frac{1}{\sin^2\pi Q_c}. \tag{9}$$

Here $\beta = 0$ represents a perfectly flat surface, whereas $\beta = 1$ is infinitely rough. The fit to the W(001) data is shown by the solid line and is clearly adequate, although models with other distributions can also fit the data. It is important to note that it is the lattice roughness, or continuation of the crystal lattice into the roughened region, that is measured by CTRs. This can be quite different from the roughness measured by X-ray reflectivity [18], which is related to the total electron density (whether crystalline or amorphous).

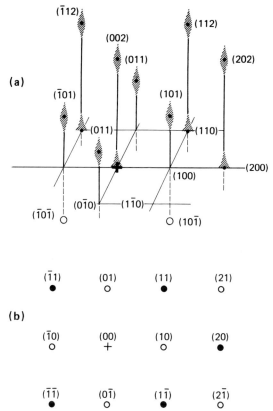

Figure 6. Crystal truncation rods for a bcc (001) surface. (A) Three dimensional view. The dark Bragg points and the diffuse CTRs are shown. (B) A slice through reciprocal space at $Q_z = 0$. The origin is shown by the "+," the CTRs by the open circles, and the Bragg points by the solid circles. The surface notation is used for labeling peaks.

E. DIFFRACTION FROM ADSORBED MONOLAYERS AND RECONSTRUCTED SURFACES

Figures 8A and B show, respectively, an incommensurate monolayer adsorbed on a (001) bcc substrate and the resulting diffraction pattern (at $Q_z = 0$). To a first approximation, the adlayer can be considered as a free standing 2D solid, and the diffraction pattern is just a superposition of that from the adlayer and the substrate. However, since there is an interaction between the adlayer and the substrate, the structure of the two will be affected. The extent of this effect depends on the relative strengths of the substrate-adsorbate and adsorbate-adsorbate interactions. For a strong substrate-adsorbate

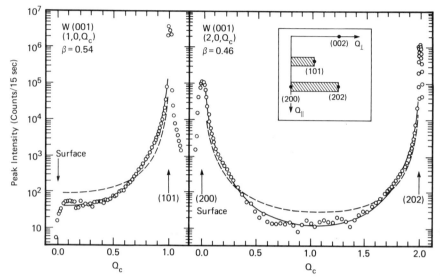

Figure 7. CTRs for a W(001) surface prepared in UHV. The perpendicular and parallel scattering vectors are Q_c and $Q_{\parallel}$, respectively. The dashed line is a fit to the data for an ideally truncated surface using Equation (9). The solid lines are independent fits to the two sets of data for the model used by Robinson and described in the text [Eq. (9)]. For the (1,0,k) rod $\beta = 0.54$, and for the (2,0,k) rod $\beta = 0.46$. In the inset, the bars show the range of the two scans in the reciprocal space. (Reprinted from Ref. [9].)

interaction, the substrate surface structure can be substantially altered due to the adsorbate. For example, the top layer of the substrate could be driven incommensurate with respect to the remainder of the substrate. For a relatively weak substrate-adsorbate interaction, only the adlayer will be affected. The azimuthal orientation of the adlayer will likely be influenced by the substrate through the creation of static distortion waves [8]. A more complete discussion of this will be presented in Section IV.C.

Next consider a commensurate layer with a larger surface lattice than the substrate. We will take a p(2x2) structure as an example and show this structure in Figure 8C. The diffraction pattern [Fig. 8D] consists of two types of diffraction peaks: the "fractional" order (half-order) peaks and the integral order peaks. The fractional order peaks [solid circles in Fig. 8D] are Bragg rods from the adsorbed monolayer. They result from the larger periodicity of the adlayer compared to the substrate. If the structure of the substrate is not changed by adsorption of the adlayer, the fractional order diffraction is due only to the adlayer, and since this is 2D, the intensity of the Bragg

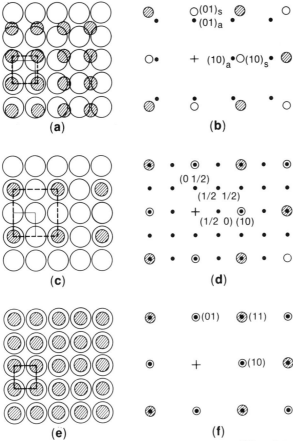

Figure 8. Real space structure and reciprocal space diffraction patterns for adsorbed monolayers on a bcc (001) surface. The bulk and adlayer lattices are shown by the thin solid and thick dashed lines, respectively. The adlayer diffraction is represented by solid circles, the substrate CTRs by open circles, and the substrate Bragg points by shaded circles. Some of the diffraction peaks are labeled with the subscripts a and s denoting the adlayer and substrate, respectively. (A) Surface structure of an incommensurate adlayer. (B) Diffraction pattern for the structure shown in (A). (C) Surface structure of a p(2x2) commensurate adlayer. (D) Diffraction pattern for the structure shown in (C). Since the adlayer lattice spacing is twice the substrate lattice spacing, the adlayer reciprocal lattice spacing is half that of the substrate. (E) Surface structure of a p(1x1) commensurate adlayer. (F) Diffraction pattern for the structure shown in (E).

rods at the fractional order positions is independent of Q_z. If the surface structure is changed upon adsorption, the intensity of the Bragg rods at the fractional order positions will depend on Q_z, since both the adlayer and the substrate have the larger periodicity of the adlayer, and hence, the structure is not completely 2D. By measuring the dependence of the Bragg rod intensity on Q_z, which is generally slow, it is possible to determine the atomic positions of the adlayer and substrate perpendicular to the surface. Such an analysis has been made for Pb and Sn on Ge(111) [19].

The integral order diffraction originates from both the adlayer and the substrate. For integral order diffraction that coincides with a bulk Bragg peak (e.g., the (11) peak), this is obvious. In general, though, this is not so. For example, the (10) peak in Figure 8D corresponds to the (100) bulk substrate reflection, which is not an allowed reflection. However, substrate CTRs necessarily occur at the same position in reciprocal space as the integral order diffraction from the adlayer. Thus, both the substrate and adsorbate contribute to all integral order diffraction. Since the adatoms are in specific sites on the substrate, the adsorbate and substrate scattering amplitudes add coherently, and the measured intensity of the integral order diffraction is

$$|f_{bulk}(\mathbf{Q})F_{CTR}(\mathbf{Q}) + e^{i\phi}f_{surf}(\mathbf{Q})F_{surf}(\mathbf{Q})|^2 , \qquad (10)$$

where the phase factor ϕ depends on the adatom bonding site (e.g., adlayer registry). Here $f_{bulk}(\mathbf{Q})$ and $f_{surf}(\mathbf{Q})$ are, respectively, the bulk and surface atomic form factors [Eq. A3], and $F_{CTR}(\mathbf{Q})$ and $F_{surf}(\mathbf{Q})$ are, respectively, the CTR and surface interference functions. As can be seen from Equation (10), the integral order intensity depends on ϕ, which is related to the bonding site. Thus, by measuring the intensity at integral order diffraction peaks, it is possible to determine bonding sites for adsorbed layers or surface reconstructions. Such measurements have been reported by Feidenhans'l et al. for (vapor deposited) Ge(111) $\sqrt{3} \times \sqrt{3}$ -Pb and the registry of the adsorbed Pb determined [20].

For an adsorbed monolayer that forms a (1x1) commensurate structure, there is no fractional order diffraction and no new diffraction peaks will be visible. However, just as for the p(2x2), the integral order diffraction will contain a contribution from the adsorbate, as well as the substrate. Thus, measurements of this diffraction can yield the atomic positions of the adlayer.

Surface reconstructions can be considered a special, and interesting, class of adsorbed layers, where the adsorbate atomic species is the same as the substrate. Surface reconstructions can be incommensurate, commensurate with a larger surface lattice (e.g., p(2x2)), or commensurate with unchanged surface lattice (necessarily (1x1)). (The latter case is usually referred to as surface relaxation). Thus, surface reconstructions can be studied using X-ray scattering in much the same way as foreign adlayers, and the discussion above is completely valid.

For surface crystallographic measurements that involve the determination of atomic positions in relatively large unit cells, many reflections must be accurately measured, and appropriate methods of data analysis must be employed to determine the positions from the measured intensities. Since this type of measurement has not yet been carried out for surfaces at the solid-liquid interface and since the subject has recently been reviewed for the surfaces at the vacuum-solid interface, we will not discuss this topic in detail. The interested reader is referred to the reviews by Als-Nielsen [18] and Robinson [21].

An interesting property of true 2D solids is that they do not posses long-range crystalline order [Eq. 1] and thus do not have δ-function type Bragg peaks [22]. Instead, 2D solids have a more subtle form of translational order, which is called bond-orientational or quasi-long range order. This topological order produces diffraction peaks with a peak shape described by $|\mathbf{Q} - \mathbf{G}|^{-2 + \eta_G}$, where $\eta_G = (kTG^2)/(4\pi K)$ and K is a combination of elastic constants [23, 24]. When instrumental resolution is taken into consideration (see next Section), this power law dependence is very difficult to distinguish from a δ-function [25]. It requires very high resolution experiments and very high quality samples. In addition, the presence of a substrate can have a strong influence on the quasi-long-range order of adsorbed monolayers [25]. Despite this, in high resolution synchrotron X-ray diffraction experiments on monolayers of Xe physically adsorbed on graphite [26, 27] and on free standing liquid crystals [28] this quasi-long-range order has been reported. Although this type of order probably exists for incommensurate electrochemically adsorbed monolayers, it will likely be very difficult to measure, because of the limitations of sample quality, high background levels caused by the diffuse scattering from the electrolyte, and strong interactions between substrate and adsorbate.

3 EXPERIMENTAL ASPECTS OF SURFACE X-RAY SCATTERING

A. SYNCHROTRON X-RAY RADIATION

Since surfaces inherently have a small number of atoms ($\sim 10^{15}/\text{cm}^2$), surface X-ray diffraction requires very intense X-ray sources. Previous experiments [29, 30] have demonstrated that surface diffraction is feasible with conventional (rotating anode) sources of X-ray radiation, particularly for strong X-ray scatterers, and thus, synchrotron radiation is not always required. However, synchrotron radiation greatly facilitates the execution of surface X-ray scattering experiments and makes possible experiments that are impossible with conventional sources. Robinson has demonstrated this with calculations of the expected count rates for several different surfaces using high-power rotating anode and synchrotron radiation sources [21, 31]. Because of the intimate connection between surface X-ray scattering and the unique properties of synchrotron radiation, we will briefly expand on the discussion of this light source given in the chapter on EXAFS. For the interested reader, several handbooks are available [32-36] and discussions of the different types of conventional sources of X-ray radiation can be found in a number of textbooks [3, 5, 6].

For X-ray diffraction, the brightness, or spectral brilliance, instead of the total photon flux, is the important characteristic quantity. Brightness is defined as the total number of photons emitted per sec per unit solid angle per unit source area in a given bandwidth (usually 0.1%), e.g., the phase-space density of the photon flux. High brightness is advantageous when high spatial and angular resolution is needed, because high brightness corresponds to a large photon flux into a small spatial and angular region. Since a small grazing incidence angle is used for surface scattering experiments, the projected sample size is quite small, and the very high brightness of synchrotron radiation compared to conventional sources is a great advantage. There may be additional advantages, depending on the angular resolution or collimation required for a particular experiment. The increase in X-ray brightness from synchrotron sources relative to conventional sources is shown in Figure 9. It is this six to eight orders of magnitude increase in brightness which has led to such a renaissance in X-ray spectroscopies.

Another characteristic of synchrotron radiation that is important for X-ray scattering is its high collimation ($\sim$0.2 milliradian (mrad) = 0.012°). This contributes to the high brightness, ensures a small irradiated area at the large source-to-sample distances typical for

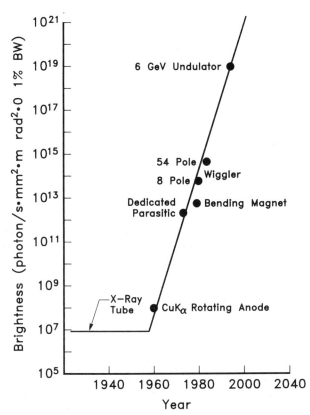

Figure 9. Brightness or spectral brilliance of various X-ray sources by year of implementation. (Reprinted from [34].)

synchrotron radiation experiments, and permits a high flux for high resolution experiments. The broad spectral range of synchrotron radiation is also advantageous, since it enables a wide selection of X-ray energy. For experiments probing the solid-liquid interface, high energies are usually selected, since the absorption cross-section of water is smaller than at lower energies. One further useful property is the high degree of linear polarization (of the electric field) in the horizontal plane. Recall that when the electric field is polarized in the plane of scattered X rays, the scattering cross section is decreased by $\cos^2(2\theta)$ compared to the cross section for perpendicular polarization [3-5]. This is one factor that leads to the use of a vertical scattering geometry, as is discussed below.

B. X-RAY BEAM LINES

In addition to the source of synchrotron radiation itself (typically, electron storage rings), the "beam line" is an integral part of the X-ray source. The purpose of a beam line is to bring as much of the synchrotron radiation emitted by the orbiting electrons onto the experimental sample as possible and to provide suitable monochromation. An X-ray beam line for surface scattering and its associated optics must provide: a) high efficiency to ensure a high incident flux; b) adequate resolution of the scattering vector ΔQ (the stringency of this will depend on the nature of the experiment being performed); c) a tunable energy range; and d) suitably monochromatic radiation. Although there are several other designs in use [13, 37-40], each with its particular set of advantages and disadvantages, we will use beam line 7-2 at SSRL (Stanford Synchrotron Radiation Laboratory) [41] as a prototype for discussing the design of beam lines. Figure 10 shows a schematic of this beam line.

The two basic optical elements of a beam line are a torodial focusing mirror and a double crystal monochromator. Although the natural angular divergence of synchrotron radiation is quite small, the electrons in the storage ring are continuously orbiting and emit radiation into the entire 2π of the orbit plane. Since the distance from the synchrotron radiation source to the experimental sample is several tens of meters, the X-ray spot size is large (typically 20 mm x 4 mm). In the grazing incidence geometry used for surface X-ray scattering, focusing this large X-ray beam onto the sample can result in a significant increase in intensity. This focusing can be achieved by employing X-ray mirrors that collect the divergence (or spot size) and focus the X-ray radiation onto the experimental sample. The torodial focusing mirror provides point-to-point focus and can increase the X-ray flux density (photons/sec-cm^2) by a factor of up to one hundred [42]. It is a bent cylinder, with a small radius of curvature ($\sim$10 cm) in the horizontal direction and a very large radius ($\sim$km) in the vertical

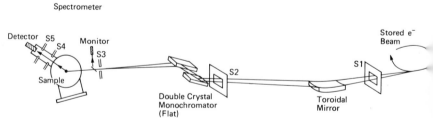

Figure 10. Schematic representation of the SSRL beam line 7-2. The slits are labeled S1-S5.

direction.   With an optimal radius in the horizontal, or sagittal, direction, the mirror effectively collects several mrad of the synchrotron radiation (e.g., several cm of the beam) and focuses it onto the sample. This horizontal acceptance is limited by mirror aberrations to about 5 mrad (about 5cm beam size).   In addition to horizontal focusing, the bend of the mirror in the vertical or meridian direction focuses the radiation vertically [42].   X-ray mirrors use the property (to be discussed below) that x-ray radiation is totally reflected at sufficiently small grazing incidence angles.   The critical angle for total external reflection is principally determined by the electron density of the mirror and the X-ray energy.   Since the grazing incidence angle is usually fixed, this results in a cutoff energy above which the mirror will not reflect X rays and is useless. The cutoff at high energies can, however, be used as an advantage to filter the incident radiation and ensure that unwanted harmonics from the monochromator are absorbed by the mirror before they reach the monochromator. Typical mirrors consist of a substrate (e.g., silica, quartz, aluminum) coated with a dense metal (e.g., Pt, Ni). For more detail on mirror principles and designs, the interested reader is referred to the literature [43-45].

The next optical element in the beam line is a double crystal monochromator, which uses Bragg diffraction to filter one energy slice from the continuous spectral distribution of the synchrotron radiation. The first crystal is the primary monochromator, and because its heat load is high ($\sim 100\text{W/cm}^2$), it is cooled to prevent thermal distortion, typically with water [41]. The second crystal renders the output beam parallel to the input beam, and if it is slightly detuned from the first crystal, can be used to filter out higher-order harmonics [46], although this results in loss of flux. To maximize the flux at the sample, the monochromator crystals should have a large bandwidth $\Delta E/E = \Delta\theta_M \cot\theta_M$, where θ_M is the monochromator Bragg angle and $\Delta\theta_M$ is the width of the diffraction peak. Monochromator crystals are most often "perfect" single crystals and the diffraction from them must be treated with the dynamical theory, unlike the kinematic discussion of diffraction given in Section II and Appendix A. Currently, limitations on $\Delta E/E$ are imposed by the Darwin width $\Delta\theta_M$ of perfect single crystalline materials. Symmetrically cut Ge(111), Si(220), and Si(111) crystals are often used and have bandwidths $\Delta E/E \sim 10^{-4} - 10^{-3}$ [46]. Less commonly used alternatives that can increase the bandwidth include asymmetrically cut crystals [47] and artificial multilayers [48-50], which consist of many alternating layers of materials with large electron density differences.   Another alternative is to place the monochromator before the mirror [38].   This can be advantageous, since it substantially reduces thermal loading on the mirror; however, it creates other problems. For more detailed information on crystal monochromators, the interested reader is referred to one of the excellent discussions in the literature [43, 46, 51].

The electron current in the storage ring ($\simeq$100mA), and hence the X-ray intensity, decays with time after the electrons are initially injected into the ring. Thus, a detecting device must be placed after the optics to monitor the intensity incident onto the experimental sample. The output from this "I_0" monitor is then used to normalize the intensity of the detected X rays. There are several types of "I_0" monitors, for example, ionization chambers or beam splitters with scintillation counters. The slits shown in Figure 10 are an important part of the beam line. Slits S1 and S2 provide the vertical collimation of the beam and can strongly affect the resolution in high resolution experiments [41]. The slits S3 and S4 define the size of the beam on the sample and reduce background radiation.

C. FOUR CIRCLE DIFFRACTOMETERS

A four circle diffractometer is generally used to access all points in the full 3D reciprocal space of the sample. Figure 11 shows a schematic representation of this instrument and defines the four angles ϕ, χ, θ, and 2θ [52]. The axes of the diffractometer are concentric to within $10\mu m$ and accurate to 0.005°. All angular motions are driven with stepper motors, which are controlled by a local computer. The computer also calculates the nonlinear transformation from a point in reciprocal space (represented by Q_a, Q_b, and Q_c) to the angular setting ϕ, χ, θ, and 2θ [52]. It can be used to scan through reciprocal space in an arbitrary direction, as was done to obtain data shown in Figure 7 [9]. To adequately constrain the calculation from three reciprocal space coordinates to four angles, a certain convention is specified [52]. Depending on the experimental approach, measurements are also made using certain modes of diffractometer operation. These have been recently discussed by Robinson [21], and we will only briefly describe the vertical, "symmetric" four-circle mode here [52], since it was used to obtain the data presented in Section 4.

The four-circle diffractometer shown in Figure 11 is operating in the vertical, symmetric mode. The sample is mounted so the diffractometer ϕ-axis is parallel to the normal to the sample surface. (More precisely, the ϕ-axis is parallel to the **G** vector of the crystal planes that are (nominally) parallel to the sample surface.) The azimuthal orientation of the sample is solely determined by ϕ, and symmetry equivalent reflections only differ by rotations of ϕ. Typically, sample alignment is first done optically and can then be improved by

Four–Circle Diffractometer

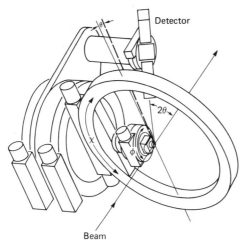

Beam

Figure 11. Schematic representation of a vertically mounted four-circle diffractometer. The scattering angle is 2θ and is the angle between the incidence beam and the detector, whereas the sample rotation angle is ϕ. The angle θ is the angle between the plane normal to the incident beam and the χ-circle, whereas the angle χ is between the sample normal and the scattering plane (plane containing the detector, sample, and incident beam).

checking that the positions and intensities of equivalent bulk reflections do not change as ϕ is rotated. The scattering plane in this mode is vertical, which means that the motion of the detector (which changes as 2θ is varied) is vertical. The vertical alignment of the scattering plane avoids intensity losses due to the natural horizontal polarization of synchrotron radiation and increases the overlap between the resolution function and the 2D Bragg rod, which will be discussed in detail below. In the symmetric mode, the diffractometer is operated such that $\theta = (2\theta)/2$. In other words, the χ-axis is half-way between the incident beam and the detector. The relationship between χ and the incidence and exit angles of the X rays relative to the sample surface, α and δ, respectively, is [52]

$$\sin \alpha = \sin \delta = \sin \chi \sin \theta. \tag{11}$$

Thus, for $\chi = 0$ the incident and exit beams are both exactly parallel to the sample surface ($\alpha = 0$). The optimal setting for χ, or equivalently α, depends on the particular experiment and will be discussed below.

There are several types of analyzers of the scattered X rays. Perfect single crystals (e.g., Si(111), etc.) are used to obtain high resolution in experiments where this is necessary. For experiments where such high resolution is not needed, there are several options: "imperfect" crystals with a mosaic spread (e.g., LiF, graphite); Soller slits, which consist of a set of closely spaced, thin metal plates [3]; or two sets of receiving slits spaced a suitable distance (~ 20-50 cm) apart. After passing through the analyzer, the scattered X rays are counted, typically with a scintillation counter. With a position sensitive detector, parallel detection is also possible [49, 50, 53].

D. RESOLUTION FUNCTION

The resolution function of an X-ray scattering instrument defines the precision in reciprocal space with which the scattering vector $\mathbf{Q}$ can be determined. It is often represented by a resolution volume, which is the volume in reciprocal space enclosed by the 50% contour of the resolution function. Since $\mathbf{Q}$ has three components, there are three directions and dimensions associated with the resolution volume, two in the scattering plane and one perpendicular to it. These can be approximately described by a) a longitudinal component ΔQ_l, which is parallel to $\mathbf{Q}$ and in the scattering plane, b) a transverse component ΔQ_t, which is in the scattering plane and perpendicular to $\mathbf{Q}$, and c) an out-of-plane component ΔQ_p, which is, naturally, perpendicular to the scattering plane. The two in-plane components are coupled together, but to first-order, ΔQ_p is decoupled from these and is independently adjustable [54].

In the vertical scattering geometry, the three components of the resolution volume are approximately [21, 54]

$$\begin{aligned}
\Delta Q_l &= k(\Delta\theta_M + \Delta\theta_A)\cos\theta \\
\Delta Q_t &= k(\Delta\theta_M + \Delta\theta_A)\sin\theta \\
\Delta Q_p &= k(\Delta\Theta),
\end{aligned} \tag{12}$$

where $k = 2\pi/\lambda$, $\theta = (2\theta)/2$ is half the scattering angle, $\Delta\theta_M$ is the Darwin width of the monochromator, and $\Delta\theta_A$ is the angular acceptance of the analyzer, which is either the analyzer crystal's Darwin width, if a perfect analyzer crystal is used, or the acceptance of the slit arrangement, if slits are used. Here $\Delta\Theta$ is the quadratic average of the horizontal acceptance of the mirror and the acceptance of horizontal slits (which is L_h/R_s, where R_s is the distance from the sample to the slit and L_h is the horizontal slit width) [21]. Since X-ray mirrors collect several mrad of horizontal radiation and since a wide horizontal slit width is used on the analyzer, $\Delta Q_p \sim 0.1 - 0.02\text{Å}^{-1}$. For low resolution experiments using slits as an analyzer, ΔQ_l and $\Delta Q_t \sim$ 0.01-0.005 Å^{-1}, while for high resolution experiments with perfect crystal analyzers, ΔQ_l and $\Delta Q_t \sim 10^{-3}$ Å^{-1}. The important point here is that the resolution volume is highly anisotropic; it is narrow in the scattering plane, but broad perpendicular to it. This anisotropy has important implications on the experimental geometries used to maximize the measured intensity from surfaces and will be discussed below.

One reason a vertical scattering geometry is used is that the small vertical divergence of the synchrotron radiation is in the scattering plane and matches the high resolution direction of the four-circle diffractometer. This is also why the monochromator and analyzer crystals scatter vertically. The focusing mirror has the disadvantage of coupling the horizontal divergence of the X-ray beam to the vertical divergence [41]. Thus, for the highest resolution ($\Delta Q_l \sim 4 \times 10^{-4}$ Å^{-1}), it is necessary to decrease the horizontal acceptance of the mirror to about one mrad [41].

The discussion of the resolution function given above is only a first approximation, and a complete description is much more complicated. The in-plane components of the resolution volume describe an ellipse, and in general, the two principal axes of this ellipse are not parallel and perpendicular to **Q**; the ellipse is oriented at a nonzero angle to **Q**. A thorough discussion is beyond the scope of this review, and the interested reader is referred to the literature for more detail [54, 55].

E. TOTAL EXTERNAL REFLECTION OF X RAYS

The final element of surface scattering is the use of a grazing incidence geometry. For all materials, the index of refraction at X-ray energies is slightly less than one [6, 56-58]. This phenomenon was first noted by Darwin and occurs because X rays traveling through matter are weakly scattered in the forward direction, with the scattered wave undergoing a phase shift very close to $-\pi/2$ [4]. This forward scattered wave interferes with the incident wave and builds up a wave that travels through the material with a phase velocity that is slightly larger than the velocity of light c. Thus, the refractive index is less than one and depends on the scattering cross section, which is proportional to the total electron density. We give a brief description of total external reflection below. A more detailed account is given in Appendix B.

Since for X rays the forward scattering is small, the index of refraction is close to unity and is typically written $n = 1 - \delta - i\beta$ [4, 6, 56-58], where

$$\delta = \frac{e^2\lambda^2}{2\pi mc^2} N_0 \frac{\rho(Z+f')}{A} = 2.70 \times 10^{-6} (\frac{Z+f'}{A})\rho\lambda^2, \quad (13)$$

and

$$\beta = \frac{\lambda\mu}{4\pi}. \quad (14)$$

Here N_0 is Avogadro's number, Z is the average atomic number, A is the average atomic mass, ρ is the mass density (in gm/cc), f' is the average (over the atomic concentration) of the real part of the anomalous scattering factor, λ is the X-ray wavelength (in Å), and μ is the linear absorption.   The term β accounts for absorption losses. Typically, f' is small compared to Z, so that δ is proportional to the total electron density ($Z\rho/A$). As Table 1 shows, typical values for δ and β in the hard X-ray region are quite small with $\delta \sim 10^{-6}$-10^{-5} and $\beta \sim 10^{-9}$-10^{-6}.

Since the refractive index is less than one, it is possible for X rays to undergo total external reflection (TER).   Consider the situation shown in Figure 12, where X rays are incident from a medium with refractive index n onto a medium with refractive index n'. Snell's law is

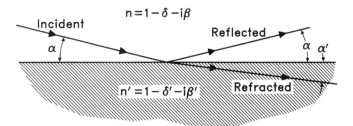

Figure 12. Reflection and refraction of X rays that are incident onto an interface between two materials with indices of refraction n and n'. The angles of incidence and reflection are α, and the refracted angle is α'. The x-and z-directions are parallel and perpendicular to the surface, respectively.   For simplicity, **E** is assumed to be parallel to the interface.   Since α is small, the reflection and refraction for this polarization is the same as for **E** perpendicular to the interface.

$n \cos \alpha = n' \cos \alpha'$. Since δ is small and we are primarily concerned with small angles, Snell's law accurately reduces to

$$\alpha'^2 = \alpha^2 - 2(\delta' - \delta). \tag{15}$$

From this, it is seen that the critical angle for TER is $\alpha_c = \sqrt{2(\delta' - \delta)}$. Table 1 gives α_c for air/water, air/metal, and water/metal interfaces for Al and Ag at 8.04 and 17.44 keV. The critical angles for air/metal interfaces are much larger than air/water interfaces, since metals have much higher electron densities than water. Similarly, the difference

between α_c for air/metal and water/metal interfaces is small.

By using Snell's law and applying Fresnel boundary conditions to the interface shown in Figure 12, it is easy to determine the fields and intensities of the reflected and transmitted (refracted) X-ray beams [59, 60]. These are the classic Fresnel equations [59]. The intensity of the reflected beam is proportional to the specular reflectivity R and Figure 13A shows the Fresnel reflectivity for an ideally smooth water/Ag interface at 8.04 and 17.44 keV. For $\alpha < \alpha_c$, R is approximately one and any deviation of R from one is dependent on absorption, in particular, the ratio $(\beta' - \beta)/\alpha_c^2$. Near α_c, R falls quickly to small values, with the steepness of the decrease again dependent on absorption. For $\alpha \gg \alpha_c$, $R \approx (\alpha_c/(2\alpha))^4$. For rough interfaces or materials consisting of several layers, the specular reflectivity is modified from that shown in Figure 13A, and measurements of the reflectivity can provide important information about interfacial roughness and the density and thicknesses of the layers [18, 61-63].

The electric field for the transmitted beam is $E(\mathbf{r}) = E_0 \exp i(\mathbf{k'} \cdot \mathbf{r})$, where E_0 is the electric field at the surface of the solid (normalized to unity incident field) and $\mathbf{k'}$ is the (complex) wavevector of the transmitted X rays. The intensity of the transmitted X rays decays into the second material (either because of total external reflection or absorption) and the depth (z) dependence of intensity of the transmitted X rays is $I(z) = |E_0^2(\mathbf{r})| = I_0 \exp(-z/D)$, where the intensity of the transmitted X rays at the surface I_0 and the X-ray intensity penetration depth D are given in Appendix B. Figures 13B and C show I_0 and D calculated for a water/Ag interface at 8.04 and 17.44keV. For $\alpha < \alpha_c$, the X rays are evanescent within the material and penetrate only a few tens of Ångstroms. As α increases and becomes equal to α_c, D rapidly increases and for angles above α_c, D approaches that expected purely from absorption (e.g., $(\sin \alpha)/\mu$). I_0 is small for $\alpha \ll \alpha_c$ and increases (approximately quadratically) to slightly less than four near the critical

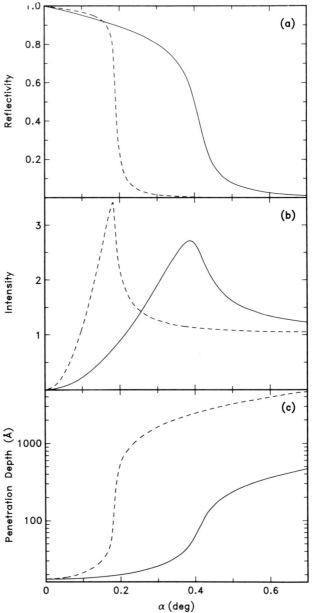

Figure 13. Dependence of reflectivity, X-ray penetration depth, and X-ray intensity on incidence angle α for an interface between Ag ($\rho = 10.5$ gm/cc) and water. The dashed lines are for 17.44 keV x rays (Mo K_α), which has $\alpha_c = 0.19°$, and the solid lines are for 8.04 keV X rays (Cu K_α), which has $\alpha_c = 0.41°$. (A) Reflectivity, R. (B) Surface X-ray intensity, I_0. (C) Penetration depth, D. Note that at $\alpha = 0$, D is a minimum that is independent of λ, $D_{\min} = \lambda/(4\pi\alpha_c) = 34\mathring{A}/(\sqrt{\rho Z/A}\,)$.

angle.   For angles greater than α_c, I_0 falls off toward unity. Experimental verification of $I_0(\alpha)$ has been reported for 10keV X rays incident on InSb(111) [38].

F. GIXS GEOMETRY

Figure 14 shows the grazing incidence X-ray scattering (GIXS) geometry used in most surface X-ray scattering experiments, with its first use reported by Eisenberger and Marra [30] and Marra, Eisenberger, and Cho [64]. Since α is small, the scattering vector **Q** is predominately in the surface plane, and the experiments probe atomic correlations in this plane. This differs from LEED experiments, where **Q** has components both in the surface plane and perpendicular to it, with the result that LEED is sensitive to in-plane and out-of-plane atomic positions.   To measure perpendicular atomic positions with surface X-ray scattering, it is necessary to scan out along the crystal truncation or Bragg rods, which involves experimental conditions where α (and thus Q_z) become large.

There are several reasons the GIXS geometry is favorable for surface scattering experiments. The most important one concerns the overlap of the resolution volume with the surface diffraction features. Recall that the resolution volume is highly anisotropic, having a small component (ΔQ_l) in the scattering plane and large component (ΔQ_p) normal to this plane. The scattering from surfaces (e.g., Bragg rods or CTRs) is also very anisotropic and is narrow in the surface plane of the crystal but diffuse normal to this.   The observed intensity is a convolution (overlap) of the resolution function with the scattering.

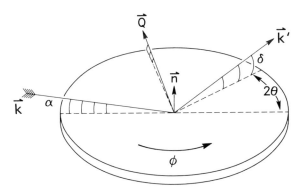

Figure 14. Grazing incidence X-ray scattering geometry showing the incident angle α, the exit angle δ, the scattering angle 2θ, and the azimuthal angle ϕ. The incident and diffracted wave vectors are **k** and **k'**, respectively, and the scattering vector is $\mathbf{Q} = \mathbf{k'} - \mathbf{k}$.

Clearly, it will be a maximum when the diffuse direction of the rod is aligned along the long direction of the resolution volume. This is the case for GIXS.

A second advantage of the GIXS geometry is a significant reduction in background scattering, both thermal diffuse and fluorescent, from the bulk substrate. This background scattering is weak, but since there are many more atoms in the substrate than at the surface, it can overwhelm the surface signal. In the GIXS geometry, the small penetration depth [Fig. 13C] effectively limits this background. The importance of this depends on the extent of atomic order in the surface layer. If the surface is well-ordered, then a high resolution detector can be used. The background is generally quite small, and the advantage is not that great. However, for less well-ordered or disordered surfaces or thin films, the advantage gained in the reduction in background by choosing $\alpha \lesssim \alpha_c$ can be very important [65, 66].

The enhancement of the transmitted X-ray intensity near α_c [Fig. 13B] can also be an advantage for the GIXS geometry. Note, however, that the angular range where there is an enhancement is small. Thus, it is not possible to use both this advantage and that gained with a relaxed out-of-plane resolution, since the relaxed resolution results in an angular spread that is comparable to α_c. For this reason, experiments with focusing optics often use conditions where this enhancement is not important (e.g., $\alpha > \alpha_c$). In cases where no focusing is used, full advantage can be taken of the enhancement of the transmitted beam due to refraction [38, 67].

For surface crystallographic measurements that involve the determination of atomic positions in a large unit cell, it is necessary to measure the intensity of many different surface reflections. Imperfect crystal alignment or slight sample miscut will cause α to vary slightly from one reflection to another. Because of refraction, this can strongly affect the accuracy of the data. Thus, to avoid this, it is often better to use α equal to several times α_c [21].

The kinematic approximation is generally used to interpret surface diffraction data obtained in a grazing incidence geometry. Since TER is inherently a dynamical effect, this approach is, strictly speaking, inadequate. However, Vineyard [68] has pointed out that a simple distorted-wave approximation based on a homogenous scatterer adequately describes the scattering essentials. This is the approach we have just taken, where the two media shown in Figure 12 are considered to have a homogeneous index of refraction. The distorted wave is the wave traveling through these homogeneous media and is described by Equations (B3)-(B7). Since the surface scattering regions are imperfect, the scattering of this distorted wave can then be accurately treated in the kinematic approximation. The validity of this approximation greatly simplifies data interpretation.

G. ELECTROCHEMICAL CELL DESIGN

Hard X rays have a considerable penetration depth (absorption length) in water as shown in Figure 15. Despite this, for in situ surface X-ray scattering measurements at electrochemical interfaces, it is advantageous to use a thin layer cell geometry and a highly X-ray transparent window. This geometry is favorable because absorption of the incident and diffracted X rays by the electrolyte can be minimized, and the small electrolyte volume limits the intensity of X rays scattered by the electrolyte (which significantly contribute to background in these experiments). This approach has been used by Chianelli et al. [2], Dahn et al. [1], and more recently, by Fleischmann et al. [69, 70]. This is also the general approach taken by a number of authors who have applied surface EXAFS to electrochemical systems [71-78]. The requirement for an X-ray transparent window coupled with the desire for a relatively thin layer of electrolyte is, however, in many ways incompatible with the electrochemical requirements. This incompatibility is exacerbated with a grazing incidence geometry.

Consider X rays impinging onto a 1 cm sample at an incidence angle of 0.5°. If the thickness of the layer of electrolyte is greater than 44 μm, the path length of the X rays through solution will be about 0.5 cm (44 μm/sin 0.5°). This is because an X-ray beam that strikes the center of the sample is only 44 μm above the sample surface at the sample edge. From Figure 15, it is clear that even at 12 keV, the cutoff energy for many X-ray mirrors, the path length is significantly larger than the X-ray absorption length and relatively few photons would reach the surface to be scattered. Since the scattered X rays are also absorbed, even fewer would reach the detector. Thus, it is essential that the electrolyte layer be kept as thin as possible. This is equally valid for the cell window. The cell used by Samant et al. [79, 80] is illustrated in Figure 16. The cell is fabricated from Kel-f® and is approximately 3 cm in diameter and 2 cm in height. The electrodes are 1.25 cm in diameter and held in place by small Kel-f® clamps under which electrical contact to a wire is made. When placed in the cell, the electrode surface extends slightly above the outer lip of the cell, allowing grazing incidence geometry to be used. A Ag/AgCl (3 M KCl) reference electrode is used along with a Pt coil counter electrode. Solutions are added (and removed) from the cell through ports, which are sealed when not in use. The electrolyte is contained between a thin

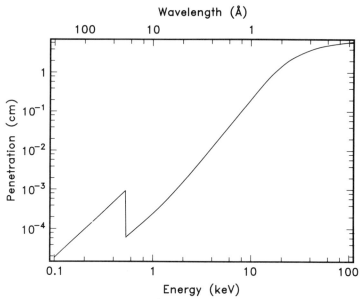

Figure 15. Dependence of the penetration depth of X rays in water on X-ray energy or wavelength. The sudden drop at 0.53 keV is due to the oxygen absorption edge.

(6μm) polypropylene film and the electrode. This film is attached to the cell with an O-ring. The electrochemistry is preformed after adding solution to the cell so that the polypropylene film distends somewhat. This eliminates the large iR drops associated with this cell design when in the thin layer configuration. After scanning to the desired potential, solution is removed, leaving only a thin layer of electrolyte between the electrode and polypropylene window. In this cell, the diffuse X-ray scattering observed from the remaining liquid is of the same order as the scattering from an adsorbed monolayer.

Another requirement in grazing incidence geometry is a flat surface. Any macroscopic roughness both shadows parts of the surface and increases the penetration depth into the sample in areas where the incidence angle exceeds the critical angle. This leads to a decrease in the surface signal and an increase in the diffuse background, respectively. To obtain the required surface, Samant et al. [79, 80] used Ag or Au epitaxially deposited on cleaved mica in the cell described above. Although not shown, the electrochemical cell is mounted on a Huber goniometer head which, in turn, mounts directly on a four-circle diffractometer.

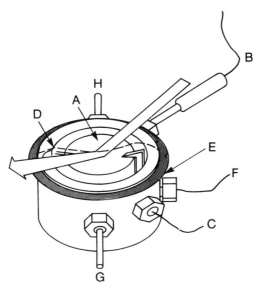

Figure 16. An electrochemical cell used in GIXS experiments. A) Silver (111) electrode, B) Ag/AgCl reference electrode, C) Platinum counter electrode, D) Polypropylene window, E) O-ring holding polypropylene to cell, F) External electrical connection to the working electrode, G) Solution inlet, and H) Solution outlet.

4 APPLICATIONS

A. AG(111)

As evident from the discussion in previous sections, the requirements for surface X-ray scattering are stringent, since there are inherently a small number of surface atoms. For this reason, and because it is important to characterize the substrate, it is useful to measure both the bulk diffraction and the CTRs from the electrode before attempting measurements from adsorbed layers [79, 80]. Since the intensity of the CTRs is of the same order as scattering from a monolayer and the crystallographic order in an adsorbed layer rarely exceeds that of the substrate, it is unlikely that scattering from an adsorbed layer can be observed if the CTRs are not easily seen.

To date, the most extensive surface diffraction measurements of electrochemical systems have been made on underpotentially deposited

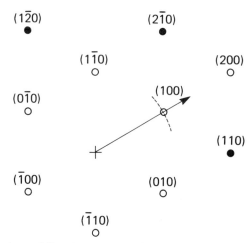

Figure 17. In-plane diffraction pattern for Ag(111). The bulk diffraction is denoted by solid circles and CTRs by open circles. The reflections are labeled using the surface notation, and the " + " indicates the origin. The solid and dashed lines indicate, respectively, radial and azimuthal scans.

Pb on Ag (111) electrodes. We will therefore first consider the scattering from an Ag(111) substrate. Figure 17 shows the in-plane diffraction pattern for a clean Ag (111) surface, which is identical to the LEED pattern observed from this surface. The in-plane Bragg peaks and CTRs are denoted by the filled and open circles, respectively. The surface notation used to label the reflections is [12]

$$(100)_s = \frac{1}{3}(\bar{4}22)_b \quad (010)_s = \frac{1}{3}(\bar{2}4\bar{2})_b \quad (001)_s = \frac{1}{3}(111)_b, \quad (16)$$

where the subscripts b and s refer to the bulk and surface, respectively. Note that the $(100)_s$ and the $(010)_s$ reflections are CTRs, while the $(110)_s$ reflections are bulk Bragg peaks. To convert this surface notation to the normal LEED notation, the last index is dropped.

Figure 17 also illustrates two types of diffraction scans. A radial scan is shown by the solid line and corresponds to measuring the intensity along a radial scattering vector at a fixed angle ϕ. This involves moving the X-ray detector by $\Delta 2\theta$ and the θ-circle of the four-circle diffractometer [Fig. 11] by $\Delta \theta$, such that $\Delta \theta = (\Delta 2\theta)/2$. The dashed line shows an azimuthal (or rocking) scan, which corresponds to measuring the intensity along an azimuthal arc at a fixed Q. It involves rotating the ϕ-circle of the diffractometer, while holding 2θ and θ constant. The third type of scan, a rod scan, measures the intensity perpendicular to the surface and is made, to first order, by scanning χ, with some motion of θ and 2θ necessary to account for changes in Q.

Figure 18 shows scans of the $(100)_S$ CTR from a clean Ag(111) electrode surface obtained in situ in 0.5 M sodium acetate and 0.1 M acetic acid at open circuit [79, 80]. From the radial and azimuthal scans shown in Figure 18A and B, respectively, it is evident that the Ag electrode surface is of high quality, since the diffraction peaks are fairly sharp. It is interesting to note that these peak widths are smaller when the electrode is immersed than when it is exposed to air, which suggests that immersion increases the surface order. For the CTR scan shown

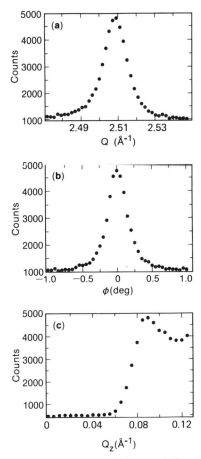

Figure 18. Scans of $(100)_S$ crystal truncation rod for a Ag(111)/electrolyte interface. The Ag ($\bar{2}11$) direction is defined as $\phi = 0.0°$. (A) Radial scan at $Q_z = 0.09$ Å^{-1} and $\phi = 0.0°$. (B) Azimuthal scan at $Q_z = 0.09$ Å^{-1} and $Q = 2.51$ Å^{-1}. (C) Crystal truncation rod scan at $Q_{\parallel} = 2.51$ Å^{-1} and $\phi = 0.0°$.

in Figure 18C the intensity is measured along $(10\,Q_z)_s$, with $Q_z = 2k \sin \alpha$. Although the range of Q_z is rather limited, the maximum near the critical angle is clearly visible at about 0.09 Å^{-1}. Scans to much larger Q_z ($Q_z \sim 2$Å^{-1}) are necessary to measure the lattice roughness of the Ag electrode, as discussed in Section II.D.

We note that surface X-ray scattering offers the potential of directly measuring the atomic scale roughness of electrode surfaces. Surface roughening is caused by the creation of steps and kinks in an atomically smooth surface and has recently been investigated theoretically and experimentally. The thermal roughening in UHV of the (110) faces of Cu [13] and Ag [14] were studied by measuring the CTR peak widths and intensities, demonstrating that CTRs are good probes of roughening. The surfaces are found to roughen at a certain transition temperature (the "roughening temperature"), where the CTR intensity decreases abruptly [13, 14]. Although for Ag(110) the width of the CTR increases at the roughening transition, it does not for Cu(110). The experimental work, however, is limited to the solid-vacuum interface, where roughening is entropically driven. Since surface reconstructions can be induced by applied potential, it might be expected that a reversible surface roughening at the solid-liquid interface could also be induced by changes in the applied potential. Thus, measurements of roughening at electrode surfaces represent a very exciting potential use of surface X-ray scattering.

B. SURFACE RECONSTRUCTION - AU(111)

Before proceeding to a discussion of scattering from electrochemically adsorbed layers, we note that the surface unit cell of the Ag(111) electrode is the same as that expected from a truncated bulk crystal, which is more the exception than the rule. This is so because the creation of a surface produces dangling bonds and changes the coordination and electronic structure of the surface atoms, which leads to a rearrangement of the surface atoms from their bulk positions. If this rearrangement results in an increase in the surface unit cell size, it is referred to as reconstruction. There have been extensive studies of surface reconstruction in UHV in the past 20 years, but for electrode surfaces only a few in situ experiments have been conducted. We will briefly discuss the Au(111) surface reconstruction here. In addition, Fleischmann and Mao [70, 81] have measured the reconstruction of Pt(110).

The (111) faces of most face-centered cubic (fcc) metals do not reconstruct. Gold, however, is a notable exception, probably due to its high malleability and ductility. The Au(111) surface in UHV

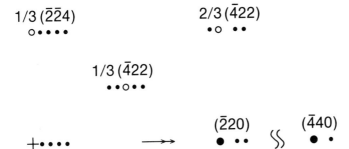

Figure 19. Diffraction pattern of one domain of the rectangular ($\sqrt{3}$ x22) reconstruction of Au(111). Bulk Au diffraction is denoted by the large solid circles, Au CTRs by open circles, and the superlattice peaks by small solid circles. Only the Bragg points and CTRs are labeled. For clarity the spacing between superlattice peaks has been magnified by two in the ($\bar{1}$10) direction, and only a few of the possible peaks are shown. Since only limited X-ray data exists, the pattern is only an approximation.

reconstructs into a rectangular ($\sqrt{3}$ x22) superlattice [82-84], and the diffraction pattern from one domain of this reconstruction is shown in Figure 19. The observed diffraction pattern is a superposition of this pattern and one rotated 120° and 240° from this [82-84]. Although the reconstruction of Au(111) at the solid-liquid interface has not been investigated in situ with X-ray diffraction, Ross et al. have made interesting ex-situ GIXS measurements [85]. The Au(111) surface is prepared by 300°C annealing of a thin film of Au evaporated in UHV onto cleaved mica. The sample is transferred in vacuum to an electrochemical cell containing 0.3M HF and 0.1mM CsF, emersed at either -0.2 or +0.5V (RHE), and transferred through air to the diffractometer. The diffraction scans are then made under flowing He gas.

Figures 20A and B show scans along the ($\bar{1}$10) direction for samples emersed at the anodic (+0.5 V) and cathodic (-0.2 V) potentials, respectively, with the scan direction in reciprocal space shown in Figure 19. Note the logarithmic scale and the dynamic range of better than 1000. At the anodic potential there is no indication of the ($\sqrt{3}$ x22) reconstruction, whereas the cathodic scan clearly shows superlattice peaks. This is likely due to the presence of Cs^+ ions on the surface at the cathodic potential, which lowers the work function and drives the reconstruction. These data suggest that the reconstruction can also be induced, probably reversibly, in situ. Although it is difficult to resolve the spots in the LEED data taken on this sample, the superlattice peaks are easily visible in the X-ray scans

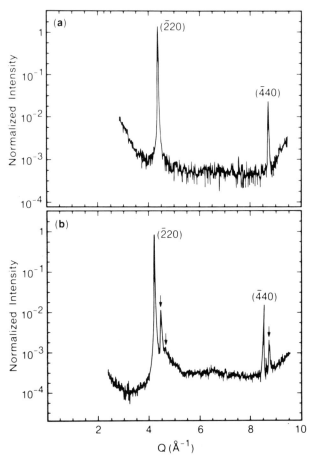

Figure 20. Diffraction scans along the (110) direction of Au(111). (A) Emersion at anodic potential (+0.5 V). The surface is not reconstructed. (B) Emersion at cathodic potential (-0.2 V). The surface is reconstructed into the rectangular ($\sqrt{3}$ x22) and the superlattice peaks are marked with the arrows.

[85]. This demonstrates the superior resolution and dynamic range of X-ray scattering compared to LEED.

C. PB ON AG(111)

Underpotentially deposited monolayers are in many ways ideal systems to probe with X-ray scattering. Many of the metals of interest have a high atomic number and hence a comparatively large scattering cross-section. The monolayers are stable, reproducible, and presumably well-ordered. In addition, they are of fundamental interest because of

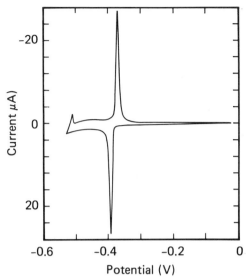

Figure 21. Voltammogram for the deposition of Pb on Ag(111). Potentials are reported relative to Ag/AgCl. Scan rate 20 mV/s, 5 x 10⁻³ M Pb acetate, 0.1 M sodium acetate, 0.1 M acetic acid. The voltammogram was recoded in the cell used for the GIXS, with a thick layer of electrolyte covering the electrode.

their unique chemical properties and their pronounced effect on subsequent metal deposition. In this section, we will describe GIXS measurements on underpotentially deposited Pb on Ag(111). The electrochemical deposition of Pb onto Ag (111) from an acetate electrolyte occurs in two distinct steps [86-95]. The first peak at approximately -350 mV (vs Ag/AgCl) corresponds to the deposition of the UPD monolayer [Fig. 21], whereas the second step corresponds to the deposition of bulk Pb. This system has received considerable attention, and previous workers have shown that the electrosorption valency is near unity (the Pb monolayer is fully discharged) and the full monolayer coverage is consistent with a close packed, incommensurate, monolayer of Pb [86-95].

1. Monolayer Structure: Figure 22A and B show, respectively, radial and azimuthal scans from a monolayer of Pb adsorbed on Ag(111) at a potential slightly negative than for monolayer completion [79, 80]. The data were taken at SSRL beam line 7-2 with an X-ray energy of 8.1 keV, and the relatively large background is primarily due to scattering from the thin layer of solution covering the electrode. The diffraction was confirmed to result from the Pb monolayer by repeating

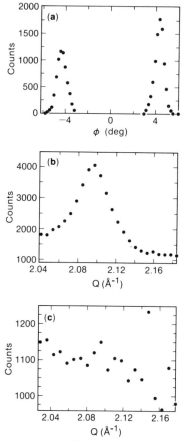

Figure 22. The (10) reflection of UPD Pb on Ag(111). The Ag ($\bar{2}11$) direction is defined as $\phi = 0$. (A) Azimuthal scan at $Q = 2.10$ Å^{-1}, showing peaks from both domains. The potential is slightly negative of that for monolayer completion, and the background has been subtracted. (B) Radial scan at $\phi = 4.5°$ for a potential slightly negative of that for monolayer completion. The 0.037 Å^{-1} width of the peak indicates a domain size of about 150 Å. Similar values are obtained using the width of the (11) and (20) diffraction peaks. (C) Radial scan at $\phi = 4.5°$ for a potential of 0 V where no monolayer is present. No diffraction is observed.

the scans with the electrode held at 0 V (vs. Ag/AgCl). At this potential, Pb is oxidized to Pb^{2+} and dissolves in the electrolyte, and the monolayer and its diffraction peaks are not observed, as is clearly seen in Figure 22C. At potentials where the monolayer is stable, identical diffraction peaks are observed at 60° intervals, consistent with the expected six fold symmetry for a hexagonal layer. The (11) and

(20) reflections from the adlayer are also observed, again each with six fold symmetry. These data show the Pb monolayer forms an incommensurate hexagonal closed packed layer. The Pb-Pb near-neighbor (*nn*) distance can be calculated from the position of the scattering vector at the diffraction peak as $a_{nn} = (4\pi)/(\sqrt{3}\,Q)$, and just after monolayer formation, a_{nn} is 3.45 Å.

The azimuthal scan through the Pb(10) peaks [Fig. 22A] shows two diffraction peaks rotated $+4.5°$ and $-4.5°$ from the Ag $(\bar{2}11)$ direction ($\phi = 0°$). This shows the Pb lattice is aligned 4.5° from the Ag $(\bar{2}11)$, which is not unexpected for an incommensurate monolayer. A discussion of this rotational epitaxy or alignment along nonsymmetry directions will be given below. The $+/-$ symmetry with respect to the substrate results from diffraction from different domains of Pb. There is no energetic difference between a Pb domain orientated at $+4.5°$ and one oriented at $-4.5°$, and any given domain has an equal chance of possessing either alignment. The intensities of the reflections at $+4.5°$ and $-4.5°$ are comparable but not equal, differing by almost 30% in the (10) and 15% in the (11) reflection. Since the monolayer is stripped and redeposited between these scans, this is likely a result of slightly different electrolyte layer thicknesses leading to different amounts of X-ray absorption by the electrolyte. However, it is possible that this difference is real, since a similar intensity asymmetry has been observed for O_2 on graphite using LEED [96]. The observed intensity anisotropy could be caused by an anisotropic nucleation process.

A section of the in-plane diffraction pattern constructed from these data is shown in Figure 23B, and the diffraction from both of the Pb domains is shown, with one of the domains marked by arrows. Figure 23A shows the structure of one domain of the Pb monolayer deduced from this diffraction pattern. The open circles represent the underlying Ag atoms and the shaded circles, the atoms in the incommensurate Pb adlayer. This structure agrees with that suggested by electrochemical data where the charge measured for the UPD is consistent with the formation of a closed packed monolayer of Pb atoms, assuming that two electrons are transferred in the deposition of each Pb^{2+} atom. The electrochemical experiments are not precise enough to measure the lattice spacing and, of course, contain no information on the rotational epitaxy angle. From the integrated intensities of the (10), (11), and (20) diffraction peaks, the in-plane vibrational amplitude is estimated as 0.4 Å, which is a rather large value. This could be due to static disorder in the adlayer or could indicate the Pb monolayer is very soft and possibly anharmonic.

It is reasonable to expect that some fraction of the deposited Pb adlayer will be disordered and will not diffract. An estimate of the

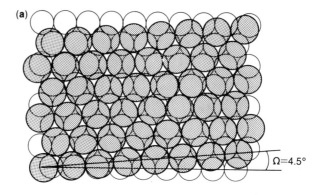

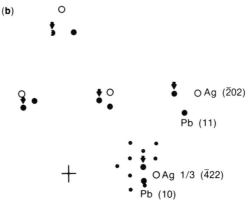

Figure 23. (A) Schematic representation of one domain of monolayer Pb on Ag(111). Open circles represent the Ag atoms of the (111) surface and shaded circles represent the Pb atoms. The rotational epitaxy angle between the Ag and Pb lattices is $\Omega = 4.5°$. (B) Schematic section of the in-plane diffraction pattern for Pb/Ag(111). Diffraction from the Ag is denoted by open circles and that from Pb by large solid circles. The expected positions of several of the satellite peaks caused by the periodic modulation of the adlayer are shown by the small solid circles.

fraction of Pb that is ordered can be obtained by comparing the integrated intensities of the Pb (10) reflection E_{Pb} and the Ag crystal truncation rod E_{Ag}. Using Equations (A15) and (A19), which neglect certain geometric factors, these are

$$E_{Pb} = N_{Pb}|F_{Pb}(\mathbf{Q})|^2 dQ_z$$

$$E_{Ag} = N_{Ag}|F_{Ag}(\mathbf{Q})|^2 \left[\frac{(1-\beta)^2}{1+\beta^2-2\beta\cos 2\pi Q_c} \frac{1}{2\sin^2 \pi Q_c} \right] dQ_z. \tag{17}$$

Recent measurements of the CTRs for Ag(111) in solution suggest that $\beta \simeq 0.1$ [97]. Using this and noting that $Q_c = 1/3$ for a $1/3(\bar{4}22)$ CTR, the term in brackets is 0.48.[1] The integrated intensities can be calculated from the data and are $E = I_{max}\Delta Q\Delta\phi$, where I_{max} is the peak count rate and ΔQ and $\Delta\phi$ are, respectively, the radial and azimuthal peak widths. Using the data shown in Figures 18 and 22, the intensity ratio is

$$\frac{E_{Pb}}{E_{Ag}} = \frac{2(2500)(0.88°)(0.037\text{Å}^{-1})}{(4000)(0.31°)(0.027\text{Å}^{-1})} = 4.9, \tag{18}$$

where the factor of two in the numerator accounts for the two domains of Pb. Using Equations (17) and (18) and the atomic form factors for Pb and Ag [98], the Pb coverage is estimated as $N_{Pb}/N_{Ag} = 0.6$. If the geometric factors that are neglected in Equation (17) are taken into account (see Robinson [21]) this is increased to $N_{Pb}/N_{Ag} \simeq 0.9$. Since the ratio of the Pb surface unit cell-to-the Ag unit cell area is 1.4, a completely ordered monolayer has $N_{Pb}/N_{Ag} = 0.7$. Because of the approximations used and the likelihood of slightly different electrolyte thicknesses for the two measurements, this comparison indicates that the Pb adlayer is almost completely ordered.

The monolayer Pb-Pb *nn* distance of $a_{nn} = 3.45$ Å is about 1.4% smaller than the bulk Pb *nn* spacing of 3.50 Å. This contraction is probably caused by the stronger Pb-Ag bonds compared to the Pb-Pb bonds, which is reflected in the 0.3 eV excess adsorption energy (underpotential shift) [90, 93]. For an incommensurate layer, this makes it energetically favorable to pack more Pb atoms on a Ag (111) surface than on a Pb (111) surface. We also note, however, that the Pb-Pb interaction in the adlayer may be different from bulk Pb and this may also affect the bond contraction [99, 100]. This contraction has

---

[1] Since the vapor deposited Ag films have both ABC and CBA stacking, it is actually necessary to average the contributions to the CTR intensity [Eq. 22] from both these stacking sequences. This is done by noting that ABC stacking has $Q_c = 1/3$, whereas CBA stacking has $Q_c = 1/6$. An average of these gives $1/7$ for the bracketed term in Equation 22.

important implications on the growth of subsequently deposited Pb, as will be discussed in Section IV.E.

The diffraction pattern and structure shown in Figure 23 are essentially the same as observed for vapor deposited Pb on Ag (111), although the contraction of the Pb lattice observed in these experiments is less than observed here [90, 91, 101]. This similarity is surprising considering the significant difference between the two environments: in solution, the monolayer is covered by a large concentration of water and other ions, whereas in vacuum, there is essentially nothing above the monolayer. This similarity suggests that at least in the case of this UPD system the presence of water and any adsorbed anions has a small effect on the structure of UPD Pb on Ag(111).

2. Potential Dependence: Figure 24 shows radial and azimuthal scans for the Pb (10) peak at two different potentials: $V = -425$ mV (A and B) and $V = -550$ mV (C and D). These data were taken on the focused 54-pole wiggler beam line 6-2 at SSRL with an incident X-ray energy of 12.35 keV (1.003 Å) [102, 103]. The ratio of the diffraction peak intensity to the background is increased compared to the data shown in Figure 22 (8.1 keV). This is likely caused by the smaller absorption of the electrolyte at this higher energy and illustrates the benefits of using higher X-ray energies.

From the peak widths of the radial scans shown in Figures 22A and 24, the size of the coherently diffracting Pb domains L can be estimated using Equation (A13). The widths and Pb surface domain sizes for the samples in Figure 22A and Figure 24 are $\Delta Q = 0.037$ and 0.02 Å^{-1} and $L \approx 150$ and 300 Å, respectively. The difference between the two samples almost certainly results from the different quality of the Ag substrates, because the Ag surface domain size estimated from ΔQ of the CTRs is $L \approx 200$ Å for the sample in Figure 22, whereas $L \approx 450$Å for the sample in Figure 24. Since the Pb and Ag surface domain sizes on both samples are similar, the Pb domain size is limited by the defects in the Ag crystal. Note that the surface domain size for UPD Pb/Ag(111) is comparable to that observed for a Pb monolayer on copper (110) in UHV [104].

The most striking and significant change shown in Figure 24 is the increase in the Pb scattering vector Q (or decrease in a_{nn}) at the more cathodic potential. The plot of a_{nn} versus electrode potential in Figure 25 shows that a_{nn} decreases linearly with potential until the onset of bulk deposition. At this potential, $a_{nn} = 3.40$ Å, which is a 2.8% contraction from bulk Pb. It is important to note that no

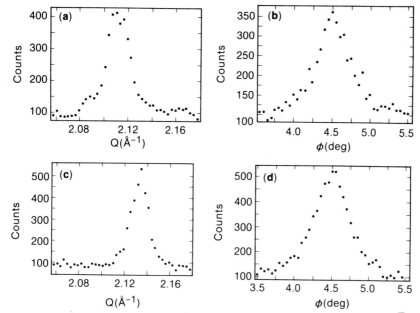

Figure 24. Potential dependence of the Pb (10) reflection. The Ag ($\overline{2}11$)
direction is defined as $\phi = 0$. (A) $V = -425$ mV. Radial scan at
$\phi = 4.5°$. (B) $V = -425$ mV. Rocking scan at $Q = 2.11$ Å^{-1}. (C)
$V = -550$ mV. Radial scan at $\phi = 4.5°$. (D) $V = -550$ mV. Rocking
scan at $Q = 2.13$ Å^{-1}. The 0.02 Å^{-1} width of the peak indicates a
domain size of about 300 Å.

systematic changes in the line shape or line width with varying potential
are observed, which indicates the monolayer has achieved equilibrium.

   To understand the compression of the monolayer with applied
potential, consider a UPD monolayer in equilibrium with its cations in
solution and at a potential where the monolayer has just formed. As
the applied potential is made more cathodic (the Fermi level is
lowered), there is a thermodynamic driving force to pack more Pb
atoms on the Ag surface. The compression is a direct result of the
increased packing density. An alternative way of viewing this
phenomena is to consider an experiment where the concentration of Pb
ions above the adsorbed monolayer is varied with the electrode held at
a constant potential. As the concentration of Pb ions is increased, the
equilibrium packing density of Pb atoms on the surface will increase.
This is completely analogous to vacuum experiments on the adsorption
of rare gases where an increase in the vapor pressure causes the
compression of the adsorbed monolayer [105-108].

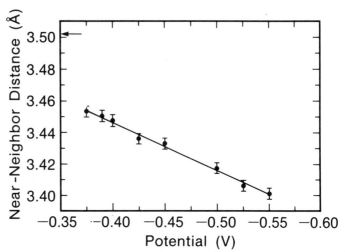

Figure 25. The Pb-Pb *nn* distance vs electrode potential. The 3.501 Å *nn* distance for bulk Pb is shown by the arrow.

The change in a_{nn} with applied potential is interpreted as a measure of the 2D compressibility of the Pb monolayer [102]. We will only briefly discuss this quantitative interpretation here, since it has recently been published. By analogy with bulk matter, the isothermal compressibility of a 2D layer is [109]

$$\kappa_{2D} \equiv -(\frac{1}{a})(\frac{\partial a}{\partial \phi})_T = -(\frac{\partial a}{\partial \mu})_T, \qquad (19)$$

where ϕ is the 2D spreading pressure, a is the atomic area, and μ is the chemical potential. The thermodynamic driving force for the compression is the increase in μ and for a UPD monolayer in equilibrium with its ions in solution this is

$$d\mu = -Z e \, dV, \qquad (20)$$

where Z is the number of electrons transferred per atom deposited and V is the applied potential [93]. From this it is seen that κ_{2D} is readily determined from equilibrium measurements as a function of applied potential

$$\kappa_{2D} = \frac{\sqrt{3} \, a_{nn}}{Ze} (\frac{\partial a_{nn}}{\partial V})_T, \qquad (21)$$

since $a = (\sqrt{3}\,(a_{nn})^2)/2$. Evaluating the slope from Figure 25 and substituting above, we find $\kappa_{2D} = 0.91$ Å^2/eV.

Since for most bulk metals, the compressibility is dominated by the electron compressibility [110], a similar domination is expected for metal monolayers. With this in mind, a very simplified model for an adsorbed metal monolayer is a 2D free electron gas [110], in which the electrons are treated as non-interacting spin-1/2 particles. Using this model, it is a classic graduate-level problem to calculate

$$\kappa_{2D} = \frac{m}{\pi(\hbar n)^2}, \qquad (22)$$

where m is the electron mass and $\hbar$ is Plank's constant over 2π. Here n is the free electron density ($n = Z_v/a$), where Z_v is the number of valance, or free, electrons. With Equation (22), we estimate $\kappa_{2D} = 0.3$ Å^2/eV for 2D Pb ($Z_v = 4$.). This is in reasonable agreement with the measured value, which is probably a result of the free-electron nature of Pb. While this agreement is gratifying, a more realistic calculation is desirable and would involve a 2D band structure calculation that included effects of the Ag substrate.

The interpretation given above is predicated on several conditions. The first is that the monolayer is in equilibrium. This is very reasonable, since no kinetic effects are observed for Pb/Ag(111) in the potential range of the experiments described above, although nonequilibrium effects are observed at more anodic potentials [88]. The second is that the Ag substrate is rigid and does not participate in the adlayer compression. The validity of this is not immediately obvious and remains to be carefully tested.

Previous experimental measurements of κ_{2D} have been reported for physisorbed rare gas monolayers on graphite and metals [105-108]. These have used the equilibrium relationship $d\mu = k_B T (dlnP)_T$, which holds for a physisorbed monolayer in equilibrium with its vapor [109]. Similar experiments on metallic adlayers have not been possible because the very low vapor pressure of metals necessitates the use of nonequilibrium conditions. In contrast, an equilibrium measurement is possible for UPD monolayers because the chemical potential is easily varied and the in-plane nn distance measured using GIXS.

3. Rotational Epitaxy: The alignment of the incommensurate Pb lattice along a nonsymmetry direction is not unexpected, since such an alignment, referred to as rotational epitaxy, has been observed for incommensurate monolayers of inert gases physically adsorbed on graphite and metals and for incommensurate monolayers of alkali atoms chemisorbed on metals [111-115]. A model for rotational epitaxy of incommensurate adlayers was first developed by Novaco and McTague [8] (before any experimental evidence - an unusual occurrence in surface physics).   Novaco and McTague found that the periodic adsorbate-substrate interaction potential (the potential energy of an adatom as it moves over the surface) creates a static-distortion wave (SDW) in the adlayer.   This periodic modulation of the adatom positions from lattice site to lattice site occurs because the adatoms prefer to occupy positions close to the minimum energy sites of the substrate.   Figure 26 illustrates such a modulation in one dimension. Although the energy of the SDW is translationally invariant, it does depend on the orientation of the adlayer relative to the substrate and on the energy required to create shear and compressive waves in the adlayer (e.g., the longitudinal and transverse sound velocities).   Since the energy required to create a shear wave is less than for a compressive wave, the adlayer orientation with the lowest energy is not a high symmetry direction.   Instead, the adlayer prefers to rotate to nonsymmetry directions, taking advantage of the lower energy shear wave.

Novaco and McTague [8] made the following assumptions in their calculation of the SDW energy: a) the interaction between adatoms is harmonic; b) the substrate is rigid; c) the temperature is zero; and d) the adlayer responds linearly to the modulation caused by the adatom-substrate potential (valid for weakly modulated adlayers far from commensurability).   If $\mathbf{R}_j$ is the equilibrium position of an adatom when there is no substrate-adlayer interaction, then the adatom is displaced from its equilibrium position by

Figure 26. One dimensional illustration of an SDW. The circles with solid lines show the adatom positions when the adsorbate-substrate potential is zero, whereas the circles with dashed lines show their positions when the sinusoidal adsorbate-substrate potential is applied. The shift in position from the solid to dashed positions caused by adsorbate-substrate interaction (u_j) has been exaggerated for clarity.

$$\mathbf{u}_j = \sum_{\mathbf{q}} \sum_{\tau} \mathbf{u_q} \sin(\mathbf{q} \cdot \mathbf{R}_j)\ \delta_{\mathbf{q};\ G - \tau}\ , \qquad (23)$$

where δ is the Kronecker delta, τ an adlayer reciprocal lattice vector, $\mathbf{G}$ a substrate reciprocal lattice vector, and $\mathbf{u_q}$ depends on the ratio of adatom-substrate to adatom-adatom interactions. Here $\mathbf{q}$ is a SDW wavevector and the Kronecker delta requires that $\mathbf{q} \equiv \mathbf{q}_{SDW} = \mathbf{G} - \tau$. The $\sin(\mathbf{q} \cdot \mathbf{R}_j)$ term in Equation (23) shows the periodic modulation in the displacements $\mathbf{u}_j$.

When considering the problem of rotational epitaxy, the adsorbate-substrate interaction potential is decomposed into Fourier components $V_{\mathbf{G}}$ [116]. For most adsorbate-substrate combinations, only one set of rotationally equivalent terms $V_{\{\mathbf{G}\}}$ dominate this expansion. In this case and in the long wavelength limit, Novaco and McTague find that the orientation of the adlayer is independent of $V_{\{\mathbf{G}\}}$. By minimizing the SDW energy with respect to the adlayer orientation, the rotational epitaxy angle is

$$\cos \Omega = \frac{1 + z^2(1 + 2\eta)}{z(2 + \eta(1 + z^2))}\ , \quad \eta \geq 1/z$$

$$\Omega = 0\ , \qquad\qquad \eta < 1/z \qquad\qquad (24)$$

where $\eta = (c_L/c_T)^2 - 1$, $z = \tau/G$, and c_L and c_T are the adlayer longitudinal and transverse sound velocities, respectively.

To calculate Ω from Equation (24), it is necessary to know the ratio of the longitudinal to transverse sound velocities for the Pb monolayer. Although these have not been measured, we can make several estimates. First, if we assume the adlayer is a 2D Cauchy solid, then $c_L/c_T = \sqrt{3}$ and $\eta = 2$ [8]. This is a good approximation for rare gases and has been proven for self-bound Lennard-Jones systems [117], but may not be valid for Pb. We, thus, make a second estimate and assume the monolayer is a thin plate of Pb with the (111) direction normal to the plate [118] and use the bulk Pb elastic constants [119]. This yields $\eta = 2.4$, which is close to that for a Cauchy solid. With these estimates, Equation (24) predicts the rotational epitaxy angle for Pb/Ag (111) is $\Omega \approx 5\text{-}6°$, with its exact value depending on a_{nn} (through τ).

As Figures 22 and 24 show, the rotational epitaxy angle for Pb/Ag(111) is $\Omega = 4.5°$, which is slightly smaller than predicted above.

This disagreement is not surprising, considering the uncertainty in η. However, it is unexpected that Ω does not appear to change as the Pb nn spacing decreases from 3.45 to 3.40 Å. This is different from the Novaco-McTague model, which predicts that Ω changes by 0.5° (e.g., from 5.9 to 5.4° for $\eta = 2.4$). One possible explanation for this is that the response of the adlayer is nonlinear (Novaco and McTague assumed a linear response), because the interaction potential between the Pb adlayer and substrate is large or because the adlayer is close to commensurate. We note the Pb layer is close to a $(\sqrt{28} \, x \sqrt{28})R40.9°$ "higher order" commensurate superlattice, which has $a_{nn} = 3.501$ Å and $\Omega = 4.3°$ and has been proposed for Pb on Au (111) [120].

The problem of nonlinear response of the adlayer (large modulation in adatom-substrate energy) has been considered by Shiba using a continuum model [121, 122]. The model accounts for the hexagonal dislocation network that forms for a strong modulation and contains a parameter that describes the adlayer modulation. For a strongly modulated adlayer, Ω is found to be smaller than predicted by the Novaco-McTague model, and as the modulation decreases, Ω approaches the predictions from Novaco and McTague. This might seem to explain the Pb/Ag(111) data; however, Shiba's model indicates the change in Ω as a_{nn} decreases is more than that predicted by the Novaco-McTague model. Recall that no change in Ω is observed.

The periodic modulation of the adlayer atomic positions (SDW) induced by the substrate [Eq. 23] will also cause satellite diffraction at $Q = \tau - q_{SDW}$ [8, 121, 122]. The expected positions of several of the satellite peaks for Pb/Ag(111) are shown by the reciprocal space schematic in Figure 23B. The diffraction intensity will be larger for strong modulation than for weak modulation. In our measurements of Pb/Ag(111) [102], we are unable to detect any satellite diffraction, although the presence of diffuse scattering from the electrolyte prevents the observation of a satellite with less than 3% of the intensity of the Pb(10) peak.

The reason for the lack of agreement with the models of rotational epitaxy is unclear, although at least three alternatives are possible. First, the surface of the Ag substrate may be significantly affected by the Pb adlayer, negating the assumption of a rigid substrate. Second, the harmonic approximation assumed for the Pb adlayer may be invalid, since the melting temperature of Pb is low and the Pb vibrational amplitudes are large. Third, very small amounts of impurities may adsorb on the surface and affect the rotational epitaxy in some way. Since the SDW energy is quite small, trace impurities could have a significant effect.

We note for completeness that an alternative model of the orientation of adlayers has been proposed by Fuselier, Raich and Gillis [123]. Here the adlayer is not considered to be incommensurate, but takes a high order commensurate structure that is dependent on a_{nn}. However, it is found that the relationship between a_{nn} and Ω is not significantly different from that predicted for by the Novaco-McTague model.

D. TL ON AG AND AU

Fleischmann and co-workers [124] have used in situ X-ray diffraction to study Tl deposited on roughened polycrystalline Au and Ag electrodes. The measurements are not done using GIXS but are performed in a reflection geometry with a conventional X-ray tube and a position sensitive detector [69, 124]. Since a roughened electrode is used, the resulting diffraction pattern is a powder pattern. Thus, only the d-spacings from the adlayers can be measured, and it is not possible to gain orientational information of the type discussed in the previous section. However, data collection is greatly simplified, since only one type of diffraction scan (a radial scan) is needed, and this is done efficiently with the position sensitive detector. To obtain an adequate signal-to-noise ratio, eight hours of data collection time are necessary and a modulation technique is employed. Data are taken at a potential where the adlayer is not adsorbed on the electrode and are subtracted from data taken at a potential with the monolayer is adsorbed. When 15 point smoothing is used, this results in a signal from the surface of about 1000 counts and a noise signal of 50 counts. The powder-diffraction peak shapes from a 2D lattice have been discussed by Warren [5].

Thallium on a roughened Ag electrode was studied at a potential where two monolayers of Tl are deposited on the electrode. The major feature in the data from Fleischmann and Mao [124] is the enhancement of the Ag(111) diffraction peak, which is attributed to the addition of a Tl (11) surface diffraction peak to the normal Ag(111) diffraction. This is interpreted as the formation of a commensurate first monolayer of Tl on Ag(111), which requires this layer to be remarkably compressed. Two less defined features are also observed and are attributed to diffraction from a second layer with an oblique lattice that is incommensurate with the first monolayer. At potentials cathodic to that where bulk Tl is deposited, the Tl(101) bulk peak is observed, which indicates the bulk Tl is highly oriented.

The interconversion of Tl and TlI in 0.1 M KI solutions was also investigated by Fleischmann and Mao [124]. A single diffraction peak

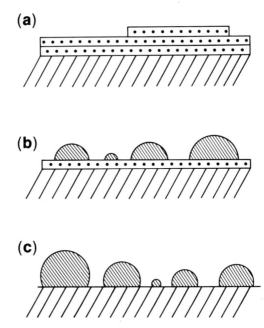

Figure 27. The three growth modes for adsorbed films. (A) Frank-van der Merwe, layer-by-layer, or complete wetting. The film forms by an infinite sequence of uniform layers.   (B) Stranski-Krastanov or incomplete wetting.   The film initially forms one or more uniform monolayers, and subsequently, clusters of bulk material nucleate on top of the layers. (C) Volmer-Weber or nonwetting. Clusters of bulk form directly on the substrate.

from the TlI is observed at $Q = 2.02$ Å^{-1} and is attributed to diffraction from a monolayer of TlI. The proposed structure of this layer is rectangular and is similar to the (010) of orthorhombic ThI. The fast conversion between adsorbed Tl and TlI is explained by the fact the Tl packing density in this rectangular structure is about the same as for the adlayer of Tl.

E. GROWTH OF BULK PB ON AG(111)

Since the properties of electrochemically deposited materials are strongly dependent on the material's microstructure, an understanding of the relationship between this microstructure and the structure of the initially adsorbed layers is of great importance.   Despite this, the relationship between the initial adlayer and the growth of subsequently deposited material has not been extensively studied.   In contrast, a substantial body of information exists on vacuum deposition and epitaxial growth [125]. As illustrated in Figure 27, there are essentially three growth modes [126]: a) layer-by-layer or Frank-van der Merwe growth; b) the formation of bulk clusters on top of one or more layers or Stranski-Krastanov growth; and c) the formation of bulk clusters directly on the substrate or Volmer-Weber growth. The influence of substrate-adsorbate and adsorbate-adsorbate interactions on the growth mode of physisorbed gases has been considered by several researchers and theories developed to predict the growth mode [127]. Originally, a strongly attractive substrate was expected to produce layer-by-layer growth, while a weakly attractive substrate would produce Stranski-Krastanov growth. More recent theories have identified compressive strain in the initial layers, which results from a large substrate-adsorbate interaction, as a critical parameter producing Stranski-Krastanov growth [128-130]. Although in electrochemical deposition, the adsorption of the solvent and electrolyte are known to have a pronounced effect, many of the ideas developed for vacuum deposition may be relevant to electrochemical growth.

For electrochemically adsorbed layers, the lack of information on the relationship between an initially adsorbed adlayer and the subsequent growth is largely a result of the lack of experimental techniques capable of microscopically probing the initial stages of growth in situ. GIXS, however, is well-suited to study this relationship, and in this section, we briefly discuss the application of GIXS to the study of the initial stages of growth of Pb on Ag(111). A more detailed discussion of this subject has recently been published [103].

Recall that the first peak in the electrochemical deposition of Pb onto Ag (111) corresponds to the deposition of the UPD monolayer, whereas the second step corresponds to the deposition of bulk Pb [Fig. 21]. In our study of the growth of the bulk deposit, a thin layer cell is used (see Section III.G) and a predetermined amount of bulk Pb is electrochemically deposited at a constant potential (following the initial deposition of the monolayer) before removing solution and reconfiguring the cell into the thin layer configuration. The amount deposited is determined from the electrochemical current and is measured in "equivalent monolayers." This is the amount of Pb contained in one geometric monolayer ($300 \ \mu C/cm^2 = 10^{15} atoms/cm^2$) and does not imply that the Pb grows in a layer-by-layer manner. Note that since the thin layer of electrolyte contains a small amount of Pb^{2+} ions, several equivalent monolayers may have been deposited after reconfiguration and this represents the uncertainty in the amount deposited.

After the deposition of 2-3 equivalent monolayers of bulk Pb, no change was observed in the scattering from the adlayer. This, together

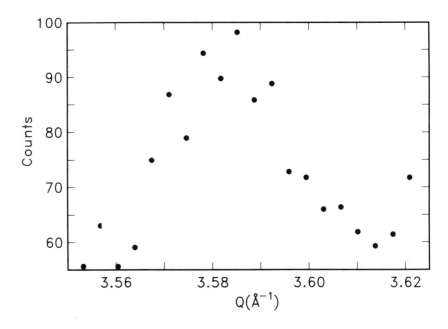

Figure 28. Radial scan of the Pb (220) reflection after the deposition of
approximately 30 mC/cm² (about one hundred "equivalent"
monolayers) of Pb onto Ag(111). This scan is along the Ag ($\bar{2}$11)
direction ($\phi = 0.0°$) and has $\alpha = \delta = 0.8°$.

with the fact the chemical potential is that for the formation of bulk Pb,
shows that bulk Pb is deposited atop the UPD monolayer and there is
no epitaxial second layer. The grown mode is Stranski-Krastanov.

After the deposition of five or more "monolayers," the previously
observed scattering from the adlayer disappears. Even at the critical
angle, the penetration depth of the X rays is much greater than the
thickness of the Pb adlayer, and hence, the disappearance of the adlayer
diffraction peaks must result from a restructuring of the layer itself. No
diffraction from the bulk Pb is observed until approximately 100
equivalent monolayers have been deposited. The Pb (220) reflection is
then observed and is shown in Figure 28. The Pb unit cell constant
calculated from these data is $a_0 = 4.96$ Å, in good agreement with bulk
Pb. The bulk Pb clusters are not well oriented in the plane of the
substrate, and this results in a significant decrease in the signal, since the
scattering intensity is spread over a 360° radial arc, as is indicated by the
diffraction pattern shown in Figure 29. If the bulk deposit has, for

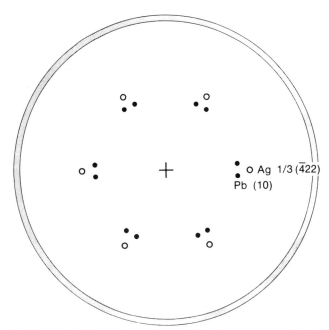

Figure 29. Schematic illustration of the diffraction pattern for bulk Pb on Ag(111). Since the bulk clusters of Pb have a (111) fiber texture, only the (220) peak is observed and is represented by the shaded region. The Ag reflections are indicated by the open circles and the Pb monolayer reflections by the solid circles. Note that after five monolayers of Pb are deposited, the monolayer diffraction is not observed. This figure illustrates the following point: Since the monolayer is well-oriented with respect to the substrate, its diffraction is localized in a small azimuthal range and is more intense than the diffraction from the approximately 100 monolayers of bulk Pb, which is spread over a large azimuthal range.

example, a (111) texture but is randomly oriented in the plane of the surface, its signal would be approximately

$$(N_l) \frac{6 \, (\Delta\phi)_{mono}}{360°} I_{mono}, \tag{25}$$

where $(\Delta\phi)_{mono}$ is the azimuthal width of the monolayer peak with intensity I_{mono} and N_l is the number of deposited layers. Using the data from Figure 22, this indicates the bulk Pb intensity should about 1/2 that of the monolayer, if 100 equivalent monolayers are deposited.

This is in reasonable agreement with Figure 28, in view of the approximations involved.

As discussed above, the Pb adlayer orders into an incommensurate triangular closed packed monolayer, which is similar to the Pb (111) surface, except for the absence of the underlying Pb layers. Since for an fcc crystal the (111) surface has the lowest surface free energy, it is reasonable to expect bulk Pb to grow epitaxially and in a layer-by-layer manner on this template. Clearly, this does not occur. The failure of Pb to grow in this manner appears to result from the fact the monolayer *nn* spacing is smaller than for bulk Pb. This causes a compressive strain or lattice mismatch between the first and "second" layer. For layers adsorbed on smooth substrates, the importance of compressive strain on the growth of subsequently adsorbed material has been recognized only recently. Originally, theories suggested that, for sufficiently strong adsorbate-substrate interaction relative to the adsorbate-adsorbate interaction, layer-by-layer growth would occur [127], since in this growth mode the number of atoms near the substrate are maximized and the atoms can take advantage of the strongly attractive substrate. However, experiments on inert gases physisorbed on graphite have shown that this is not so [128]. The discrepancy between the theories and these experiments has recently been attributed to the fact that the theories ignored the compression in the layers, which results from the strong substrate-adsorbate interaction [128-130]. The decrease in energy that results from adsorption near the substrate is overwhelmed by the increase in strain energy that would be built up in layer-by-layer growth. This quenches the epitaxy of further layers and results in the growth of bulk crystallites. The short range of interactions in metals limits the energy gained when Pb atoms are close to the substrate and further augments the tendency toward Stranski-Krastanov growth.

Although these theories were developed for physisorption and the detailed calculations are not applicable in our case, the idea that compressive strain is a determining factor is relevant. The significantly stronger Pb-Ag interaction compared to the Pb-Pb interaction [90, 93] causes the large (2.8%) lattice parameter mismatch between the Pb monolayer and bulk Pb. This mismatch then results in the Stranski-Krastanov growth mode.

The apparent restructuring of the Pb monolayer after the deposition of five equivalent monolayers is interesting, and we offer one possible explanation. The bulk Pb crystallites grow atop the compressed monolayer, and since the lattice spacing between the two are different, there is an interfacial strain. As additional Pb is deposited, the bulk crystallites grow, and this increases the interfacial strain energy.

At some crystallite size, this energy becomes larger than the energy gained by having extra atoms in the compressed monolayer, and the initial monolayer restructures, perhaps becoming "epitaxial" with the bulk crystallites and taking the same structure as the clusters of Pb. The monolayer is still on the Ag surface, but its structure and orientation are now the same as the overlying bulk Pb clusters.

One reason that the importance of strain in the first adlayer on electrochemical growth has not attracted more attention is that X-ray diffraction is one of the few techniques capable of measuring such small changes. The compression of the monolayer between -400 mV and -550 mV represents the addition of only 7 $\mu C/cm^2$ of Pb. Electrochemically, it is very difficult to distinguish this small faradiac charge above the capacitive charging. Likewise, the uncertainties in the electrode area and the electrosorption valency are too large to permit an observation of the 1.4% compression upon formation of the UPD layer by a measurement of the faradiac current associated with the deposition. The compression is also difficult to address using standard ex-situ methods. In addition to questions of possible structural changes upon removal from potential control and transfer into UHV, 1% changes in lattice spacings are near the limit of resolution using conventional LEED. However, these "small" changes in the lattice spacing may be the dominant force in determining the morphology of subsequent growth. Before the structure of electrochemically deposited metals can be predicted from the properties of the first monolayer, both a greater understanding of the influence of the strain on the initial stages of metal deposition and the influence of the substrate on the strain will be required.

An important question that these studies pose is: What happens between one and one hundred layers? As discussed above, the bulk Pb does not appear to have a strong preferential orientation in the substrate plane, and hence, the diffraction from it is weak and difficult to detect, making GIXS a rather poor method for addressing this question. X-ray reflectivity, however, does not depend significantly on this crystallographic order, and the signal can be very strong. In Section III.E, we briefly mentioned that X-ray reflectivity probes interlayer order and interfacial roughness and density perpendicular to the surface. Thus, this is one promising technique that can address the structural evolution between one and one hundred layers.

In addition to heterogeneous growth, surface X-ray scattering can also be used to study, directly and on an atomic scale, the evolution of surface morphology during homogeneous electrodeposition. For example, measurements of CTRs can determine whether the electrodeposit grows in a completely layer-by-layer manner, with 2D nucleation of each layer, or whether the growth of a new layer begins before the layer beneath it has completely formed. In the later case, the surface becomes rougher as the growth progresses and this roughening can be quantified. Such measurements have recently been reported for the UHV evaporation of Ge on Ge(111) [131]. Similar measurements on electrodeposits may yield insight into the relationship between electrochemical growth conditions and the resulting properties of the deposit.

5 CONCLUDING REMARKS

In this Chapter, we have described surface X-ray scattering and its application to in situ structure determination at electrochemical interfaces. X-ray scattering provides a *direct* determination of the positions of atoms at this interface, which contrasts with the more often used optical methods, such as infrared, Raman, second harmonic generation, and others, which are inherently indirect. This structural knowledge is a prerequisite to understanding many of the chemical and dynamical processes that occur at electrochemical interfaces. The area is still in its infancy, with only a limited number of studies having been reported. However, the potential for surface X-ray scattering to improve our understanding of electrochemical interfaces is tremendous.

In the near future, the use of in situ surface X-ray scattering as a probe of electrochemical interfaces is likely to grow considerably. Although most of the experiments to date have concentrated on UPD monolayers, since the scattering from these is surface specific, future experiments will probe other aspects of electrochemical interfaces. One of these aspects is reconstruction and roughening on clean electrode surfaces, and a few initial, ex-situ investigations have been discussed. In electrochemical experiments it is easy to control the chemical potential, which contrasts to UHV experiments, where such control is difficult to achieve. This ability of easily controlling chemical potential will aid in our understanding of the forces that drive surface reconstructions and roughening. Another exciting potential use of in situ X-ray scattering is to directly probe the structure of passive oxide films and the interfacial region between these films and the underlying metal substrate. These experiments can relate the structural properties of the passive film to film's corrosion resistance, and hence, can improve our understanding of these protective films. We discussed the application of surface X-ray scattering to the initial stages of heterogeneous electrochemical growth.

The combination of this technique with X-ray reflectivity and further studies of additional electrochemical systems will improve our understanding of this important area, as well as homogeneous electrochemical growth.

One further application is the study of the structure of the double layer. The experiments on UPD monolayers that were discussed above have probed some aspects of the inner Helmholtz layer and similar experiments can be used to probe the structure and thermodynamics of specifically adsorbed anions and adsorbed water molecules. Whereas these GIXS experiments primarily probe atomic correlations parallel to surfaces, X-ray reflectivity probes density correlations perpendicular to surfaces. It is, thus, a complementary technique, which will provide additional information on the double layer structure.

Finally, we note that one enjoyable aspect of these experiments is their interdisciplinary nature and the requirement of close collaboration between electrochemists, surface physicists, and surface chemists. This interaction ensures the introduction of new ideas into these fields and ensures their continued growth.

6 ACKNOWLEDGMENTS

We wish to express our appreciation to Gary Borges for his aid in preparing some of the artwork, Phil Ross for sharing unpublished data with us, Ian Robinson for giving us permission to show Figure 7, and Ian Munro for permission to use Figure 9. Finally, we would like to thank Gary Borges, Phil Ross, Mahesh Samant, Joe Gordon, Jeff Kortright, Larry Sorensen, and Dennis Yee for assistance and useful discussions.

7 APPENDICES

APPENDIX A. X-RAY DIFFRACTION

In this Appendix we elaborate on the introduction to diffraction from 2D and 3D crystals given in the main text and include a discussion of the von Laue or reciprocal lattice approach to diffraction, diffraction from crystals with more than one atom per unit cell, and the effect of some types of crystalline defects on diffraction peaks. The von Laue approach to diffraction from a free standing (2D) layer and a description of the scattered intensity from CTRs are also presented.

1. Von Laue Approach to Diffraction: To calculate the scattering intensity from 3D crystals, we note the important fact that the scattering of X rays from electrons is weak, and hence, the kinematic approximation is valid (at least for crystals that are not "perfect"). Thus, the scattering amplitude A can be calculated in the Born approximation (no multiple scattering) by summing the contribution from each individual electron,

$$A = A_e \int \rho(\mathbf{r}) e^{i\mathbf{Q} \cdot \mathbf{r}} d^3 r. \qquad (A1)$$

Here $\rho(\mathbf{r})$ is the electron density, $A_e = e^2/(mc^2 R_s)$ is the X-ray scattering from a single electron (neglecting polarization), and R_s is the distance between the sample and the X-ray detector. The total electron density is essentially the sum of the electron density of each atom $\rho_a(\mathbf{r})$ over all atoms in the crystal

$$\rho(\mathbf{r}) = \sum_{n,m,p} \rho_a(\mathbf{r} - \mathbf{R}_{nmp}) \qquad (A2)$$

where the atomic positions $\mathbf{R}_{nmp}$ are given by Equation (1). Using this, Equation (A1) becomes (for one atom per unit cell)

$$A = A_e \left[\int \rho_a(\mathbf{r}) e^{i\mathbf{Q} \cdot \mathbf{r}} d^3 r \right] \left[\sum_{n,m,p} e^{i\mathbf{Q} \cdot \mathbf{R}_{nmp}} \right]$$

$$= A_e \, f(\mathbf{Q}) \, F(\mathbf{Q}), \qquad (A3)$$

which defines the atomic form factor $f(\mathbf{Q})$ as the Fourier transform of $\rho_a(\mathbf{r})$ and the interference function as $F(\mathbf{Q}) = \sum \exp(i\mathbf{Q} \cdot \mathbf{R}_{nmp})$. For small scattering vectors, $(Q \lesssim 1 \text{Å}^{-1})$, $f(\mathbf{Q})$ is approximately constant and is equal to the number of electrons on each atom Z. As Q (or 2θ) increases, $f(\mathbf{Q})$ monotonically decreases. The scattering intensity I is the amplitude squared and is

$$I = |A|^2 = A_e^2\, |f(\mathbf{Q})|^2\, |F(\mathbf{Q})|^2 e^{-2W}, \qquad (A4)$$

where $2W$ is the Debye-Waller factor and has been added to account for thermal vibrations.

Now that we have obtained the scattering intensity I, we can determine the conditions necessary for diffraction to occur. To do this we express $\mathbf{Q}$ in terms of the primitive reciprocal lattice vectors of the crystal $\mathbf{a^*}$, $\mathbf{b^*}$, and $\mathbf{c^*}$

$$\mathbf{Q} = Q_a\, \mathbf{a^*} + Q_b\, \mathbf{b^*} + Q_c\, \mathbf{c^*}, \qquad (A5)$$

where the primitive reciprocal lattice vectors are

$$\mathbf{a^*} = 2\pi\, \frac{\mathbf{b \times c}}{V} \qquad \mathbf{b^*} = 2\pi\, \frac{\mathbf{c \times a}}{V} \qquad \mathbf{c^*} = 2\pi\, \frac{\mathbf{a \times b}}{V}, \qquad (A6)$$

and $V = \mathbf{a \cdot b \times c}$ is the unit cell volume. With this substitution the interference function becomes

$$|F(\mathbf{Q})|^2 = |F(Q_a, Q_b, Q_c)|^2 = \left| \sum_{n=1}^{n=N_a} \sum_{m=1}^{m=N_b} \sum_{p=1}^{p=N_a} e^{2\pi i (nQ_a + mQ_b + pQ_c)} \right|^2$$

$$= \frac{\sin^2 \pi N_a Q_a}{\sin^2 \pi Q_a}\, \frac{\sin^2 \pi N_b Q_b}{\sin^2 \pi Q_b}\, \frac{\sin^2 \pi N_c Q_c}{\sin^2 \pi Q_c}, \qquad (A7)$$

where N_a, N_b, and N_c are the total number of unit cells in the $\mathbf{a}$, $\mathbf{b}$, and $\mathbf{c}$ directions, respectively. For large N_a, N_b, and N_c, $|F(\mathbf{Q})|^2$ is a sharply peaked function and has a maximum when

$$Q_a = h, \quad Q_b = k, \quad \text{and} \quad Q_c = l, \qquad (A8)$$

where h, k, and l are integers. Since $|F(\mathbf{Q})|^2$ is a rapidly varying function of $\mathbf{Q}$, and the other terms in Equation (A4) are all slowly varying, Equations (A8) describe the conditions for diffraction from the crystal and are known as the three Laue conditions.

Using the identity that as M tends to infinity, $(\sin Mx / \sin x)^2 \to M\delta(x - \pi h)$, where δ is the Dirac delta function, Equation (A7) can be written as

$$|F(\mathbf{Q})|^2 \to (N_a N_b N_c)\delta(Q_a - h)\delta(Q_b - k)\delta(Q_c - l)$$
$$= N\delta(\mathbf{Q} - \mathbf{G}_{hkl}),$$
(A9)

where $N = N_a N_b N_c$ is the total number of atoms in the crystal. The reciprocal lattice vector $\mathbf{G}_{hkl} \equiv h\mathbf{a}^* + k\mathbf{b}^* + l\mathbf{c}^*$ is perpendicular to the hkl lattice planes and has a magnitude $G = 2\pi/d_{hkl}$. When the Laue conditions are satisfied and diffraction is observed,

$$\mathbf{Q} = \mathbf{G}_{hkl}$$
(A10)

and thus $Q = G_{hkl} = 2\pi/d_{hkl}$ This is equivalent to Bragg's law and demonstrates the equivalence between the von Laue and Bragg approaches.

It is often useful to calculate the total integrated intensity in the diffraction peak E_{3D}, since it is independent of crystal imperfections and instrumental resolution and is used for crystallographic analysis. A complete treatment of this is given by Warren [5], but for our purposes, it is sufficient to obtain an estimate of E_{3D}. This is easily obtained by neglecting some geometric factors, such as the Lorentz correction, receiving surface size, and so forth, and by using Equations (A4) and (A9). Thus,

$$E_{3D} \propto \int_{\text{det}} I(\mathbf{Q}) d^3Q = N(\frac{e^2}{mc^2})^2 |f(\mathbf{Q})|^2 e^{-2W},$$
(A11)

where the integral is taken over the acceptance of the detector.

2. Crystallography: In the proceeding discussion, we examined the diffraction from a crystal with a unit cell having only one atom per cell. Most crystals have more than one atom per unit cell, and the atoms are often of different types. In this case, the atomic form factor $f(\mathbf{Q})$ in Equation (A3) must be replaced by the structure factor

$$S(\mathbf{Q}) = \sum_{j=1}^{n} f_j(\mathbf{Q}) e^{i\mathbf{Q} \cdot \mathbf{r}_j},$$
(A12)

where the sum is over the atoms j in the unit cell that have atomic position r_j, and atomic form factor $f_j(\mathbf{Q})$ is defined in Equation (A3). Since $\mathbf{Q} = \mathbf{G}_{hkl}$ at a diffraction peak, $S(\mathbf{Q})$ is often written as S_{hkl}.

In a crystallographic experiment, the experimenter measures the diffracted intensity I_{hkl} at a number, often a very large number, of hkl reflections. A series of corrections (for angular velocity, Lorentz factor, etc.) is then applied to I_{hkl} to obtain a quantity proportional to $|S_{hkl}|^2$. The experimenter then determines the atomic positions in the unit cell from $|S_{hkl}|^2$. This is often a difficult task, since only the magnitude of S_{hkl} is measured and not the phase. This topic is beyond the scope of this review; for a more complete discussion, see several of the texts on X-ray diffraction [4, 5, 132].

3. The Shape of Diffraction Peaks: Real crystals in 3D (and in 2D) are often imperfect, containing various types of extended or localized defects, which can be nonrandom and anisotropic in their distribution. Many imperfect crystals consist of a number of coherently diffracting regions (e.g., grains or particles), with the orientation of the crystal lattice differing from region to region. The entire range of the crystal lattice orientations within the imperfect crystal can be large or small. In addition, each coherently diffracting region may not contain a large number of atoms. Thus, the shapes of the Bragg peaks are not perfect δ-functions as given by Equation (A9), but instead the peaks are broadened. Figure A1 shows a schematic representation of the diffraction pattern from a real crystal. The radial broadening of the scattering vector is ΔQ and the azimuthal angular broadening in the plane that is shown is $\Delta Q_\phi = Q\Delta\phi$. There is also an angular broadening in the direction perpendicular to the page, which is not shown. Some of the crystal imperfections that cause the broadening are described in the following paragraphs.

For a polycrystalline aggregate with a completely random distribution in orientation angles of the crystal lattice planes (e.g., perfect powder), the diffraction pattern can be generated by rotating the reciprocal lattice of a single crystal through all possible orientations about the origin. Each $\mathbf{G}_{hkl}$ generates a sphere of radius G_{hkl} about the origin. The intersection of the Ewald sphere with these reciprocal lattice spheres produces the well-known Debye rings of a perfect powder. In general, the crystal has a distribution in orientation angles for the crystal lattice that is not random, and the material is said to have preferred orientation or texture. The anisotropic angular distribution creates an anisotropic diffraction pattern, where the intensity of the reciprocal lattice spheres depends on the angular

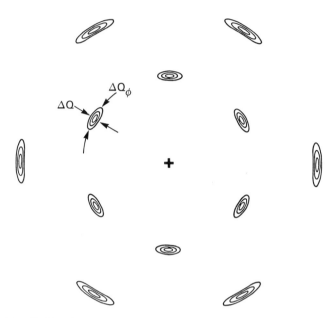

Figure A1. Diffraction pattern from an imperfect crystal. This is a 2D cross section of the entire 3D pattern. The curves near each diffraction peak represent contours of equal scattered intensity. The radial broadening is ΔQ and the azimuthal broadening is ΔQ_ϕ. There is an additional broadening of the peaks in the plane perpendicular to the page.

position in reciprocal space. Thus, the intensity of the Debye rings is angularly dependent and will also depend on sample orientation. The diffraction pattern in Figure A1 shows an example of preferred orientation. Highly textured materials have a high degree of preferred orientation, and their diffraction patterns are localized near several angles in reciprocal space. The angle $\Delta\phi = (\Delta Q_\phi)/Q$ [Fig. A1] is often used to describe the degree of texture and is referred to as the mosaic spread.

The average particle size L often determines radial broadening ΔQ and from Equation (A7) we can estimate ΔQ (defined as the full-width half maximum (FWHM) broadening of Q) as

$$\Delta Q \approx \frac{2\pi}{L}. \tag{A13}$$

The factor 2π is dependent on the model used to describe the particles [4]. Different models will yield different factors, but they are all close to 2π. Because of this and since other factors (e.g., inhomogeneous strain) can also affect the diffraction peak shape, Equation (A13) only provides an estimate of L. Since $Q = (4\pi/\lambda) \sin \theta$, Equation (A13) is equivalent to the well-known Scherrer formula.

4. Two Dimensional Diffraction: Diffraction in 2D can be understood by taking the von Laue approach and considering a free standing monolayer as a bulk crystal, but consisting of only ONE layer of atoms. The formalism presented above (in A.1) is then used.   We take the c-direction of the crystal as parallel to the surface normal (z-direction). Thus, Equation (A7) can be applied with $N_c = 1$ and interference function describing the scattering from the monolayer is

$$|F(Q_a, Q_b, Q_c)|^2 = \frac{\sin^2 \pi N_a Q_a}{\sin^2 \pi Q_a} \frac{\sin^2 \pi N_b Q_b}{\sin^2 \pi Q_b} . \qquad (A14)$$

This shows that for a diffraction peak to occur it is only necessary to fulfill the two Laue conditions in the plane of the monolayer, $Q_a a = h$ and $Q_b b = k$, There is NO Laue condition that must be satisfied for the component of the scattering vector perpendicular to the monolayer. Thus, the diffraction from a monolayer consists of lines of diffuse scattering perpendicular to the monolayer (the Bragg rods), which is simply due to the loss of translational symmetry perpendicular to the monolayer.

As with the 3D case, it is useful to estimate the intensity integrated over the diffraction peak E_{2D}. Neglecting the same geometric factors as in Section A.1, we find

$$E_{2D} \propto \int_{\text{det}} I_{2D}(\mathbf{Q}) d^3 Q = (N_a N_b)(\frac{e^2}{mc^2})^2 |f(\mathbf{Q})|^2 e^{-2W} \delta Q_z, \qquad (A15)$$

where δQ_z is the amount of Q_z that passes through the detector. For a more complete treatment of this, in the spirit of Warren's discussion [5], the reader is referred to the review by Robinson [21].

5. *Crystal Truncation Rods:*   To estimate the scattered intensity from CTRs [9] recall that the interference function from a bulk crystal with lattice vectors **a**, **b**, and **c** and dimensions N_a, N_b, and N_c is

$$|F(Q_a, Q_b, Q_c)|^2 = \frac{\sin^2 \pi N_a Q_a}{\sin^2 \pi Q_a} \frac{\sin^2 \pi N_b Q_b}{\sin^2 \pi Q_b} \frac{\sin^2 \pi N_c Q_c}{\sin^2 \pi Q_c} . \qquad (A16)$$

Here **a** and **b** are parallel to the crystal surface, and **c** is normal to it. Now consider the situation where only two of the three Laue conditions are satisfied. We take these to be the Laue conditions in the plane of the surface, $Q_a = h$ and $Q_b = k$, and with this, the interference function becomes

$$|F(h, k, Q_c)|^2 = (N_a N_b)^2 \frac{\sin^2 \pi N_c Q_c}{\sin^2 \pi Q_c} . \qquad (A17)$$

At positions in reciprocal space that are between Bragg points (e.g., far from reciprocal space positions where the third Laue condition $Q_c = l$ is satisfied), the rapidly varying oscillatory term $\sin^2(N_c \pi Q_c)$ averages out to $1/2$ and the interference function becomes

$$|F(h, k, Q_c)|^2 = (N_a N_b)^2 \frac{1}{2 \sin^2 \pi Q_c} . \qquad (A18)$$

We can now estimate the intensity integrated over the CTR diffraction peak by using this equation and neglecting the same geometric factors as in Section A.4 with the result

$$E_{CTR} \propto \int_{\text{det}} I_{CTR}(\mathbf{Q}) d^3 Q = (\frac{e^2}{mc^2})^2 (N_a N_b) \frac{|f(\mathbf{Q})|^2 e^{-2W} \delta Q_z}{2 \sin^2 \pi Q_c} . \qquad (A19)$$

This shows that the ideally truncated surface causes streaks of intensity that connect Bragg points (at $Q_c = l$) along directions normal to the surface and have the same order of magnitude as that obtained for a single free standing monolayer [Eq. A15]. Thus, the scattering intensity from CTRs should be similar to that from a monolayer, although, in contrast to a monolayer, it is not independent of Q_c, but has a $(\sin \pi Q_c)^{-2}$ shape. An example of the intensity from a CTR is shown in Figure 5.

As we have mentioned previously and will demonstrate below, the exact shape of a CTR is quite sensitive to surface topography [9-11]. To understand this, it is useful to recall that the scattering amplitude is the Fourier transform of the electron density [11]. The electron density of an ideally truncated surface can be considered as the product of a) a step function, which represents the surface truncation, and b) a periodically varying function of infinite extent, which, inside the surface, is the electron density. The Fourier transform of this is then the convolution of the transforms of a step function and an infinite, periodic electron density. The first of these Fourier transforms is $1/iQ_c$, while the later is the sum over hkl of functions sharply peaked at **G**. The scattering intensity is the magnitude squared of this convolution and is proportional to

$$\sum_{hk} \frac{1}{2\sin^2 \pi Q_c} \delta(Q_a - h)\delta(Q_b - k), \qquad (A20)$$

which is essentially the same as Equation (A18). If the surface termination is not ideally sharp but is broadened, then its Fourier transform will be sharper than $1/Q_z$ and the resulting shape of the CTR will have more intensity close to the Bragg points and less in the region of reciprocal space between them [9, 11].

This observation also explains why CTRs are not experimentally observed along directions other than close to the surface normal. For a faceted crystal, ideally truncated at all sides, CTRs connect the Bragg points along all directions normal to the facets. However, the spatial decay of the four edges of the X-ray beam along the sample surface occurs very slowly and the X rays have limited penetration into the sample. This is equivalent to a broad termination of the crystal in these five directions. Thus, the intensity of the rods parallel to these directions is concentrated near the Bragg points and is not observable away from these points. The only observable rods of diffuse scattering are along directions normal to the surface.

APPENDIX B. TOTAL EXTERNAL REFLECTION OF X RAYS

As we noted in the main text, the refractive index at X-ray energies is typically written $n = 1 - \delta - i\beta$ [4, 6, 56-58], where

$$\delta = \frac{e^2\lambda^2}{2\pi mc^2} \sum_i N_i f_i(0) = \frac{e^2\lambda^2}{2\pi mc^2} N_0 \frac{\rho(Z+f')}{A} \tag{B1}$$

and

$$\beta = \frac{e^2\lambda^2}{2\pi mc^2} \sum_i N_i f_i{}'' = \frac{e^2\lambda^2}{2\pi mc^2} N_0 \frac{\rho f''}{A} = \frac{\lambda \mu}{4\pi}, \tag{B2}$$

Here N_i is the atomic density, $f_i(0)$ is the scattering factor [Eq. A4], and $f_i{}''$ is the imaginary part of the anomalous scattering factor for the atoms of type i in the material. N_0 is Avogadro's number, Z is the average atomic number, A is the average atomic mass, ρ is the mass density, f' (f'') is the average (over the atomic concentration) of the real (imaginary) part of anomalous scattering factor, μ is the linear absorption, and λ is the X-ray wavelength. Table 1 in the main text shows typical values for δ and β in the hard X-ray region. The values for β are $\sim$ 10-9-10-6, and are generally much less ($\lesssim$ 10%) than δ. Often, and particularly at high X-ray energies, β is less than a few percent of δ. Thus, absorption is only important close to the critical angle.

It is straightforward to determine the fields and intensities of the reflected and transmitted (refracted) X-ray beams at an interface between two materials [Fig. 12], by using Snell's law and applying Fresnel boundary conditions [59, 60]. These are the classic Fresnel equations [59] with the intensity of the reflected beam

$$R = \frac{\left[(\alpha - p)^2 + q^2\right]}{\left[(\alpha + p)^2 + q^2\right]}, \tag{B3}$$

where

$$q = \frac{\left[\sqrt{(\alpha^2 - \alpha_c^2)^2 + 4(\beta' - \beta)^2} + \alpha_c^2 - \alpha^2\right]^{1/2}}{\sqrt{2}} \tag{B4}$$

and

$$p = \frac{\left[\sqrt{(\alpha^2 - \alpha_c^2)^2 + 4(\beta' - \beta)^2} - \alpha_c^2 + \alpha^2\right]^{1/2}}{\sqrt{2}}.$$ (B5)

Recall that $\alpha_c = \sqrt{2(\delta' - \delta)}$ is the critical angle for TER. The intensity of the transmitted X rays decays into the second material (either because of total external reflection or absorption) as $I(z) = I_0 \exp(-z/D)$, with the surface intensity of the transmitted X rays, I_0, given by

$$I_0(\alpha) = \frac{4\alpha^2}{(p + \alpha)^2 + q^2},$$ (B6)

and the X-ray intensity penetration depth D given by

$$D(\alpha) = \lambda/4\pi q.$$ (B7)

Figure 13 shows calculations of the reflectivity, penetration depth, and surface intensity for a Ag/water interface at 8.04 and 17.44 keV.

In the above discussion, we treated TER of X rays as a boundary-value problem for reflection and refraction of a plane electromagnetic wave at an interface between two uniform, absorbing dielectrics. This results in Snell's law and the Fresnel equations. It is not immediately obvious that this approximation is valid, since the X-ray wavelength is comparable to the interfacial width. However, it has been shown that the Ewald-Oseen extinction theorem, which is generally only valid when the light wavelength is large compared with the dimensions of the scatterers, is also applicable when the incident radiation frequency is high compared to atomic transition frequencies [133]. Since this is true for X-ray radiation, the use of Snell's law and the Fresnel equations is likely a good approximation.

8 REFERENCES

1. Dahn, J., Py, R., and Haering, R., *Can. J. Phys.* 60 (1982): 307.
2. Chianelli, R., Scanlon, J., and Rao, B., *J. Electrochem. Soc.* 125 (1978): 1563.
3. Cullity, B., *Elements of X-Ray Diffraction.* Reading: Addison-Wesley, 1978.
4. James, R., *The Optical Principles of the Diffraction of X-Rays.* Woodbridge: Ox Bow Press, 1982.
5. Warren, B., *X-Ray Diffraction.* Reading: Addison-Wesley, 1969.
6. Compton, A., and Allison, S., *X-rays in Theory and Experiment.* Princeton: Van Nostrand, 1935.
7. Woodruff, D., and Delchar, T., *Modern Techniques of Surface Science.* Cambridge: Cambridge University Press, 1986.
8. McTague, J., and Novaco, A., *Phys. Rev. B* 19 (1979): 5299.
9. Robinson, I., *Phys. Rev. B* 33 (1986): 3830.
10. Afanas'ev, A., Aleksandrov, P., Fanchenko, S., Chaplanov, V., and Yakimov, S., *Acta Cryst.* A42 (1986): 116.
11. Andrews, S., and Cowley, R., *J. Phys. C* 18 (1985): 6427.
12. Robinson, I., Waskiewicz, W., Tung, R., and Bohr, J., *Phys. Rev. Lett.* 57 (1986): 2714.
13. Mochrie, S., *Phys. Rev. Lett.* 59 (1987): 304.
14. Held, G., Jordan-Sweet, J., Horn, P., Mak, A., and Birgeneau, R., *Phys. Rev. Lett.* 59 (1987): 2075.
15. Gibbs, D., Ocko, B., Zehner, D. M., and Mochrie, S., *Phys. Rev. B* 38 (1988): 7303.
16. Ocko, B., and Mochrie, S., *Phys. Rev. B* 38 (1988): 7378.
17. Takahashi, T., Nakatani, S., Ishikawa, T., and Kikuta, S., *Surf. Sci.* 191 (1987): L825.
18. Als-Nielsen, J., In *Structure and Dynamics of Surfaces*, ed. W. Schommers and P. von Blanckenhagen, Vol. 2, 181. Berlin: Springer-Verlag, 1987.
19. Pedersen, J., Feidenhans'l, R., Nielsen, M., Kjaer, K., Grey, F., and Johnson, R., *Surf. Sci.* 189/190 (1987): 1047.
20. Feidenhans'l, R., Pedersen, J., Nielsen, M., Grey, F., and Johnson, R., *Surf. Sci.* 178 (1986): 927.
21. Robinson, I., In *Handbook on Synchrotron Radiation*, ed. D.E. Moncton and G.S. Brown,. Amsterdam: North Holland, 1990.
22. Landau, L., and Lifshitz, E., *Statistical Physics.* Reading: Addison-Wesely, 1969.
23. Imry, Y., and Gunther, L., *Phys. Rev. B* 3 (1971): 3939.

24. Jancovici, B., *Phys. Rev. Lett.* 19 (1967): 20.
25. Nagler, S., Horn, P., Rosenbaum, F., Birgeneau, R., Sutton, M., Mochrie, S., Moncton, D., and Clarke, R., *Phys. Rev. B.* 32 (1985): 7373.
26. Dimon, P., Horn, P., Sutton, M., Birgeneau, R., and Moncton, D., *Phys. Rev. B* 31 (1985): 437.
27. Heiney, P., Birgeneau, R., Brown, G., Horn, P., Moncton, D., and Stephens, P., *Phys. Rev. Lett.* 48 (1982): 104.
28. Moncton, D., Pindak, R., Davey, S., and Brown, G., *Phys. Rev. Lett.* 49 (1982): 1865.
29. Robinson, I., *Phys. Rev. Lett.* 50 (1983): 1145.
30. Eisenberger, P., and Marra, W., *Phys. Rev. Lett.* 46 (1981): 1081.
31. Robinson, I., In *Structure of Surfaces*, ed. M.A. Van Hove and S.Y. Tong, 60. Berlin: Springer-Verlag, 1985.
32. Koch, E., *Handbook on Synchrotron Radiation.* Vol. 1,. Amsterdam: North-Holland, 1983.
33. Kunz, C., *Synchrotron Radiation Techniques and Applications.* Berlin: Springer-Verlag, 1979.
34. Marr, G., *Handbook on Synchrotron Radiation.* Vol. 2,. Amsterdam: North Holland, 1987.
35. Moncton, D., and Brown, G., *Handbook on Synchrotron Radiation.* Amsterdam: North Holland, 1990.
36. Winick, H., and Doniach, S., *Synchrotron Radiation Research.* New York: Plenum Press, 1980.
37. Takahashi, R., Izumi, K., Ishikawa, T., and Kikuta, S., *Surf. Sci.* 183 (1987): L302.
38. Feidenhans'l, R., Bohr, J., Nielsen, M., Toney, M., Johnson, R., Grey, F., and Robinson, I., *Festkorperprobleme* XXV (1985): 545.
39. Mills, D., Henderson, C., and Batterman, B., *Nucl. Instr. Meth.* A246 (1986): 356.
40. Phillips, J., Baldwin, K., Lehnert, W., LeGrand, A., and Prewitt, C., *Nucl. Instrum. Meth.* A246 (1986): 182.
41. Moncton, D., and Brown, G., *Nucl. Instr. Meth.* 208 (1983): 579.
42. Howell, J., and Horowitz, P., *Nucl. Instr. Meth.* 125 (1975): 225.
43. Hastings, J., *J. of Appl. Phys.* 48 (1977): 1576.
44. Heald, S., In *X-ray Absorption: Principles, Applications, Techniques of EXAFS, SEXAFS, and XANES*, ed. D.C. Koningsberger and R. Prins, 119. New York: Wiley, 1988.
45. West, J., and Padmore, H., In *Handbook on Synchrotron Radiation*, ed. G.V. Marr, Vol. 2, 21. Amsterdam: North-Holland, 1987.

46. Matsushita, T., and Hashizume, H., In *Handbook on Synchrotron Radiation*, ed. E.E. Koch, Vol. 1, 261. Amsterdam: North-Holland, 1983.

47. Kohra, K., Ando, M., Masushita, T., and Hashizume, H., *Nucl. Instr. Meth.* 152 (1978): 161.

48. Bilderback, D., Lairson, B., Barbee Jr., T., Ice, G., and Sparks Jr., C., *Nucl. Instr. Meth.* 208 (1983): 251.

49. Stephenson, G., *Nucl. Instr. Meth.* A266 (1988): 447.

50. Stephenson, G., Ludwig, K., Jordan-Sweet, J., Brauer, S., Mainville, J., Yang, Y., and Sutton, M., *Rev. Sci. Instrum.* 60 (1989): 1537.

51. Hart, M., *Rep. Prog. Phys.* 34 (1971): 435.

52. Busing, W., and Levy, H., *Acta Cryst.* 22 (1967): 457.

53. Bohr, J., Kjaer, K., Nielsen, M., and Als-Nielsen, J., *Nucl. Instr. Meth.* 208 (1983): 555.

54. Pynn, R., Fujii, Y., and Shirane, G., *Acta Cryst.* A39 (1983): 38.

55. Als-Nielsen, J., "Resolution in Diffraction", *Lecture Notes for Vienna Summer School on Synchrotron Radiation*, 1980.

56. Darwin, C., *Phil. Mag.* 27 (1914): 315.

57. Darwin, C., *Phil. Mag.* 27 (1914): 675.

58. Compton, A., *Phil. Mag.* 45 (1923): 1121.

59. Born, M., and Wolf, E., *Principles of Optics*. Oxford: Pergamon Press, 1970.

60. Jackson, J., *Classical Electrodynamics*. New York: John Wiley & Sons, 1975.

61. Parratt, L., *Phys. Rev.* 95 (1954): 359.

62. Boite, M. L., Traverse, A., Nevot, L., Pardo, B., and Corno, J., *Nucl. Instr. Meth.* B29 (1988): 653.

63. Lucas, C., Hatton, P., Bates, S., Ryan, T., Miles, S., and Tanner, B., *J. Appl. Phys.* 63 (1988): 1936.

64. Marra, W., Eisenberger, P., and Cho, A., *J. Appl. Phys.* 50 (1979): 6927.

65. Fuoss, P., Norton, L., Brennan, S., and Fischer-Colbrie, A., *Phys. Rev. Lett.* 60 (1988): 600.

66. Fuoss, P., and Fischer-Colbrie, A., *Phys. Rev. B* 38 (1988): 1875.

67. Bohr, J., Feidenhans'l, R., Nielsen, M., Toney, M., Johnson, R., and Robinson, I., *Phys. Rev. Lett.* 54 (1985): 1275.

68. Vineyard, G., *Phys. Rev. B* 26 (1982): 4146.

69. Fleischmann, M., Oliver, A., and Robinson, J., *Electrochim. Acta.* 31 (1986): 899.

70. Fleischmann, M., and Mao, B., *J. Electroanal. Chem.* 229 (1987): 125.

71. Elder, R., Lunte, C. E., Rahman, A., Kirchhoff, J., Dewald, H., and Heineman, W., *J. Electroanal. Chem.* 240 (1988): 361.
72. Smith, D., Elder, R., and Heineman, W., *Anal. Chem.* 57 (1985): 2361.
73. Smith, D., Heeg, M., Heineman, W., and Elder, R., *J. Amer. Chem. Soc.* 106 (1984): 3053.
74. Melroy, O., Samant, M., Borges, G., Gordon, J., Blum, L., White, J., Albarelli, M., McMillan, M., and Abruna, H., *Langmuir* 4 (1988): 728.
75. Samant, M., Borges, G., Gordon, J., Blum, L., and Melroy, O., *J. Amer. Chem. Soc.* 109 (1987): 5970.
76. Blum, L., Abruna, H., White, J., Gordon, J., Borges, G., Samant, M., and Melroy, O., *J. Chem. Phys.* 85 (1986): 6732.
77. Kordesh, M., and Hoffman, R., *Nucl. Instr. Meth.* A222 (1984): 347.
78. Bosio, L., Cortes, R., Defrain, A., and Froment, M., *J. Electroanal. Chem.* 180 (1984): 265.
79. Samant, M., Toney, M., Borges, G., Blum, L., and Melroy, O., *Surf. Sci.* 193 (1988): L29.
80. Samant, M., Toney, M., Borges, G., Blum, L., and Melroy, O., *J. Phys. Chem.* 92 (1988): 220.
81. Fleischmann, M., and Mao, B., *J. Electroanal. Chem.* 247 (1988): 311.
82. Harten, U., Lahee, A., Toennies, J., and Woll, C., *Phys. Rev. Lett.* 54 (1985): 2619.
83. Heyraud, J., and Metois, J., *Surf. Sci.* 100 (1980): 519.
84. Van Hove, M., Koestner, R., Stair, P., Biberian, J., Kesmodel, L., Bartos, I., and Somorjai, G., *Surf. Sci.* 103 (1981): 189.
85. Ross, P., Kortright, J., and Van Hove, M., unpublished, 1988.
86. Muller, R., and Farmer, J., *Surf. Sci.* 135 (1983): 521.
87. Bewick, A., and Thomas, B., *J. Electroanal. Chem.* 84 (1977): 127.
88. Siegenthaler, H., and Juttner, K., *Electrochim. Acta* 24 (1979): 109.
89. Melroy, O., Kanazawa, K., Gordon, J., and Buttry, D., *Langmuir* 2 (1986): 697.
90. Takayanagi, K., Kolb, D., Kambe, K., and Lehmpfuhl, G., *Surf. Sci.* 100 (1980): 407.
91. Takayanagi, K., *Surf. Sci.* 104 (1981): 527.
92. Dickertmann, D., Koppitz, F., and Schultze, J., *Electrochim. Acta* 21 (1976): 967.
93. Kolb, D., Przasnyski, M., and Gerischer, H., *J. Electroanal. Chem.* 54 (1974): 25.

94. Staikov, G., Juttner, K., Lorenz, W., and Budevski, E., *Electrochim. Acta* 23 (1978): 319.
95. Lorenz, W., Schmidt, E., Staikov, G., and Bort, H., *Faraday Symp.* 12 (1978): 14.
96. Toney, M., and Fain Jr., S., *Phys. Rev. B* 36 (1987): 1248.
97. Toney, M., Gordon, J., Kau, L., Borges, G., Melroy, O., Samant, M., Wiesler, D., Yee, D., and Sorensen, L., unpublished, 1990.
98. Ibers, J., and Hamilton, W., *International Tables for X-Ray Crystallography.* Vol. IV,. Birmingham, England: The Kynoch Press, 1974.
99. Wimmer, E., *Surf. Sci.* 134 (1983): L487.
100. Batra, I., *J. Vac. Sci. Technol. A* 3 (1985.): 1603.
101. Rawlings, K., Gibson, M., and Dobson, P., *J. Phys. D* 11 (1978): 2059.
102. Melroy, O., Toney, M., Borges, G., Samant, M., Kortright, J., Ross, P., and Blum, L., *Phys. Rev. B* 38 (1988): 10962.
103. Melroy, O., Toney, M., Borges, G., Samant, M., Kortright, J., Ross, P., and Blum, L., *J. Electroanal. Chem.* 258 (1989): 403.
104. Brennan, S., Fuoss, P., and Eisenberger, P., *Phys. Rev. B* 33 (1986): 3678.
105. Shaw, C., and Fain, S., *Surf. Sci.* 83 (1979): 1.
106. Shaw, C., and Fain, S., *Surf. Sci.* 91 (1980): L1.
107. Bruch, L., and Phillips, J., *Surf. Sci.* 91 (1980): 1.
108. Unguris, J., Bruch, L., Moog, E., and Webb, M., *Surf. Sci.* 109 (1981): 522.
109. Dash, J., *Films on Solid Surfaces.* New York: Academic Press, 1975.
110. Ashcroft, N., and Mermin, N., *Solid State Physics.* Philadelphia: Saunders College, 1976.
111. Shaw, C., Fain, S., and Chinn, M., *Phys. Rev. Lett.* 41 (1978): 955.
112. Kern, K., *Phys. Rev. B* 35 (1987): 8265.
113. Aruga, T., Tochihara, H., and Murata, Y., *Phys. Rev. Lett.* 52 (1984): 1794.
114. Doering, D., and Semancik, S., *Phys. Rev. Lett.* 53 (1984): 66.
115. Cousty, J., and Riwan, R., *Surf. Sci.* 204 (1988): 45.
116. Steele, W., *The Interaction of Gasses with Solid Surfaces.* Oxford: Pergamon Press, 1974.
117. Villain, J., *Phys. Rev. Lett.* 41 (1978): 36.
118. Nye, J., *Physical Properties of Crystals.* London: Oxford University Press, 1957.
119. Hirth, J., and Lothe, J., *Theory of Dislocations.* New York: McGraw-Hill, 1968.

120. Perdereau, J., Biberian, J., and Rhead, G., *J. Phys. D* 4 (1974): 798.
121. Shiba, H., *J Jap. Phys. Soc.* 46 (1979): 1852.
122. Shiba, H., *J Jap. Phys. Soc.* 48 (1980): 211.
123. Fuselier, C., Raich, J., and Gillis, N., *Surf. Sci.* 92 (1980): 667.
124. Fleischmann, M., and Mao, B., *J. Electroanal. Chem.* 247 (1988): 297.
125. Matthews, J. New York: Academic Press, 1975.
126. Bauer, E., *Z. Kristallogr.* 110 (1958): 372.
127. Pandit, R., Schick, M., and Wortis, M., *Phys. Rev. B* 26 (1982): 5112.
128. Bienfait, M., Seguin, J., Suzanne, J., Lerner, E., Krim, J., and Dash, J., *Phys. Rev. B* 29 (1984): 983.
129. Gittes, F., and Schick, M., *Phys. Rev. B* 30 (1984): 209.
130. Ebner, C., Rottman, C., and Wortis, M., *Phys. Rev. B* 28 (1983): 4186.
131. Vlieg, E., Gon, A. D., Veen, J. v., Macdonald, J., and Norris, C., *Phys. Rev. Lett.* 61 (1988): 2241.
132. Lipson, H., and Cochran, W., *The Determination of Crystal Structures.* Ithaca: Cornell University Press, 1966.
133. Oxtoby, D., Novak, F., and Rice, S., *J. Chem. Phys.* 76 (1982): 5278.

CHAPTER 3

ELUCIDATION OF STRUCTURAL ASPECTS OF ELECTRODE/ELECTROLYTE INTERFACES WITH X-RAY STANDING WAVES

James H. White

Department of Chemistry
Baker Laboratory
Cornell University
Ithaca, N.Y. 14853-1301

CONTENTS

I. INTRODUCTION

The study of the structure of electrode/electrolyte interfaces has recently been stimulated by the adaptation of X-ray techniques to these problems. The highly penetrating nature of X rays and the atomic level information provided by their interaction with matter make them, potentially, important probes in the study of interfaces in general. The nature of these interactions allows for the possibility of the examination of geometric, as well as, electronic structure.

The diffraction of X rays has extensively contributed to the study of the structures of crystalline materials. These phenomena arise because of the interference between X rays scattered from collections of atoms and, as such, require some periodicity of the scatterers in order to allow structural or distributional information to be obtained. It is possible, utilizing such interactions, to extract crystallographic information, (i.e. unit cell), including that from a solid surface. However, the positions of atoms within the unit cell cannot be determined without analysis of the scattered intensities. Even then, the treatment of diffraction that is employed determines whether an unambiguous assignment can be made. This is the so-called "phase problem," which arises from the fact that, in a kinematic treatment, scattered intensity (the square of scattered amplitude) does not contain a reference to the sign of the structure factor.

In the more general treatment of X-ray diffraction from perfect crystals, intensity expressions can contain structure factor terms with definite signs. Thus, in principle, the phase problem can be solved, and position within a unit cell can be extracted from scattered intensity measurements .

One of the major shortcomings of using elastic scattering of X rays as a structural probe is the lack of selectivity of X rays of fixed energy toward different elements (the X-ray scattering cross section varies approximately with the atomic number, Z). This is a particularly grave problem if one is interested in structural information concerning an impurity atom in the presence of more substantial concentrations of other scatterers. Such a case would arise in such instances as impurity doping of semiconductors, co-adsorption on surfaces, and small concentrations of a particular ion in the diffuse double layer at an electrode surface. In these examples, the small concentrations of impurity would not cause appreciable differences in the scattered intensity. Techniques utilizing the detection of a signal proportional to the absorption coefficient, and changes in the same, would be anticipated to allow considerably more selectivity to be obtained, since absorption edges occur at highly characteristic energies.

Changes in the X-ray absorption coefficient are brought about by modulation in the final state of the absorption process or by modulation of the X-ray electric field within the material under scrutiny. At strong reflections in perfect crystals, the X-ray electric field, as a function of depth in and above the crystal, is modulated in some manner which is proportional to the Bloch wave representation of the electron density of the material [1]. This variation of electric field intensity with the periodic structure of the crystal is, under conditions in which the incident and reflected amplitudes are comparable, referred to as an X-ray standing wave. A change of the relative phases of the incident and diffracted beams corresponds to changing the phase of the standing wave relative to the periodic structure. Thus, it would be anticipated that some quantity proportional to the X-ray absorption coefficient of an absorber within the extinction length of the incident X rays (such as photoelectron, Auger electron, or fluorescence yield) will be modulated in a manner which depends on the position and distribution of the absorber relative to the period of the standing wave.

II. THEORY

The standing wave effect is the result of the coherent interference between two traveling waves at a strong reflection. The strength of reflection required is such as to demand a nearly perfect crystal and to require a dynamical approach to the treatment of the diffracted intensity.

Dynamical diffraction theories typically involve consideration of the interaction between beams within the diffracting crystal, as opposed to the kinematical approach, which treats diffraction as the summation of independent scattering events from independent volume elements within the crystal. As such, the usual approach is to calculate wave field amplitudes within the crystal, subject to a diffraction condition (Bragg's Law). This normally involves establishment of a wave equation ("dispersion" equation) in terms of the wave vectors for the beams under consideration.

An illustration of the wave representation of dynamical diffraction can be obtained by consideration of analogous effects in scattering theory in the form of the Born series approximation

$$\psi^{(n)}(r) = \frac{\mu}{4\pi} \int \frac{\exp^{(-ik|r-r'|)}}{|r-r'|} \; \phi(r') \, \psi^{(n-1)}(r')dr', \tag{1}$$

where $\psi^{(n)}$ represents the nth scattered beam (ψ° represents the incident beam), and $\phi(r')$ is a function representative of the potential encountered by the incident and scattered radiation. This merely serves as a convenient representation of the multiple scattering aspect of dynamical diffraction of X rays. This more general representation reduces to that for kinematical (geometric) diffraction, when for $n>1$, the contribution of these waves to the total amplitude is negligible.

In addition to multiple scattering processes, a thorough treatment of dynami-

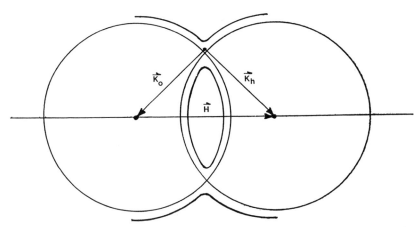

Figure 1. *Ewald representation of two beam Bragg diffraction for which a refractive index correction has been applied. The asymptotes about the intersection of the two Ewald spheres are the dispersion surfaces.*

cal diffraction must take into account loss of intensity due to removal of energy from the incident beam (primary extinction), an increase in the phase velocity of radiation relative to vacuum (refractive index <1, or, more generally, the effect of the strength of interaction of radiation with matter represented by the potential function in Equation (1)), and absorption. Several treatments for dynamical diffraction of X rays have been proposed, including those of Darwin [2], Ewald [3], and von Laue [4]. More recent expositions of these theories are to be found in James [5] and Warren [6] as well as by Batterman [1]. The treatment by Batterman is particularly appropriate to a discussion of the X-ray standing wave effect. The formulation as developed in this article consists, in summary, of finding the wave field in a perfect crystal, subject to both Bragg's Law and Maxwell's equations for a medium described by a periodic complex dielectric constant having the form of a Bloch function. The essential results for the two beam Bragg case were depicted in the form of dispersion surface which can be geometrically represented by the Ewald construction (Fig. 1). This approach will be discussed here, but first, a brief introduction to the Ewald construction will be presented.

The Ewald construction is a geometric representation of the diffraction condition. In the Bragg case emphasized here, a vector of length equal to the inverse of the wavelength of the incident radiation and in the direction of the incident beam is drawn to the origin of reciprocal space from the center of a sphere. From any other point on the sphere, the radial vector from the center of the sphere to that point represents the direction of a diffracted beam. The fact that the index of refraction of X rays in the diffracting medium is less than unity (by about 1 part in 10^5 or 10^6) causes the center of the sphere to be shifted slightly inward. Variation of the angle of incidence causes the refractive index corrected point to trace out a locus of points referred to as a dispersion surface. In general, for each beam considered, one Ewald sphere can be drawn. For example, in the two beam case, one sphere is drawn for the incident beam, and one is drawn for the diffracted beam. The intersection of these spheres represents the dispersion surfaces.

The dispersion equations for the two beam case can be cast as follows:

$$[k^2(1-\Gamma F_0) - (\mathbf{k_0 \cdot k_0})]E_0 - k^2 P \Gamma F_{\overline{H}} E_H = 0$$

and   (2)

$$-k^2 P \Gamma F_H E + [k^2(1-\Gamma F_0) - (\mathbf{k_0 \cdot k_H})]E_H = 0,$$

where k = wave vector in vacuum
k_0 = incident wave vector in crystal
k_H = diffracted wave vector in crystal
Γ = $(e^2/4\pi\varepsilon_0 mc^2)1^2/\pi V$
E_0 = electric field amplitude of incident beam
E_H = electric field amplitude of diffracted beam
P = polarization factor
= 1 for σ polarization (E perpendicular to plane of incidence)
= $\cos 2\theta$ for π polarization (E in the plane of incidence)
F_H = structure factor for h,k,l reflection
$F_{\overline{H}}$ = structure factor for $\overline{h},\overline{k},\overline{l}$ reflection
and F_0 = structure factor for 000 term in the Fourier expansion of the complex dielectric constant.

The determinant of the matrix representing these equations must equal zero to obtain non-trivial solutions.

The permitted solutions for the dispersion equations give rise to the surfaces in the Ewald construction as shown in Figure 1. The equation describing this surface is given by

$$\varepsilon_0 \varepsilon_H = \frac{1}{4}k^2 P^2 \Gamma^2 F_H F_{\overline{H}},$$ (3)

where $2k\varepsilon_0 = k^2(1-\Gamma F_0) - (\mathbf{K_0 \cdot K_0})$

and $2k\varepsilon_H = k^2(1-\Gamma F_0) - (\mathbf{K_H \cdot K_H})$.

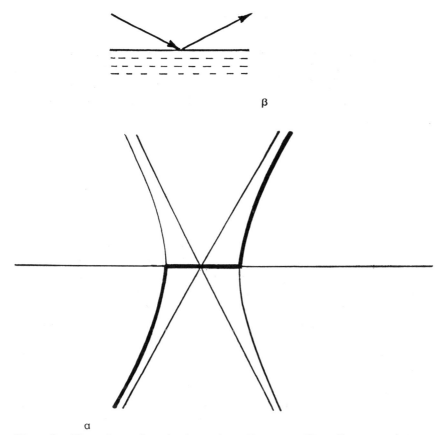

β

α

Figure 2. *Dispersion surfaces for the two beam Bragg case. Heavy line represents the excitation encountered in a standing wave experiment with a changing angle of incidence of radiation.*

It should be pointed out that the structure factors contain corrections for resonance and absorption processes (the Hönl corrections).

The typical X-ray standing wave experiment may thus be regarded (in the Ewald construction) as sweeping along the dispersion surface from the α branch (low angle side) to the β branch (high angle side) as shown in Figure 2. The tie points on the dispersion surfaces (any point on the dispersion surface intersected by incident and reflected beams) give the ratio of reflected to incident field amplitudes.

$$E_H/E_o = -kP\Gamma F_H/2\varepsilon_H .\qquad(4)$$

At the diameter points (those corresponding to the Bragg reflection), the coherent incident and reflected beams have equal electric field amplitudes. A standing wave (a time averaged periodic modulation of the electric field amplitude) exists along the planes of atoms with an electric field intensity given by the relationship

$$I = |E_{tot}|^2$$

$$= |E_o|^2[1 + (E_H/E_o)^2 + 2P(E_H/E_o)\cos(v - 2\pi H \cdot r)]\qquad(5)$$

The fact that the structure factors in Equation (3) are complex, including an absorption correction, means that, as a tie point on either branch is excited, the absorption coefficient for a given angle of incidence will be proportional to the electric field amplitudes represented by Equation (4). Since absorption of X rays produces core holes, secondary processes whose probabilities are proportional to the number of core holes occur with intensities proportional to the electric field intensity as a function of angle. Note that the term $(E_H/E_o)^2$ is simply the reflectivity. Thus, Equation (5) provides a relationship between two experimentally measurable variables, the yield of a secondary process (such as fluorescence, photoelectron, Auger, or secondary electron emission) and reflectivity.

The real space representation of the standing wave is shown in Figure 3, where the oscillatory nature of the electric field intensity is evident. It will be noted that the periodicity of the standing wave is that of the underlying diffracting element, and that considerable intensity outside the crystal surface still exists, pointing to the standing wave effect as a probe of interfacial structure in the broadest sense.

If an impurity atom is located at a given position with respect to the diffracting planes, the X-ray electric field experienced by this absorber will be given by Equation (5). The fluorescence yield will likewise show this dependence on angle of incidence. A family of curves representative of the electric field and fluorescence yield for various positions of the absorber with respect to the diffracting planes is shown in Figure 4.

The above relationship assumes that all absorbers appear at a single coherent position within a d-spacing. In practice, this is never the case and appropriate corrections must be made for the distribution of the absorber. The anticipated fluorescence yield will, in general, be obtained by incorporating the distribution function $f(x)$ into the integral for the fluorescence yield

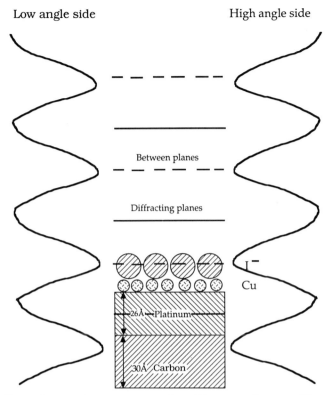

Figure 3. *Real space representation of X-ray standing wave. The variation of electric field intensity with depth corresponds to the two permitted solutions of the dispersion equations.*

$$Y = \int_{-0.5}^{0.5} If(x)dx, \tag{6}$$

where the limits of integration refer to fractions of a d-spacing of the diffracting element. In crystalline materials, the absence of perfect coherence of absorbers is usually taken into account by introducing a coherent fraction, which is defined as the mth coefficient of the Fourier series representation of the distribution of absorbers, into the electric field intensity equation.

$$I = |E_0|^2\{(1+R)(1-f_c) + [(1+R+2P\sqrt{R}\ \cos(v-2\pi\mathbf{H}\cdot\mathbf{r})]f_c\} \tag{7}$$

The coherent fraction (f_c) represents the fraction of absorbers occupying a

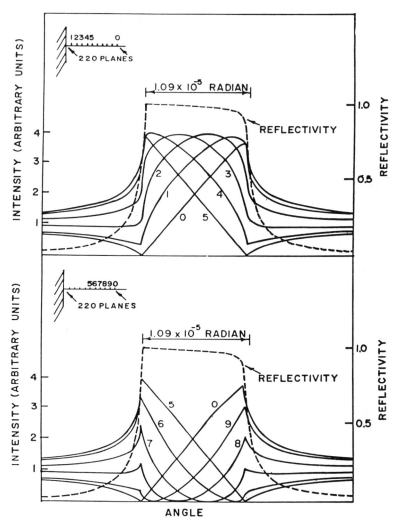

Figure 4. *Electric field intensities for various test positions of an absorber. (Reprinted from Reference 26.)*

given coherent position. If several coherent positions are possible, a single measurement will not be sufficient to unambiguously assign the positions of the absorbers. Thus, measurements in the specular reflection region or higher order measurements must be performed to allow such an assignment. The specular measurement is particularly useful in cases where changes in position across one or more d-spacings occur above the surface of the crystal, since the periodicity of the standing wave in this regime is of the order of several hundred angstroms.

It should be noted from the integral form of the fluorescence yield [Eq. (6)] that the extension of largely incoherently distributed absorbers across many d-spacings can cause reduction in the coherent yield, even if the majority of the absorbers occur within one d-spacing, as is the case, for example, in an adsorbed layer at a smooth surface.

III. BACKGROUND

The X-ray standing wave technique has begun to be employed only relatively recently. A short, but not exhaustive, survey of the literature would seem to be appropriate and is presented below.

The modulation of the fluorescence yield as a function of angle of incidence at a strong Bragg reflection was demonstrated by Batterman [7], using the (220) reflection of a germanium single crystal. The presence of an X-ray standing wave field was indicated by the asymmetry of the fluorescence yield. The position of arsenic implanted in silicon was subsequently deduced by Batterman [8], indicating the potential of the standing wave effect in locating impurity atoms in crystal lattices. The effect of atomic position and extinction on the fluorescence yield were demonstrated there. Subsequent experiments more clearly emphasized features of the fluorescence modulation due to variation in position of impurity atoms and polarization condition [9,10]. It should be noted that all of these experiments were carried out using conventional X-ray sources under a two beam diffraction case.

The presence of X-ray standing wave fields external to the surface of a silicon crystal was demonstrated by Cowan, et al. [11] who followed the fluorescence yield of bromine on the surface of a silicon crystal at the (220) reflection. This also represented the first case in which an adsorbate was examined using this technique [12].

The registry of adsorbed impurity atoms (Br) with respect to the substrate (Si(lll)) was established using the fluorescence yields corresponding to two different reflections [13]. The necessity of using this triangulation technique derives from the fact that the distribution of absorbers is such as to produce two coherent positions, each requiring a Fourier coefficient to give the coherent fraction produced with this distribution. The in-plane distribution of bromine atoms on Si(lll) was examined using a Laue (transmission) geometry, with a Bonse-Hart X-ray interferometer to generate a standing wave parallel to this plane. The diffraction of evanescent X-rays during total external reflection (DEXTER) also gives rise to a standing wave in the direction parallel to the crystal surface, thus allowing distributions to be determined in planes parallel to the surface. Such an approach was utilized by Cowan, et al. in examining the surface of Ge(111) [14]. In addition, it was proposed that depth selective probing of interfaces could be accomplished using this methodology. The use of a combination of photoelectron and fluorescence yields was demonstrated to allow layer-by-layer sampling via the X-ray standing wave effect [15].

The extension of the X-ray standing wave technique from single crystals to synthetic structures was achieved by Barbee and Warburton [16] at a platinum-carbon multilayer coated with a thin film of hafnium [17]. It was later demonstrated that the standing wave field extended hundreds of angstroms above the surface of the microstructure by monitoring the fluorescence yield from hafnium atop a silent layer. X-ray standing wave fields at a Bragg reflection from the layer were found to exist in a Langmuir-Blodgett layer of lead stearate [18]. Heterostructures of Langmuir-Blodgett films of manganese and lead stearate were characterized with X-ray standing waves [19]. Here, the spacing between a manganese atom plane and the nearest lead atom plane was determined.

IV. EXPERIMENTAL

The typical X-ray standing wave experiment consists of monitoring some signal proportional to the standing wave electric field intensity as a function of the angle of incidence of the radiation at a strong reflection. An experimental setup that allows these measurements to be made is shown in Figure 5.

Typically, the incident beam is collimated by a pair of slits and is then measured with a detector (generally an ion chamber). The reflected beam is

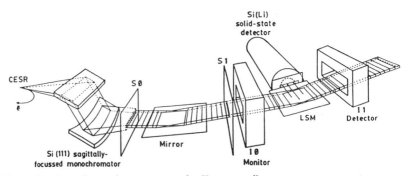

Figure 5. *Experimental arrangement for X-ray standing wave measurements.*

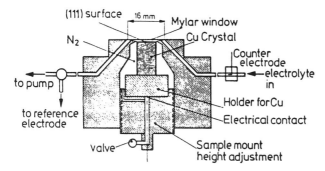

Figure 6. *Cell for X-ray standing wave/electrochemistry experiments with a Cu(lll) electrode (Reprinted from Reference 22.)*

monitored by means of another detector after the sample. Contributions from scattered radiation are reduced by a pair of slits just before the device detecting the signal proportional to electric field intensity. In general, for in situ studies of electrode surfaces, this will be a solid state fluorescence detector.

Signal from the fluorescence detector is passed through a pulse height analyzer to discriminate against unwanted contributions to the signal. With an energy dispersive semiconductor detector, an inelastic X-ray energy spectrum can be obtained with a multichannel pulse height analyzer for each angle of incidence. Subsequent analysis permits undesirable contributions and background to be subtracted from the total signal, thus yielding a fluorescence signal which could be related to reflectivity, as required by Equation (5).

The design of the electrochemistry/spectroscopy cell for these measurements may be critical, particularly if the in situ measurement is to be made on a metal single crystal, since dislocations may be induced in the crystal under a very slight stress. A design for such a cell is shown in Figure 6. A teflon window allowed transmission of incident and reflected beams as well as permitting the establishment of a thinlayer condition necessary for minimization of attenuation of these beams and the fluorescence. A small pump was used to apply a negative pressure to the entrapped liquid to form a thin-layer of solution of constant thickness (20-50 microns). Electrical contact was made by means of a graphite holder.

A similar cell design has been used by us in the employment of the X-ray standing wave technique in the in situ examination of electrolyte/layered synthetic structure interfaces (Fig. 7). The cell consists essentially of a teflon body

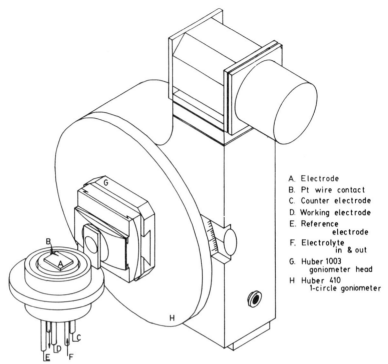

A. Electrode
B. Pt wire contact
C. Counter electrode
D. Working electrode
E. Reference
      electrode
F. Electrolyte
      in & out
G. Huber 1003
      goniometer head
H. Huber 410
      1-circle goniometer

Figure 7. *Cell for X-ray standing wave and electrochemistry experiments at a layered synthetic microstructure.*

with feedthroughs for electrode connections and electrolyte flows. A thin (6 micron) polypropylene or teflon film is held down by an outer teflon ring. Negative pressure is maintained by means of a gas tight syringe.

The requirements for an X-ray standing wave experiment of this sort are quite rigorous. First, one must be able to precisely control angle of incidence, necessitating high resolution goniometer drives, particularly for monocrystalline samples, for which the reflection width may be of the order of a few microradians. Second, the condition of the substrate itself must be impeccable: a useful standing wave can only be generated in a nearly perfect crystal. This second requirement can be met by the growth of crystals from the metal by float zone methods, while subsequently avoiding any stress on the crystal. Largely for this reason, most of the standing wave measurements reported thus far have been obtained using single crystal semiconductor samples.

The production of synthetic microstructures with large *d*-spacings is possi-

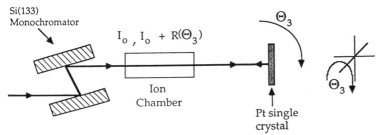

Figure 8. *Normal incidence geometry for X-ray standing wave measurement.*

ble, utilizing modern deposition techniques [16a]. Sputtering or evaporation of materials onto very smooth substrates, e.g. silicon or germanium, can produce structures of alternating low and high Z materials. The in situ monitoring of X-ray reflectivity provides a convenient means to control the quality of the crystal that will be produced.

The angular range examined in the X-ray standing wave experiment plays a part in determining the extent to which the result may be interpreted. The standing wave yield at a single reflection does not provide an unambiguous assignment of the distribution of an absorber. Rather, measurements at two or more reflections must be obtained for cases in which a single preferred position for an absorber is not obtained. Is such a case, one would be able to extract one Fourier coefficient for the distribution for each reflection.

It should be added, that, unlike surface EXAFS, it is quite possible to perform standing wave measurements with conventional X-ray sources, as the modulation of interest can be several times that for the previous technique.

The geometry of the experiment can be of considerable help in overcoming the constraints generally imposed by crystal imperfections: if a Bragg condition at near normal incidence is satisfied (Fig. 8), the angular width at the reflection is considerably broader than that in the conventional (near grazing incidence) geometry. Thus, the sensitivity of the reflectivity to crystal imperfections (mosaic spread) is considerably reduced. One could then anticipate that a strong reflection may be generated even in single crystals prepared by the usual Czholkraski method. Indeed, Woodruff et al. [20] employed this geometry in examining chlorine adsorption on Cu(111) in vacuum. Of course, it is apparent that, practically, this condition can only be satisfied for a very limited number of incident energies: thus, it is probably necessary to use synchrotron radiation to achieve any measurable signal. The reflections employed will probably have to be of greater order than one to achieve the penetrating power required for in situ studies of solid-liquid interfaces.

V. ANALYSIS OF DATA AND INTERPRETATION OF RESULTS

Analysis of X-ray standing wave data is based on a fit of the data (reflectivity and fluorescence yield) to those predicted from theory. However, the data must first be treated to extract yields corrected for background and other contributions. In general, the fluorescence yield is recorded as a function of angle of incidence. An energy dispersed spectrum for each angle is recorded in digital memory. Fitting of the desired emission line to an assumed functional form (usually a combination of Gaussian functions) and subtraction of an extrapolated polynomial background serve to render the data in a form suitable for reconstruction of the fluorescence yield as a function of the angle of the incident radiation.

The electric field intensity at a given point in the crystal must either be calculated from dynamical theory (i.e. wave field amplitude from the dispersion equations) or from a computational approach. The latter approach is generally based on a stratified medium formalism in which the medium is divided into parallel slabs [16b,21]. The continuity of the tangential components of the electric and magnetic fields at each of the resulting interfaces is an essential requirement that is invoked, and a recursion relation (containing the Fresnel coefficients) is used to calculate electric field intensity as a function of angle of incidence. Such a treatment is applicable to the total external reflection condition as well as to diffraction.

The layered medium approach is particularly well suited for analysis of standing wave electric fields in multilayered structures [16b,27]. The recursion relation employed generally has the following form:

$$R_{j,j+1} = a_j^4 \left[\frac{R_{j+1,j+2} + F_{j,j+1}}{1 + R_{j+1,j+2} F_{j,j+1}} \right], \tag{7}$$

where

$R_{j,j+1}$ =   ratio of reflected wave amplitude to incident wave amplitude for j^{th} layer

$R_{j+1,j+2}$ =   ratio of reflected wave amplitude to incident wave amplitude for $j+1^{th}$ layer

$F_{j,j+1}$ =   Fresnel coefficient for j^{th} layer

a_j =   complex amplitude factor at the $j,j+1$ interface.

The reflectivity at a given interface is the squared modulus of $R_{j,j+1}$. The total reflectivity at a given angle of a structure consisting of n layers is obtained by applying the recursion relation n-1 times from the substrate (or from the extinction length) to the topmost layer.

The reflectivity in the total external reflection region is that of the topmost layer. It should be noted that in this region, the electric field intensity is a continuous function of angle of incidence. At the surface of the crystal, the electric field intensity is given by [22]

$$I(O) = |E_0|^2[1+|R_{1,2}|^2 + 2|R_{1,2}|\cos(v)] \tag{8}$$

In general, the E field intensity in the total external reflection region can be determined from

$$I(z) = |E_0|^2[1+|R_{1,2}|^2 + 2|R_{1,2}|\cos(v-4\pi\Theta_{inc}z/\lambda)] \tag{9}$$

Thus, one would anticipate a continuously periodic standing wave (of period D = $\lambda 2\sin\Theta$) starting with an infinitely long periodicity at zero angle of incidence. This type of measurement has recently been employed in the examination of phase transitions in trilayers of cadmium and zinc stearates on a W/Si LSM [23].

The coherent position of an absorber is obtained by fitting the observed fluorescence yields to Equations (5) or (9). Incorporation of coherent fraction into these equations allows a fit to be obtained in terms of three parameters: normalized coverage of absorber, coherent position, and coherent fraction. In a Bragg diffraction standing wave experiment, the coherent position is extracted modulo d.

VI. EXAMPLES OF X-RAY STANDING WAVE STUDIES OF ELECTRODE/ELECTROLYTE INTERFACES

The number of studies of electrochemical interfaces using the X-ray standing wave technique is very small. (To this author's knowledge, only three such experiments have been published). The dearth of experimental results is due, in part, to the experimental difficulties alluded to previously. This section will review these experiments.

The first experiment was that of Materlik et al. [24], who followed the Tl fluorescence from thallium underpotentially deposited on Cu(lll). The voltammetry for the deposition is shown in Figure 9. The standing wave measurements were performed at various coverages in situ, with little positional change being noted for changes in coverage (Fig. 10). However, it was noted that the coherent

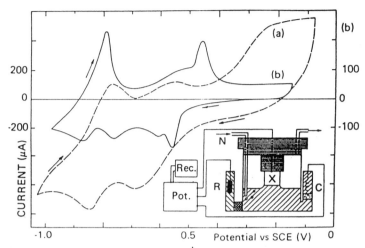

Figure 9. *Cyclic voltammetry for Tl$^+$ (1 mM) in 0.5 M Na$_2$SO$_4$ (A) containing a trace of oxygen and (B) purged with nitrogen. (Reprinted from Reference 22.)*

fraction decreased with increasing Tl coverage, indicating preferred deposition at certain sites on the electrode surface.

The measurements were also performed ex situ. It was observed that a marked difference in coherent position between the two cases could be seen, the sample having been exposed to the atmosphere upon emersion. Coherent positions of 2.27 ± 0.04 and 2.67 ± 0.02Å were observed for the emersed and in situ cases, respectively. It is possible that this difference is due to an adsorbate induced relaxation of the substrate surface, i.e. adsorption of oxygen.

It should be pointed out that these measurements were performed in the absence of dissolved thallium, a point that is crucial when discussing in situ standing wave experiments and one that will be remarked on in reference to a later example. In any event, it is impressive that these investigators were able to obtain results under in situ conditions, since perturbation of the mosaic of the crystal would be anticipated with the pressure of electrolyte and containing films on top of the crystal.

The difficulties encountered in X-ray standing wave experiments with single crystal substrates have led us to perform several experiments with layered synthetic microstructures (LSMs). Two particularly salient examples will be discussed here. The first involved following the evolution of the structure of an adsorbate system [25]. The second was concerned with examination of the extended part of the interfacial region of an electrode/electrolyte system.

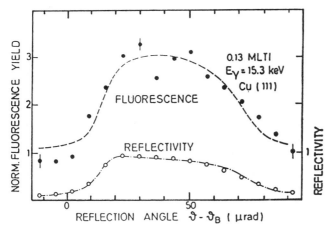

Figure 10. *(A) Position and (B) coherent fraction as a function of total Tl coverage. (Reprinted from Reference 22.)*

The underpotential deposition of copper on Pt(lll) was studied by Stickney et al. [26] using LEED, Auger, and electrochemistry. It was concluded from the relative intensities of iodine and copper Auger signals that, at all coverages, copper deposits directly onto the platinum substrate, displacing iodine from the surface. With the standing wave technique, one has the capacity to directly determine these structural changes.

Approximately one-half of a monolayer of copper was underpotentially deposited on a Pt/C LSM (56Å d-spacing with Pt as the top-most layer) initially pretreated with an aqueous iodide solution. Figure 11 shows the reflectivity and $I_{L\alpha}$ fluorescence yield for the LSM after exposure to the aqueous iodide solution and that for $Cu_{K\alpha}$ yield after electrodeposition of copper. The fact that the peaks in the fluorescence yields were considerably greater than 1+R and were not coincident with the reflectivity profile indicates that the copper and iodine layers were correlated with respect to the substrate. The phase difference between the fluorescence yields indicates a difference in the position of each absorber (within a single d-spacing) at the surface of the multilayer. Fitting of the data to theory as described previously indicated that the copper and iodine layers were found at about 0.7 ± 0.5 and 4.0 ± 0.5Å from the LSM surface. Coherent fractions of about 0.5 were obtained for both species. The uncertainty in these measurements is large because of the large d-spacing employed (recall d-spacing was 56Å). Nevertheless, these results show that the structural course of an electrochemical process could be followed with this technique.

The preceding example concerned the ex situ study of an electrochemical

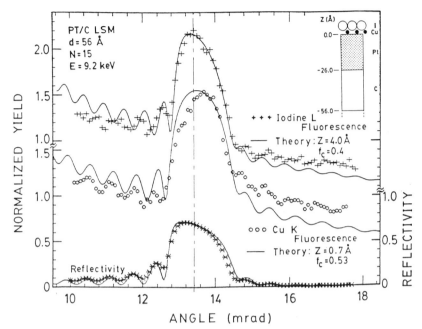

Figure 11. *Reflectivity and fluorescence (I_L and Cu$K\alpha$) from iodide and underpotentially deposited copper on Pt/C LSM. (d = 56 angstroms). Incident energy = 9.2 keV.*

system at various stages of evolution. A more intriguing example of this technique in studying electrochemical interfaces has recently emerged. In this experiment, the fluorescence yield for iodide electrosorbed on a Pt/C LSM was monitored in situ as a function of applied potential. This data, along with measured reflectivity and preliminary fits are shown in Figure 12. What is clear from this illustration is that there are definite amplitude, phase, and coverage changes with the applied potential. The initial fits seem to indicate that coherence is largely destroyed and that there is some change in the position of the centroid of the iodine density as the potential is adjusted. What is most striking, however, is that the fitting parameter corresponding to the decay length of iodide exhibits a maximum at about +0.35V, suggesting the possibility that, about the point of zero charge, distributional changes in the diffuse layer are occurring. It should be noted that the extension of iodide across many d-spacings requires that an E-field weighted fluorescence yield must be used. This will, in general, lead to a rather complicated expression for the yield, which must be fitted to the data.

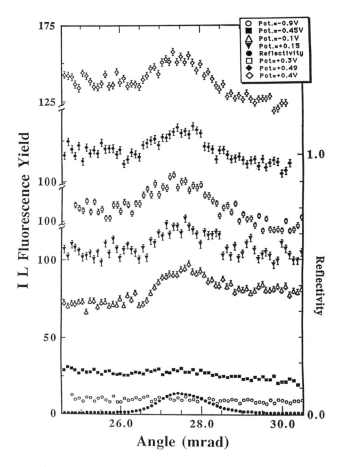

Figure 12. *Reflectivity and fluorescence yield (IL) from Pt/C LSM (d = 40Å) in 0.01 mM NaI and 0.1 M Na₂SO₄ (pH = 6.7). Incident energy = 6.0 keV.*

VII. PROSPECTS FOR THE USE OF X-RAY STANDING WAVES IN THE STUDY OF ELECTRODE/ELECTROLYTE INTERFACES

The lack of a substantial data base for XSW studies of electrochemical systems is an impetus for accelerated application of this technique to these problems. Indeed, there are several areas in which the technique has rather substantial promise. These areas will be commented on briefly here.

First, investigation of the diffuse double layer or extended part of the interface is going to be essential in in situ investigations of any problem with this technique, since the presence of even relatively small amounts of absorber in solution above an electrode surface with a large surface excess of this species will tend to "wash out" the measured fluorescence intensity, in addition to causing apparent phase changes. This is also an interesting topic for another reason: There are very few probes of this region, since, in general, the probe must have selectivity towards a given species, as well as have the capacity to probe a definite spatial region.

The use of the standing wave technique in investigating diffuse layer structure might be envisioned in several approaches. One problem would involve investigating the distribution of some impurity species in the double layer as a function of electrolyte composition and applied potential. One could thus extract some information concerning gross potential profiles and concentration of major species. The effect of the addition of depolarizers to solution could be examined with this approach.

The determination of point of zero charge for a given system may be possible by examination of the potential dependence of the decay length, a maximum being expected at the E_{pzc}. Variations of E_{pzc} with electrolyte concentration and composition are also possible.

The use of single crystals in investigation of diffuse layer structure would seem to be desirable. However, it would remain to be seen if sufficient intensity of the standing wave fluorescence modulation could be achieved to allow structure determination on a scale of only 2 to 3 angstroms. Such a capacity might allow exploration of diffuse layer fine structure.

Ordered solvents, such as liquid crystal media or frozen solvents might be preferable targets for such diffuse layer studies.

The use of various geometries for the standing wave experiment might allow certain advantages to be gained under circumstances as would be envisioned, for example, in the diffuse layer studies outlined above. The use of a normal incidence geometry [20,27] would improve the ease with which these experiments could be performed on single crystal substrates. Such an experimental approach would permit more detailed information on the compact layer at well defined electrode surfaces to be obtained.

The use of a grazing incidence geometry to produce a standing wave field would allow information concerning structure parallel to the electrode surface to be obtained. In combination with grazing incidence diffraction, a solution to the phase problem at electrode surfaces could be arrived at. This would be particularly valuable in the study of the structure of co-adsorbates, since one does not have, at present, a means of locating species with respect to each other within a mixed layer.

X-ray standing waves could be of enormous use in the detection of labels on adsorbed or assembled films on electrode surface. For example, the position and distribution of the label as a function of applied potential or temperature could yield new insight into the behavior of these species in phase transitions. The determination of the distribution of intercalated ions in films should also be possible.

The examination of the position and distribution of labels attached during reactions of dissolved species with adsorbed molecules could allow investigation of the chemical evolution of such systems.

VIII. CONCLUSIONS

The X-ray standing wave technique has not been extensively utilized in the study of electrochemical interfaces. This stems from the difficulty of the experiment as well as from the lack of proliferation of knowledge of the technique to those interested in these systems. The technique has great potential in the study of certain classes of electrochemical systems and is not necessarily restricted by the absence of synchrotron sources.

The use of new materials and novel experimental geometries promise to allow greater applicability of the technique. In addition, systems for which a substantial amount of structural information is not available (e.g. semiconductor/electrolyte interfaces) are ideal targets for the application of the technique.

Acknowledgments

Our work on the use of X-ray standing waves was generously supported by the Materials Chemistry Initiation of the National Science Foundation and by the Office of Naval Research.

References

1. Batterman, B. W., and Cole, H. *Rev. Mod. Phys.* 36 (1964): 681.
2. Darwin, C. G. *Phil. Mag.* 27 (1914): 315.
3. Ewald, P. P. *Acta Cryst.* 11 (1958): 888.
4. von Laue, M. *Ergeb. Exakt. Naturw.* 10 (1931): 133.
5. James, R. W. *The Optical Principals of the Diffraction of X-Rays.* Connecticut: Oxbow Press, 1982.
6. Warren, B. E. *X-Ray Diffraction,* Chap. 14, Reading, MA: Addison Wesley.
7. Batterman, B. W. *Phys. Rev.* 133 (1963): A759.
8. Batterman, B. W. *Phys. Rev. Lett.* 22 (1969): 703.
9. Golovchenko, J. A.; Batterman, B. W.; and Brown, W. L. *Phys. Rev. B* 10 (1974): 4239.
10. Andersen, S. K.; Golovchenko, J. A.; and Mair, G. *Phys. Rev. Lett.* 37 (1976): 1141.
11. Cowan, P. L.; Golovchenko, J. A.; and Robbins, M. F. *Phys. Rev. Lett.* 44 (1980): 1680.
12. Golovchenko, J. A., et al. *Phys. Rev. Lett.* 49 (1982): 560.
13. Materlik, G.; Frahm, A.; and Bedzyk, M. J. *Phys. Rev. Lett.* 52 (1984): 441.
14. Cowan, P. L., et al. *Phys. Rev. Lett.* 57 (1986): 2399.
15. Bedzyk, M. J.; Materlik, G.; and Kovalchuk, M. V. *Phys. Rev. B* 30 (1984): 4881.
16. a. Barbee, T. W. In AIP *Conference Proceedings* 75, 131, ed. D. T. Atwood and B. L. Henke. New York: AIP, 1981.
    b. Underwood, J. H., and Barbee, T. W. In *AIP Conference Proceedings* 75, 170, ed. D. T. Atwood and B. L. Henke. New York: AIP, 1981.
17. Barbee, T. W., and Warburton, W. K. *Matt. Lett.* 3 (1984): 17.
18. Iida, A.; Matsushita, T.; and Ishikawa, T. *Jap. J. App. Phys.* 24 (1985): L675.
19. Matsushita, T., et al. *Nucl. Instr. Meth. in Phys. Res.,* A246 (1986): 751.
20. Woodruff, D. P., et al. *Phys. Rev. Lett.* 58 (1987): 1460.
21. Parratt, L. G. *Phys. Rev.* 95 (1954): 359.
22. Bommarito, G. M. Master's Thesis, 1987.
23. Bedzyk, M. J., et al. *Science* 241 (1988): 1788.
24. Materlik, G., et al. *Phys. Chem.* 91 (1987): 292.
25. Bedzyk, M. J., et al. *Phys. Chem. 90* (1986) 4926.
26. Stickney, J. L.; Rosasco, S. D.; and Hubbard, A. T. *J. Electrochem. Soc.* 131 (1984): 260.
27. Bedzyk, M. J., Ph.D. Dissertation, 1982.

CHAPTER 4

MEASUREMENT OF SURFACE FORCES

Christopher P. Smith, Shelly R. Snyder, and
Henry S. White

Department of Chemical Engineering and Materials Science
University of Minnesota
Minneapolis, MN 55455

CONTENTS

I. INTRODUCTION

The role of electrostatic surface forces in determining the distribution of ions at the electrode/electrolyte interface is well established. However, surface forces also lead to the formation of a number of interesting microscopic structures of current interest to electrochemists. The adsorption of thin layers of redox active polymers onto electrode surfaces, the orientation and density of molecular films, the dispersion of semiconductor particles in photoelectrochemical cells, and the formation of ultra-thin and stable wetting layers necessary for various forms of atmospheric corrosion are a few examples where surface interactions are recognized as playing key roles. Although the characterization of microstructures on electrode surfaces is now possible by various electrochemical and spectroscopic techniques, it has proven generally difficult (and more often not considered) to directly measure the interactions between components that lead to stable systems. The possibility of directly measuring forces at electrode surfaces (and at chemically modified electrode surfaces) is an enticing proposition in that fundamental insights gained in understanding the nature of these interactions may provide clues for predicting interfacial structure.

The surfaces forces apparatus [1] described in this chapter is an experimental system for measuring the nature and magnitude of interactions between two surfaces separated by a fluid medium. The basic measurement developed by Israelachvili and coworkers, and now applied in many research laboratories, consists of bringing two ultra-smooth surfaces (typically, but not limited to, molecular smoothness) together within distances comparable to the decay length of the interaction being measured, e.g., the Debye length. Forces between the two surfaces are measured as a function of the distance separating the surfaces by means of optical and electromechanical measurements (described in detail in section II). Depending on the nature of the surface interactions, the measurements can be made over relatively large distances (e.g., 10 - 1000 Å for electrostatic forces between two electrically charged or ionized surfaces) or short ranges (e.g., <30 Å for structural forces). More often, two or more types of surface forces with different decay lengths can be quantitatively measured in one experiment, resulting in a complete force law describing the surface interactions across the fluid.

A striking result obtained from surface forces measurements that demonstrates the unique capability of this experimental approach is the measurement of the "quantization" of liquids entrapped between mica sheets [2-6] or between mica and an electrically conductive metal film [7]. An oscillatory force vs distance curve [Fig. 1] is observed due to the ordered layering of liquid molecules as the separation of surfaces is decreased below 5 to 10 molecular diameters. Other successes of this technique include experimental verification of the DLVO theory describing

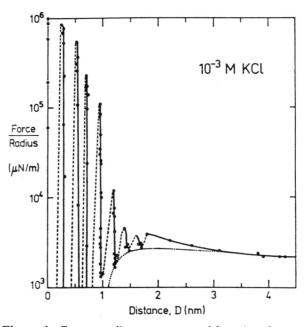

Figure 1. *Force vs. distance measured for mica sheets immersed in 10^{-3} M KCl. The oscillatory force curve below 2 nm is the result of the layering of water between negatively charged mica surfaces, partially neutralized by adsorption of K^+. The surface coverage was estimated to be ca. one K^+ per 1.2 nm^2. The forces beyond 2 nm separation result from the combination of repulsive coulombic forces (described by the Poisson-Boltzmann equation) and attractive van der Waals forces (described by the Hamaker equation). (From Reference 44. Copyright © 1985 Royal Swedish Academy. Reprinted with permission of Cambridge University Press.)*

the combined interactions of van der Waals and electrostatic forces [8], measurements of (a) long range hydrophobic forces [9-11], (b) frictional forces between surfaces separated by molecular distances [12] and (c) forces between surface adsorbed polymers [13-16]. In the past three years, surface forces apparatus techniques have begun to be applied by several research groups to study the interactions between solid metal electrodes separated by an electrolytic solution. Electrostatic forces, which are intimately related to electrode kinetics and adsorption phenomena, have been directly measured between Pt surfaces [17]. In addition, van der Waals [18], solvation [7], and adhesion forces [19] between metal surfaces have been measured by similar techniques.

Although the surface forces apparatus is capable of resolving distances between two surfaces with 1 Å resolution, it is important to note that the forces are being measured between two macroscopic surfaces. Unlike the scanning tunneling microscope [20] in which an atomically sharp tip is brought close to a single surface, no topographical information from force measurements is obtained unless it is inferred *indirectly* from the observed forces (such as in the smearing out of oscillatory forces on an atomically rough surface) [21]. On the other hand, surface properties manifest themselves by such factors as surface electrostatic charge, hydrophobicity, crystallographic orientation [22], and so forth.

In the ensuing sections, selected experimental work is presented demonstrating the use of the surface forces apparatus to measure interactions between insulating and metallic surfaces. The examples have been specifically chosen to emphasize relationships between forces and interfacial structures that are of interest to chemists and especially to electrochemists. Interfacial structure is defined broadly in this account, and includes, for example, the hydration of ionic surfaces as well as the swelling of polymer films. Our coverage is incomplete—recent advances in the understanding of adhesion forces, forces between amphiphilic layers, and frictional forces have been obtained from surface forces measurements. These investigations have had an impact in many areas of science and engineering, but have been judged to be of less interest to the electrochemical community than the topics that were chosen.

The vast majority of force measurements during the 1970s and 1980s were concerned with physical interactions between surfaces of mica; mica can be readily cleaved to yield large area specimens that are molecularly smooth and relatively inert. However, mica can be modified with metallic, polymeric, semiconductor, or surfactant overlayers or replaced entirely with other molecularly smooth surfaces, e.g., highly oriented pyrolytic graphite [19]. The study of chemical and physical interactions between these different materials is the direction that many laboratories are now pursuing.

II. SURFACE FORCES APPARATUS AND MEASUREMENT THEORY

The surface forces apparatus developed and popularized by Israelachvili [1,23] [Fig. 2] will form the basis for our description of the basic principles of force measurements. This instrument provides the only direct method by which forces within the electrode/electrolyte interface can be measured as a function of distance, anywhere from thousands of angstroms to contact with a distance resolution of ca. 1 Å. The technical requirements of the measurement are:

1. Surfaces sufficiently smooth to permit meaningful measurements;
2. A method to move the surfaces together in angstrom increments;
3. A method of measuring the separation distance between surfaces.

A. General Description
The entire apparatus is constructed of 316 stainless steel, glass, and other inert plastics or polymers such as Teflon and Kel-F. Two molecularly smooth mica samples are mounted on hemicylindrical glass supports (radius ~ 2 cm) and oriented with respect to each other in a crossed-cylindrical geometry to allow a number of possible contact positions. The lower support is secured to a weak cantilever spring which is attached to a spring assembly; the upper is secured to a plate which is contacted by a piezoelectric tube.

The surfaces mounted on the glass supports can be moved toward or away from each other in three ways. The spring assembly accomplishes a course and fine adjustment of separation distance through the motions of two micrometer rods. The upper rod is controlled by a stepper motor and is used before an experiment to coarsely adjust the surface separation. The lower

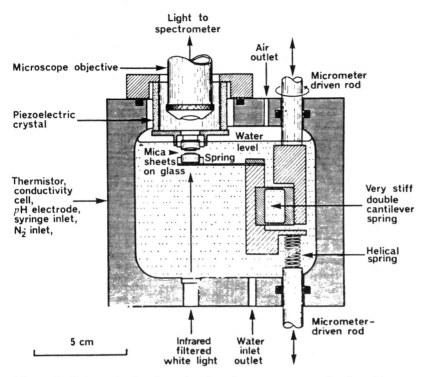

Figure 2. *Schematic drawing of surface forces apparatus developed by Israelachvili. (Reprinted by permission from* Nature *262: 774. Copyright © 1976 Macmillan Journals Limited.)*

rod is driven by a synchronous motor which affects the surface separation through a coupled spring assembly. The difference in force constants of the helical and double cantilever spring allows for a thousand-fold reduction in motion, so that a micron change in rod height is reduced to a nanometer change in surface separation. Finest adjustments of surface separation are made with the piezoelectric tube, which drives the upper surface. With a 1 nm/V expansion coefficient, separations can be controlled to within 1 Å.

The changes in surface separation are measured by optical interferometry [24]. A tungsten-halogen lamp provides an intense source of white light, which is collimated, IR filtered (to reduce heating of the apparatus), and directed to the surfaces. As it passes through the surfaces, multiple reflections take place between silver layers that are deposited onto the backsides of the mica before mounting. This results in the constructive and destructive interference of certain wavelengths over others. The transmitted intensity profile is focused and directed to a spectrometer where it is viewed as an array of fringes that correspond to the wavelengths of constructive interference. The shape, position, and separation of these fringes is uniquely determined by the refractive index and physical thickness of the materials through which the light passes.

The force acting between the surfaces is determined by measuring deflections in the single cantilever spring which supports the lower mica surface. These deflections are measured using the optical system and, when multiplied by the spring constant (~100 N/m), yield the force acting between the surfaces with a sensitivity of about 10 nN (10 µg).

In all experiments great care is taken to ensure the mechanical stability of the system through vibration isolation and thermal control. Dust particles are avoided by performing all preparatory work in a laminar flow hood and by filtering all fluids that enter the apparatus.

B. Force Measurement

To measure the force acting between the two surfaces, one must measure the deflections in the force measuring cantilever spring that holds the lower glass support. Since these deflections are only on the order of angstroms, conventional techniques of measuring displacement, e.g., a traveling microscope, are of no use. Instead, the mechanical displacements of the surfaces are monitored with optical interferometry. The combination of mechanical and optical methods allows one to deduce deflections to within a few angstroms. For example, pushing against the coupled spring assembly with the lower micrometer rod (as described above) is one method of controlling the separation between the surfaces. Displacements of the rod are monitored by using a high precision linear potentiometer attached to the synchronous motor which drives this rod.

At a distance where no forces are encountered (several thousand angstroms), a calibration curve is started by recording the initial separation distance and resistance across the potentiometer. Subsequent distances and resistances are recorded point by point as the surfaces are driven together. The calibration curve of distance D vs resistance ρ is a straight line with slope $dD/d\rho$. The theoretical change in surface separation may be computed by multiplying the change in potentiometer resistance

$\Delta \rho$ by the proportionality constant $dD/d\rho$ given by the calibration. As long as no forces are acting between the surfaces, the change in reference separation $\Delta D_{ref.}$ is equal to the change is surface separation measured optically $\Delta D_{surf.}$ [25]. Once forces are encountered, the optically measured change in surface separation is greater or less than the reference change in separation predicted from the calibration [Fig. 3]. The difference in these two values,

$$\text{Force} = K * \text{Spring Deflection} = K * \left[\Delta \begin{array}{c} \text{Surface} \\ \text{Separation} \end{array} - \Delta \begin{array}{c} \text{Reference} \\ \text{Separation} \end{array} \right]$$

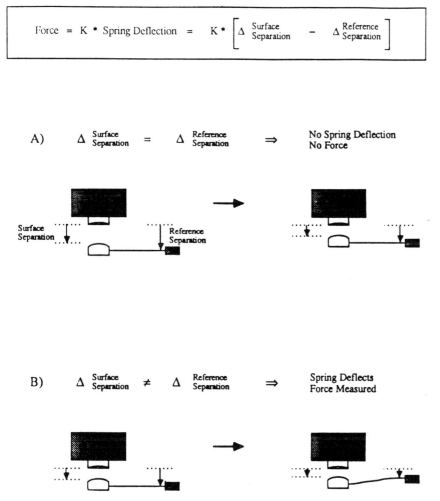

Figure 3. *Schematic description of force calculation (From Reference 25, with permission.)*

the spring deflection, is multiplied by the force constant of the spring K to yield the force between the surfaces (i.e., Hooke's law):

$$\text{Force} = K \cdot \text{spring deflection} = K \cdot [\Delta D_{surf.} - \Delta D_{ref.}]. \quad (1)$$

The sign of the force is positive or negative depending on whether the surface forces are repulsive or attractive, respectively. The spring constant may be calibrated independently by adding known masses to the spring and measuring the deflection, e.g., via a reflected laser beam. The error in measuring K ($\leq 1\%$) sets the limit on the accuracy of the forces measured.

It is worth mentioning here that the forces measured with the crossed-cylinder configuration can be related to the theoretically more tractable geometry of parallel planes through an approximation first proposed by Derjaguin [26,27]. The force between two crossed cylinders, F_{cc}, at a given nearest separation is related to the energy of interaction per unit area of two parallel plates, E/A_{pp}, at the same separation through a geometric factor, G.

$$F_{cc} = G \cdot (E/A)_{pp} \quad (2)$$

For two cylinders of radius r_1 and r_2 crossed at an angle of ω, G is $2\pi\sqrt{(r_1 r_2)}/\sin \omega$. For cylinders of equal radii, R, crossed at 90°, G is $2\pi R$. It is customary to report forces normalized by the radius, F/R, to facilitate the comparison of experimental results obtained in different laboratories.

C. Optical System and
Multiple-Beam Interferometry [24]

When the mica surfaces are in contact, the light reflected between the silver layers on the backsides of the mica develops a profile of constructive and destructive interference. This interference pattern is focused and directed to a spectrometer where the constructively transmitted wavelengths are viewed as a set of "fringes of equal chromatic order" (FECO) [Fig. 4].

The position of these fringes is measured with a ruled microscope objective that is mounted on a translating micrometer stage. This stage is calibrated with the mercury green ($\lambda = 5460.7$ Å) and doublet yellow ($\lambda = 5769.6$ or 5790.6 Å) emission lines, yielding a wavelength to displacement ratio of ~ 32 Å/mm. The smallest measurable step of the stage is 1 μm and under optimal conditions, measurements of the fringe wavelength can be made to

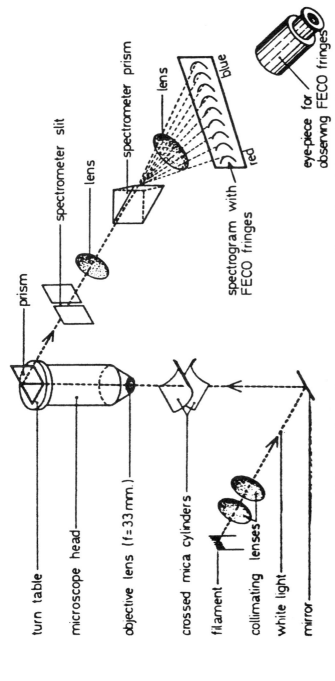

Figure 4. *Schematic of optical system used to measure fringes of equal chromatic order (FECO). (From Reference 28, with permission.)*

within 0.1 Å.

The exact position of the fringes when the surfaces are in *direct contact* depends on the mica's refractive index μ_{mica} and its physical thickness T_{mica}. Those rays with wavelengths that exit the Ag/mica/mica/Ag interferometer in phase are the wavelengths that produce the fringes in the spectrometer and satisfy the equation

$$\lambda_m^0 = \frac{2\mu_{mica}(D_{mica})}{m} \; ; \; m = 1,2,3,... \; ; \; D_{mica} = 2T_{mica}, \quad (3)$$

where the superscript "0" refers to the fringe wavelength when the surfaces are in contact and the subscript "m" identifies the fringe number. Any two successive wavelengths, λ_m^0 and λ_{m-1}^0 allow one to calculate the fringe number and the mica thickness when the refractive index of mica is known [28].

When the surfaces are separated to a distance D, the optical path length increases, and the wavelengths that pass constructively between the interferometer shift correspondingly toward longer wavelengths: $\Delta\lambda_m = \lambda_m - \lambda_m^0$. These shifts are used to calculate the separation distance between the surfaces:

$$D = \frac{m \, \Delta\lambda_{m(odd)}}{2\mu_{mica}} \quad m = 1,3,5,... \quad (4)$$

$$D = \frac{m\mu_{mica} \, \Delta\lambda_{m(even)}}{2 \, \mu_{med}^2} \quad m = 2,4,6,.... \quad (5)$$

Due to the different dependence of the fringe orders (odd, even) on the refractive index of the medium, μ_{med}, these two equations can be solved simultaneously to give the separation distance between the mica surfaces *and* the refractive index of the intervening medium.

Equations (4) and (5) are good approximations for $\Delta\lambda_m/\lambda_m^0 \ll 1$ and suffice to demonstrate the accuracy possible with the method. For $m = 22$ (corresponding to 2 μm thick mica sheets), $\mu_{mica} = 1.58$, and $\mu_{med} = 1.33$ (water), $\partial D \approx 10 \, \partial(\Delta\lambda_m)$. Under optimum conditions with the uncertainty in $\Delta\lambda_m$ equal to 0.1 Å, the uncertainty in D is about 1 Å or less. Factors which significantly alter the accuracy of the measurement include nonlinear dispersion [28] and the introduction of reflective overlayers on the mica [29]. An effect of the latter is depicted in Figure 5 where the even order fringes are obscured by reflections between the Ag and Pt layers.

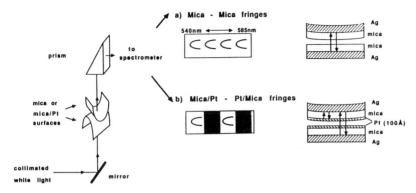

Figure 5. *Qualitative features of the FECO observed for mica and Pt coated mica surfaces. (Reprinted with permission from Reference 17. Copyright © 1988 American Chemical Society.)*

III. ELECTROSTATIC AND VAN DER WAALS FORCES

The earliest and most extensive studies of surface interactions were concerned with verification of theories describing repulsive electrostatic and attractive van der Waals forces. The combination of these opposing forces, described by the DLVO theory [30,31] (named after Derjaguin, Landau, Verwey, and Overbeek), is the basis of a variety of common phenomena, e.g., adhesion, the equilibrium thickness of soap films, and the stabilization of colloidal suspensions. In 1959, Derjaguin and coworkers, at the Academy of Sciences in Moscow, published an account [32,26] of the measurement of electrostatic forces between two smooth, 300 μm diameter Pt wires, oriented in a crossed cylindrical fashion and immersed in various aqueous and nonaqueous electrolytes. Their instrument was the forerunner of the present day surface forces apparatus, and the results they obtained caught the attention of at least one prominent electrochemist. In a 1960 review article [33] of the ionic double layer at metal surfaces, A. N. Frumkin included a part of Derjaguin's results [Fig. 6] showing the magnitude of the force barrier surmounted while bringing two Pt wires to electrical contact as a function of their potential (measured vs a calomel electrode). These curves and ones obtained in other electrolytes show a pronounced minimum in the force vs potential curve at low ionic concentrations

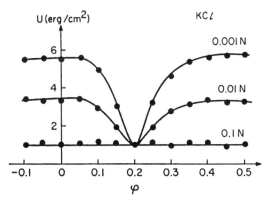

Figure 6. *Energy barrier surmounted in bringing two 300 μm diameter Pt wires together to electrical contact as a function of potential. The Pt wires were poised at the same potential (φ) referenced to a calomel electrode. (From Reference 26, with permission.)*

(corresponding to the potential of zero charge of Pt) and a potential independent force at high concentrations, qualitatively similar to capacitance curves observed for many liquid metals. Frumkin wrote:

> It is not quite clear why in this case [*viz.* surface forces measurements] we do not meet with the difficulties, which were encountered during the attempts to determine the location of the zero charge potential of platinum from the capacity minimum in dilute solutions [33].

Frumkin's early report is of some historical interest, since the technique of measuring forces was apparently not applied again to electrochemical studies until the mid 1980s; his comment also clearly points out an important advantage of surfaces forces measurement techniques applied to the study of solid electrodes. The difficulties in measuring the capacitance of Pt electrodes, referred to by Frumkin, resulted from dispersion of interfacial capacitance due to roughness and other surface heterogeneities and from psuedocapacitances arising from adsorption of hydrogen and oxygen. The force barrier, as correctly analyzed by Derjaguin, clearly resulted from the repulsion between surfaces as their diffuse double layers overlapped at close separation. The diffuse distribution of ions surrounding the electrode held near the potential of zero charge, however, was not influenced as strongly by microscopic roughness or by the adsorption of solutes. Thus, the potential of minimum electrostatic force in dilute solutions, analogous to a capacitance minimum at the p.z.c., was more readily apparent.

In Derjaguin's measurements, the roughness of the Pt wires limited quantitative determination of the separation distance to several hundred angstroms and greater; thus, the shape of the electrostatic force curve at shorter distances was not determined. The measurements of Tabor and Winterton in 1968 [34] of normal and retarded van der Waals forces between layers of cleaved muscovite mica separated by air was the first direct measurement of forces at separations below 100 Å. Besides first recognizing the utility of mica as a necessary ultra-smooth substrate for measuring short-range interactions, their experimental apparatus also made use of a piezoelectric transducer to vary the separation distance, and multiple beam interferometry (using fringes of equal chromatic order) to measure the separation distance, both of which are essential elements of the apparatus employed by most researchers today. Although fused silica and various polished glasses have been employed subsequently, mica has remained the most common choice for surface forces apparatus measurements, being used either as a bare surface or as a substrate modified by the deposition of optically transparent metal, surfactant or polymers films.

The surface forces apparatus has been employed by Israelachvili and coworkers in detailed studies of DLVO forces between bare mica surfaces immersed in aqueous electrolytes [35,1]. A general conclusion of their work is that the Poisson-Boltzmann equation and the Liftschitz theory of van der Waals interactions give good quantitative predictions of the observed forces in solutions containing symmetrical electrolytes for separations down to ca. 20 Å. Other types of forces, however, are often dominant below this distance, as will be discussed below.

Before considering the experimental observations, it is worth noting some of the chemical properties of mica. The dissociation of K^+ gives the surface of mica a net negative charge, creating an electrical double-layer whenever a bare mica surface is in contact with an aqueous solution. The mica/electrolyte double-layer structure is analogous to what electrochemists imagine exists at metal/electrolyte interfaces [36]. The force measurements unequivocally demonstrate a diffuse double-layer region, as well as a "compact" layer that is analogous to, but far more *structurally* complex than, the simplified picture that is generally drawn of the inner and outer Helmholtz layers. In nonaqueous solutions, e.g., cyclohexane, and in the absence of additional electrolyte, K^+ ions remain adsorbed onto the surface, and electrostatic forces are correspondingly absent. The notable and obvious difference between mica and metal surfaces is that mica is an excellent electrical insulator. Two consequences of this factor are that (a) the charge on the crystal surface, resulting from ionization, is spatially localized, and (b) the net charge per unit surface area in any particular experiment is determined and fixed by chemical interactions with the solution (e.g., adsorption of ions). The latter factor limits the measurement of forces to a relatively small range of surface potential ($< |150$ mV$|$) in comparison to what is possible with electrochemical systems. Cleaved mica, however, has a sufficiently high surface charge density (0.5 negative charges/nm^2) that it is generally assumed in analyzing force curves that one is dealing with a surface of uniform charge.

Figure 7 schematically shows the interactions energy between two surfaces based on the DLVO theory [8]. The total energy (solid line) can be considered as the sum of the van der Waals and electrostatic interactions (broken lines). The electrostatic force between *identical* surfaces is always repulsive, regardless of distance, and acts in the presence of attractive van der Waals dispersion forces. However, the exact shape of the interaction profile depends markedly on the solution composition. In air (or vacuum) or in non-polar solvents without added electrolyte, the electrostatic contribution is negligible relative to the van der Waals interaction and the measured forces between surfaces are attractive. In polar liquids containing a small concentration of ions, the electrostatic contribution is large, and repulsive double-layer forces can be measured from contact out to separations of 0.1 μm and beyond. At higher ionic concentrations (e.g., 1 M KNO_3), the Debye screening length ($\kappa^{-1} = 0.3$ nm) shortens to distances comparable to values over which van der Waals interactions occur, resulting in a complex force curve which may exhibit both local maxima and minima [Fig. 7].

Figure 8 shows force vs distance curves obtained by Israelachvili and Adams [1] for two mica layers separated by KNO_3 solutions of various concentrations. The forces shown in

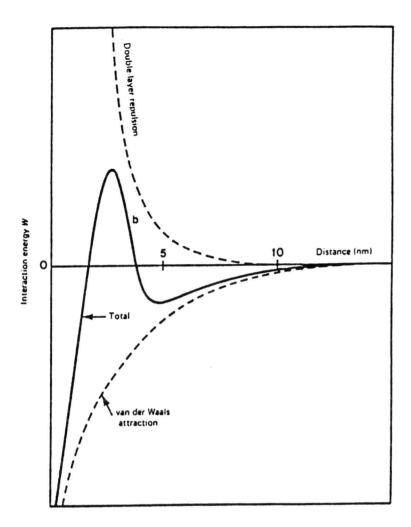

Figure 7. *Schematic representation of the interaction energy* W *as a function of distance between two surfaces. The total surface interaction (solid line) is the sum of the attractive van der Waals and repulsive electrostatic interactions (dotted lines). The maximum in the interaction energy shown schematically at ca. 3 nm corresponds qualitatively to the barrier between two Pt surfaces measured by Derjaguin [e.g., Fig. 6]. (From Reference 8, with permission.)*

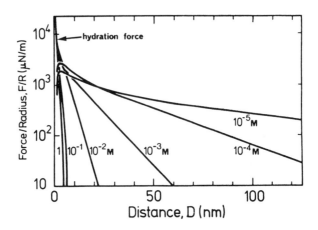

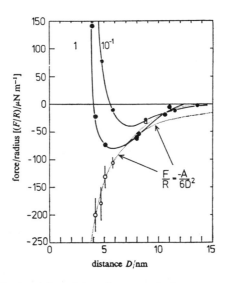

Figure 8. *(top) Repulsive electrostatic forces as a function of distance between mica in aqueous solutions containing 10^{-5} to 1 M KNO_3 (From Reference 44. Copyright © 1985 Royal Swedish Academy. Reprinted with permission of Cambridge University Press.); (bottom) DLVO forces (solid circles) as a function of separation distance in 0.1 and 1 M KNO_3. Open circles represent the resulting forces after subtraction of the electrostatic component. The dashed line represents the inverse square van der Waals force law, using a Hamaker constant of $A = 2.2 \times 10^{-20}$ Joules. (From Reference 1, with permission.)*

Figure 8 (top) at distances greater than 20 Å are long-range repulsive forces resulting from the overlapping surface double-layers. (In this and all other figures, repulsive forces are plotted as positive values and attractive forces as negative values.) These force profiles may be analyzed by fitting the linear portions of the curves to an analytical expression which is a function of the Debye length, κ^{-1}, and the surface potential, ψ_0. The analysis of electrostatic forces in this region is straightforward. The objective is to describe the variation of pressure between two planar surfaces (a much simpler geometry than crossed cylinders) as a function of distance. Once this is known, the pressure may be integrated with respect to distance to give the interaction energy per unit area, E/A. Then, using the Derjaguin approximation [Eq. (2)], this energy for two planar surfaces is converted directly to the force between the two hemicylindrical surfaces. The derivation is based on the assumption that the potential distribution is governed by the Poisson-Boltzmann (P-B) equation which, in cgs units, is

$$\frac{d\psi^2}{dx^2} = \frac{-4\pi e}{\varepsilon} \sum_i z_i n_i^0 \exp(\frac{-z_i e \psi}{kT}), \qquad (6)$$

where ψ is the potential which varies with distance x in a medium with dielectric constant ε. The summation gives the charge density, which is composed of all ionic species in the medium (subscript "i") which have bulk concentration n_i^0 and valency z_i. The constants e, k, and T are the electronic charge, Boltzmann constant, and the absolute temperature, respectively.

The electrostatic contribution to the pressure between two planar surfaces is a result of the excess osmotic pressure of the ions at the midpoint between the two planes:

$$P = kT \left(\sum_i n_i^m - \sum_i n_i^0 \right). \qquad (7)$$

The summations give the total ionic concentrations at the midplane (superscript "m") and in the bulk (superscript "0"). Both of these values are given by the Boltzmann equation

$$n_i^x = n_i^0 \exp(-z_i e \psi_x / kT), \qquad (8)$$

which describes how the ion concentrations vary from a value of n_i^0 in the bulk (where the potential is assumed equal to 0) to a greater or lesser concentration as the ions are attracted or repelled by the electric field extending from the surface.

For a symmetrical electrolyte at a bulk concentration of n^0 the values of n_i for the anion, $z_i = -z$, and cation, $z_i = +z$, evaluated at the midplane potential, $\psi = \psi_m$, and the bulk potential, $\psi = 0$, may be evaluated with Equation (8) and substituted into Equation (7) to yield

$$P = 2n^0 kT \, [\cosh(ze\psi_m/kT) - 1], \tag{9}$$

the cosh term arising from the identity $e^x + e^{-x} = 2 \cosh x$.

Equation 9 will give the desired relationship between the pressure and separation distance once the variation of the midplane potential is defined with respect to distance. Ideally, this would be accomplished by solving the Poisson-Boltzmann equation between two planar walls [37]. Although there is no analytical solution for this problem, it is possible to obtain an approximation for distances greater than the Debye length by superimposing the potential distributions from each of two such isolated surfaces that face each other in a parallel plane geometry [38]. These potential profiles are obtained by solving Equation (6) with the appropriate boundary conditions, e.g., assume that the surface potential is fixed so that $\psi(x = 0) = \psi_0$ and $\psi(x = \infty) = 0$, to yield

$$\gamma = \gamma_0 \exp(-\kappa x), \tag{10}$$

where $\gamma = \tanh(ze\psi/4kT)$ and $\kappa^{-1} = \dfrac{4\pi e^2 \Sigma_i z_i^2 n_i^0}{\varepsilon kT}$.

At distances greater than the Debye length, the potential will be small, regardless of the potential at the surface, so that the left-hand side of Equation (10) may be replaced with $ze\psi/4kT$ and rearranged to give an expression for the potential

$$\psi = \frac{4kT\gamma_0}{ze} \exp(-\kappa x). \tag{11}$$

Assuming that such profiles extend from each of the two parallel faces, the value of the potential at the midplane (where x is half of the separation distance, $D/2$) is given by the supposition of the profiles:

$$\psi_m = \frac{8kT\gamma_0}{ze} \exp(-\kappa D/2). \tag{12}$$

This is substituted into Equation (9) and, because this value of ψ_m was obtained under the assumption of small ψ, the cosh term may

be replaced with the leading terms of the power series expansion
($\cosh x = 1 + x^2/2! + x^4/4! + ...$). This yields an expression for
the pressure in terms of the Debye length and the surface potential:

$$P = 64n^0kT\gamma_0^2 \exp(-\kappa D). \tag{13}$$

Equation (13) may be integrated with respect to distance to
give the desired interaction energy per area between the planar
surfaces. To obtain this energy for surfaces at a separation of D,
the integration is performed from infinite separation (where the
pressure is zero) to D to yield

$$E/A = (64n^0kT/\kappa)\gamma_0^2 \exp(-\kappa D). \tag{14}$$

The final step in the analysis is to relate this energy to a force
between the hemicylindrical surfaces (i.e., Derjaguin
approximation [Equation (2)] by noting that $E/A = F/2\pi R$. Since
κ^{-1} is defined by the solution composition and temperature, the
only adjustable parameter is the surface potential, ψ_0.

From the foregoing analysis, a plot of $\ln(F/R)$ vs D is
expected to be linear, with a slope proportional to κ^{-1} and an
intercept related to the surface potential ψ_0. Figure 8 (top) bears
out the linearity of $\ln(F/R)$ vs D for mica separated by KNO_3
solutions over several Debye lengths, and Table 1 presents κ^{-1}
and ψ_0 values determined by this procedure.

Despite some uncertainty in the exact value of ψ_0 resulting
from variations in the chemical composition (% weight K^+) of
different mica samples [1], the measured electrostatic repulsive
forces between mica separated by dilute symmetrical electrolytes
appear to be well described by the Gouy-Chapman theory. Under

TABLE 1. **Debye Length and Surface Potential as a Function**
of Electrolyte Concentration[a]

$[KNO_3]$	κ^{-1} (theory)	κ^{-1} (expt.)	ψ_0 (expt.)
10^{-1} M	9.6 Å	11.5 Å	75 mV
10^{-2}	30	37.5	62
10^{-3}	96	99	85
10^{-4}	304	291	82

[a]Data taken from Reference 1.

other conditions, there are significant discrepancies between experiment and theory. In high concentrations of KNO_3, e.g., 1 M, κ^{-1} values are ~ 25% higher than theoretical values, and it is necessary to assume that the outer Helmholtz plane is shifted to ~2.5 nm beyond the surface in order to obtain a finite value for the surface potential. This phenomenon is now understood to result from hydration forces (or solvation forces) resulting from the structural ordering of H_2O between the surfaces and the hydration of adsorbed K^+ on the surface.

In nonsymmetrical electrolytes containing a divalent ion, e.g., $Ca(NO_3)_2$, κ^{-1} is much smaller (20-45%) than anticipated, signaling a reduction in the extent of repulsive electrostatic forces. This apparent reduction is believed to be the result of an ion correlation effect, which has only recently been theoretically predicted to occur between highly charged surfaces in solutions of high charge density [39], e.g., in solutions containing divalent ions. In essence, this effect arises because the local ion distribution not only reflects the average or mean-field imposed by the screened surface charge, but also the field imposed by other ions in solutions; i.e., there is a correlation between ions that is not accounted for by the Gouy-Chapman theory. The importance of ion-correlation effects on electrochemical double-layer structures has not been experimentally investigated to our knowledge, but appears significant enough to warrant investigation.

Van der Waals forces can be observed in aqueous KNO_3 solutions at close separations and at high ion concentrations. For example, if the force curves in Figure 8 (top) for 0.1 and 1 M KNO_3 are plotted in more detail at distances below 20 nm [1], there is a small but significant attraction between the surfaces, and the force curves pass through a distinct minimum [Fig. 8 (bottom)]. These attractive forces have been attributed to van der Waals dispersion forces, which in theory are essentially independent of the electrolyte concentration. To demonstrate this, Israelachvili and Adams mathematically subtracted electrostatic forces, extrapolated from measurements made at large separations, from the total observed forces at short ranges. The remaining van der Waals forces obtained in 0.1 and 1.0 M KNO_3 solutions were found to coincide, in agreement with theory. Further, by using an inverse square law for the force ($F/R = -A/6D^2$ where the Hamaker constant $A = 2.2 \times 10^{-20}$ J), these authors found good quantitative agreement between the experiment and nonretarded van der Waals theory.

In our laboratory, we have measured repulsive electrostatic forces between optically transparent Pt films deposited on mica [17]. These results are very preliminary, but they demonstrate that short-range forces at solid electrodes can be measured at distances comparable to those obtained using mica. Figure 9 shows the force vs distance curve obtained for two identical 4 nm thick Pt electrodes immersed in H_2O. Measurable forces are observed beginning at about 16 nm and increase approximately exponentially with decreasing separation. Typically, the closest approach of the two surfaces is about 1 nm ($D = 0$ corresponds to contact in air). That the surfaces apparently "contact" at distances greater than expected may be due to surface asperities. However, it is noteworthy that a 1 nm distance of closest approach is in reasonable agreement with the surface roughness estimated from scanning tunneling microscopy [40] [Fig. 10]. This surface roughness complicates interpretations of the interaction between metal layers at very short distances.

From electron diffraction and transmission electron microscopy, the Pt films are known to be polycrystalline, with an approximate average grain size of 20 Å or less, which is considerably smaller than the total interaction area between the crossed cylindrical surfaces. Thus, the measurements we have made result from interactions between numerous grains with different crystallographic orientations. Calculated force curves, using the nonlinear Poisson Boltzmann equation to describe the forces [41], are in good agreement with the data. Average values of $|\psi_0| = 51 \pm 13$ mV and $\kappa^{-1} = 65 \pm 22$ nm were obtained from a set of independent measurements in H_2O. The screening length κ^{-1} is much shorter than expected for pure H_2O and corresponds roughly to an impurity ion concentration (1:1 electrolyte) of 10^{-3} M. The reasonable agreement between the experimental and measured force curves has led us to believe that the excess surface charge is associated with ionized surface-adsorbed species or to localized charge induced in the film during sputter deposition.

IV. STRUCTURAL FORCES [42] AND HYDRODYNAMIC FLOW

As mentioned in the preceding section, the DLVO theory fails to adequately predict the repulsive short-range forces observed between mica layers immersed in concentrated KNO_3 solutions. This phenomenon is not specific to KNO_3; similar discrepancies

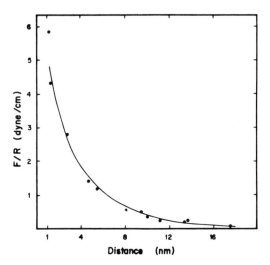

Figure 9. *Force versus distance for Pt coated mica surfaces separated by water. The solid line represents the best fit of the data using the non-linear Poisson-Boltzmann equation. (Reprinted with permission from Reference 17. Copyright © 1988 American Chemical Society.)*

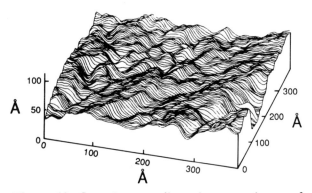

Figure 10. *Scanning tunneling microscope image of 40 Å thick Pt film r.f. sputtered deposited on cleaved mica. (Reprinted with permission from Reference 40. Copyright © 1989 American Chemical Society.)*

between fluid-based continuum theories and experimental force measurements at very small separations have been measured in aqueous solutions containing various electrolytes, and in a number of nonpolar organic solvents, for example, cyclohexane and n-hexadecane [5]. The consensus of laboratories studying these interactions is that these discrepancies are the effect of an additional force (or forces) resulting from hydration of surface adsorbed cations on mica and/or organization of solvent in diffuse layers confined to the molecularly narrow enclosure. The observation of structural forces is not limited to force experiments using mica. They also appear in the swelling of clays and and are related to the lubrication of surfaces.

Figure 11 shows an example of structural forces observed between mica and a thin silver film deposited on mica [7]. The solvent is octamethylcyclotetrasiloxane, OMCTS, a nonpolar liquid that consists of a quasi-spherical molecule with a mean molecular diameter of 8 Å. The force curve is qualitatively similar to that observed between two bare mica surfaces separated by OMCTS and other nonpolar liquids, demonstrating the extreme smoothness of the metal layer. A decaying oscillatory force is observed as a function of distance separating the surface, with a periodicity equal to the molecular diameter of OMCTS. A similar oscillatory function is often, but not always, observed for bare mica separated by aqueous solutions [Fig. 1] although the periodicity is reduced to 2.4 Å, corresponding to the mean diameter of H_2O.

The correlation between the periodicity of the force oscillations with the molecular diameter of the liquid molecule suggests that

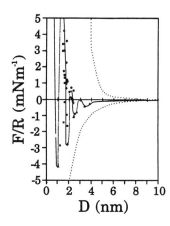

Figure 11. *Oscillatory force curve between Ag and mica separated by OMCTS. (From Reference 7, with permission.)*

confinement of a liquid between two surfaces results in a layering of the fluid molecules. This structural effect is very short ranged, limited to separations of several molecular diameters, as indicated by the rapid decay in the oscillations. The layering of the solvent does not appear to involve, at least in the case of nonpolar liquids, specific chemical interactions with the surfaces.

Observations of structural liquid layering between mica surfaces are relatively recent and are not completely understood. These interactions cannot be described by a continuum fluid theory. The oscillations reflect the graininess of the liquid, and one expects that successful models will take into account molecular instead of bulk properties of the liquid. A simplified explanation, for instance, uses a space filling model [43] to account for the density of spherical molecules such as OMCTS entrapped between the mica surfaces [Fig. 12]. At separations that allow close packing of the spheres (corresponding to integral values of the molecular diameter), the density of the fluid will be greatest. At any other separation distance, the average fluid density will fall below the bulk value. Thus, as the wall

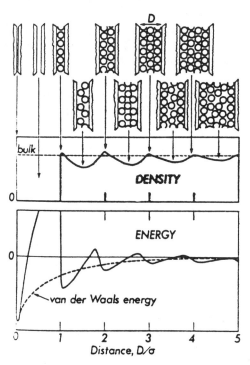

Figure 12. *Schematic diagram of the layering of nonpolar spherical fluid molecules (e.g., OMCTS) between two flat walls. The coarseness of the fluid at the molecular scale produces maxima and minima in the density profile that occur at multiples of the molecular diameter, σ. The oscillating density profile resulting from this solvent layering leads to a measurable oscillating interaction energy and "quantized" fluid flow between two closely (D < 5-10 σ) separated mica layers. (From Reference 43 (a), with permission.)*

separation is varied, the van der Waals interactions occur across a liquid with a periodically rising and falling mean density, causing the forces to undergo a similar oscillation.

The structural forces observed in aqueous solutions are more complex and dependent on chemical interactions, i.e., adsorption, between solutes and the surface [44,45]. In addition to oscillatory forces that probably arise for similar reasons as described above, a monotonically decaying repulsive or attractive structural force is often observed on hydrophilic and hydrophobic surfaces, respectively. These forces are referred to in the literature as hydration and hydrophobic structural forces, and their origin is not completely resolved. As an example, we consider the work of Pashley and coworkers [45] on hydration forces observed between ionized mica in electrolyte solutions, which bears a resemblance to electrode interfaces. In this study, strong repulsive hydration forces were observed in solutions containing chloride salts of Li^+, K^+, Na^+, and Cs^+, resulting from electrostatic binding of the cation to the negatively charged surface. The evidence supporting this includes: (a) no hydration forces were observed in pure water; (b) the magnitude of forces increases with the hydration of the bound layer in the order: $Li^+ = Na^+ > K^+ > Cs^+$; and (c) the hydration forces are nearly independent of the concentration at high concentrations corresponding to saturation coverage. Pashley has used a mass-action law to describe the competitive surface binding of metal cations and H^+ (or H_3O^+) in order to explain the observed dependence on the cation concentration. These workers also concluded that the extra hydration force resulted from "dehydrating" the adsorbed metal cation in a multistep process as the surfaces were pushed together.

The structure of hydrated metal cations on mica, implied by force measurements, is analogous to the conceptual model of a Stern layer of ions adsorbed at a finite distance, δ, from the surface. The Stern layer model has been implicitly applied by Claesson et al. in analyzing force curves obtained in concentrated solutions of a series of tetraalkylammonium bromide salts [46] [Fig. 13]. In these measurements, the distance of closest approach of the two surfaces (defined by an apparent hard wall contact) corresponds to twice the molecular diameter of the large organic cation adsorbed on the mica surface. The DLVO theory gives a good fit to the data beyond a separation distance of 2δ assuming a plane of charge located at a distance δ from each surface.

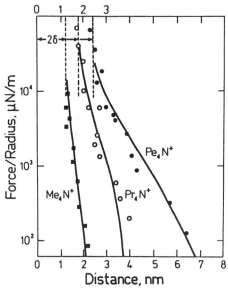

Figure 13. *Forces between mica as a function of distance in concentrated aqueous solutions of $R_4N^+Br^-$ salts. Me = methyl, Pr = propyl, and Pe = pentyl. The continuous curves assume a Stern layer of thickness δ that corresponds roughly to the thickness of the adsorbed cation. (From Reference 44. Copyright © 1985 Royal Swedish Academy. Reprinted with permission of Cambridge University Press.)*

The oscillatory and hydration forces directly observed through force measurements are related to other interfacial parameters of interest, which have been investigated by both experimental and computational methods, e.g., molecular dynamics [47,48]. One parameter, the effective molecular diffusivity in a pore (e.g., zeolite or polymer), has been indirectly related to transport limited rates measured at electrodes of nanoscopic dimensions [49]. Hydrodynamics in narrow enclosures have also been experimentally investigated by Chan and Horn [2] and Israelachvili [3], using transient force measurement techniques. In Chan and Horn's experiment, the lower mica surface is driven at a constant rate towards the upper surface. The hydrodynamic drag of the moving surface slows its movement, which is detected by interferometry using a video recording system and analyzed on the basis of Reynolds theory to, in effect, yield the liquid viscosity as a function of separation distance. An example of one experiment is shown in Figure 14, where the two surfaces were mica (in a crossed cylindrical orientation), and the liquid was OMCTS (qualitatively similar results have been obtained in liquid alkanes). At large separations (>50 nm), Chan and Horn found good quantitative agreement between theory and experiment, indicating that the viscosity within this region is equal to the bulk value. At shorter distances, the rate of the movement of the lower surface was slower than predicted, indicating an increase in viscosity. The magnitude of this increase is small, but the values are experimentally significant. A more interesting behavior is observed at distances less than 2 nm. In this regime, the movement of the lower surface is no longer a monotonic function of time, but instead occurs in a jump-wise fashion, with the size of each jump equal to the mean diameter of OMCTS. Further, the

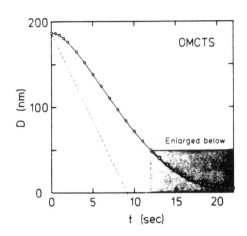

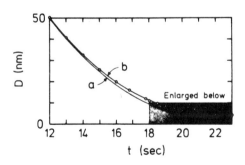

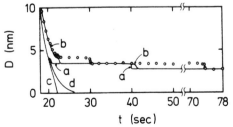

Figure 14. *Plot of the rate of drainage between two mica sheets immersed in OMCTS. In this experiment, one of the mica surfaces is driven at a constant rate, 20.5 nm/s, towards the opposing surface. The open circles represent the measured distance between the surfaces as a function of time. The top frame shows the measured distance as a function of time (the surface separation is 185 nm at t = 0 s) and the predicted response (solid line) based on Reynolds theory for hydrodynamic flow. The middle frame shows the same quantities for distances below 50 nm and at longer times where there is a small but significant deviation between the experiment and theory, indicating an increase in the apparent fluid viscosity. At very small separations (< 5 nm), bottom frame, OMCTS molecules flow out between the surfaces in a series of discrete jumps. The jump size is 0.75 nm, which corresponds to the OMCTS molecular diameter. Solid curves labeled (a)-(d) are theoretical predictions described in the original report. (From Reference 2, with permission.)*

time interval between jumps becomes progressively longer with each jump, indicating that the fluid is becoming progressively more difficult to squeeze out. This type of flow is indicative of the ordering of fluid molecules that can be obtained in narrow pores.

V. FORCES BETWEEN POLYMER FILMS

Several groups have extended the use of the surface forces apparatus to the study of adsorbed polymers [13-16]. Knowing the intermolecular forces that occur between polymer layers and substrates and how these forces are affected by temperature, solvent, and so forth, can provide clues to predict polymer conformations on solid substrates.

Klein measured both the forces [13] between adsorbed polystyrene on mica in cyclohexane and the refractive index n of the medium between the two surfaces as a function of separation distance [Fig. 15]. Refractive index measurements allow the volume fraction of polymer between the surfaces to be estimated. The force diagram shows attractive van der Waals forces starting at a separation distance of ca. 65 nm and an attractive minimum at 20 nm. Compression below 20 nm leads to a repulsive force. The results can be qualitatively explained in terms of the phase behavior for polystyrene in cyclohexane [Fig. 16]. In the region where there are no measurable forces ($D > 65$ nm), the polymer layers are not yet in contact, and the measured refractive index n corresponds to that of bulk cyclohexane. With a decrease in D, the effective polymer volume fraction in the region where the chains overlap, ϕ_{OV}, increases and leads to a two phase system with reduced free energy. This is experimentally seen as an attractive well in the force curve and an increase in the refractive index. When the compression increases past ϕ_2, a one phase region again exists. In this region, compression causes the chain density to increase and, thus, the free energy to increase. The configurational entropy of the polymer between the mica surfaces also decreases in this region, contributing to the repulsive part of the force-distance curve experimentally observed.

Force measurements have been made by Hadziioannou et al. [15] on block copolymers of poly(vinyl-2-pyridine)/polystyrene (PV2P/PS). The PV2P segment of the polymer is adsorbed in a flattened configuration on the mica surfaces; the PS segment is

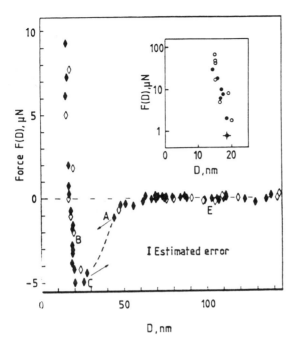

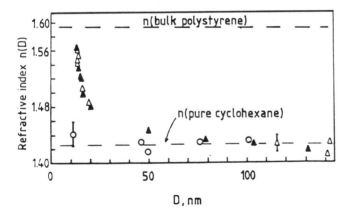

Figure 15. *(top) Forces between adsorbed polystyrene on mica in cyclohexane; (bottom) Refractive index of adsorbed polystyrene on mica as a function of surface separation. (From Reference 13 (a), with permission.)*

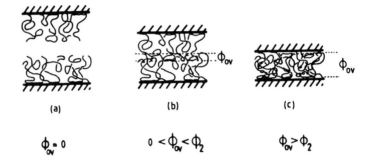

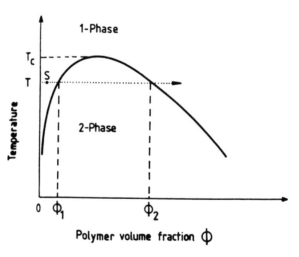

Figure 16. *(top) Schematic showing the overlap of the polystyrene layers as a function of surface separation; (bottom) The equilibrium phase diagram for polystyrene in cyclohexane. (From Reference 13 (a), with permission.)*

covalently bound to the PV2P segment and is oriented towards the solution phase. This configuration eliminates the possibility of the individual PS macromolecules bridging the gap and adsorbing directly on mica. (The bridging configuration is thought to cause additional attraction in the case of the adsorbed PS homopolymer). In a good solvent such as toluene, the PS chains are in an extended configuration away from the surface, and compression of the surfaces causes an overlap of the PS chains as previously. The subsequent repulsion observed for the block copolymer, however, begins at 10 R_g (where R_g is the radius of gyration of the polymer), as compared to the 3 R_g of homopolystyrene. Changing the solvent to cyclohexane substantially reduces the repulsive range to about 4 R_g. This reduction of the repulsive range is due to the configurational contraction of the PS chains and a decrease of the binary interactions between the polymer segments. Use of the copolymer allows observation of the thermodynamic segmental interaction between the PS layers without the added attractive contribution due to bridging. The authors also measured an increase in the onset of repulsive forces with increasing molecular weight of the polystyrene [Fig. 17]. They attribute this to terminally attached and extended polystyrene chains, which form a layer of uniform density whose thickness increases with the molecular weight of the polystyrene block.

VI. ULTRA-THIN-LAYER ELECTROCHEMISTRY

In a unique application, Bard and coworkers have employed a modified surface forces apparatus to construct a dual-electrode thin-layer electrochemical cell where the spacing between working electrodes can be varied from tens of microns to less than 1 nm. In these experiments, the surface forces apparatus is used to control the separation between two Pt or highly oriented pyrolytic graphite (HOPG) electrodes, oriented in a crossed cylindrical geometry, while monitoring forces and/or faradaic currents between the electrodes [19,50,51]. In a typical experiment, one electrode is biased at a potential to effect the oxidation (or reduction) of a soluble redox species, e.g., $Fe(CN)_6^{-4} \rightarrow Fe(CN)_6^{-3} + e^-$, which diffuses across the gap where it is rereduced (or reoxidized) at the second electrode. The electrochemical cell circuit is similar to that of conventional dual-electrode cells, allowing steady-state and transient electrochemical

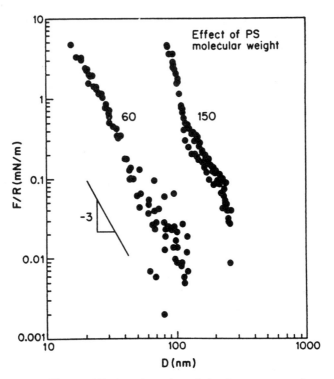

Figure 17. *Log-log plot of the force versus distance curve for two molecular weights (60,000 MW and 150,000 MW) of PS in the block copolymer PV2P/PS adsorbed on mica. (Reprinted with permission from Reference 15. Copyright © 1986 American Chemical Society.)*

measurements to be performed. Of interest is the fact that the electrode gap can be reduced to essentially molecular dimensions, allowing processes to be investigated that would not be possible in a conventional cell. For instance, in experiments with the $Fe(CN)_6^{-4/-3}$ couple, Fan and Bard [50] found that the current-distance behavior between two Pt electrodes could be separated into three regimes: (a) at large separations, $D > 300$ Å, the steady-state current could be accounted for by normal diffusional transport of the electroactive species across the gap, taking into account the crossed cylindrical electrode geometry; (b) at intermediate distances ($10 < D < 300$ Å), the current is somewhat larger than expected for a mass-transport controlled reaction, indicating that new factors, such as an altered reactant concentration resulting from double-layer electrostatic forces or a change in fluid viscosity near the electrode surfaces, are effecting the transport controlled rate; and (c) at short distances ($D < 10$ Å), the current shows a nearly exponential increase with decreasing distance suggesting electron tunneling directly between the two surfaces. In the same paper, these authors also demonstrated electron-transfer between two redox active polymer coated Pt electrodes as the surfaces were brought into contact.

In an experiment combining faradaic electrochemistry and surface force measurements, Lee and Bard [19] measured the adhesion forces between unactivated and activated HOPG surfaces immersed in aqueous Na_2SO_4 and correlated their findings with the activation kinetics observed for $K_3Fe(CN)_6$ reduction on the same surfaces. The adhesion force for unactivated (hydrophobic) HOPG in the aqueous solution was found to be approximately equal to the value measured in air (50 μN), indicating little hydration of the unactivated surface. Activated HOPG, produced by pulsing the electrode potential between 1.5 V and -1.5 V vs SCE, resulted in a dramatic decrease in the adhesion force (2 μN) and a marked increase in rate of $Fe(CN)_6^{-3}$ reduction. Both effects were ascribed to the more hydrophilic nature of the activated surface.

VII. CONCLUSIONS

The selected experimental results presented in this chapter demonstrate how detailed pictures of interfacial structure can be obtained from force measurements. Although the majority of past work has dealt with forces between mica surfaces, it appears feasible to make similar measurements with electrodes of smoothness comparable to that of mica. The technical problems in preparing ultra-smooth electrode surfaces are obvious, but not insurmountable. Materials such as HOPG [19] and layered compound semiconductors (e.g., WSe_2) are natural candidates, as they can be cleaved to obtained molecularly smooth surfaces. The deposition of solid and liquid metal thin films, while providing a greater range of materials for study, will be more technically demanding in their preparation.

The very high resolution and sensitivity of the surface forces apparatus allows interfacial structure to be probed over distances which range from the size of a macromolecule to the thickness of the Helmholtz plane. It should be possible to extract similar detailed information on a myriad of structures with dimensions intermediate between these extreme cases. Force measurements appear particularly well suited for in situ studies of modified electrodes (e.g., thin oxide coatings and organic films), simultaneously providing molecular structure, e.g., orientation and coverage, and the potential distribution across these interfaces. The most fundamental and direct information of double-layer structure and ion adsorption has been obtained from force measurements by investigators whose primary interests concern colloid chemistry. There are, however, a rich variety of questions regarding double-layer structure at metal electrodes that have yet to be explored by a direct experimental technique. As an example, the dependence of structural or hydration forces at metal surfaces, where the electronic charge is uniformly smeared out (vs localized ionic charge on mica), has not been measured. Forces at metals can be made over a wide range of potentials and charges not available using mica, extending our knowledge of double layer phenomena.

The ability to perform chemistry between surfaces separated by an inter-electrode gap of nanometers or less, as in the initial studies by Bard and coworkers, makes possible new types of experiments to explore chemical dynamics. For instance, one can imagine using the surface forces apparatus to measure the electron transfer rate as a *function of distance* (with angstrom resolution) between redox species immobilized on the two surfaces or to measure the distance dependence of energy transfer between a luminescent polymer and a metal surface. These exciting possibilities await further development, but are likely to provide new insights into chemistry occurring at interfaces.

References

1. Israelachvili, J. N., and Adams, G. E. *J. Chem. Soc. Faraday Trans. I* 74 (1978): 975.
2. Chan , D. Y. C., and Horn, R. G. *J. Chem. Phys.* 83 (1985): 5311.
3. Israelachvili, J. N., *J. Colloid and Interface Sci.* 110 (1986): 263.
4. Pashley, R. M., and Israelachvili, J. N. *J. Colloid and Interface Sci.* 101 (1984): 511.
5. Christenson, H. K.; Horn, R. G.; and Israelachvili, J. N. *J. Colloid and Interface Sci.* 88 (1982): 79.
6. McGuiggan, P. M., and Pashley, R. M. *J. Phys. Chem.* 92 (1988): 1235.
7. Parker, J. L., and Christenson, H. K. *J. Chem. Phys.* 88 (1988): 8013.
8. Israelachvili, J. N. *Intermolecular and Surface Forces.* London: Academic Press, 1985.
9. Claesson, P. M. and Christenson, H. K. *J. Phys. Chem.* 92, (1988): 1650.
10. Israelachvili, J. N., and Pashley, R. M. *J. Colloid and Interface Sci.* 98 (1984): 500.
11. Pashley, R. M. et al. *Science* 229 (1985): 1088.
12. Israelachvili, J. N.; McGuiggan, P. M.; and Homola, A. M. *Science* 240 (1988): 248.
13. (a) Klein, J. *Adv. Colloid and Interface Sci.*, 16 (1982): 101; (b) Klein, J. *Nature*, 288 (1980): 248.
14. Israelachvili, J. N., et al. *Macromolecules* 17 (1984) 204.
15. Hadziioannou, G., et al. *Am. Chem. Soc.* 108 (1986): 2869.
16. Marra, J., and Hair, M. L. *J. Phys. Chem.* 92 (1988): 6044.
17. Smith, C. P., et al. *J. Phys. Chem.* 92 (1988): 199.
18. van Blokland, P. H. G. M., and Overbeek, J. T. *J. Chem Soc., Faraday Trans. I* 74 (1978): 2637.
19. Lee, C.-W., and Bard, A. J. *J. Electrochem. Soc.* 135 (1988): 1599.
20. Binning, G., and Rohrer, H. *Helv. Phys. Acta* 55 (1982): 726.
21. Christenson, H. K. *J. Phys. Chem.* 90 (1986): 4.
22. McGuiggan, P. M., and Israelachvili, J. N. *Chem. Phys. Lett.* 149 (1989): 469.
23. Israelachvili, J. N., and McGuiggan, P. M. *Science* 241 (1988): 795.
24. Tolansky, S. *Multiple Beam Interferometry.* Oxford: Clarendon Press, 1948.
25. Vanderlick, T. K. *Ph.D. Thesis.* Minneapolis: University of Minnesota, 1988.
26. Derjaguin, B. V., et al. *J. Colloid Sci.* 19 (1964): 113.
27. (a) Derjaguin, B. V. *Kolloid-Z.* 69 (1934): 155; (b) Barouch, E.; Matijevic, E.; and Parsegian, V. A. *J. Chem. Soc., Far. Trans. I* 82 (1986): 2801.
28. Israelachvili, J. N. *J. Colloid and Interface Sci.* 44 (1973): 259.
29. Clarkson, M. T. *J. Phys. D: Appl. Phys.* 22 (1989) 475.
30. Derjaguin, B. V., and Landau, L. *Acta Physicochem. URSS* 14 (1941): 633.
31. Verwey, E. J. W., and Overbeek, J. T. G. *Theory of the Stability of Lyophobic Colloids.* Elsevier: Amsterdam, 1948.
32. Voropajeva, T.; Derjaguin, B.; and Kabanov, B. *Compt. Rend. Acad. Sci. U.R.S.S.* 128 (1959) 981.
33. Frumkin, A. N. *J. Electrochem. Soc.* 107 (1960): 461.
34. Tabor, D., and Winterton, R. H. S. *Nature* 219 (1968): 1120.
35. Israelachvili, J. N., and Adams, G. E. *Nature* 262 (1976): 774.
36. Bard, A. J., and Faulkner, L. R. *Electrochemial Methods.* New York: Wiley,

1980.

37. Devereux, O. F., and de Bruyn, P. L. *Interactions of Plane-Parallel Double Layers*. Massachusetts: M.I.T. Press, 1963.

38. Hiemenz, P. C. *Principles of Colloid and Surface Chemistry*, 2nd ed., 12.7. New York: Marcel Dekker, 1986.

39. Guldbrand, L., et al. *J. Chem. Phys.* 80 (1984): 2221.

40. Scott, E. R.; White, H. S.; and McClure, D. J. *J. Phys. Chem.* 93 (1989): 5249.

41. Chan, D. Y. C.; Pashley, R. M.; and White, L. R. *J. Colloid and Interface Sci.* 77 (1980): 283.

42. For recent advances in this field, see the Proceedings from the Conference on "Hydration Forces and Molecular Aspects of Solvation," (Orenas, Sweden, June 1984), *Chemica Scripta* 25 (1985): 1.

43. (a) Israelachvili, J. N. *Adv. Colloid and Interface Sci.* 16 (1982): 31. (b) Ninham, B. N. *J. Phys. Chem.* 84 (1980): 84.

44. Israelachvili, J. N. *Chemica Scripta* 25 (1985): 7.

45. Pashley, R. M. *Chemica Scripta* 25 (1985): 22.

46. Claesson, P.; Horn, R. G.; and Pashley, R. M. *J. Colloid and Interface Sci.* 100 (1984): 250.

47. Bitsanis, I., et al. *J. Chem. Phys.* 89 (1988): 3152.

48. Davis, H. T., et al. *ACS Symposium Series No. 353, Supercomputer Research in Chemistry and Chemical Engineering*, ed. K. F. Jensen and D. G. Truhlar, 1987.

49. Morris, R. B.; Franta, D. J.; and White, H. S. *J. Phys. Chem.* 91 (1987): 3559.

50. Fan, F.-R. F., and Bard, A. J. *J. Am. Chem. Soc.* 109 (1987): 6262.

51. Davis, J. M.; Fan, F.-R. F.; and Bard, A. J. *J. Electroanal. Chem.* 238 (1987): 9.

CHAPTER 5

SURFACE ENHANCED
RAMAN SCATTERING

Jeanne E. Pemberton

Department of Chemistry
University of Arizona
Tucson, AZ 85721-0001

CONTENTS

I. INTRODUCTION

The extreme sensitivity to chemical environment of many heterogeneous processes that occur at solid-liquid interfaces has stimulated much research into the development of spectroscopic methods capable of providing a detailed molecular picture of the interface. Electrochemistry is one area where considerable interest in these developments exists because of the sensitivity of the electron transfer event to the molecular nature of the interface. Development of an understanding of the molecular nature of the electrochemical double layer is of both fundamental and technological interest. In order that the electron transfer between a redox species in solution and an immersed electrode be completely understood, it is of critical importance that the impact of molecular double layer structure be adequately assessed. Once this understanding is achieved, improvements in electrochemical devices of technological interest, such as energy conversion and storage devices, should follow.

Within the last decade, significant advances have been made along these lines through the successful application of various spectroscopic probes to the characterization of the electrochemical double layer. Spectroscopic probes which have proven useful include both optical spectroscopy on in situ and emersed electrodes and electron spectroscopies on emersed electrodes. The advent of spectroscopic probes that are molecularly specific provides the potential for ultimately understanding the relationship between the electrochemical double layer and the electron transfer event.

Techniques which appear to be most promising in this regard are the vibrational spectroscopies. The potential of these approaches lies in the extreme sensitivity of molecular vibrations to chemical environment. In terms of applications to in situ electrochemical systems, promising experimental approaches must meet several criteria: adequate sensitivity to detect species on the order of 10^{14} to 10^{15} molecules cm^{-2}, applicability to a wide range of experimental systems, and interfacial selectivity. This last criterion is critical for minimal spectral interference from the solvent and from species in bulk solution, which are generally at much higher concentration levels than those confined to the interfacial region. Without interfacial selectivity, adsorbate spectra are observed as only weak features, which may be shifted in position from that of the solution components due to interaction with the surface. These goals have begun to be realized through recent successful application of infrared (IR) and Raman spectroscopic methodologies.

Raman spectroscopy provides several attractive features that address certain limitations of the IR spectroelectrochemical techniques discussed elsewhere in this book. Firstly, Raman scattering in aqueous media is very weak. Therefore, many common aqueous electrochemical systems are readily amenable to study with Raman spectroscopy. Moreover, the low frequency region down to ca. 5 to 10 cm^{-1} is accessible in Raman spectroscopic investigations. Thus, despite the poor sensitivity normally inherent in light scattering methods, Raman spectroscopy has the potential to provide a wealth of information not readily obtainable with these other methods.

Several enhancement approaches have been used to successfully overcome the inherent sensitivity limitations of Raman spectroscopy for the study of interfacial species in electrochemical systems. Van Duyne and coworkers were the first to demonstrate the power of resonance Raman spectroscopy for the study of electrochemically generated species of a transient nature [1-6]. Since this original work, other researchers have utilized resonance Raman spectroscopy to study monolayer and submonolayer quantities of adsorbed species in electrochemical systems.

A second enhancement approach, which allows for the investigation of the electrochemical double layer and which is the focus of this chapter, is surface enhanced Raman scattering or SERS. The origins of SERS are intimately connected with electrochemical systems and date back to pioneering work by Fleischmann and coworkers [7]. In this 1973 paper, they reported the use of Raman spectroscopy to study Hg_2Cl_2, Hg_2Br_2, and HgO on a thin film Hg electrode supported on a Pt substrate. They were able to obtain Raman spectra of quite reasonable signal-to-noise ratio from thin films (two or more monolayers) of these mercurous halide and mercuric oxide species on relatively high surface area electrodes. The spectra resembled those of the respective bulk compounds, and although not particularly exciting from a surface chemistry perspective, these experiments did demonstrate the feasibility of using Raman spectroscopy as a probe of electrochemical interfaces.

These researchers later expanded this approach to the study of Ag electrodes using pyridine as a surface adsorbed probe molecule [8]. Their approach was to increase the number of surface pyridine molecules sampled in the Raman scattering experiment by increasing the surface area of the electrode by electrochemical roughening through multiple oxidation-reduction cycles in an aqueous Cl^- media. In their report of this work in 1974, they presented spectra of very good quality for adsorbed pyridine on these roughened Ag electrodes. Recognizing that the spectra of Fleischmann and coworkers were of higher signal-to-noise ratio than could be rationalized on the basis of an increase in surface area, Jeanmaire and Van Duyne [9] and later Albrecht and Creighton [10] followed this original study with more careful investigations of this observation. Both groups independently recognized that some form of enhancement responsible for a 10^5 to 10^6 increase in intensity relative to an equivalent amount of pyridine in solution was operable in these systems.

Since the first report of surface enhancement, a staggering amount of research has been undertaken with the intent of elucidating the mechanisms responsible for SERS and using this phenomenon to study a wide variety of solid-liquid, solid-gas, and solid-solid interfaces. A significant fraction of the research on SERS has been performed in electrochemical environments. Since the original observations at Ag by Van Duyne and Creighton, SERS has been extended to other metal electrodes as well, most notably Cu and Au. Indeed, thousands of papers in this area have been published in the last decade.

Obviously, all of the preceding work cannot be reviewed in the space of this chapter. Rather, the intent is to give an overview of SERS as it has been applied to electrochemical systems. The characteristics of SERS that make it an attractive probe of the electrode-solution interface are presented first. This section is followed by a qualitative description of current theories of the mechanisms causing surface enhancement and the evidence for the operation of these mechanisms in electrochemical systems. The emphasis of this discussion is on the implications of the different mechanisms in terms of suitable preparation of electrodes for SERS studies. The problems encountered in the application of SERS to electrochemical systems, the novel approaches devised to overcome some of these problems, and examples of electrochemical systems of fundamental or technological interest successfully probed with SERS are presented in the remaining part of the chapter. The reader is referred to the many recent reviews for more detailed descriptions of work in this vast area [11-26].

In reading this chapter, it must be kept in mind that, although the focus is on electrochemical systems, much of the understanding of the phenomenon has been gleaned from SERS studies performed in nonelectrochemical environments. Indeed, studies of SERS on colloids and metal films fabricated in ultrahigh vacuum have contributed considerable insight into surface enhancement. Unfortunately, limitations of space preclude inclusion of the significant work on these other systems.

II. FUNDAMENTAL CHARACTERISTICS OF SERS IN ELECTROCHEMICAL SYSTEMS

Several features associated with SERS make it particularly useful for the investigation of electrochemical interfaces. Of perhaps greatest importance is its sensitivity to submonolayer quantities of species confined in the vicinity of an appropriately prepared electrode. In general, the SERS intensity for a surface confined species tends to follow the surface coverage at a given excitation wavelength. Good experimental evidence in support of this has been presented by Weaver and coworkers [27] in a combined electrochemical-SERS study of the surface coverage of Ag electrodes by simple anionic adsorbates as a function of potential. However, this trend is not absolute in all cases due to the complexity of the surface enhancement mechanisms and sensitivity of the SERS response to experimental conditions such as adsorbate orientation and properties of the ambient environment.

The absolute sensitivity of SERS is intimately related to the enhancement factor operating in these systems, which in turn, is dictated by the preparation conditions as will be described in greater detail in the next section. In general, however, estimation of the enhancement factor for a given system requires assumption of the orientation of the species on the electrode surface and knowledge of certain experimental system parameters such as laser beam size, surface roughness factor, and spectrometer efficiency. Although few investigators have attempted to quantitatively estimate enhancement factors in electrochemical SERS studies, values of enhancement factors reported for Ag electrodes are typically on the order of 10^6. A careful study of enhancement factors by Weaver and coworkers demonstrated that the values are remarkably insensitive to the electronic structure of the adsorbate and the corresponding scattering cross section of the molecule in solution [28].

It is important to note that these enhancement factors are also sensitive to excitation wavelength [29-32]. Maximum enhancement factors estimated for Cu and Au SERS electrodes are ca. 10^5 with excitation in the red [32-34]. It should be noted that these enhancement factors are usually evaluated under conditions of optimal surface preparation and take no account of the distance dependence of the adsorbate from the electrode surface.

SERS possesses sufficient sensitivity to allow electron transfer events to be monitored at the electrode surface. The study of redox reactions should continue to reveal the influence of interfacial structure due to the unparalleled molecular specificity of this approach. Selected investigations are discussed at greater length in the last section of this chapter.

A second feature of the SERS phenomenon making it a viable in situ probe of electrode-electrolyte interfaces is its selectivity for the interfacial region. This behavior is largely due to the characteristics of the mechanisms believed to give rise to SERS. Experimental evidence suggests that enhancement is greatest for the first monolayer and decreases dramatically with distance from the surface [35-38]. Hence, a majority of the SERS response arises from species in the inner and outer Helmholtz planes in electrochemical systems. Perhaps more importantly, Raman scattering from the bulk solution species is usually observed as bands of considerably lower intensity than those from the surface species. This selectivity confers certain experimental advantages on SERS relative to other vibrational spectroscopic approaches devised for the in situ investigation of the electrochemical double layer. Most notably, SERS spectra can be acquired while the potential of an electrode is maintained at a constant value. This is in contrast to the recently developed approach of electrochemically modulated infrared reflectance spectroscopy (EMIRS) wherein the electrode potential is modulated between two values to achieve surface selectivity [39-43].

SERS also possesses advantages relative to two other IR approaches that have been used to study electrochemical interfaces, internal reflection IR and IR reflection-absorption spectroscopy (IRRAS) [40-46]. Bulk foil electrodes can be used with SERS in contrast to internal reflection IR spectroscopic approaches, and no polarization modulation apparatus is necessary as in IRRAS.

One important question regarding interfacial selectivity that remains to be unequivocally answered is whether SERS actually probes the average electrode surface species. Uncertainty regarding the mechanisms that underlie SERS compounds this dilemma. Mechanisms which rely on the existence of a fraction of chemically unique surface sites at which the enhancement preferentially occurs may be predicted to give spectra representative of only those unique surface sites and not of the average surface site. This issue has been addressed recently by Weaver and coworkers [47,48] and Seki and coworkers [49,50]. In general, these researchers find that for simple anionic adsorbates such as CN^-, N_3^-, and SCN^-, the SERS and IRRAS responses are essentially identical. Such results are certainly encouraging; however, similar studies should be performed on more complex systems before these results are considered to be general.

SERS can be successfully used in a variety of electrochemical environments. Although the majority of work has been performed in aqueous media, recent SERS studies in nonaqueous electrochemical environments have been reported [51-62] It is likely that, once surface roughening schemes are devised for electrodes in nonaqueous media, SERS will find greater application in technologically important environments. Recent efforts to observe SERS in molten salt electrolytes have proven unsuccessful [63]. Further efforts aimed at developing appropriate roughening schemes for electrodes in these media will likely result in the fruitful application of SERS to these fascinating solvent systems. Considerations of roughening electrodes for SERS in nonaqueous media are treated in more detail in the next section.

Another characteristic of SERS that has important ramifications for the study of the electrochemical interface is the universality of the enhancement with respect to the chemical nature of the adsorbate. As noted above, enhancement factors for adsorbates typically are on the order of 10^6, and these enhancement factors describe the SERS behavior of a range of molecular adsorbates. Seki has compiled lists of adsorbates studied with SERS that are current through ca. 1985 [64,65]. Perusal of these lists indicates that virtually any molecule, organic or inorganic, adsorbed at an appropriately roughened electrode is observable with SERS. The types of molecules successfully probed to date include simple and complex organic and inorganic species as well as polymeric species at electrode surfaces. Coupled with the fact that SERS can be used with a variety of electrochemical solvents, the vast range of adsorbates studied thus far suggests that the absolute number of electrochemical systems that can be probed with this approach is indeed very large and continually increasing.

Easy access to the low frequency region of the spectrum (<400 cm^{-1}) is one of the more important advantages of SERS relative to its IR counterparts. Critical information regarding adsorbate-electrode bonding that may directly bear on questions of adsorbate orientation and strength of adsorption can be found in this frequency region. The accessibility of this region has been amply demonstrated in electrochemical systems through the study of adsorbed monatomic ions. Hundreds of such studies exist which are too numerous to detail here. However, the interested reader is referred to a nice example in an electrochemical environment provided by the work of Chang and coworkers [66].

Additionally, the low frequency region has been shown to contain vibrational information about the metal surface. A very low frequency mode or VLFM [67-69] is observed for SERS-active Ag surfaces at ca. 8 cm^{-1} -12 cm^{-1}. This mode was first observed by Weitz, Gersten and coworkers [70,71] in 1980. Its position is generally independent of the nature of the adsorbate but, surprisingly, dependent on the excitation frequency. This mode was originally assigned to acoustical vibrations of the Ag surface resulting from large scale roughness features and thought to be good evidence for the importance of electromagnetic models for SERS [72]. However, recent evidence by Wall and coworkers [67-69] suggests that it may be related to the presence of surface roughness on the order of 50-100 Å in size which is generally agreed to fall outside the size range normally associated with electromagnetic effects. Despite this remaining question regarding the origins of the VLFM, its observation clearly demonstrates the accessability of the low frequency region in SERS. As the application of SERS to electrochemical interfaces continues to expand, it is likely that researchers will further avail themselves of the information contained in this region. Recent low frequency results for the presence of Ag clusters on SERS-active surfaces are discussed in more detail below.

From the standpoint of fundamental molecular information, determination of adsorbate orientation on electrode surfaces has been realized through development of an understanding of SERS "surface selection rules." These selection rules have been independently presented in a formalism which readily allows their use in the interpretation of spectra from surface species by Moskovits [73-76] and Creighton [77,78]. The origins of these selection rules are several-fold. For vibrations which are Raman-allowed, surface selection rules at smooth surfaces have been generally presented in terms of image dipoles which are screened by their image when they are parallel to the surface and enhanced by their image when they are perpendicular to the surface. This is the basis for the surface selection rules operating in surface infrared and HREELS experiments where the transition dipole moment is the critical parameter. However, as pointed out by Campion [79], with surface Raman spectroscopy, the three-dimensional dipole polarizability is the important parameter giving rise to "propensity rules" rather than strict selection rules. Moskovits has provided more exact treatments involving the interference of incident and reflected electric fields [75,76] for both flat (smooth) and curved (rough) metal surfaces.

An alternate way to treat surface propensity rules in SERS is in terms of surface complexes of distinct symmetry formed between the adsorbate and the surface upon adsorption. Complex formation results in a reduction in symmetry of the free molecule through proximity to the surface, resulting in the appearance of vibrational bands that are not Raman-allowed in the free molecule, but which are Raman-allowed in the surface complex [76]. It is not unequivocally known at this time which of these two explanations for the observation of Raman-inactive vibrations at smooth surfaces is correct.

It is important to realize, however, that for SERS-active surfaces, the radius of curvature of the surface confers an additional level of complexity on the operational surface propensity rules. An electromagnetic geometrical effect dependent on the dielectric properties of the curved metal particle and surrounding medium exists which alters the magnitudes of the electric field components normal and tangential to the metal surface [76]. The result is that the relative intensity of these electric field components depends on the proximity of the excitation frequency to the plasma mode frequency of the metal particle which, in turn, is a function of the dielectric properties of the particle. When excitation is far to the red of the plasma frequency, the electric field normal to the surface is dominant, and only vibrations with a significant component in this direction are observed. On the other hand, as the excitation frequency approaches the plasma frequency, the tangential component becomes increasingly significant, providing correspondingly greater intensity to vibrational modes parallel to the surface. Furthermore, for excitation to the blue of the plasma frequency, the tangential component of the electric field can even be greater than the normal component under certain conditions. Moskovits and coworkers have demonstrated the validity of this treatment for a variety of organic molecules adsorbed onto Ag sols [75,76,80]. However, the essence of the treatment is similar to that used by Creighton in the determination of the orientation of pyridine at a Ag electrode surface [77]. Although few reports of the success of this approach for the determination of orientation of adsorbates at electrodes have appeared, it seems likely that a wealth of information will be available on electrochemical interfaces using this approach. It is therefore expected that this approach will receive considerable attention by electrochemists in the future.

It is generally agreed that the major limitation of SERS with respect to the study of the electrochemical double layer is the fact that enhancement does not occur at all metal surfaces. The metals commonly associated with surface enhancement in electrochemical environments are Ag, Cu, and Au. Claims of surface enhancement at other electrodes including Pt [82,83], Cd [84], Pd [85], ß-PdH [86], and Hg [87,88] have been reported. However, these claims have been difficult to validate. The majority of SERS in electrochemical systems has been performed using Ag, Cu, and Au. Therefore, the main focus of this chapter will be on work done with these metals.

It is important to remember that electrode surfaces used for SERS must be appropriately roughened before they will support significant surface enhancement. This aspect of the enhancement, coupled with the limited number of metals which readily support enhancement, greatly limits the generality of SERS. In fact, the majority of commonly used metal electrodes are not enhancing.

Recent efforts to extend the generality of SERS in electrochemical systems have generated significant success. One approach taken in several laboratories has been to electrochemically deposit small quantities of a nonenhancing metal onto an enhancing metal substrate. This approach had as its genesis studies of the effect of underpotentially deposited monolayers of nonenhancing metal films on the SERS response of enhancing electrodes. This work was pioneered by Furtak in a study of the effect of submonolayers of Au on the SERS response of pyridine at Ag electrodes with 514.5 nm excitation [89]. These studies were followed by investigations in a number of research groups in which other nonenhancing metal films were deposited onto enhancing Ag or Au electrodes. The deposited metals studied to date include Pb [90-101], Tl [91,101,102], Cd [90], Cu [90,103,104], and Hg [101]. It is generally observed that, upon deposition of the first monolayer, the SERS signals for adsorbates are greatly decreased. This effect has been explained as a combination of changes in surface electronic properties and alteration of the microscopic Fermi energy at unique surface sites, known as "active sites," thought to be important in the chemical enhancement mechanism for SERS [98]. However, despite the significant decrease in overall signal intensity, a measurable signal still remains which can be used to study adsorbates on these thin films.

This approach has been further extended to encompass not only monolayer films, but also thin multilayer films of foreign metals on enhancing substrates. Fleischmann and coworkers have reported diminished SERS (DSERS) from thin layers of Pb [100], Tl [100], Ni [105,106], Co [105,106], Cu [105], Zn [105], and Fe [107] on roughened Ag electrodes with adsorbates such as pyridine, CN^-, acetate, and benzotriazole. Weaver and coworkers have reported similar success with thin deposited layers of Hg, Tl, and Pb with halide ion and pyridine adsorbates [101], and Pt and Pd with CO as the adsorbate [108] on SERS-active Au electrodes. Despite the decrease in intensities relative to SERS on the substrate metal, spectra of good quality can still be obtained.

[Figs. 1 and 2] are examples of spectra that are obtained from these metal-modified electrodes. [Fig. 1] shows a spectrum of pyridine at -0.8 V versus SCE adsorbed at a thin film equivalent to ca. 30 monolayers of Fe deposited onto a SERS-active Ag electrode at -1.0 V for 3 seconds from 0.1 M $FeSO_4(NH_4)_2SO_4$ in 0.1 M KCl [107]. [Fig. 2] shows spectra for the C-O stretching region and the low frequency region for CO adsorbed at a Pt-modified Au electrode [108]. These data demonstrate the quality of spectral information available from these surfaces. This approach certainly holds a great deal of promise for future work in terms of extending the generality of SERS to more commonly used electrode materials.

A second approach which has enjoyed success in partially overcoming the limitations imposed by the electronic properties of the metal surface is electrochemical deposition of small quantities of an enhancing metal onto a nonenhancing substrate electrode. The first successful application of this

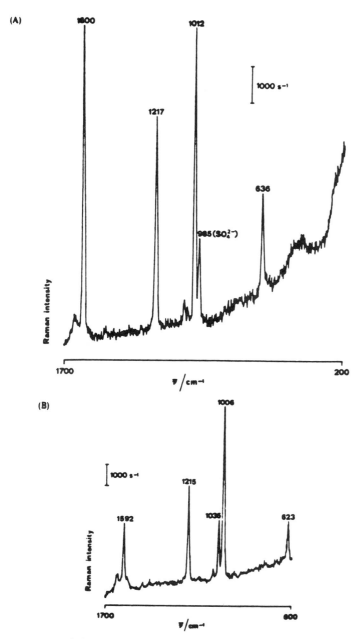

FIGURE 1 (A) Spectrum of pyridine at -0.80 V adsorbed on an Fe electrode formed by depositing Fe on a SERS-active Ag electrode for 3 s at -1.0 V from a solution of 0.1 M $FeSO_4(NH_4)_2SO_4$ + 0.1 M KCl; pyridine added at -0.8 V to make solution 0.05 M. (B) Spectrum of pyridine at -0.9 V adsorbed at a Ag electrode from a solution 0.1 M KCl + 0.05 M pyridine at pH 3.5. (Reprinted with permission from Reference 107.)

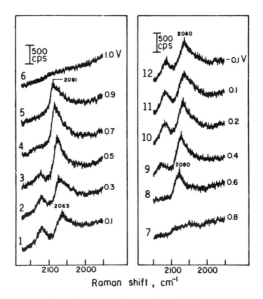

FIGURE 2 Potential-dependent SER spectra in the C-O stretching region for CO adsorbed on a Pt-coated Au electrode. Electrolyte was 0.5 M H_2SO_4 saturated with CO. Spectra were obtained at the indicated potentials sequentially as numbered. Laser excitation was 50 mW at 647.1 nm. (Reprinted with permission from Reference 108.)

variation on the above theme was reported by Marinyuk and coworkers in their 1982 study of pyridine on thin Ag films electrochemically deposited onto Pt electrodes [109]. This work was followed by successful application of the Ag deposition technique to the study of molecules at n-GaAs [60,61], p-GaAs [61,110], and Si [61] semiconductor electrodes. Further work on SERS at electrochemically deposited thin Ag films on Pt electrodes was pursued in this laboratory [111] and that of Furtak [112,113], using pyridine as the adsorbate probe molecule.

One further variation of this approach was recently reported by Weaver and coworkers [114]. In this study, SERS spectra were reported for Cl^-, Br^-, SCN^-, benzonitrile, and pyridine adsorbed at monolayers of Cu and Ag deposited at underpotential on electrochemically roughened Au electrodes. Excitation in these studies was at 647.1 nm where Ag, Cu, and Au all support surface enhancement. Therefore, these studies represent use of an enhancing metal film on an enhancing metal surface. The SERS intensities found for these mixed-metal surfaces were commonly comparable to or higher than those observed for the bulk metal electrodes. Moreover, the signals exhibit the reversibility with respect to positive-negative potential excursions that is characteristic of the underlying Au substrate but not of bulk Ag and Cu surfaces. These surfaces therefore exhibit desirable SERS properties which suggest their possible application in electrochemical studies requiring surfaces with Ag- or Cu-like properties, but having a greater potential range afforded by stabilization of the overlayer [114].

One further point with respect to the limitation of SERS imposed by the relatively small number of metals which support surface enhancement is important to note. As advances in surface Raman instrumentation and methodologies are realized, reliance on surface enhancement for study of the electrochemical double layer will continue to decrease. These advances will allow surfaces with smaller enhancement factors to be studied, ultimately down to an enhancement factor of unity, representing normal surface Raman spectroscopy. Evidence for the potential success of normal surface Raman spectroscopy in electrochemical systems comes from a recent report by Campion on unenhanced (normal) Raman spectroscopy of 4-cyanopyridine at a Rh electrode [115]. These researchers present spectra shown in [Fig. 3] in which the intensity of the C-N stretch of the cyano group at 2248 cm^{-1} is dependent on the polarization of the incident radiation. These observations are evidence that the Raman scattering is arising from surfacea confined species and not solution species. They interpret the observed spectrum in terms of 4-cyanopyridine bound to the surface through the ring nitrogen and oriented along the surface normal. These results are extremely exciting and point the way toward the future for normal surface Raman scattering as a probe of the electrode-electrolyte interface.

III. SERS MECHANISMS AND SURFACE ROUGHNESS IN ELECTROCHEMICAL SYSTEMS

A. Types of Surface Roughness in Electrochemical Systems and Enhancement Mechanisms for SERS.

The features of SERS described above suggest that a wealth of useful information may be available about the electrochemical

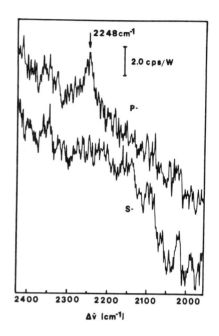

FIGURE 3 Raman spectra of 4-cyanopyridine adsorbed on a Rh electrode at open circuit potential as a function of the incident laser polarization. (Reprinted with permission from Reference 115.)

interface from these studies. However, further advances in the utilization of SERS for electrochemical systems will only occur in parallel with development of a better understanding of the origins of surface enhancement. This section is intended to present an overview of the two classes of mechanisms thought responsible for surface enhancement phenomena. The aim of this section is not absolute rigor. Rather, it is hoped that an appreciation of the fundamental issues involved in these mechanisms and the intimate relationship between surface preparation and enhancement in electrochemical systems can be developed.

The observation of surface enhancement relies upon the existence of the appropriate roughness of the electrode surface. From a historical perspective, the production of surface roughness in Fleischmann's original work [8] was intended only to increase the surface area of the electrode such that a greater number of scattering molecules could be sampled in the Raman experiment. Despite the rather serendipitous nature of this approach, the realization that the observed intensities were inexplicably large and dependent on the presence of roughness [9,10] started furious activity to establish the link between surface enhancement and surface preparation that has continued for over a decade. Thus, it is quite remarkable that a detailed understanding of surface enhancement phenomena has yet to be achieved in light of the enormous effort that has been expended.

In electrochemical systems, the necessary roughness is usually produced through an electrochemical procedure known as an oxidation-reduction cycle (ORC). In this process, the electrode surface is first oxidized to form either a soluble cation or a slightly soluble salt which precipitates on the surface. The electrode is then reduced back to the metallic state leaving a surface which is mildly roughened. This process is thought to generate two types of surface roughness which are proposed to be important in the enhancement phenomenon.

The first type of roughness is known as large-scale roughness and has dimensions on the order of 5 to 10 nm or larger. Large-scale roughness is predominantly associated with classical electromagnetic (EM) enhancement mechanisms. These theories are attractive, because they adequately predict, although not exactly, many experimentally observed aspects of SERS, including quantitative values for the enhancement factor, the excitation dependence of SERS, which metals can support surface enhancement, and the distance dependence of the intensities. The enhancement arises from the amplification of the incident and scattered electromagnetic fields at the interface between a polarizable solid of complex dielectric function $\hat{\epsilon}_1$ and some ambient medium of dielectric constant ϵ_2. The enhancement can be calculated from Maxwell's equations assuming a small particle of known geometry as a model. As long as the particle is small relative to the wavelength of light, the calculations are made in the electrostatic limit (also known as the Rayleigh approximation). The sphere represents the limit of simplicity that these calculations can assume. Thus, this was a logical starting point for these calculations, and one that many researchers chose to employ [116-122].

Kerker has presented calculations for classical enhancement for a molecule adsorbed at the surface of a sphere in a uniform electric field normal to the scattering plane [117]. The Raman enhancement G for this molecule is given by

$$G = 5 \, |(1 + 2 \, g_0) \, (1 + 2 \, g) \, |^2,$$

where

$$g_0 = \frac{[\hat{\epsilon}_1(\omega_L) / \epsilon_2(\omega_L)] - 1}{[\hat{\epsilon}_1(\omega_L) / \epsilon_2(\omega_L)] + 2}$$

and

$$g = \frac{[\hat{\epsilon}_1(\omega) / \epsilon_2(\omega)] - 1}{[\hat{\epsilon}_1(\omega) / \epsilon_2(\omega)] + 2} \ .$$

For a monolayer of molecules on the sphere with oscillating dipoles normal to the surface, the average enhancement is given by

$$G = |(1 + 2g_0)(1 + 2g)|^2$$

As $[\hat{\epsilon}_1 / \epsilon_2] \to -2$, the value of G gets very large. It is prohibited from going to infinity by the finite value of the imaginary part of the dielectric function of metals. However, the smaller the imaginary part of the dielectric function under these resonance conditions, the greater the enhancement. Thus, free-electron-like metals such as Ag, Cu, Au, Li, and Na are predicted [123] and observed to give very large enhancements. Additionally, the above equations predict a minor dependence of the enhancement on the dielectric properties of the surrounding medium. This result has important consequences for electrochemical systems, because as the dielectric constant of the surrounding medium increases, the maximum enhancement is predicted to increase and shift to lower energies. These trends are followed for Ag structures produced in vacuum environments and immersed into different media [124] and, as suggested by preliminary evidence from this laboratory, for Ag electrodes in nonaqueous pyridine solutions as well [125].

As the shapes used as models become more complex, depolarization factors are added to the calculations to account for the shape-dependent properties of the electromagnetic response. Numerous calculations have appeared on ellipsoids of varying aspect ratio [126-132].

Calculations on spheres and ellipsoids have been quite useful in understanding the experimental parameters which affect the overall enhancement factor; however, they are far from realistic models of an electrode surface roughened with an ORC. Several researchers have attempted to address this problem through calculations of electromagnetic enhancement at spherical and elliptical protuberances on flat surfaces [133-137]. Although these models do adequately predict the frequency dependence of surface enhancement, the absolute magnitudes of the predicted enhancements differ from those experimentally observed by several orders of magnitude [137]. As the computational complexity applied to understanding these phenomena increases, it is anticipated that better agreement between theoretical models and experiment will be achieved.

The second type of roughness thought to be generated in the ORC and important in SERS is known as atomic-scale roughness. Generally, this roughness is believed to be on the order of molecular dimensions. These roughness features have been variously termed active sites, activated complexes, adatoms, and adatom clusters. The most popular picture of how these species are involved in chemical surface enhancement is through photoassisted charge transfer (CT) between adsorbate and metal electronic levels at sites of atomic-scale roughness. This model was first proposed in 1979 [138,139] and has been cited by several other workers as an important contribution to the overall surface enhancement in both electrochemical and UHV systems [140-143]. In this model, the incident photon excites a charge-transfer process between metal levels associated with microscopic surface defect sites such as adatoms and adsorbate levels, which are broadened and made accessible through interaction with the metal surface. The direction of charge transfer depends upon the chemical nature of the adsorbate. For certain anionic adsorbates [141,144,145] and saturated organic adsorbates [146], the charge transfer is thought to occur between filled adsorbate levels and vacant metal levels at the Fermi energy. This pathway is often described as adsorbate-to-metal charge transfer. Conversely, unsaturated organics such as pyridine undergo a metal-to-adsorbate charge transfer in which an electron is transferred from filled metal levels to empty adsorbate levels [146].

Metal-to-adsorbate charge transfer has received more attention in the literature and, although the details of the charge transfer mechanism are not completely understood, a model for CT to adsorbed pyridine is outlined in [Fig. 4]. The Figure shows an idealized schematic of the electrode/electrolyte interface. The left-hand side of the diagram represents the metal electrode, which can be described in terms of a Fermi energy, E_f, and the work function, ϕ. It is important to note that the Fermi energy at microscopic defect sites has been shown to differ significantly from the bulk value [147,148].

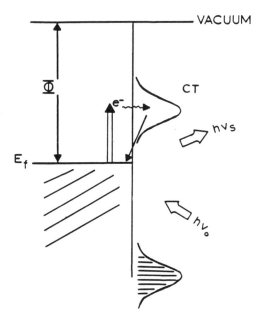

FIGURE 4 General model for metal-to-
adsorbate charge transfer excitation for
pyridine. (Reprinted with permission from
Reference 98.)

For example, the work function at coordinatively unsaturated
surface sites such as adatoms has been shown to be lower than
that at other surface sites [149]. A decrease in work function
at these sites may allow CT excitation that might not otherwise
be accessible with visible radiation.

The right-hand side of the diagram represents the solution
interfacial region. The diagram shows empty adsorbate levels
at energies higher than the Fermi energy and filled levels lying
below the Fermi energy. According to UV photoemission
studies of pyridine on Ag by Demuth [150], the highest filled
electronic levels of adsorbed pyridine are most likely π levels.
Upon adsorption, the nitrogen lone pair level is stabilized with
respect to the π levels due to chemical interaction with the
substrate. Ueba has proposed that the empty level associated
with charge transfer is most likely a new electronic level
which arises due to chemisorption [151]. Both molecular levels
are broadened and shifted in energy due to interaction with
the surface.

In photoassisted charge transfer, the incident photon excites an electron from the Fermi energy to empty metal levels higher in energy. If the photon is sufficiently energetic, the excited electron can tunnel to vacant levels on the adsorbate, momentarily creating a negatively charged adsorbate. Upon recombination of the electron and the hole generated in the Fermi level, a Raman scattered photon is generated, because the molecule has been left in a vibrationally excited state. A similar scheme can be envisioned for adsorbate-to-metal charge transfer where excitation of an adsorbate-based electron to empty levels slightly above the Fermi energy occurs.

It is clear from the above discussion that the ability to promote CT excitation depends on three factors: the excitation wavelength, the Fermi energy of the metal, and the energy and broadness of the adsorbate electronic levels. If a significant density of empty adsorbate levels exists at an energy corresponding to an excited electron, maximum SERS intensities are predicted. If the photon energy is significantly higher or lower than that shown in [Fig. 4], the CT process moves out of resonance, resulting in lower SERS intensities.

The Fermi energy of the metal electrode is also an important factor in the CT process. The Fermi energy can be altered by changing the applied potential to the electrode. Negative potential excursions result in an increase in the Fermi energy, while positive going excursions decrease the Fermi energy. This is shown schematically in [Fig. 5]. At fixed excitation frequency, changes in the electrode potential can move the CT process into or out of resonance. Such changes in SERS intensity as a function of applied potential have been observed experimentally [141,152].

This model also predicts that the potential of maximum SERS intensity should shift as the excitation frequency is altered [141,144,146,152,153]. [Fig. 6] shows intensity-potential plots for six adsorbates at two excitation frequencies. The adsorbates separate into two categories, depending on how the potential of their maximum SERS intensities changes with excitation frequency. For pyridine and 2-methylpyridine, the potential of maximum SERS intensity shifts to more negative values as the excitation frequency decreases. This behavior is indicative of metal-to-adsorbate charge transfer. The other adsorbates exhibit the opposite trend as is indicative of adsorbate-to-metal charge transfer. A plot of the incident photon energy as a function of applied potential is shown in

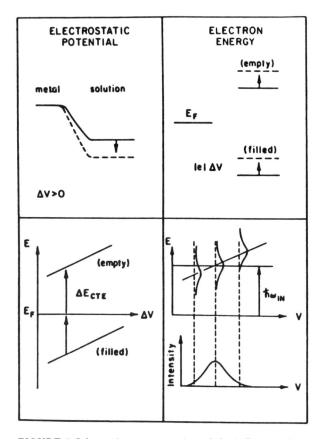

FIGURE 5 Schematic representation of the influence of potential on the charge transfer excitation enhancement mechanism. (A) Spatial distribution of the electrostatic potential. The effect of a positive change in the voltage applied to the metal is shown. (B) Spatial representation of the energy states on the metal at the Fermi level and the molecule. (C) Energy transitions are indicated. (D) Illustration of the effect of tuning the voltage to bring charge transfer into resonance with fixed incident photon energy. (Reprinted with permission from Reference 141.)

[Fig. 7]. Data plotted in this fashion clearly show the energy separation between the states at the interface. Moreover, the sign of the slope in these plots is diagnostic for either metal-to-adsorbate (positive slope) or adsorbate-to-metal (negative slope) charge transfer.

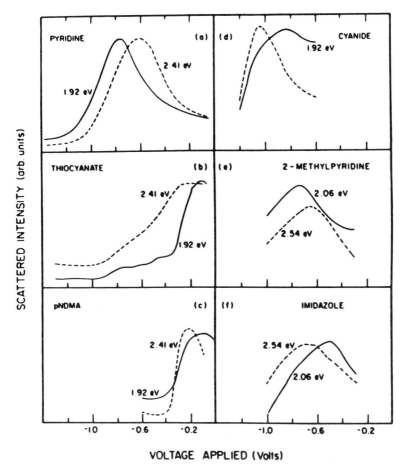

FIGURE 6 Examples of the tuning effect explained in Figure 5D. In each case, the Raman intensity is plotted as a function of the voltage for two excitation energies. The Ag substrate was electrochemically roughened in each case prior to the Raman experiment. The vertical scales vary among the curves: (A) 1008 cm^{-1} ring breathing mode of pyridine; (B) 2105 cm^{-1} CN stretch mode of SCN^{-}; (C) 1160 cm^{-1} phenyl-nitroso stretch mode of p-nitrosodimethylaniline; (D) 2114 cm^{-1} CN stretch mode of CN^{-}; (E) 1008 cm^{-1} ring breathing mode of 2-methylpyridine; (F) 1163 cm^{-1} mode of imidazole. (Reprinted with permission from Reference 141.)

A wealth of information in support of the existence of atomic-scale roughness and its importance in SERS in electrochemical systems exists. However, the majority of the evidence is indirect due to the fact that this roughness is relatively unstable, low in absolute surface coverage, and difficult to study.

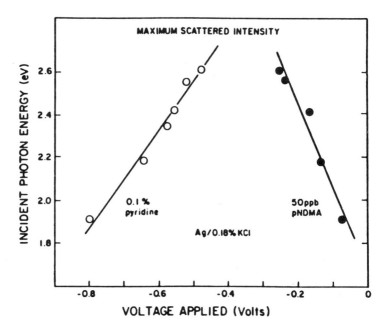

FIGURE 7 From data like those shown in Figure 6 at several excitation energies, the optimum conditions for charge transfer resonance can be identified for a given molecule. This shows how the separation of the energy states involved in the charge transfer changes as a function of the voltage for pyridine (slope 2.2 eV/V) and p-nitrosodimethylaniline (slope -3.4 eV/V). (Reprinted with permission from Reference 141.)

Potential excursion experiments in electrochemical systems have shown that a large portion of the initial SERS intensity is irreversibly lost when the potential reaches values where adsorbates are no longer strongly adsorbed [154-158]. This effect is more severe for roughened Ag electrodes than for Au [159] or Cu [160]. This observation implies that atomic-scale roughness on Cu and Au electrodes is more stable than that on Ag.

Observation of the continuum background that is ubiquitous in SERS spectra [161-163] has been explained in terms of atomic-scale roughness. This background results from excitation of electrons and holes, in the s,p-band of the metal surface in the presence of atomic scale roughness, that recombine to give the background inelastic scattering [68].

Additional indirect evidence for the existence of atomic-scale roughness on SERS-active surfaces comes from quenching experiments using the underpotential deposition of foreign metal films. The decrease in SERS intensity that occurs as a result of deposition of submonolayer to monolayer quantities of a foreign metal (see discussion in previous section) is irreversible after quantitative stripping of the foreign metal film. In one previous study, details of the recovery of the SERS for pyridine and Cl⁻ adsorbed at Ag electrodes after deposition and quantitative stripping of Pb were presented [93]. The recovery of the SERS signal was found to depend on the coverage of the surface by the deposited Pb before stripping as shown in [Fig. 8]. For coverages less than ca. 0.6 monolayer Pb, the recovery of the original SERS intensity of both the 1013 cm⁻¹ pyridine band and the 235 cm⁻¹ Cl⁻ band is almost complete. However, when the coverage exceeds this amount, the recovery drops rapidly to 40% at one Pb monolayer for pyridine and 85% at one Pb monolayer for Cl⁻. Further kinetic studies of this effect demonstrated that the inability to recover the original SERS intensity during monolayer formation could be attributed to a structural rearrangement of the Pb overlayer on the surface as it achieved its final hexagonal close-packed configuration [93]. Similar irreversible losses in intensity upon

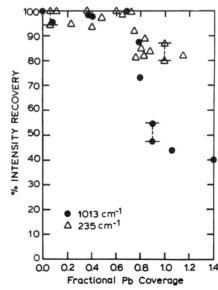

FIGURE 8 Percent intensity recovery after deposition and quantitative stripping of varying submonolayer amounts of UPD Pb on Ag: (Δ) Ag-Cl stretch at 235 cm⁻¹; (●) pyridine ring breathing mode at 1013 cm⁻¹. (Reprinted with permission from Reference 93.)

deposition of submonolayer and monolayer quantities have been observed by other workers [90-102,104,105].

The importance of atomic-scale roughness in SERS is also evident from the successful use of surfaces formed from the electrochemical deposition of small quantities of an enhancing metal onto a nonenhancing substrate for SERS. As discussed, Furtak and coworkers have investigated SERS at Au electrodes modified by small amounts of electrochemically deposited Ag with 514.5 nm excitation where Au is not enhancing [89], and at Pt electrodes modified with small amounts of electrochemically deposited Ag [112,113]. This latter system has also been investigated in this laboratory [111] and by Marinyuk and coworkers [109]. Additionally, SERS at Cu adatoms electrochemically deposited onto Ag has been observed by Pettinger and coworkers [90,103] and in this laboratory [104].

Despite the indirect evidence implicating the importance of atomic-scale roughness in SERS, very little quantitative information is available regarding the energetics of these atomic-scale roughness features and their interactions with adsorbates. Recently, a sensitive method for probing the energetics of Ag atomic-scale roughness-adsorbate interactions in an electrochemical environment was reported [164]. This method is based on the thermally-induced irreversible decay of SERS intensity for pyridine and Cl^- adsorbed at Ag electrodes. The decay of SERS intensities at constant electrode potential has been observed previously in electrochemical systems. However, the kinetics of this decay have remained somewhat elusive [156,165]. In this study, a thermally-induced first order decay of the SERS intensity was observed at a constant surface temperature. The surface temperature was established at these roughened Ag surfaces through the use of different laser powers from 50 mW to 1 W giving a usable temperature range from ambient temperature to ca. 312K.

Interestingly, two types of decay behavior were observed for both pyridine and Cl^- adsorbates on Ag electrodes roughened under illumination. These were termed type A and B, respectively. Application of the Arrhenius expression allowed calculation of the activation energies associated with these laser-induced thermal processes. Arrhenius plots for both pyridine and Cl^- are shown in [Fig. 9]. The activation energies associated with the type A kinetics were 12.8 ± 3.2 kcal/mol for pyridine and 11.1 ± 2.4 kcal/mol for Cl^-. The activation energies found for type B kinetics were significantly greater

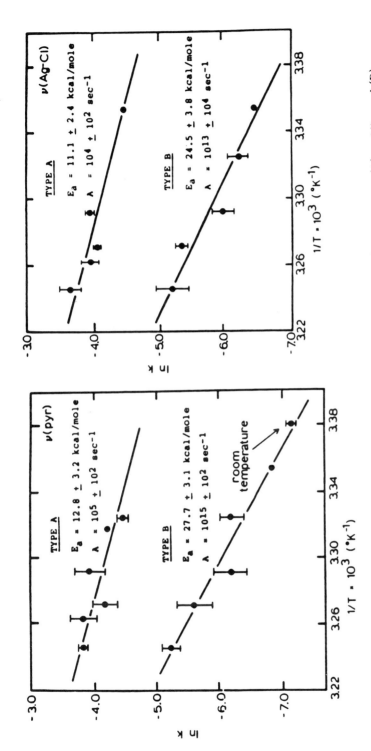

FIGURE 9 Arrhenius plots obtained for decay of SERS at -0.6 V after an illuminated ORC for (A) pyridine and (B) Cl⁻ (Reprinted with permission from Reference 164.

than for type A and were 27.7 ± 3.1 kcal/mol and 24.5 ± 3.8 kcal/mol for pyridine and Cl⁻, respectively. These energies were interpreted in terms of disruption of an adatom complex involving Ag atomic-scale roughness and the adsorbates allowing the former to be irreversibly incorporated into the Ag lattice. The two types of kinetic behavior were attributed to the existence of these surface complexes at distinct sites on the electrode surface, such as terraces and steps or kinks, which would stabilize the surface complexes to different extents [164].

Further direct evidence for the existence of atomic-scale roughness comes from the work of Furtak and Roy. These researchers have provided convincing spectral data and interpretations consistent with the presence of tetrahedral Ag_4^+ species on the surfaces of electrochemically roughened Ag electrodes [141,166-168]. This cluster is pictured to exist on the surface coadsorbed with stabilizing adsorbates such as pyridine and Cl⁻ as shown in [Fig. 10]. Spectral bands for these clusters are observed in the low frequency region at 73, 110, and 161 cm^{-1} in many SERS environments, including the electrochemical interface. These bands are weak in intensity and difficult to distinguish above the Rayleigh background, but [Fig. 11] demonstrates quite clearly the presence of these bands. Further evidence that the clusters are the tetrahedral Ag_4^+ species proposed by Roy and Furtak comes from calculations of the vibrational modes of such a cluster on an electrode surface [167]. Four bands are predicted from these calculations at 75, 100, 118, and 170 cm^{-1} which correspond very well with the three bands observed. In terms of providing an avenue for enhancement of Raman scattering, these clusters are proposed to possess intrinsic resonances with which the vibrational modes of coadsorbed species such as Cl⁻ can couple in a process similar to the resonance Raman effect [167].

In general, evidence for the existence of atomic-scale roughness and its importance in SERS in electrochemical systems is quite persuasive. Therefore, it is likely that chemical enhancement mechanisms contribute at least partially to the overall enhancement in these systems. Hopefully, a more quantitative definition of the respective roles of electromagnetic and chemical enhancement will result from further study of this exciting phenomenon.

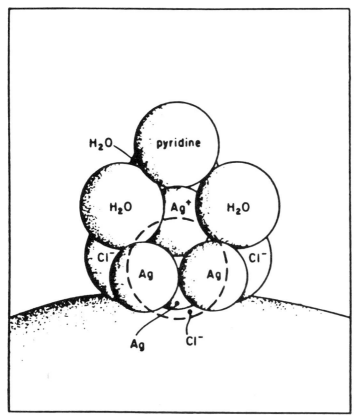

FIGURE 10 Hypothetical model for the adatom complex involving a tetrahedral Ag_4^+ cluster, one pyridine molecule, and three Cl^- species. (Reprinted with permission from Reference 141.)

B. Production and Control of Roughness in Electrochemical Systems.

Obviously, surfaces which support SERS in electrochemical environments are quite heterogeneous due to the complexityof the surface and solution chemistry occurring during the ORC. This aspect of SERS has made reproducibility of intensities between researchers poor. Several methods for performing the ORC on electrodes have been published including both potential sweep and potential step techniques. This assortment of ORC techniques leads to a variety of electrode surface morphologies. Moreover, the surface morphology obtained using a particular ORC method can vary if an experimental parameter, such as the amount of charge

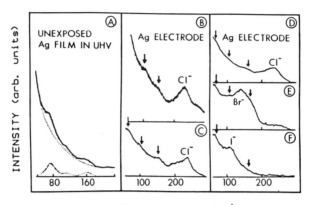

PHOTON ENERGY SHIFT (cm⁻¹)

FIGURE 11 Low frequency region of SERS on Ag collected
under different experimental conditions: (A) on cold Ag
films in UHV; (B) on a dry Ag electrode at room
temperature initially roughened by an ORC in 1 M KCl;
(C) on a dry Ag electrode under similar conditions to (B),
but recorded at liquid nitrogen temperature; (D-F) on a
dry Ag electrode at room temperature for ORCs in Cl⁻,
Br⁻, and I⁻ containing solutions, respectively. (Reprinted
with permission from Reference 167.)

passed, is altered. Thus, experiments designed to understand,
systematize, and control ORC procedures are essential for the
acquisition of reproducible SERS data. Steps have been taken
along these lines by various workers. Evans and coworkers
have demonstrated that the surface concentration of Ag
nodules formed during an ORC is critically dependent upon
the amount of charge passed [169]. These workers also noted
that the nodule size was fairly independent of the total amount
of charge passed during potential sweep ORCs. Schultz and
coworkers presented scanning electron microscopy data
demonstrating differences in the surface morphologies of Ag
electrodes subjected to potential step as opposed to potential
sweep ORCs [170].

A typical cyclic voltammogram for a potential sweep ORC
on a Ag electrode in 1 M NaCl solution is shown in [Fig. 12].
As the potential is scanned to more positive values, the
currentincreases essentially linearly once the oxidation process
begins.This current-voltage behavior can be exploited to
control the rate of the oxidation process [171] and helps to
explain the strategy behind the use of the symmetric double
potential step ORC procedure used in this laboratory. Stepping
the potential of the electrode to a particular value of

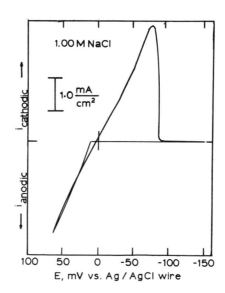

1.00 M NaCl

i cathodic

$1.0 \frac{mA}{cm^2}$

i anodic

100   50   0   -50   -100   -150

E, mV vs. Ag / AgCl wire

FIGURE 12 Cyclic voltammogram for Ag electrode in aqueous 1 M NaCl; scan rate = 20 mV s^{-1}. (Reprinted with permission from Reference 171.)

overpotential for the Ag oxidation process causes this process to occur at essentially a constant rate. The greater the magnitude of the potential step, the greater the oxidation rate.

The surface morphology of the Ag electrode subjected to these ORC procedures varies as a function of the rate of the electrochemical oxidation reaction and has been established using scanning electron microscopy (SEM) [171,172]. It is important to note that only the large-scale surface roughness features greater than ca. 30 nm could be studied with SEM, as this represents the resolution of the microscope. Surface morphological data from micrographs of electrodes roughened with this symmetric double potential step ORC method in 1 M NaCl solution are shown in [Table 1]. Due to the tilt angle of 0° for which SEMs presented here were acquired, the only measurement of the surface roughness features that could be made with any degree of accuracy was nodule diameter.

In general, the data in [Table 1] suggest that an increase in the rate of the ORC coincides with a decrease in the nodule diameter, an increase in the surface concentration of roughness features, and an increase in the internodule distance. More importantly, these data demonstrate that some degree of control of surface roughness can be achieved in electrochemical systems. At low rates, large, elongated nodules that tend to form clusters with large, barren patches between them predominate. In addition, three-dimensional growth into

TABLE 1. Ag Surface Morphological Data From SEM
As A Function Of Anodic Current Density
In 1 M NaCl

Current Density $mA\ cm^{-2}$	Nodule Width, nm			Inter feature Dist,nm	Conc. Nodules μm^{-2}
	Lgst	Smst	Avg		
1.0	370	110	190±20	Clust'd	3-D Gr.
3.5	300	75	160±10	Clust'd	3-D Gr.
5.3	520	70	180±20	Clust'd	3-D Gr.
6.6	390	75	150±10	30±10	21
9.8	260	75	130±10	39±13	33
12	210	60	140±10	41± 6	44
15	210	50	100± 5	51± 6	54
18	180	40	100±10	62± 5	54

Reproduced with permission from Reference 171.

solution occurs. At higher rates, the nodule diameters are significantly smaller, predominantly hemispherical, distributed more evenly across the surface, and demonstrate no three-dimensional growth.

The data in [Table 1] are shown as a function of anodic current density, because it has been demonstrated that the rate of oxidation dictates the surface morphology in a symmetric double potential step ORC [171]. An understanding of the relationship between surface morphology and oxidation rate comes from consideration of the chemical mechanism of the ORC of a Ag electrode in aqueous Cl⁻ media. This chemistry has been proposed to occur according to the following steps by Katan and coworkers [173,174]:

$$Ag \longrightarrow Ag^+ + e^- \quad \text{(dissolution)} \tag{1}$$

$$Ag^+ + (n+1)\ Cl^- \longrightarrow AgCl_{n+1}^{-n} \quad \text{(complex formation)} \tag{2}$$

$$AgCl_{n+1}^{-n}\ (a) \longrightarrow AgCl_{n+1}^{-n}\ (b) \quad \text{(solution transport)} \tag{3}$$

$$AgCl_{n+1}{}^{-n} \longrightarrow AgCl \text{ (s)} + n \text{ } Cl^- \quad \text{(deposition \& growth)} \quad (4)$$

It has been proposed that at lower rates, [Equation 4] is the rate-determining step. Under these conditions, deposition takes place at energetically more favorable sites of continued AgCl growth. Consequently, the roughness features are large and develop outward into solution. At faster oxidation rates, [Equation 3] becomes the rate-determining step. The imposition of a "high rate" potential in these experiments decreases the time for the solution transport step such that the number of nodules increases. This reasoning leads to the further conclusion that the nodules must be smaller and the distance between them increased.

The SERS intensity of the 235 cm^{-1} ν(Ag-Cl) vibration of specifically adsorbed Cl^- was monitored as a function of oxidation rate during the ORC and therefore, the surface morphology. SERS spectra were obtained at -0.20 V versus a Ag/AgCl reference electrode subsequent to ORCs carried out at different rates in the dark. The data indicate that as the oxidation rate increases and the surface nodules get smaller, the intensities of both the ν(Ag-Cl) band and the background increase. A plot of the intensity of this vibrational band as a function of Ag surface nodule diameter, taken from SEM data, is shown in [Fig. 13]. These data show a maximum in the observed intensity at a nodule diameter of 90 to 100 nm for ORCs in 1 M NaCl.

From a purely theoretical basis, it is difficult to predict what combination of particle size, surface concentration, and interfeature distance will produce the maximum enhancement. The magnitude of enhancement calculated from electro-magnetic theory depends sensitively on the specific shape and size of the roughness feature used as the model. Electro-chemical control of the size and shape of the surface roughness may never be achieved at the level necessary to validate or invalidate these models. It is useful, however, to compare the trends in SERS intensity (and therefore, enhancement factor) observed with surfaces fabricated by controlled electro-chemical ORCs with the trends predicted by theoretical calculations.

These data are qualitatively in agreement with electromagnetic theories for SERS [126-137]. A discrepancy does exist, however, between the maximum particle diameter observed to give the largest SERS intensities and that predicted

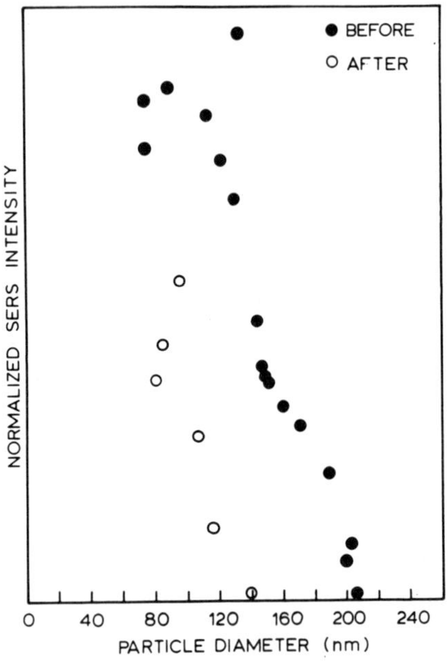

FIGURE 13 Normalized SERS intensity of ν(Ag-Cl) as a function of average particle diameter in nm before (•) and after (o) the destruction of a majority of atomic-scale roughness by a negative potential excursion. (Reprinted with permission from Reference 171.)

to give the largest SERS intensities on the basis of electromagnetic theories. Calculated values of particle diameter at which the optimum enhancement factor should be realized typically range from 10 to 50 nm, depending on the shape of the roughness feature assumed in the calculation. These values are significantly smaller than the 90 to 100 nm at which the maximum SERS intensity for the ν(AgCl) vibration is observed in this study. This discrepancy may be the result of the fact that the relatively crude surfaces produced with the electrochemical ORC do not closely approximate the model systems used for the calculations. Although it is likely that the ideal surface features required for these calculations will never be produced electrochemically, the adherence of the experimental intensity data to the trends predicted by electromagnetic calculations suggests that the SERS behavior of these surfaces is dictated, at least in part, through electromagnetic effects associated with these large-scale roughness features.

A series of experiments were designed to assess the role of atomic-scale roughness features in these data as well [171]. In these experiments, electrodes roughened with a double potential step were subjected to a cathodic potential sweep to

-0.80 V to destroy the atomic-scale roughness [154-158] before the spectra were acquired. These intensities are shown in [Fig. 13] as a function of large-scale roughness feature diameter along with the intensities measured before the destruction of the atomic-scale roughness. The absolute intensities decrease ca. 50-60% upon destruction of the atomic scale roughness, even though scanning electron microscopy shows that the surfaces are essentially unchanged by the negative potential excursion. Moreover, the nodule diameter at which the maximum SERS intensity is observed remains the same. These results were interpreted in terms of contributions from both electromagnetic and chemical effects to the overall surface enhancement operating in these systems.

Results from similar experiments performed in 0.05 M pyridine/0.1 M KCl were also obtained [175]. The Ag surface morphology as assessed by SEM is quantitated in [Table 2]. In general, the results obtained in this medium parallel those obtained in 1 M NaCl. Thus, the faster the rate of oxidation, the smaller the average Ag nodule diameter. This trend in the pyridine/Cl⁻ medium has been explained in a manner analogous to that presented above in terms of the combined solution and surface chemistry occurring during the oxidation process [172].

TABLE 2.   Ag Surface Morphological Data From SEM As A Function of Anodic Current Density In 0.05M Pyridine/0.1 M KCl

Current Density mA cm⁻²	Nodule Width, nm		
	Largest	Smallest	Average
1.5	210	95	136±27
2.3	215	95	131±18
5.9	202	71	119±25
10	149	54	92±18
15	167	41	94±13

Reproduced by permission from Reference 172.

The plot of SERS intensity of the 1008 cm^{-1} pyridine band as a function of Ag nodule diameter as taken from the SEMs of these surfaces is shown in [Fig. 14]. The intensities are reported as values normalized to the maximum intensity that can be observed over the range of rates studied. The intensities increase as the average Ag nodule diameter decreases between 140 and 125 nm. The maximum SERS intensity is observed for an average Ag nodule diameter of ca. 125 nm. Beyond this maximum, the SERS intensities again decrease to unmeasurable values as the average nodule diameter decreases to 85 nm.

As with the study in Cl$^-$ only, these trends are in qualitative agreement with electromagnetic models for SERS. A discrepancy does exist, however, between the optimum particle diameter predicted from theory and the nodule diameter at which the maximum SERS is observed for adsorbed pyridine and Cl$^-$. Of perhaps greater significance is the observation that the nodule diameter at which maximum SERS intensity is observed for the ν(AgCl) vibration in 1 M NaCl is ca. 95 nm while that observed for the pyridine ring breathing vibration in pyridine/Cl$^-$ media is ca. 125 nm. This difference has been proposed to result from several factors [175]. First, the SEM of these surfaces demonstrates that the shapes of the roughness features produced with the symmetric double potential step technique in these two different chemical environments are significantly different [172]. Moreover, the

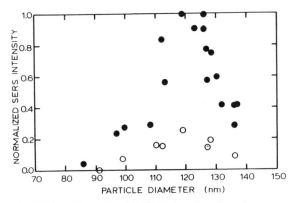

FIGURE 14 Normalized SERS intensity of ν_1 ring breathing vibration of pyridine as a function of average particle diameter in nm before (●) and after (○) the destruction of a majority of atomic-scale roughness by a negative potential excursion. (Reprinted with permission from Reference 171.)

surface roughness features produced in complex electrochemical ORC processes do not resemble the model shapes
used in electromagnetic calculations. Additionally, the
differences are probably due, in part, to the role of chemical
enhancement occurring at sites of atomic-scale roughness in
these systems which is not directly monitored with SEM.

The behavior of these surfaces after the destruction of
atomic-scale roughness is also shown in [Fig. 14]. The pyridine
bands typically decrease ca. 75% with the destruction of
atomic-scale roughness.

Perhaps the greatest significance of this work is the
demonstration that methods capable of providing control of
the ORC chemistry, and hence, resulting morphology, can be
developed. Hopefully, these approaches will take some of the
"black-magic" out of electrochemical pretreatment of surfaces
for SERS.

All of the above studies, and in fact, the majority of
electrochemical SERS studies have been carried out in
electrolyte media possessing an anion with which the cation
derived from the metal electrode can form a sparingly soluble
precipitate. Roughening the electrode to an adequate degree in
a solution where no such precipitate can be formed is much
more difficult. This situation applies to aqueous solutions
containing anions such as ClO_4^-, SO_4^{2-}, and NO_3^-, and many
nonaqueous solutions containing any anion. [Fig. 15] shows a
potential sweep ORC of a Ag electrode in 0.1 M $HClO_4$. As can
be seen by comparison with the cyclic voltammogram shown in
[Fig. 12], the amount of charge recovered on the cathodic
sweep in ClO_4^- media is significantly less than in Cl^- media
due to the solubility of Ag^+ in ClO_4^- solution. The ramification
of this behavior with respect to surface roughening is that a
much smoother surface is obtained for an identical potential
sweep ORC procedure. Although the surface roughened in
ClO_4^- media does support surface enhancement, the intensities
observed are considerably less than observed at the surface
roughened in Cl^-.

Similar problems are encountered when working in
nonaqueous media. In fact, early difficulties in obtaining
SERS in nonaqueous media were probably related to the
inability to appropriately roughen the electrode surface using
ORC schemes similar to those used in aqueous halide media.
As an example of the problems encountered in nonaqueous

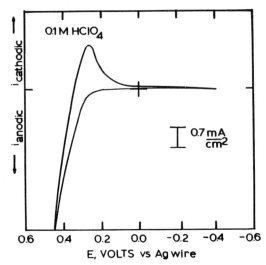

FIGURE 15 Cyclic voltammogram for Ag
electrode in 0.1 M $HClO_4$; scan rate = 20 mV s^{-1}.

solutions, consider the cyclic voltammogram for a Ag electrode
in 1 M tetra-n-butylammonium chloride in neat pyridine shown
in [Fig. 16]. It resembles the voltammetric behavior shown for
Ag in ClO_4^- media, because AgCl is quite soluble in pyridine
solutions. Although SERS has been successfully reported from
solutions of neat pyridine [51], the intensities are somewhat
irreproducible if the ORC chemistry and conditions are not
strictly controlled. The implications of this work for
nonaqueous SERS are that the ORC should be carefully
characterized and optimized using a combination of cyclic
voltammetry, scanning electron microscopy, and SERS for each
system studied. Potential sweep and step techniques should be
investigated, as should multiple or repetitive applications of an
ORC scheme for the best SERS. Although this approach may be
somewhat tedious, it is expected that with sufficient attention
to optimization of the roughening procedure, SERS should be
observable in the majority of electrochemical environments
commonly employed.

C.   Enhancement   Mechanisms   and   Prospects   for
Electrochemistry.

Several ramifications of the above roughness-related
enhancement mechanisms for the future use of SERS in

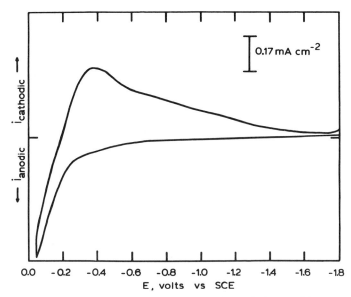

FIGURE 16 Cyclic voltammogram for Ag electrode in 0.25 M tetra-n-butyl-ammonium chloride in pyridine; scan rate = 20 mV s^{-1}.

electrochemical systems should be noted. Most importantly, even though the enhancement mechanisms are not completely understood, Raman spectral data of excellent quality for a significant number of electrochemical systems can be obtained. The quality of this spectral data is currently unmatched by any other in situ vibrational probe of the electrochemical double layer. Thus, the continued use of SERS for the study of electrochemical systems seems justified.

The demonstrated role of electromagnetic enhancement in electrochemical SERS has several consequences. First, the long-range nature of this enhancement means that the SERS signals will be integrated over the entire double layer. The species closest to the surface are enhanced to the greatest extent, but information on species in the outer Helmholtz plane and into the diffuse double layer region should also be observed. Secondly, the physical nature of this enhancement confers generality with respect to the chemical nature of the surface species on electrochemical SERS studies, as demonstrated in the literature [64,65]. Thirdly, electromagnetic enhancement allows successful fabrication of novel electrode geometries, which have extended the generality of SERS with respect to the nature of the electrode [101,105-108]. It is expected that further developments in this area may be realized through the use of ultramicroelectrodes whose sizes and geometries are approaching those needed for efficient electromagnetic enhancement of SERS [176]. Furthermore, the use of these electrode geometries coupled with Raman microscopy as successfully demonstrated by Van Duyne and coworkers [177] could provide insight into the electrochemical double layer at a microscopic level not previously envisioned.

Chemical contributions to surface enhancement in electrochemical systems has other important ramifications. In using SERS to study the electrochemical double layer, one must remain cognizant of the instability of the SERS response. Although the stability of SERS on Au and Cu appears to be considerably greater than on Ag [159,160], the SERS response must be considered much more dynamic than when using other techniques on smooth electrodes.

The importance of atomic-scale roughness raises an additional question regarding the importance of specific chemical interactions between the adsorbate and atomic-scale roughness features that may bear directly on the type and quality of information available from a SERS study in a particular electrochemical system. The extent of interaction of a particular molecule with an adatom cluster may impact on the SERS intensity and stability of the observed response. Poor SERS signals may erroneously be equated with inappropriate roughening schemes or weak molecular adsorption. Additionally, the chemistry associated with the molecule-adatom cluster may, in some cases, give rise to misleading spectral results that are unique to the cluster and not to the general adsorbate.

In summary, the roles of surface roughness in SERS of electrochemical systems are varied and complex casting a negative specter on the technique in the eyes of some scientists. From a more optimistic perspective, however, the complexity that enshrouds SERS in electrochemical systems may also be viewed as the challenge inherent in using SERS to study electrochemical systems. From either perspective, electrochemists using SERS would be well-served to remain aware of these complexities so as not to misinterpret or over-interpret their results.

IV. EXPERIMENTAL ASPECTS OF SERS IN ELECTRO-CHEMICAL SYSTEMS

The critical parts of an instrumental system for SERS are of course the spectrometer and associated laser source. The majority of SERS investigations have been performed using visible wavelength excitation, usually from an ion laser or an ion laser-pumped dye laser. The choice of laser is somewhat dependent on the nature of the metal surface under investigation, due to the excitation dependence of the enhancement, which varies from metal to metal. Ag electrodes support enhancement throughout the blue, green, and red regions of the visible spectrum. Although the enhancement is greatest with red excitation, argon ion lasers with output in the blue and green regions of the spectrum have been very commonly used. For Cu and Au electrodes, which only support enhancement with red excitation, krypton ion lasers have been very popular. A suitable alternative to the krypton ion laser, which actually provides more flexibility, is an ion laser-pumped dye laser. With these excitation sources, excellent SERS for Ag, Cu, and Au electrodes can be obtained at excitation frequencies throughout the red region of the visible and even into the near-IR region. In fact, excellent SERS at Ag, Cu, and Au electrodes has been recently obtained using the 1064 nm line of a continuous wave Nd:YAG laser and a Fourier Transform Raman spectrometer by Chase and Parkinson [178].

Laser powers typically employed are minimal due to the good sensitivity of SERS. Adequate spectra can be acquired from Ag, Cu, and Au electrodes at their optimum excitation wavelength using only 50 to 100 mW of power. In fact, it is advantageous to keep the power at or below these levels, whenever possible, on these roughened surfaces to minimize heating which renders the surface features unstable [164].

Two dispersion device/detector combinations have routinely been used to acquire SERS spectra. Traditionally, SERS has been performed on a conventional scanning system consisting of a double monochromator with a PMT detector used in the photon counting mode. The PMT should be one with a high-sensitivity photocathode such as GaAs for best sensitivity. SERS spectra of excellent S/N can be easily acquired with such a system.

The major disadvantage inherent to the use of a scanning system is one of speed. Acquisition of even a portion of a spectrum usually takes on the order of several minutes, making kinetic studies on a time scale faster than this impossible. In electrochemical systems, the accessible time scale of several minutes precludes facile study of reacting redox systems. The use of multichannel detectors with appropriate dispersion devices has helped to overcome this limitation. The detector most commonly employed has been either the intensified or unintensified photodiode array, IPDA or PDA, respectively. Another multichannel detector that has been used recently in Raman spectroscopy [179-181] is the charge-coupled device (CCD) detector. This detector is theoretically superior to the best IPDA and PDA detectors because of its high quantum efficiency and essentially noiseless operation [182,183]. The CCD looks promising for the study of systems with significantly lower enhancement, possibly down to an enhancement factor of unity, and will probably be receiving considerable attention as a detector for SERS in the future.

For electrochemical SERS studies, multichannel detectors are typically used with a triple monochromator system. The first two stages of these systems are coupled in subtractive dispersion (no net dispersion at the exit of the second stage) to eliminate stray radiation, and then the radiation is dispersed in the third stage before impinging on the detector. SERS spectra of good S/N can usually be acquired with such systems in one to several seconds, making them more amenable to the study of reacting electrochemical systems. Examples of such studies are detailed in the next section.

Cells for electrochemical SERS investigations are relatively straightforward to design and construct. Glass is a suitable cell material, because Raman spectroscopy is carried out in the visible region of the spectrum where glass does not absorb appreciably. The ready availability of cell materials is a distinct advantage of SERS over its IR counterparts.

In designing a cell for electrochemical SERS studies, relatively few criteria must be met. The design must allow the incident laser beam to strike the surface of the electrode, preferably at controlled angle, with subsequent efficient collection of the Raman scattered radiation. It should possess adequate electrochemical characteristics to provide the option of performing the ORC in the spectroelectrochemical cell and the acquisition of spectra under potential control. Additional capability for a variable thickness solution layer between the electrode surface and the cell window can be useful in solvent systems other than aqueous, in which minimization of the bulk solvent signal is desirable.

The literature is replete with descriptions of instrumental schemes and spectroelectrochemical cells for SERS that will not be repeated here. The reader is referred to the excellent descriptions in several recent reviews for these details [11-26].

V. SELECTED EXAMPLES OF SERS APPLICATIONS IN ELECTROCHEMICAL SYSTEMS

SERS has been used to study a myriad of electrochemical systems, all of which cannot be reported here. Instead, selected examples will be presented that reflect the breadth of information available about electrochemical environments from SERS investigations.

A. SERS of Interfacial Solvent Molecules.

SERS has been used to probe the double layer structure of solvent molecules in both aqueous and nonaqueous electrochemical systems. From these studies has come a greater understanding of the influence of potential and electrolyte on the orientation, extent, and type of interaction of the solvent with the metal electrode surface. Information of this sort is of paramount importance at the most fundamental level if knowledge of the influence of molecular double layer structure on the electron transfer event is ever to be achieved.

A considerable amount of effort has been expended in investigation of H_2O in the double layer [184-194]. The spectra of the interfacial H_2O species are characterized by the presence of the ν_1 O-H stretch vibrational mode, the ν_2 O-H bend vibrational mode, and the $2\nu_2$ Fermi resonance mode superimposed on the continuum background scattering. Chang and coworkers have utilized an optical multichannel detector system to monitor the behavior of these modes during potential cycling at Ag electrodes. [Fig. 17A] shows a cyclic voltammogram of an ORC of a Ag electrode in 1 M KBr solution [188]. [Figs. 17B and 17C] show the SERS spectra of the O-H stretching vibration and O-H bending vibration, respectively, as the potential is linearly ramped positive from -0.86 V and back. At potentials too positive to initiate oxidation, weak scattering from bulk H_2O, invariably sampled in this in situ arrangement, is observed. However, these bulk bands become difficult to observe as the AgBr layer forms on

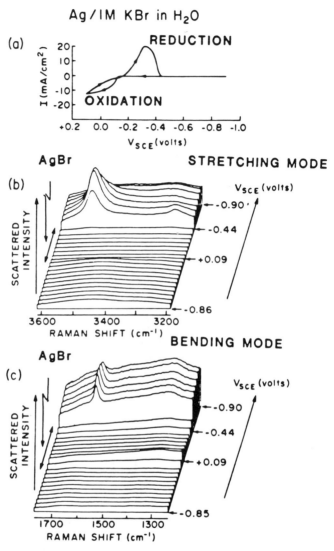

FIGURE 17 (A) Cyclic voltammogram for Ag electrode in 1 M
KBr; scan rate = 5 mV s^{-1}. During the first ORC, the temporal
evolution of the SERS spectra for the (B) O-H stretch mode and
(C) O-H bend mode. (Reprinted with permission from Reference
188.)

the Ag electrode. As the ORC is completed, new vibrational features at 3510 cm^{-1} (ν_1), 1615 cm^{-1} (ν_2) and 3230 cm^{-1} ($2\nu_2$) are readily observed in the spectra. The corresponding bands are observed in D_2O KBr electrolyte solutions at 2580 cm^{-1} (ν_1), 1190 cm^{-1} (ν_2), and 2380 cm^{-1} ($2\nu_2$), as shown in [Fig. 18].

Several features of the peaks in these spectra are noteworthy. First, the lines are considerably narrower and higher in frequency by ca. 100 cm^{-1} than the corresponding bands in bulk solution. Secondly, the frequencies of the bands are voltage dependent. Finally, the continuum background is observed even after the intensities of these bands have dropped considerably. All of these observations support the contention

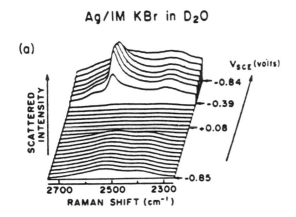

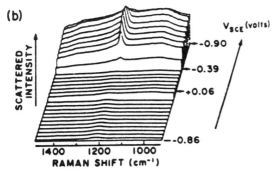

FIGURE 18 Same as Figure 17 except in D_2O instead of H_2O. (Reprinted with permission from Reference 188.)

that the spectra arise from H_2O and D_2O species in the interface. Qualitatively, these spectra are similar to those observed for bulk H_2O at high temperatures in the presence of a high concentration of a structure-breaking salt [195,196]. From this similarity, it has been concluded that the interfacial H_2O species exist as monomers due to disruption of hydrogen bonding by interaction with the surface and adsorbed anions [197]. Besides functioning to disrupt intermolecular hydrogen-bonding between H_2O species, anions are also necessary for stabilization of atomic-scale roughness without which the SERS of H_2O is not observable in electrochemical systems.

SERS of H_2O and D_2O at Ag electrodes is also extremely sensitive to the nature of the electrolyte cation [184-186,189-191]. Chang and coworkers were the first to recognize that the observed effects were correlated to the hydration energy of the cations. [Fig. 19] shows the SERS spectra in the vicinity of the ν_1 region for H_2O solutions of a variety of Cl⁻ electrolytes [191]. These spectra can be grouped into two categories. The ν_1

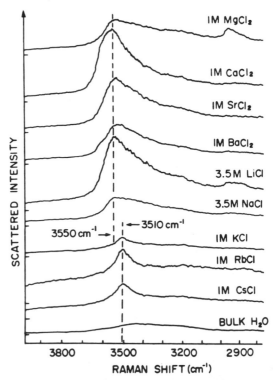

FIGURE 19 SERS spectra from different H_2O electrolytes just after reduction of AgCl layer produced in the ORC. (Reprinted with permission from Reference 191.)

band for the CsCl, RbCl, and KCl electrolytes is narrow, symmetric, and at ca. 3510 cm^{-1}. This band in NaCl, LiCl, BaCl$_2$, SrCl$_2$, CaCl$_2$, and MgCl$_2$ is broad, asymmetric, and observed at ca. 3550 cm^{-1}. The explanation for these differences is related to the hydration energy associated with each of these two groups [191]. The first group of cations (Cs$^+$, Rb$^+$, K$^+$) have low hydration energies allowing the H$_2$O dipoles to be oriented with their O ends toward the metal surface. However, the high hydration energy cations reorient in the double layer such that their O ends are solvating the cations in the outer Helmholtz plane.

The effect of cation on SERS in D$_2$O solutions is similar, as can be seen by the spectra in [Fig. 20]. Interestingly, when mixed H$_2$O-D$_2$O solutions containing these electrolytes are investigated, the spectra change considerably, relative to either pure H$_2$O or D$_2$O, due to the presence of HOD species. This effect is seen in the spectra in [Fig. 21] in which the behavior from D$_2$O and H$_2$O-D$_2$O mixtures are compared for LiCl, NaCl,

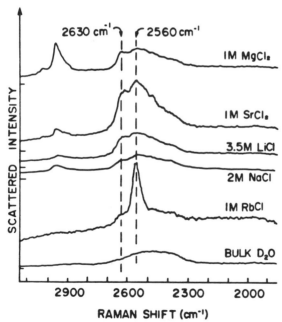

FIGURE 20 Same as in Figure 19 except in D$_2$O instead of H$_2$O. (Reprinted with permission from Reference 191.)

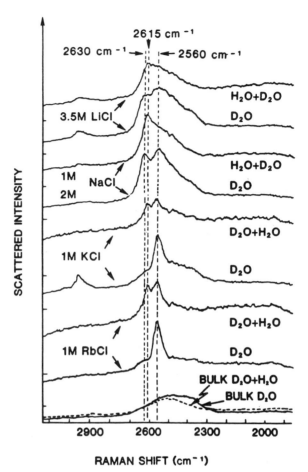

RAMAN SHIFT (cm⁻¹)

FIGURE 21 SERS spectra from different electrolytes in
D_2O and in an equal mixture of H_2O and D_2O just
after reduction of AgCl layer produced in the ORC.
Curves at the bottom are the normal Raman spectra of
bulk D_2O and of an equal mixture of D_2O and H_2O in
1 M RbCl. (Reprinted with permission from reference
194.)

KCl, and RbCl electrolytes [194]. The differences in the
spectra are explained by the presence of H_2O, D_2O, and HOD
in the interface for cations of both high and low hydration
energy. A schematic of the interface explaining the influence
of cation and HOD on the resulting spectra in the frequency
region associated with D_2O is shown in [Fig. 22]. This picture
explains the multiplicity of peaks observed in this region,

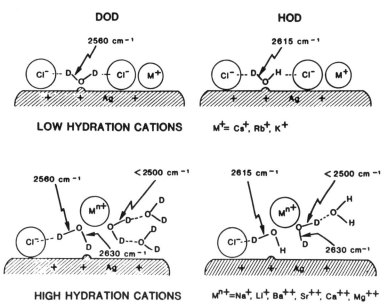

FIGURE 22 Model for interfacial DOD and HOD molecules in electrolytes with low and high hydration cations. (Reprinted with permission from reference 194.)

particularly for the case of cations of high hydration energy [194].

Reports of the observation of OH⁻ and OD⁻ in the double layer have also appeared in the literature [198,199]. Two relatively narrow peaks are observed for OH⁻ species at 3680 and 3595 cm⁻¹ and for OD⁻ at 2685 and 2670 cm⁻¹. These have been assigned to two different types of OH⁻ or OD⁻ species existing in the interface [198]. The first type consists of OH⁻ or OD⁻ species in the inner Helmholtz plane with their oxygen atoms pointing toward the electrode. These species give rise to the bands at 3680 and 2685 cm⁻¹, respectively. The second type of OH⁻ or OD⁻ species is proposed to be in the inner Helmholtz plane with the oxygen atom pointing away from the electrode surface, interacting with a cation in the outer Helmholtz plane.

Studies in nonaqueous solvent systems analogous to those discussed in aqueous solvent systems have also appeared in the recent literature [51,56-58,62]. Irish and coworkers were the first to report the use of SERS for determination of the interaction of solvent molecules in nonaqueous systems with electrode surfaces. These researchers reported a SERS study of Ag in 1 M LiI in acetonitrile [57]. The CN stretching region for interfacial acetonitrile molecules is shown in [Fig. 23] as a

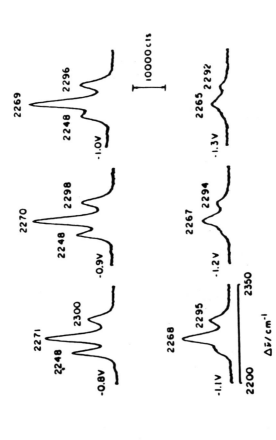

FIGURE 23 SERS in the CN stretching mode region at different electrode potentials for the system Ag/1 M LiI/CH$_3$CN (water content ≈ 4 x 10^{-4} M). (Reprinted with permission from Reference 57.)

function of potential. The bands at 2271 and 2300 cm^{-1} shift to lower frequencies as the potential is made more negative. Moreover, when Li$^+$ is replaced with Na$^+$ as the electrolyte cation, these two bands disappear at the expense of a band at 2262 cm^{-1}. Therefore, these bands are sensitive to the nature of the cation in solution. The position of the bands at 2248 cm^{-1} in Li$^+$ and 2252 cm^{-1} in Na$^+$ are relatively insensitive to potential. On the basis of comparison with the Raman spectral behavior of electrolyte solutions of acetonitrile, these researchers assign the bands at 2271 and 2300 cm^{-1} in Li$^+$ and 2262 cm^{-1} in Na$^+$ to acetonitrile molecules at the electrode surface solvating cations in the outer Helmholtz plane. The second type of solvent molecule is proposed to be at the surface but interacting with another solvent molecule instead of a cation.

The molecular picture of the interface deduced by these researchers is shown in [Fig. 24]. The acetonitrile molecules are weakly bonded to the Ag electrode surface through adsorbed I$^-$. Those molecules solvating cations are represented as solvent-separated ion pairs at the electrode surface.

Investigations in methanol solutions have yielded similar information regarding the orientation of solvent molecules at the Ag electrode-electrolyte interface [62]. [Fig. 25] shows SERS spectra in the ν(C-O) and ν(C-H) regions for LiBr

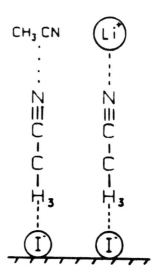

FIGURE 24 Model for two different types of surface acetonitrile molecules at Ag electrode. (Reprinted with permission from Reference 57.)

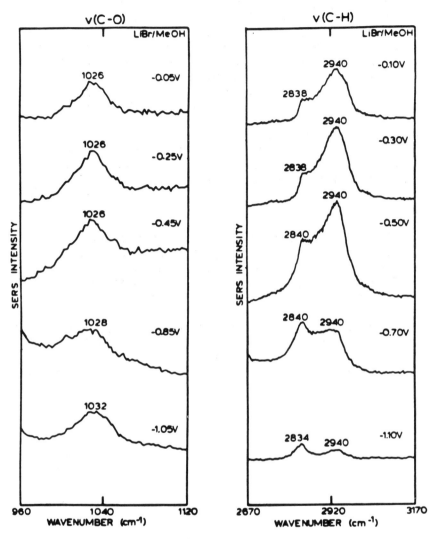

FIGURE 25: SERS spectra of (A) ν(C-O) and (B) ν(C-H) regions of methanol at Ag electrode in 0.4 M LiBr/MeOH solutions.

solutions of methanol at a Ag electrode as a function of potential. The ν(C-O) band for methanol is observed to decrease in frequency upon interaction with the Ag electrode surface. The frequency of this band increases slightly as the potential of the electrode is made more negative, but it never increases enough to become equivalent to that observed for bulk solution methanol.

The ν(C-H) bands for surface methanol do not change in frequency relative to the solution behavior. However, they do show an interesting reversal in intensity between the symmetric and asymmetric modes. In solution, the symmetric ν(C-H) mode is more intense than the asymmetric mode. However, for the surface species, the reverse is true. Moreover, the relative intensity ratio for these two bands is extremely sensitive to the potential of the electrode. The intensity ratio approaches that observed in solution as the potential is made more negative.

A summary of the SERS behavior of methanol at Ag electrodes in solutions of LiBr and LiCl electrolytes as a function of potential as compared to solution methanol is shown in [Table 3]. These data are interpreted in terms of methanol molecules interacting with the Ag surface through the oxygen end of the molecule as shown in [Fig. 26]. At more positive potentials, the strength of this interaction is proposed to be quite strong, leading to a considerable lowering in frequency of the ν(C-O) band. The methyl end of the molecule is proposed to be held close to the surface at an angle, giving rise to the reversal in intensity of the symmetric and asymmetric ν(C-H) modes due to the surface propensity rules. As the potential is made more negative, the methanol molecule interacts less strongly with the Ag surface and attains an orientation with the C-O bond more perpendicular to and further away from the surface. This change in orientation results in an increase in the frequency of the ν(C-O) band, due to decreased interaction with the surface, and restoration of an intensity ratio between the symmetric and asymmetric ν(C-H) bands indicative of bulk methanol.

B. SERS of Adsorbed Ions.

The information provided by SERS investigations of interfacial solvent molecules should help electrochemists to build an increasingly accurate molecular picture of the double layer. This picture can then be broadened through studies involving systems of greater complexity. Obviously, the next step in this process is elucidation of interactions between solution electrolyte species, most importantly anions, and the electrode surface. SERS has enjoyed great success in deciphering interactions between halide and pseudohalide ions

TABLE 3. Raman Spectral Information For Methanol Solutions And Methanol Adsorbed At Ag Electrodes

MeOH	Solution Frequencies LiCl/MeOH	LiBr/MeOH	SERS LiCl/MeOH	LiBr/MeOH	Assign.
1036	1040	1038	1026-1034	1026-1032	ν(C-OH)
1112	1106	1108	NO[a]	NO	ν(C-OH)
1454	1453	1455	1456	1456	δ(C-CH)
2836	2842	2840	2836	2838	ν(C-H)$_{sym}$
2944	2950	2947	2940	2940	ν(C-H)$_{asym}$
			3242-3256	3256-3266	ν(O-H)
3337	3361	3380	3340	3346-3354	ν(O-H)

[a]Not observed.

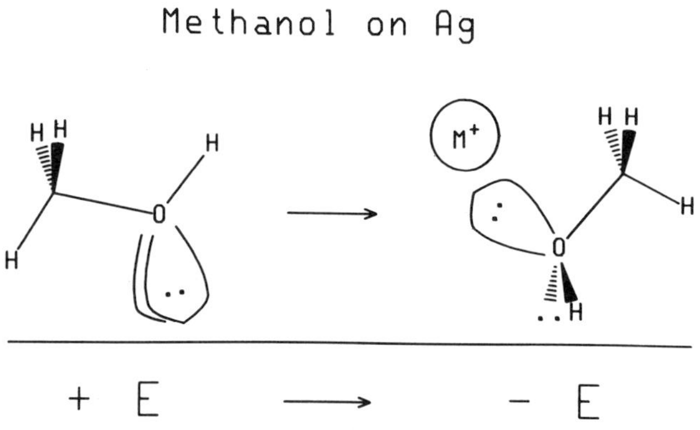

Methanol on Ag

FIGURE 26 Model for orientation of methanol solvent molecules at the Ag electrode surface as a function of potential.

and Ag electrodes. These ions are attractive for such studies due to their structural simplicity and strong adsorption at solid metal electrodes. SERS is a viable approach for investigating the adsorption of these ions, because the low frequency region where the metal-ion vibrations are observed is readily accessible. The ability to easily compare electrochemical and spectroscopic measures of adsorption provides a useful independent check on the quality of the SERS information obtained.

Recently, reliable measures of the interaction of these ions with Au surfaces have appeared [200]. These will be discussed here in some detail to demonstrate the quality of information attainable from such studies. [Fig. 27] shows a series of SERS spectra reported by Weaver for Cl⁻, Br⁻, and I⁻ adsorbed at a Au electrode at a variety of potentials [200]. For Cl⁻, a broad band (FWHM 45-50 cm⁻¹) centered at ca. 265 cm⁻¹ is observed. This band is assigned to the vibration of Cl⁻ against the Au electrode surface. The intensity of this band decreases as the potential is made more negative, indicating desorption of the ions. Similar bands are observed for adsorbed Br⁻ and I⁻ at 185 cm⁻¹ and 120 cm⁻¹, respectively. However, the intensities of these bands remain essentially constant until potentials in the hydrogen evolution region are reached. Comparisons between the SERS intensities and the differential double layer capacitance (C_{dl}) plots as a function of potential shown in [Fig. 28] indicate that the SERS response is almost independent of potential for a major portion of the potential region studied. The conclusion from these observations is that SERS is seen

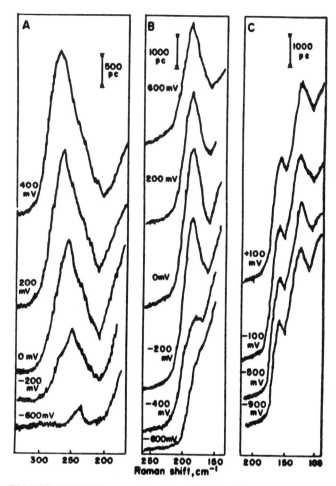

FIGURE 27 SERS spectra for (A) Cl⁻, (B) Br⁻, and (C) I⁻
adsorbed at Au at various electrode potentials. Electrolytes are
0.1 M potassium halides. Excitation was at 647.1 nm.
(Reprinted with permission from Reference 200.)

only from the more strongly bound halide ions associated with
the larger C_{dl} peak at more negative potentials.

From these data, surface-halide force constants can be
calculated [200] using the following equation

$$f_{M-X} = 4\pi^2 \nu_{M-X}^2 c^2 \mu,$$

where c is the velocity of light and μ is the effective mass of
the vibrating bond taken to be equal to the halide mass.
Although certain assumptions of this treatment may not be

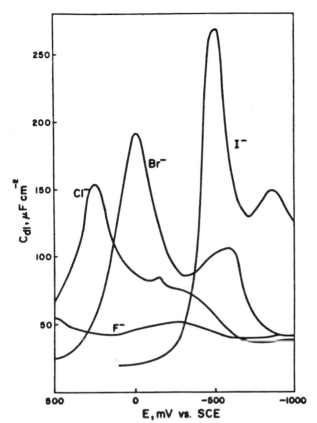

FIGURE 28 Differential double layer capacitance, C_{dl}, for SERS-active Au surface in contact with 0.1 M potassium halide versus electrode potential. (Reprinted with permission from Reference 200.)

strictly accurate, it provides a means of estimating force constants for the surface-halide bonds which become useful when comparing different ions or different surfaces. [Table 4] demonstrates this utility. It shows the SERS information and force constants determined for Cl⁻, Br⁻, and I⁻ adsorbates at Ag and Au electrodes. The force constants for the Au-halide bonds are consistently higher than those for the Ag-halide bonds. The significance of this comparison becomes even greater when it is realized that the force constants calculated at 500 mV at Au and at -200 mV on Ag are for electrodes at approximately the same excess surface charge. Weaver and coworkers interpret these results to indicate a greater degree of covalency between the Au surface and the halides than for the Ag surface. This conclusion is supported by Raman results on the corresponding bulk phase materials.

TABLE 4. Frequency And Force Constant Information For Halide Adsorption At Au And Ag Electrodes From SERS

Vibration	Medium	ν_{M-X} cm^{-1}	Force Constant 10^5 dyne cm^{-1}
Au-Cl	Au/Cl⁻, H_2O		
	500 mV	275	1.6
	-400 mV	245	1.25
Au-Cl	Ag/Cl⁻, H_2O		
	-200 mV	238	1.2
Au-Br	Au/Br⁻, H_2O		
	500 mV	186	1.6
	-400 mV	181	1.55
Ag-Br	Ag/Br⁻, H_2O		
	-200 mV	158	1.2
Au-I	Au/I⁻, H_2O		
	500 mV	124, 158	1.15, 1.87
	-400 mV	120, 158	1.10, 1.87
Ag-I	Ag/I⁻, H_2O		
	-200 mV	115	1.0

Reproduced with permission from Reference 200.

C. SERS of Electrochemically Reactive Adsorbates.

The next level of complexity that one can confer upon an electrochemical system is the addition of a molecule that will undergo electron transfer through interaction with the surface. One example of a reversible redox couple successfully studied with SERS is pentaammine(pyridine)osmium(III)/(II) at Ag electrodes [201]. Spectra in three frequency regions at representative potentials are shown in [Fig. 29]. At potentials positive of -500 mV, the SERS frequencies are essentially

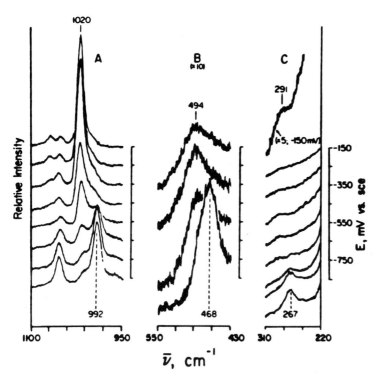

FIGURE 29 Potential-dependent SERS of $Os(NH_3)_5Py(III)/(II)$ at roughened Ag from 0.1 mM $Os(NH_3)_5Py(III)/0.1$ M NaBr/0.1 M HCl. (Reprinted with permission from Reference 201.)

identical to those for bulk $Os(NH_3)_5Py(III)$. However, as the potential is made more negative, significant changes are observed in the bands corresponding to the Os-Py stretch at 291 cm^{-1}, the Os-NH_3 stretch at 494 cm^{-1} and the pyridine ring breathing vibration at 1020 cm^{-1}. The intensities of these bands decrease sharply between -500 and -700 mV and are replaced by bands ca. 20-30 cm^{-1} lower in frequency. It was further found that these changes were reversible upon returning the potential to more positive values. The spectral changes are shown to be due to the one-electron reduction of Os(III) to Os(II). [Fig. 30] shows the potential dependence of the SERS intensities for the pyridine ring breathing vibrations at 1020 and 992 cm^{-1}. Assuming that the intensities are proportional to the corresponding surface concentration of Os(III) and Os(II), respectively, a formal potential of ca. -630 mV is determined for the reduction. This value is similar to that determined electrochemically.

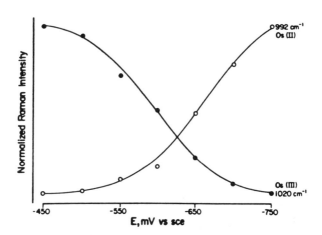

FIGURE 30 Normalized intensity of the symmetric ring
breathing mode of pyridine in $Os(NH_3)_5Py$ as a function
of electrode potential. Os oxidation states are indicated.
(Reprinted with permission from Reference 201.)

A similar approach has been taken with molecules which
undergo irreversible electron transfer. Two representative
examples which have been studied with SERS are the
electroreduction of nitrobenzene and the electrooxidation of
benzidene. These studies are also useful to consider, because
they represent a greater level of molecular and electron
transfer mechanistic complexity than the $Os(NH_3)_5Py$ example
discussed above.

Nitrobenzene adsorbed at Ag and Au electrodes has been
studied by several groups using SERS [201-205]. The electron
transfer process is irreversible and gives rise to several
products through complicated schemes not yet understood even
after extensive study by electrochemical methods. [Fig. 31A]
shows a SERS spectrum of nitrobenzene adsorbed at Au at
potentials more positive than the onset of reduction from a 3
mM solution in 0.1 M NaOH [203]. With the exception of the
band at 1330 cm^{-1}, the bands in the frequency region between
1000 and 1600 cm^{-1} are due to vibrational modes of the
aromatic ring and are not changed significantly from the
corresponding bands of bulk nitrobenzene. The band at 1330
cm^{-1} is due to the symmetric N-O stretch and is significantly
downshifted and broadened compared to bulk nitrobenzene,
indicative of coordination of the nitro group to the Au surface
[202].

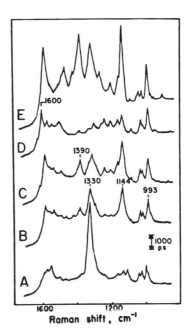

FIGURE 31 SERS spectra for nitrobenzene and reduction products at Au electrode in 3 mM $C_6H_5NO_2$ in 0.1 M NaOH. Potential for each spectrum: (A) −100 to −300 mV vs SCE, (B) −500 mV, (C) -600 mV, (D) -850 mV, (E) after return to -200 mV. (Reprinted with permission from Reference 203.)

As the potential is made more negative, the spectra shown in [Figs. 31B-E] are observed. Several spectral changes are noteworthy. First, the intensity of the symmetric N-O stretch is reduced considerably, and new bands appear at 1145, 1390, and 1595 cm^{-1}. The band at 1390 cm^{-1} is diagnostic for nitrosobenzene at the Au surface during the reduction process. Thus, this study establishes quite convincingly the importance of nitrosobenzene in the reduction mechanism between nitrobenzene and further reduction products including azobenzene and phenylhydroxylamine.

A related analysis that has appeared in the literature is study of the oxidation of benzidene [206]. At pH 4.35, solution benzidene undergoes two one-electron oxidations at ca. 380 and 480 mV versus the SCE. Adsorbed benzidene also gives two voltammetric waves at ca. 400 and 590 mV under these pH conditions, but they are not as reversible as their solution oxidation counterparts. The oxidation processes proposed to occur are as follows

$$H_3\overset{+}{N}-\bigcirc-\bigcirc-NH_2 \rightleftharpoons H_3\overset{+}{N}=\bigcirc=\bigcirc=\overset{+}{N}H_2 + e^-$$

$$H_3\overset{+}{N}=\bigcirc=\bigcirc=\overset{.}{N}H_2 \rightleftharpoons H_2\overset{+}{N}=\bigcirc=\bigcirc=\overset{.}{N}H_2 + e^- + H^+$$

The SERS behavior for benzidene is shown in [Fig. 32A-E]. [Figs. 32A and B] are the spectra obtained at 0 and 375 mV, respectively, before the onset of oxidation. The ring vibrations at 830 and 1600 cm^{-1} are shifted downward by ca. 15 cm^{-1} indicating flat adsorption of the benzidene at the Au surface [202]. Upon oxidation at 400 mV, spectral changes are observed ([Figs. 32c and d]) suggestive of oxidation of the benzidene precursor to its corresponding cation radical. The clearest indicators of the presence of this cation radical are the C=C bond vibration at 1350 cm^{-1} and the C=N vibration at 1505 cm^{-1}, as has been shown by solution Raman spectroscopy on this system [207].

Further oxidation yields the dication species whose SERS spectrum is shown in [Fig. 32E]. Four major bands are observed in the spectrum at 1200, 1360, 1440, and 1585 cm^{-1}. The intensities of these bands are increased over those of the cation radical species, most likely due to additional resonance Raman enhancement.

The two SERS studies just discussed have confirmed previous postulates regarding reaction mechanisms in these systems. They also demonstrate the power of SERS for elucidating various aspects of electrochemical reaction pathways not necessarily evident in the electrochemical characterization alone. The outstanding molecular specificity of SERS makes it quite likely that its use in detailing electrochemical reaction schemes will continue.

VI. CONCLUSIONS

It is reasonable at this point to ask where the future of SERS lies with respect to its use in electrochemistry. Intense investigation of the SERS phenomenon in electrochemical systems over the past decade has provided important insight necessary to answer this question. It is quite clear that issues

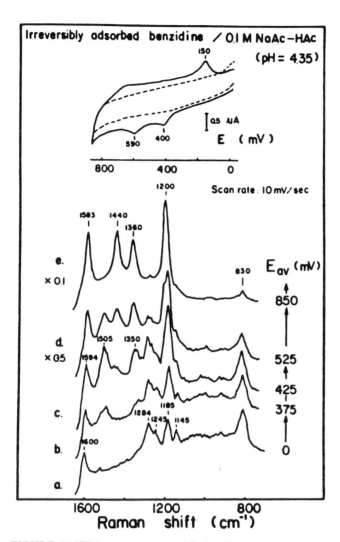

FIGURE 32 SERS spectra acquired during linear sweep
voltammetric oxidation of adsorbed benzidene at potentials
indicated. The cyclic voltammogram shown above was obtained
simultaneously. (Reprinted with permission from Reference 206.)

regarding the detailed mechanisms of SERS will continue to be
debated for quite some time to come. However, the
considerable effort that has been directed towards developing
SERS into a scientific, controllable phenomenon, as opposed to
the witchcraft it was once considered to be, is beginning to pay
enormous dividends in terms of our understanding of the
electrochemical interface. As electrochemists continue to amass

documentation that SERS is capable of providing reliable information about the electrochemical interface, the acceptance of SERS as a routine method of interfacial characterization will expand. Parallel developments in Raman instrumentation and methodology should help to partially relieve reliance on poorly understood enhancement phenomena for acquisition of this information. However, it should be borne in mind that recent developments that have occurred in the application of Raman spectroscopy to the study of the electrochemical interface have been greatly catalyzed by the fervent interest in SERS. For the time being, at least, SERS remains an important tool for the characterization of interfaces in electrochemical systems.

ACKNOWLEDGMENTS

I am truly grateful to all of my students who have explored the area of SERS with me over the past few years and whose significant contributions have helped to improve our understanding of this phenomenon. I am also grateful to the National Science Foundation for financial support (CHE-8309454 and CHE-8614955) of our work in this area.

References

1. Jeanmaire, D.L.; Suchanski, M.R.; and Van Duyne, R.P. *J. Am. Chem. Soc.* 97 (1975): 1699.
2. Jeanmaire, D.L., and Van Duyne, R.P. *J. Am. Chem. Soc.* 98 (1976): 4029.
3. Jeanmaire, D.L., and Van Duyne, R.P. *J. Am. Chem. Soc.* 98 (1976): 4034.
4. Suchanski, M.R., and Van Duyne, R.P. *J. Am. Chem. Soc.* 98 (1976): 250.
5. Jeanmaire, D.L., and Van Duyne, R.P. *J. Electroanal. Chem.* 66 (1975): 235.
6. Van Duyne, R.P., et al. *J. Am. Chem. Soc.* 101 (1979): 2832.
7. Fleischmann, M.; Hendra, P.J.; and McQuillan, A.J. *J. Chem. Soc. Chem. Comm.* 3 (1973): 80.
8. Fleischmann, M.; Hendra, P.J.; and McQuillan, A.J. *Chem. Phys. Lett.* 26 (1974): 163.
9. Jeanmaire, D.L., and Van Duyne, R.P. *J. Electroanal. Chem.* 84 (1977): 1.
10. Albrecht, M.G., and Creighton, J.A. *J. Am. Chem. Soc.* 99 (1977): 215.

11. Van Duyne, R.P. In *Chemical and Biochemical Applications of Lasers*, Vol. 4, ed. C.B. Moore, 101. New York: Academic Press, 1979.

12. Chang, R.K., and Furtak, T.E. eds. *Surface Enhanced Raman Scattering*. New York: Plenum Press, 1981.

13. Birke, R.L.; Lombardi, J.R.; and Sanchez, L.A. In *Electrochemical and Spectrochemical Studies of Biological Redox Components*, ACS Symposium Series No. 201, 69. Washington, D.C.: American Chemical Society, 1982.

14. Ayra, K., and Zeyher, R. In *Light Scattering in Solids* IV, ed. M. Cardona, and G. Guntherodt, 419. Berlin: Springer-Verlag, 1984.

15. Otto, A. In *Light Scattering in Solids* IV, ed. M. Cardona, and G. Guntherodt, 289. Berlin: Springer-Verlag, 1984.

16. Wokaun, A. In *Solid State Physics*, ed. H. Ehrenreich, and D. Turnbull, Vol. 38, 223. New York: Academic Press, 1984.

17. Chang, R.K., and Laube, B.L. *CRC Crit. Rev. Solid State Mater. Sci.* 12 (1984): 1.

18. Metiu, H., and Das, P. *Ann. Rev. Phys. Chem.* 35 (1984): 507.

19. Metiu, H. *Prog. Surf. Sci.* 17 (1984): 153.

20. Efrima, S. In *Modern Aspects of Electrochemistry*, ed. B.E. Conway; R.E. White; and J. O'M. Bockris, No. 16, 253. New York: Plenum Press, 1985.

21. Moskovits, M. *Rev. Mod. Phys.* 57 (1985): 331.

22. Wokaun, A. *Molec. Phys.* 56 (1985): 1.

23. Campion, A. *Ann. Rev. Phys. Chem.* 36 (1985) 549.

24. Murray, C.A. In *Advances in Laser Spectroscopy*, ed. B.A. Garetz, and J.R. Lombardi, Vol. 3, 49. New York: Wiley, 1986.

25. Weitz, D.A.; Moskovits, H.; and Creighton, J.A. In *Chemistry and Structure at Interfaces*, ed. R.B. Hall, and A.B. Ellis, 197. Berlin: VCH Publishers, 1986.

26. Campion, A. In *Vibrational Spectroscopy of Molecules at Surfaces*, ed. J.T. Yates, and T.E.Madey, 345. New York: Plenum Press, 1987.

27. Weaver, M.J., et al. *J. Electroanal. Chem.* 160 (1984): 321.

28. Weaver, M.J.; Farquharson, S.; and Tadayyoni, M.A. *J. Chem. Phys.* 82 (1985): 4867.

29. Pettinger, B.; Wenning, U.; and Wetzel, H. *Surface Sci.* 101 (1980): 409.

30. Blatchford, C.G.; Campbell, J.R.; and Creighton, J.A. *Surface Sci.* 108 (1981): 411.

31. Wenning, U.; Pettinger, B.; and Wetzel, H. *Chem. Phys. Lett.* 70 (1980): 49.

32. Allen, C.S.; Schatz, G.C.; and Van Duyne, R.P. *Chem. Phys. Lett.* 75 (1980): 201.
33. Busby, C.C., and Creighton, J.A. *J. Electroanal. Chem.* 140 (1982): 379.
34. Gao, P., et al. *J. Electroanal. Chem.* 233 (1987): 211.
35. Murray, C.A.; Allara, D.L.; and Rhinewine, M. *Phys. Rev. Lett.* 46 (1981): 57.
36. Murray, C.A., and Allara, D.L. *J. Chem. Phys.* 76 (1982): 1290.
37. Murray, C.A., et al. *Surface Sci.* 119 (1982): 449.
38. Kovacs, G.J., *Langmuir* 2 (1986): 689.
39. Bewick, A., et al. *J. Electroanal. Chem.* 160 (1984): 47.
40. Foley, J.K., et al. In *Electroanalytical Chemistry*, ed. A.J. Bard, Vol. 14. New York: Marcel Dekker, 1988.
41. Bewick, A., and Pons, S. In *Advances in Infrared and Raman Spectroscopy*, ed. R.J.H. Clark, R.E. Hester, Vol. 12, 1. New York: Wiley, 1985.
42. Pons, S., et al. In *Modern Aspects of Electrochemistry*, ed. J.O'M. Bockris, and B.E. Conway, Vol. 17. New York: Plenum Press, 1986.
43. Korzeniewski, C., and Pons, S. *Prog. Analyt. Spectrosc.* 10 (1987): 1.
44. Golden, W.G.; Dunn, D.S.; and Overend, J. *J. Catal.* 71 (1981): 395.
45. Russell, J.W., et al. *J. Phys. Chem.* 86 (1982): 3066.
46. Golden, W.G., and Saperstein, D.D. *J. Electron Spectrosc. Relat. Phenom.* 30 (1983): 43.
47. Corrigan, D.S., et al. *Langmuir* 1 (1985): 616.
48. Corrigan, D.S., et al. *Langmuir* 2 (1986): 744.
49. Kunimatsu, K.; Seki, H.; and Golden, W.G. *Chem. Phys. Lett.* 108 (1984): 195.
50. Kunimatsu, K., et al. *Surface Sci.* 158 (1985): 596.
51. Pemberton, J.E. *Chem. Phys. Lett.* 115 (1985): 321.
52. Hutchinson, K.; McQuillan, A.J.; and Hester, R.E. *Chem. Phys. Lett.* 98 (1983): 27.
53. Shin, G.S., and Kim, J.J. *Surface Sci.* 158 (1985): 286.
54. Kim, J.J., and Shin, G.S. *Chem. Phys. Lett.* 118 (1985): 493.
55. Shin, G.S., and Kim, J.J. *Chem. Phys. Lett.* 120 (1985): 569.
56. Guzonas, D.A.; Atkinson, G.F.; and Irish, D.E. *Chem. Phys. Lett.* 107 (1984): 193.
57. Irish, D.E., et al. *J. Soln. Chem.* 14 (1985): 221.
58. Hill, I.R.; Irish, D.E.; and Atkinson, G.F. *Langmuir* 2 (1986): 752.
59. Stacy, A.M., and Van Duyne, R.P. *Chem. Phys. Lett.* 102 (1983): 365.
60. Van Duyne, R.P., and Haushalter, J.P. *J. Phys. Chem.* 87 (1983): 2999.

61. Van Duyne, R.P., et al. *J. Phys. Chem.* 89 (1985): 4055.
62. Sobocinski, R.L., and Pemberton, J.E. *Langmuir* 6 (1990): 43.
63. Mamantov, G. Private communication, 1988.
64. Seki, H. *J. Electron Spectrosc. Relat. Phenom.* 30 (1983): 287.
65. Seki, H. *J. Electron Spectrosc. Related Phenom.* 39 (1986): 289.
66. Owen, J.F., et al. *Surface Sci.* 125 (1983): 679.
67. Wall, K.F., and Chang, R.K. *Chem. Phys. Lett.* 129 (1986): 144.
68. Wall, K.F.; Temperini, M.L.A.; and Chang, R.K. *Chem. Phys. Lett.* 129 (1986): 253.
69. Acker, W.P., et al. *Surface Sci.* 176 (1986): 336.
70. Weitz, D.A., et al. *Phys. Rev. Lett.* 22 (1980): 4562.
71. Gersten, J.I., et al. *Phys. Rev. B* 22 (1980): 4562.
72. Weitz, D.A.; Gramila, T.J.; and Genack, A.Z. In *Surface Enhanced Raman Scattering*, ed. R.K. Chang, and T.E. Furtak, 339. New York: Plenum Press, 1981.
73. Moskovits, M., *J. Chem. Phys.* 77 (1982): 4408.
74. Moskovits, M., and Suh, J.S. *J. Phys. Chem.* 88 (1984): 1293.
75. Moskovits, M., and Suh, J.S. *J. Phys. Chem.* 88 (1984): 5526.
76. Moskovits, M.; DiLella, D.P.; and Maynard, K.J. *Langmuir* 4 (1988): 67.
77. Creighton, J.A. *Surface Sci.* 124 (1983): 209.
78. Creighton, J.A. *Surface Sci.* 158 (1985): 211.
79. Hallmark, V.M., and Campion, A. *Chem. Phys. Lett.* 110 (1984): 561.
80. Moskovits, M., and Suh, J.S. *J. Am. Chem. Soc.* 108 (1985): 6826.
81. Suh, J.S., and Moskovits, M. *J. Am. Chem. Soc.* 108 (1986): 4711.
82. Benner, R.E., et al. *Chem. Phys. Lett.* 96 (1983): 65.
83. Loo, B.H. *J. Phys. Chem.* 87 (1983): 3003.
84. Loo, B.H. *J. Chem. Phys.* 75 (1981): 5955.
85. Loo, B.H. *J. Electron Spectrosc. Relat. Phenom.* 29 (1983): 407.
86. Fleischmann, M., et al. *Chem. Phys. Lett.* 95 (1983): 322.
87. Naaman, R., et al. *J. Phys. Chem.* 84 (1980): 2692.
88. Sanchez, L.A.; Birke, R.L.; and Lombardi, J.R. *Chem. Phys. Lett.* 79 (1981): 219.
89. Loo, B.H., and Furtak, T.E. *Chem. Phys. Lett.* 71 (1980): 68.
90. Pettinger, B., and Moerl, L. *J. Electron Spectrosc. Relat. Phenom.* 29 (1983): 383.
91. Watanabe, T., et al. *Chem. Phys. Lett.* 96 (1983): 649.

92. Guy, A.L.; Bergami, B.; and Pemberton, J.E. *Surface Sci.* 150 (1985): 226.
93. Guy, A.L., and Pemberton, J.E. *Langmuir* 1 (1985): 518.
94. Guy, A.L., and Pemberton, J.E. *Langmuir* 3 (1987): 125.
95. Kellogg, D.S., and Pemberton, J.E. *J. Phys. Chem.* 91 (1987): 1127.
96. Coria-Garcia, J.C.; Pemberton, J.E.; and Sobocinski, R.L. *J. Electroanal. Chem.* 219 (1987): 291.
97. Pemberton, J.E.; Coria-Garcia, J.C.; and Hoff, R.L. *Langmuir* 3 (1987): 150.
98. Guy, A.L., and Pemberton, J.E. *Langmuir* 3 (1987): 777.
99. Pemberton, J.E., and Coria-Garcia, J.C. In *Molecular Phenomena at Electrode Surfaces*, ed. M.P. Soriaga, 398. ACS Symposium Series No. 378, Washington, D.C.: American Chemical Society, 1988.
100. Fleischmann, M., and Tian, Z.Q. *J. Electroanal. Chem.* 217 (1987): 385.
101. Leung, L.-W. H., and Weaver, M.J. *J. Electroanal. Chem.* 217 (1987): 367.
102. Kester, J.J. *J. Chem. Phys.* 78 (1983): 7466.
103. Moerl, L., and Pettinger, B. *Solid State Commun.* 43 (1982): 315.
104. Kellogg, D.S., and Pemberton, J.E. Unpublished results.
105. Fleischmann, M.; Tian, Z.Q.; and Li, L.J. *J. Electroanal. Chem.* 217 (1987): 397.
106. Fleischmann, M., and Tian, Z.Q. *J. Electroanal. Chem.* 217 (1987): 411.
107. Mengoli, G., et al. *Electrochim. Acta* 32 (1987): 1239.
108. Leung, L.-W.H., and Weaver, M.J. *J. Am. Chem. Soc.* 109 (1987): 5113.
109. Marinyuk, V.V.; Lazorenko-Manevich, R.M.; and Kolotyrkin, Y.M. *Solid State Commun.* 43 (1982): 721.
110. Mo, Y.; von Kanel, H.; and Wachter, P. *Solid State Commun.* 52 (1984): 213.
111. Pemberton, J.E. *J. Electroanal. Chem.* 167 (1984): 317.
112. Furtak, T.E., and Miragliotta, J. *Surface Sci.* 167 (1986): 381.
113. Miragliotta, J., and Furtak, T.E. *Phys. Rev. B* 35 (1987): 7382.
114. Leung, L.-W.H.; Gosztola, D.; and Weaver, M.J. *Langmuir* 3 (1987): 45.
115. Shannon, C., and Campion, A. *J. Phys. Chem.* 92 (1988): 1385.
116. McCall, S.L.; Platzman, P.M.; and Wolff, P.A. *Phys. Lett. A* 77 (1980): 381.
117. Wang, D.S.; Kerker, M.; and Chew, H. *Appl. Opt.* 19 (1980): 2135, 4159.

118. Messinger, B.J., et al. *Phys. Rev. B* 24 (1981): 649.
119. Ohtaka, K., and Inoue, M. *J. Phys. C* 15 (1982): 6463.
120. Ohtaka, K., and Inoue, M. *Phys. Rev. B* 25 (1982): 689.
121. Chew, H., and Wang, D.S. *Phys. Rev. Lett.* 49 (1982): 490.
122. Wang, D.S., and Kerker, M., *Phys. Rev. B* 25 (1982): 2433.
123. Zeman, E.J., and Schatz, G.C. *J. Phys. Chem.* 91 (1987): 634.
124. Liao, P.F. In *Surface Enhanced Raman Scattering*, ed. R.K. Chang, and T.E. Furtak, 379. New York: Plenum Press, 1981.
125. Cross, N.A., and Pemberton, J.E. Unpublished results.
126. Wang, D.S., and Kerker, M. *Phys. Rev. B* 24 (1981): 1777.
127. Adrian, F.J. *Chem. Phys. Lett.* 78 (1981): 45.
128. Wang, D.S.; Kerker, M.; and Chew, H. *Appl. Opt.* 19 (1980): 1573, 2315.
129. Gersten, J.I. *J. Chem. Phys.* 72 (1980): 5779, 5780.
130. Gersten, J.I., and Nitzan, A. *J. Chem. Phys.* 75 (1981): 1139.
131. Barber, P.W.; Chang, R.K.; and Massoudi, H. *Phys. Rev. B* 27 (1983): 7251.
132. Krauss, W.A., and Schatz, G.C. *Chem. Phys. Lett.* 99 (1983): 353.
133. Berreman, D.W. *Phys. Rev. B* 1 (1970): 381.
134. Gersten, J.I., and Nitzan, A. *J. Chem. Phys.* 73 (1980): 3023.
135. Ruppin, R. *Solid State Commun.* 39 (1981): 903.
136. Das, P.C., and Gersten, J.I. *Phys. Rev. B* 25 (1982): 6281.
137. Laor, U., and Schatz, G.C. *J. Chem. Phys.* 76 (1982): 2888.
138. Burstein, E., et al. *Solid State Commun.* 29 (1979): 567.
139. Gersten, J.I.; Birke, R.L.; and Lombardi, J.R. *Phys. Rev. Lett.* 43 (1979): 147.
140. Otto, A. In *Surface Enhanced Raman Scattering*, ed. R.K. Chang, and T.E. Furtak, 147. New York: Plenum Press, 1981.
141. Furtak, T.E., and Roy, D. *Surface Sci.* 158 (1985): 126.
142. Pettenkofer, C., and Otto, A. *Surface Sci.* 151 (1985): 37.
143. Persson, B.J. *Chem. Phys. Lett.* 82 (1981): 561.
144. Billman, J., and Otto, A. *Surface Sci.* 138 (1984): 1.
145. Otto, A., et al. *Surface Sci.* 138 (1984): 319.
146. Lombardi, J.R., et al. *Chem. Phys. Lett.* 104 (1984): 240.
147. Hulse, J., et al. *Appl. Surf. Sci.* 6 (1980): 453.
148. Kuppers, K., et al. *Surface Sci.* 88 (1979): 1.
149. Besocke, K.; Krahl-Urban, B.; and Wagner, H. *Surface Sci.* 68 (1977): 39.
150. Demuth, J.E., and Sanda, P.N. *Phys. Rev. Lett.* 47 (1981): 57.

151. Ueba, H.; Ichimura, S.; and Yamada, H. *Surface Sci.* 119 (1982): 433.
152. Furtak, T.E., and Roy, D. *Phys. Rev. Lett.* 50 (1983): 1301.
153. Furtak, T.E., and Macomber, S.H. *Chem. Phys. Lett.* 95 (1983): 328.
154. Furtak, T.E., and Roy, D. *Surface Sci.* 131 (1983): 347.
155. Owen, J.F., et al. *Surface Sci.* 131 (1983): 195.
156. Weaver, M.J., et al. *Surface Sci.* 125 (1983): 409.
157. Wetzel, H.; Gerischer, H.; and Pettinger, B. *Chem. Phys. Lett.* 78 (1981): 392.
158. Wetzel, H.; Gerischer, H.; and Pettinger, B. *Chem. Phys. Lett.* 80 (1981): 159.
159. Gao, P., et al. *Langmuir* 1 (1985): 173.
160. Bunding, K.A.; Gordon, J.G.; and Seki, H. *J. Electroanal. Chem.* 184 (1985): 405.
161. Chen, C.Y.; Burstein, E.; and Lundquist, S. *Solid State Commun.* 32 (1979): 63.
162. Birke, R.L.; Lombardi, J.R.; and Gersten, J.I. *Phys. Rev. Lett.* 43 (1979): 71.
163. Timper, J., et al. *Surface Sci.* 101 (1980): 348.
164. Sobocinski, R.L., and Pemberton, J.E. *Langmuir* 4 (1988): 836.
165. Baltruschat, H., and Heitbaum, J. *Surface Sci.* 166 (1986): 113.
166. Roy, D., and Furtak, T.E. *Chem. Phys. Lett.* 124 (1986): 299.
167. Roy, D., and Furtak, T.E. *Phys. Rev. B* 34 (1986): 5111.
168. Roy, D., and Furtak, T.E. *J. Electroanal. Chem.* 228 (1987): 229.
169. Evans, J.F., et al. *J. Electroanal. Chem.* 106 (1980): 209.
170. Schultz, S.G.; and Janik-Czachor, M.; and Van Duyne, R.P. *Surface Sci.* 104 (1981): 419.
171. Tuschel, D.D.; Pemberton, J.E.; and Cook, J.E. *Langmuir* 2 (1986): 380.
172. Pemberton, J.E., and Girand, M.M. *J. Electroanal. Chem.* 217 (1987): 79.
173. Katan, T.; Szpak, S.; and Bennion, D.N. *J. Electrochem. Soc.* 120 (1973): 883.
174. Katan, T.; Szpak, S.; and Bennion, D.N. *J. Electrochem. Soc.* 121 (1973): 757.
175. Cross, N.A., and Pemberton, J.E. *J. Electroanal. Chem.* 217 (1987): 93.
176. Cassidy, J.; Khoo, S.B.; and Pons, S. *J. Phys. Chem.* 89 (1985): 3933.
177. Van Duyne, R.P.; Haller, K.L.; and Altkorn, R.I. *Chem. Phys. Lett.* 126 (1986): 190.

178. Chase, B., and Parkinson, B. *Appl. Spectrosc.* 42 (1988): 1186.
179. Murray, C.A., and Dierker, S.B. *J. Opt. Soc. Am. A* 3 (1987): 2151.
180. Dierker, S.B., et al. *Chem. Phys. Lett.* 137 (1987): 453.
181. Pemberton, J.E., et al. *Spectroscopy* 5 (1990): 26.
182. Bilhorn, R.B., et al. *Appl. Spectrosc.* 41 (1987): 1114.
183. Bilhorn, R.B., et al. *Appl. Spectrosc.* 41 (1987): 1125.
184. Fleischmann, M., et al. *J. Electroanal. Chem.* 117 (1981): 243.
185. Fleischmann, M., and Hill, I.R. *J. Electroanal. Chem.* 146 (1983): 367.
186. Fleischmann, M., and Hill, I.R. In *Surface Enhanced Raman Scattering*, ed. R.K. Chang, and T.E. Furtak, 275. New York: Plenum Press, 1981.
187. Pettinger, B.; Philpott, M.R.; and Gordon, J.G. *J. Chem. Phys.* 74 (1981): 934.
188. Chen, T.T., et al. *Chem. Phys. Lett.* 89 (1982): 356.
189. Macomber, S.H.; Furtak, T.E.; and Devine, T.M. *Surface Sci.* 122 (1982): 556.
190. Pettinger, B., and Moerl, L. *J. Electroanal. Chem.* 150 (1983): 415.
191. Chen, T.T., et al. *Chem. Phys. Lett.* 108 (1984): 32.
192. Owen, J.F., et al. *J. Electroanal. Chem.* 150 (1983): 389.
193. Owen, J.F., and Chang, R.K. *Chem. Phys. Lett.* 104 (1984): 510.
194. Chen, T.T., and Chang, R.K. *Surface Sci.* 158 (1985): 325.
195. Ratcliffe, C.I., and Irish, D.E. *J. Phys. Chem.* 86 (1982): 4897.
196. Luck, W.A.P. In *Water and Ions in Biological Systems*, ed. A. Pullman; V. Vasilescu; and L. Packer, 95. New York: Plenum Press, 1985.
197. Chang, R.K. *Ber. Bunsenges. Phys. Chem.* 91 (1987): 296.
198. Chen, T.T.; Chang, R.K.; and Laube, B.L. *Chem. Phys. Lett.* 108 (1984): 39.
199. Dorain, P.B. *J. Phys. Chem.* 92 (1988): 2546.
200. Gao, P., and Weaver, M.J. *J. Phys. Chem.* 90 (1986): 4057.
201. Farquharson, S., et al. *J. Am. Chem. Soc.* 105 (1983): 3350.
202. Gao, P., Weaver, M.J. *J. Phys. Chem.* 89 (1985): 5040.
203. Weaver, M.J. *Ber. Bunsenges. Phys. Chem.* 91 (1987): 450.
204. Baltruschat, H.; Staud, N.; and Heitbaum, J. *J. Electroanal. Chem.* 239 (1988): 361.
205. Shindo, H., and Nishihara, C. *Surface Sci.* 158 (1985): 393.
206. Weaver, M.J., et al. *J. Electron Spectrosc. Relat. Phenom.* 45 (1987): 291.
207. Hester, R.E., and Williams, K.P.J. *J. Chem. Soc. Far. Trans.* 77 (1981): 541.

CHAPTER 6

INVESTIGATIONS OF ELECTROCHEMICAL INTERFACES BY NONLINEAR OPTICAL METHODS

Geraldine L. Richmond

Department of Chemistry
University of Oregon
Eugene, OR 97403-1253

CONTENTS

I. INTRODUCTION

Over the past decade there has been a rapid growth of interest in the use of pulsed lasers to study surfaces and interfacial behavior. Although these optical devices have been used routinely for studying bulk media, it is only recently that their value as in situ probes of the solid/liquid junction has begun to be recognized. The impetus behind the use of pulsed lasers in this area is largely due to the nonlinear optical effects associated with pulsed radiation, a phenomenon which is uniquely suited for studies probing such buried interfaces. In addition, due to recent advances in the area of ultra-fast pulse generation, chemical events occurring on time scales as short as tens of femtoseconds can be probed. Optical second harmonic generation (SHG), hyper-Raman scattering (HRS) and sum-frequency generation (SFG) are nonlinear optical processes which show particular promise in this area due to the inherent restriction of these second order processes to the symmetry breaking interface [1]. This review summarizes the use of these techniques to probe properties of the solid/liquid interface.

Of these three nonlinear optical methods, the most extensive investigations of electrochemical systems have been performed with second harmonic generation, the production of light at twice the fundamental frequency. This technique has been used to monitor a variety of adsorptive and reactive processes in situ in both a static and time-resolved mode. The description of these SH experiments and corresponding theoretical investigations will be the main topic of this review. Sum-frequency generation at surfaces is currently in a less developed state, but the initial work summarized here demonstrates its value in measuring vibrational modes in adsorbates. Both SFG and SHG can be performed on a variety of materials and do not require the surface roughening procedures necessary in the surface enhanced Raman spectroscopy (SERS) experiments described in a previous chapter. The few studies performed to date using hyper-Raman spectroscopy, the nonlinear analog to Raman spectroscopy, will also be described. This method does require surface enhancement features on the substrate and provides complementary information to SERS, since different selection rules for optical excitation of vibrational modes are operative.

II. SURFACE SECOND HARMONIC GENERATION

Of the variety of optical techniques that have been applied to the study of surfaces, optical second harmonic generation (SHG) shows particular promise. The appealing features of SHG are its experimental simplicity and its inherent sensitivity to the interfacial region. As with all second order nonlinear optical processes, this sensitivity is a result of the fact that under the electric dipole approximation, SHG is forbidden in the bulk of centrosymmetric media and is only allowed at the interface where the inversion symmetry is broken. Furthermore, because of its fast time response, the technique can investigate dynamic processes occurring over a wide range of timescales.

The first SH study of an electrochemical system appeared in 1967 [2]. The harmonic light produced in reflection from silver and silicon surfaces was found to vary with DC bias potential. Very little work was subsequently done in this area until 1981 when Chen et al. reported a more detailed analysis of the Ag/aqueous electrolyte system [3,4]. Since then, a variety of studies have ensued and are summarized below. The review begins with a brief discussion of the current state of the theory of the electrified interface. After a description of the experimental methods used, experimental studies of the SH response to ionic and molecular adsorption at smooth metal surfaces will be presented. This will be followed by a summary of the application of SHG to the study of faradaic processes, including thin film formation. Both static and time-resolved SH experiments will be incorporated into these sections. New advances in the area of in situ surface structure measurements, and the controversies that these measurements raise, will follow. A discussion of the effects of an oxidation-reduction cycle and enhancement mechanisms for second harmonic generation at roughened surfaces will complete this section. It is important to note that even with the significant advances made in this field in the past decade, the current understanding of this second order optical process is far from complete, as will be apparent from the preliminary nature of many of the experimental and theoretical works to date.

A. Theoretical Considerations

Surface second harmonic generation has been the subject of intense theoretical study following the publication of Bloembergen and Pershan's cornerstone work in 1962 [5]. Numerous theoretical studies have followed that use a variety of different models and methodologies. One of the more successful efforts has been the classical treatment of second harmonic generation in reflection from an interface developed by Shen [1], Heinz [6], and Sipe and coworkers

[7]. This theory describes surface SHG from a generalized source. Although the theory falls short in providing microscopic insight into the source of the polarizability at a given substrate, it is moderately successful in describing many experimental observations on a macroscopic level. Unfortunately, theories attempting to incorporate microscopic properties of the surface into expressions for the source of the nonlinear polarizability have only met with limited success in predicting experimental results [8]. For a more complete summary of those microscopic and macroscopic theoretical approaches, consult Reference 9.

A simple physical picture of SHG from an interface between two isotropic media is given in Figure 1. The multilayer geometry indicates that the surface atomic or molecular layers of thickness, d, generally have optical properties different from those of the bulk. Medium 1 is taken to be strictly linear with dielectric constant ϵ_1. Medium 2 is characterized by linear dielectric constant ϵ_2 and the second order nonlinear susceptibility $\chi^{(2)}$. A monochromatic plane wave at frequency ω incident from medium 1 induces a nonlinear source polarization in the surface layer and in the bulk of medium 2. This source polarization then radiates, and harmonic waves at 2ω emanate from the boundary in both the reflected and transmitted directions.

Under the electric dipole approximation, second harmonic generation is forbidden in the bulk of medium 2 because $\chi^{(2)}$ vanishes under inversion symmetry. The higher order electric quadrupole and magnetic dipole contributions to the second order nonlinearity do not vanish and must be considered. An electric dipole contribution becomes allowed at the interface where inversion symmetry is broken. Quadrupole type contributions arising from the large electric field gradient at the surface also exist.

The nonlinear polarization is conventionally treated as a sheet, placed just below the surface (at $z=0^+$), which can be described by the surface susceptibility tensor, $\chi^{(2)}_s$. This approach is equivalent to considering the surface layer thickness, d, to approach zero. The full expression for the second order nonlinear polarization induced by a single plane wave in an isotropic medium is then written as a sum of the bulk and surface contributions

$$\mathbf{P}_{s,eff}(2\omega) = (2i\omega/c)\gamma[\mathbf{E}(\omega) \times \mathbf{B}(\omega)] + \chi^{(2)}_s \delta(z): \mathbf{E}(\omega)\mathbf{E}(\omega) \qquad (1)$$

where $\delta(z)$ is a δ-function at $z=0^+$, and the frequency dependent coefficient γ describes the higher order response of the material to the incident electric field. The radiated SH fields generated by $\mathbf{P}_{s,eff}(2\omega)$ are found by solving the wave equation [10], given the new boundary conditions imposed by the presence of the dipole layer [6]. The intensity of the SH signal is proportional to the square of the SH field, $[\mathbf{E}(2\omega)]^2$.

For excitation by a plane wave of frequency ω and polarization $\mathbf{e}(\omega)$, the SH intensity generated in reflection with polarization $\mathbf{e}(2\omega)$ is

$$I(2\omega) = \frac{32\pi^3\omega^2 sec^2\theta_{2\omega}}{c^3 A} \left| \mathbf{e}(2\omega)\cdot\chi^{(2)}_{s,eff}:\mathbf{e}(\omega)\mathbf{e}(\omega) \right|^2 I^2(\omega) \quad (2)$$

where $\theta_{2\omega}$ is the angle of the radiated SH light with respect to the surface normal and A is the cross-sectional area of the beam [1,6,7]. The expression explicitly shows the quadratic dependence of the SH intensity on the intensity of the fundamental light, $I(\omega)$. It also contains the polarization and frequency dependences. The effective surface nonlinear susceptibility $\chi^{(2)}_{s,eff}$ incorporates the surface nonlinear susceptibility $\chi^{(2)}_s$ and the higher order bulk contributions to the nonlinearity. For isotropic media, there are only three nonzero independent elements of $\chi^{(2)}_s$, namely $\chi^{(2)}_{s,zii}$, $\chi^{(2)}_{s,izi} = \chi^{(2)}_{s,iiz}$, and $\chi^{(2)}_{s,zzz}$ where i = x,y.

The expression, in Equation (2) above, for reflected second harmonic intensity has been derived from a general expression for the second order nonlinear polarization without regard to the microscopic source of the nonlinearity in a given medium. A large number of theoretical studies have considered the microscopic source of the polarization, especially in the case of metals [9]. The bulk nonlinear response for centrosymmetric media is relatively well understood and can be calculated from the lowest order nonlocal terms, with reasonable accuracy, for insulating materials or for materials with free-electron behavior.

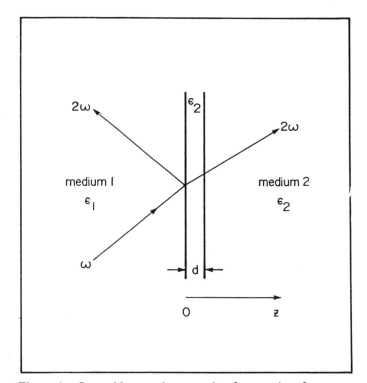

Figure 1. *Second harmonic generation from an interface between two isotropic media. The z-direction is taken as zero at the interface between the media and is positive going into medium 2.*

However, at the surface, the problem is made difficult by an inadequate knowledge of the surface electronic structure. The surface contribution is of considerable importance. A crude estimate of the relative contributions of the surface and the bulk to the second harmonic signal is given by Shen [1] as approximately $(d/a)^2$, where d is the surface layer thickness and a is the size of the atoms or unit cells. This quantity is on the order of, or larger than, unity. This ratio can be enhanced by various surface modification schemes such as roughening, resonances, or polarization selection. Unfortunately, it is not possible to separately determine the elements of the surface susceptibility and the material constants characterizing the bulk sources. In particular, the elements that always appear together in a linear combination are $\chi_{s,zii}$ and γ [11].

Pertinent to the electrochemical studies to be described, Terhune et al. [12] first noted that an additional contribution to the SH response from a material can be induced with an applied DC electric field. In these studies of calcite, it was found that the SH signal was proportional to the square of the applied field. This DC field dependence is attributed to a third order effect that adds to the second order nonlinear polarization given by Equation 2 such that

$$\mathbf{P}(2\omega) \propto \chi^{(3)} : \mathbf{E}_{dc} \cdot \mathbf{E}(\omega) \cdot \mathbf{E}(\omega). \tag{3}$$

This effect can be significant for electrochemical interfacial studies where the DC field at the surface can be on the order of 10^6 - 10^7 V/cm. This potential dependence in the SH response was first demonstrated by Lee and coworkers in 1967 [2] at a silver/aqueous electrolyte interface and has been the focus of many studies in the 1980s, as will be described later.

B. Experimental Methods

Several experimental geometries have been developed to examine a range of diverse systems. Two of the most common configurations are described here, the reflection geometry and the attenuated total reflection (ATR) geometry. Among the measurable characteristics of the SH response from an interface are the phase, the magnitude of the susceptibility tensor, the frequency, polarization and angular dependencies, and the transient change following a perturbation. The experimental considerations involved in such characterizations are also described.

A schematic diagram illustrating the standard reflection geometry is shown in Figure 2. Linearly polarized pulsed laser light of frequency ω strikes the surface at an angle θ from the surface normal. The harmonic light of frequency 2ω generated at or near the angle of specular reflection (determined by the frequency dependent Fresnel factors) is analyzed for polarization and is detected following rejection of the reflected fundamental beam by color filters and usually a monochromator. The latter is useful to verify the monochromaticity of the measured light and to confirm the absence of luminescence. Quadratic variation of the SH intensity, $I(2\omega)$, with average incident laser intensity serves as another check. By coupling a fraction of the fundamental beam into a doubling medium and detecting the SH light in a reference channel, normalization of the SH signal against laser power fluctuations can be achieved.

Q-switched lasers provide sufficient pulse energy to generate detectable SH signals from most materials. One of the more commonly used Q-switched excitation sources is a Nd:YAG laser producing 10 to 30 pulses per second. For

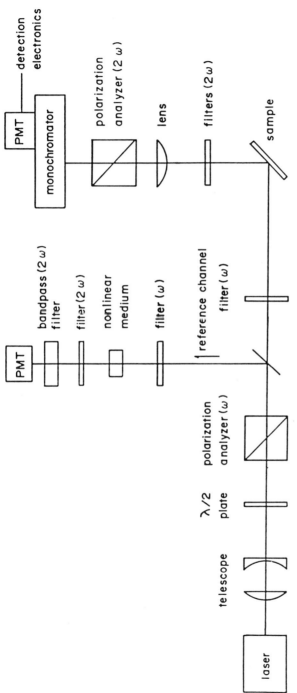

Figure 2. Schematic diagram of the second harmonic generation experimental apparatus with the sample in the reflection geometry. The polarization analyzers are set to transmit p polarized light at the frequency labeled in the figure. The ($\omega/2\omega$) filters transmit the (fundamental/harmonic) light while blocking the (harmonic/fundamental) light. The inset shows the ATR sample geometry in the Otto configuration.

example, Equation (2) predicts a response of 10^4 SH photons/pulse from a surface with $|\chi^{(2)}| \approx 10^{-15}$ esu for excitation with a 10 nsec, 20 mJ pulse at 1.064 μm in a spot size of 0.2 cm^2 [1]. Gated electronics are usually used for detection, although single photon counting is useful for particularly low signal levels. SH experiments using a cw mode-locked Nd:YAG laser with [13] and without [14] Q-switching in conjunction with photon counting detection have also been reported. The fundamental light must be tightly focused in order to achieve requisite energy densities. Tunable laser pulses produced by pumping a dye laser with either type of laser allow measurement of the frequency dependence of SHG. For example, by tuning the dye laser to a resonance between ω or 2ω and an electronic transition in the substrate or an optical transition of an adsorbate, the SH response can be enhanced to afford greater sensitivity to selected properties of the system.

For continuous interrogation of a transient event at the surface, a cw laser is the ideal source. However, low signal levels are expected from cw lasers in the absence of enhancement. By using a cw mode-locked laser, these signal levels can be improved. The mode locked systems also have an advantage over the Q-switched lasers. The experimental time resolution is typically about 12 nsec in the former case and ranges from 30 to 100 msec in the latter case, unless the laser repetition rate is externally controlled [16]. Time-resolved pump-SH probe studies with subnanosecond time resolution have been reported [17-21] in surface/vacuum and surface/air studies.

Determination of the orientation of a molecular adlayer requires measurement of the phase or polarization dependence of the SH field [e.g. 22-27]. Although these studies have not been done unambiguously at the solid/liquid interface, they have been performed on surfaces in air and in vacuum. The relative phase of the SH field can be measured by interfering the sample SH field with that from a quartz plate in the beam path at a variable distance following the sample [7,28]. A pressure scanning interferometric method was first introduced by Chang, Ducuing and Bloembergen [29]. If the phase of the reference material bulk nonlinear susceptibility is known, the absolute phase of the SH from the interface can be measured [24,25].

Variations on the standard reflection geometry shown in Figure 2 include two geometries useful when investigating the symmetry and surface order of single crystal surfaces. In one geometry [e.g. 30], the surface is rotated about its normal for fixed incoming fundamental and outgoing harmonic beam polarizations as shown in Figure 3. The modulation in the SH intensity, as the angle between the plane of incidence and a crystal axis or direction [Fig. 3] is changed by rotating the crystal, is referred to as rotational anisotropy. In another approach [e.g. 31], the fundamental light strikes the fixed sample at normal incidence. The polarization of the incoming beam is rotated and the SH light generated is analyzed along two orthogonal directions. The utility of SH rotational anisotropy as a monitor of surface symmetry and order is currently being explored, as detailed later in this review.

The reflection geometry described above is useful for investigating many different systems. A complementary approach uses the attenuated total reflection (ATR) geometry which couples surface plasmon waves to the incident electric field and enhances the SH production. Metallic thin films are the most common materials studied with this technique. In the Otto configuration, a gap exists between the metal and the prism [32]. In the Kretschmann configuration, the gap is filled with an index matching fluid or the metal is deposited directly on the prism [32]. The incident light launches a surface polariton along the surface,

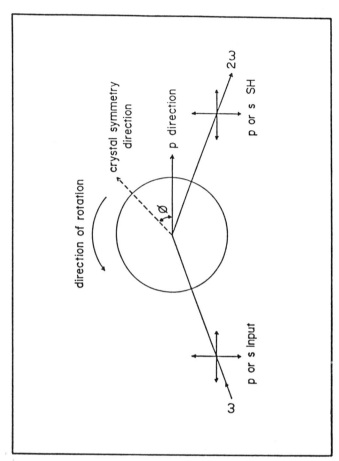

Figure 3. *Schematic diagram of the SH rotational anisotropy experimental geometry.*

defined as the x-direction, when the x-component of the incident wave vector equals that of the surface polariton. SHG can then occur provided the phase matching condition is met. A second harmonic photon is produced only at the plasmon angle of incidence, θ_p, such that the x-component of the second harmonic wave vector equals twice that of the surface polaritons [16]. The efficiency of the coupling depends on the thickness of the metal film or the air gap in the respective configurations.

As for all surface analytical methods, careful surface preparation is critical to the SH technique. The ideal case is to perform the surface preparation in ultra high vacuum with inert transfer into the optical electrochemical cell. In the experiments described, the metal electrode surfaces are mechanically polished and, in most cases, are electrochemically polished to remove the damage layer and oxides. Metal electrodes subject to oxidation are prepared under an inert atmosphere and placed in a purged spectroelectrochemical cell. Thin metal films, as studied in the ATR geometry, are prepared by vapor deposition.

C. Simple Potential Induced Phenomena on Smooth Surfaces

1. Ionic Adsorption. As a metal electrode is biased in a simple aqueous electrolyte at potentials within the ideally polarizable region, the electrode-electrolyte interface charges, analogous to a charging capacitor. In the absence of the interfacial electron transfer, a charge, q_m, accumulates on the metal surface as the bias is varied. An equal and opposite charge, q_s, builds on the solution side of the junction with a spatial distribution of electrolyte ions described by various double layer models [33]. An example of the charging current associated with this process is shown in Figure 4(A) for polycrystalline Ag in $KClO_4$. The corresponding SH response during this sweep is found to vary with potential in a highly reproducible manner, as shown in Figure 4(B) for two concentrations of $KClO_4$, 100 mM and 500 mM. The SH signal is reversible when the potential is swept in either direction between this limit [34-36]. This response correlates qualitatively with the increasing perchlorate anion adsorption at the silver electrode as the surface increases in positive polarity from -1.3 V to -0.1 V. The onset of the increase in SHG near -1.0 V directly agrees with the reported potential of zero charge (PZC) at -1.0 V for this system as measured by differential capacitance (DC) [35,36].

This sensitivity to ionic adsorption has been explored in several studies [16,35-41] with the goal of using SHG to obtain thermodynamic parameters for ionic adsorption at a given potential. Requisite to this goal is an evaluation of the relative contribution of the surface and the adsorbed ions to the polarizability at the boundary. The nonlinear polarizability of the interface must include the electric dipole contribution from the adjoining water or molecular adsorbates (a), the ions (i), and the surfaces (s). The overall boundary susceptibility $\chi^{(2)}$ is then the sum

$$\chi^{(2)} = \chi^{(2)}_a + \chi^{(2)}_i + \chi^{(2)}_s. \tag{4}$$

As noted above, in the presence of a DC electric field, the additional third order contribution can be significant [2]. It is important to note that whereas third order effects are allowed in the surrounding bulk media, the dimensions of the applied electric field are limited to the surface of the metal and to several hundred angstroms into the solution, again restricting the SH response to the interfacial region. By incorporating the potential dependence into the $\chi^{(3)}$ term, the authors assume that $\chi^{(2)}$ is potential independent. Although this work by Lee et al. [2] was done on ill-defined and relatively rough polycrystalline surfaces, the results were the first to demonstrate that SHG was capable of probing the solid/liquid interface.

Actual values for the different contributions to the overall SH response are difficult to calculate, due in part to a lack of experimental data. However, based on the small magnitude of the nonlinear susceptibility of the water near the surface relative to that for silver [42-44], one would expect the SH light from the silver metal to dominate over

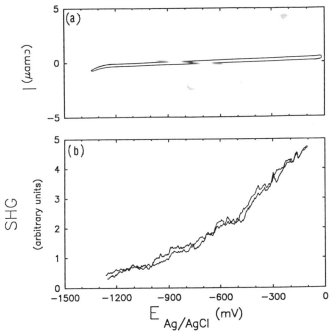

Figure 4. (A) *Cyclic voltammogram for smooth polycrystalline silver biased in 100 mM NaClO$_4$ within the limits of the IPR at pH 6.7.* (B) *SH response as a function of potential for 100 mM and 500 mM NaClO$_4$ at pH 6.7. SH wavelength at 532 nm. Scan rate, 5 mV/sec. (Reprinted from Reference 39).*

the contribution from the adjacent water molecules. The observed potential dependence must therefore be attributed to either the susceptibilities of the surface, $\chi^{(2)}_s$, or of the adsorbing ions, $\chi^{(2)}_i$, or possibly to the $\chi^{(3)}$ contribution from the surface as $\mathbf{E}_{dc}$ changes in magnitude [Eq. (3)]. With regards to the relative magnitude of these two factors, simple calculations indicate that although the third order susceptibility is several orders of magnitude smaller than either $\chi^{(2)}_i$, the magnitude of the DC electric field within the double layer ($\sim 10^7$ V/cm) should balance this difference. Further investigation of the relative magnitude has currently been the focus of several investigations described below.

Second harmonic generation measurements have consistently shown that the $\chi^{(3)}$ contribution from the silver surface plays a dominant role when the electrode is polarized in simple electrolyte solutions [16,35-41]. The results demonstrate a strong potential dependence for ions which have little or no contact adsorption at silver, such as F⁻, ClO_4^- and SO_4^{2-}. As with differential capacitance measurements for these nonspecifically adsorbing systems, the SH response does not vary with concentration, as shown in Figure 4(B), for the two concentrations of $NaClO_4$. The interaction of these solvated anions with the charged metal surface involves only long-range electrostatic forces. Since the nonlinear susceptibility of the water molecules hydrating the anions and the surface is small, the potential dependent SH response must originate from the surface itself. Additional studies of Ag in other simple electrolytic solutions containing ions of variable polarizability confirm the relationship between the potential dependent SH signal and the surface electrostatics [39,40]. Richmond has shown that for Ag(111), Ag(110) and polycrystalline Ag in halide containing solutions, an excellent correlation with the PZC and the onset of the rise in SHG signal exists [35,36]. However, the observed trends in signal levels upon saturation coverage at the most positive potentials did not follow the predicted trends in adsorbate polarizability as would be expected if $\chi^{(2)}{}_i$ is significant.

Corn et al. [16,38] have proposed a model in which the surface charge density, σ_m, is explicitly incorporated in E_{dc} for a flat conducting surface [Eq. (3)]. These studies were conducted on Ag thin films using an attenuated total reflection geometry in the Kretshmann configuration. The SH light was generated from injection of surface polaritons onto the electrode surface by prism coupling techniques. As with earlier studies on bulk calcite [12], an asymmetrical parabolic SH response was observed as the surface was charged from a negative to a positive value within the IPR. These and related experiments with a silver-mica capacitor as a model of the interface suggested a correlation between the SH signal and the surface excess charge density σ_m such that

$$I(2\omega) \propto a + b^2 \left(\frac{4\pi}{\epsilon_1(0)} \sigma_m + c \right)^2 , \tag{5}$$

where a, b, and c are constants contained in the expansion of the polarizability, which are assumed to be potential independent. The coefficients a and c contain the potential independent $\chi^{(2)}$ contribution to the polarizability, whereas b is comprised of the factors responsible for the $\chi^{(3)}$ term. It is also assumed that σ_m varies linearly with the applied DC electric field. If the overall polarizability is dominated by the $\chi^{(3)}$ effect, this equation can be simplified to the form

$$I(2\omega) \propto \sigma_m^2 . \tag{6}$$

The same quadratic variation in $I(2\omega)$ with applied field has been predicted by another theory [45], which proposed that the potential dependent SH response arises from the variation in the center of gravity of the induced electron density at 2ω. The above mentioned studies all demonstrate a correlation between surface electrostatics and $I(2\omega)$. However, the parabolic plasmon enhanced SH response differs from that observed in experiments on metal surfaces performed in reflection [36] wherein the SH signal remains at a minimum for potentials negative of the PZC. This difference will be discussed in more detail later.

The correlation between $I(2\omega)$ and σ_m^2 has been tested by Richmond and coworkers [36,39,41] for Ag. By analyzing the SH response from a series of KBr concentrations, thermodynamic adsorption parameters for Br$^-$ on silver were calculated using the σ_m^2 model [Eq. (6)] in conjunction with the Frumkin isotherm [36]. The free energy adsorption, ΔG_o, for Br$^-$ was determined to be -115 kJ/mole [35], which compared well with a value of -114 kJ/mole [47] determined by differential capacitance studies at similar potentials. Good agreement between the values of the interaction parameter was also observed. Other studies have focused on the direct correlation between σ_m^2 and the SH response [Eq. (6)] by simultaneous DC and SH measurements [39,41]. As shown in Figure 5 for polycrystalline silver in perchlorate containing solutions, there is a good correlation between σ_m^2 and the SH intensity shown in Figure 4(B).

More recently, these studies have been extended to examine the validity and general applicability of the more complete expression for the relationship in Equation 5 between $I(2\omega)$ and σ_m [39]. As with the related studies above, σ_m was determined by back integration of the capacitance data. The $I(\sigma)$ data was then fit to the expression in Equation (5), and the values for the parameters a and b were derived by the best fit. As a starting point, the value of parameter c was determined from the value of σ_m at the minimum of the SH curves, where $c = 4\pi\sigma_m/\epsilon(o)$. Figure 6 shows the fits obtained for the data for ClO_4^-, Cl^-, and Br^-, from which the relative contribution from $\chi^{(2)}$ and $\chi^{(3)}$ can be calculated. In the case of ClO_4^-, at an intermediate value of $\sigma_m = 31 \mu C/cm^2$, the potential independent contribution to the overall polarizability was found from the coefficients to be only 7% of the overall signal, indicating a dominance of the $\chi^{(3)}$ term in the polarizability for silver. A good fit to the data for Br^- and Cl^- could be obtained at the initial negative potentials where lower coverages are present. When ions of higher optical polarizability are examined, the contribution from the $\chi^{(2)}_i$ of the ions themselves can be observed [48]. This has been found for SCN^- where a deviation from the model is found within the IPR at a relatively high electrolyte concentration. A similar effect is observed for some molecular adsorbates and is described below.

It is interesting to compare these results with those of electroreflectance studies in which the linear reflectivity of the surface has been measured as a function of surface charge, wavelength, and optical polarization [49-51]. Second harmonic generation and electroreflectance are quite different in that the linear reflection from the surface

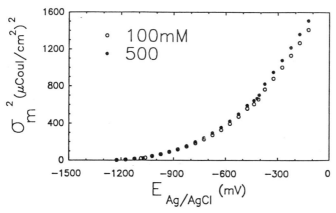

Figure 5. $\sigma_m^2(E)$ *for polycrystalline silver in NaClO$_4$ concentrations of 100 mM (O) and 500 mM (•). SH wavelength at 532 nm. (Reprinted from Reference 39.)*

atoms is overwhelmed by the dipole-allowed polarization in the bulk. Nevertheless, these studies also indicate a surface charge sensitivity. A potential dependence in $\Delta R/R$ is observed for various silver single crystals at photon energies between 0.5 and 3.0 eV [49]. Early studies that described this behavior in terms of a free electron model [49] are consistent with most observations, but cannot explain the more recent observations of polarization anisotropy that are described in section IID. Other studies suggest that this polarization anisotropy might be a consequence of electromodulation of surface states with sensitivity to surface charge density [51,52].

2. *Molecular Adsorption.* Adsorption of organic molecules on smooth surfaces biased within the IPR has been studied by several groups. Molecular adsorption of pyridine on polished Ag(111) and Ag(110) is readily observed at negative potentials near the PZC [34]. The adsorption of phthalazine on polycrystalline silver has been measured, and the potential dependent signal has been correlated with various orientations of the molecule with respect to the surface [53]. The relative contribution of phthalazine to the overall interfacial polarizability is ambiguous in these studies since, as with anion adsorption, a dipole induced $\chi^{(3)}$ contribution can again occur at the surface as the adsorbing molecules approach. Differential capacitance measurements are sensitive to the change in the electrostatics of the surface upon adsorption of pyridine [54]. To separate the $\chi^{(3)}$ contribution from the $\chi^{(2)}_a$ contribution of the adsorbate, simultaneous SH and DC studies have been performed for pyridine on polycrystalline silver in aqueous electrolytes [39]. It was found that at low concentrations ($< 10^{-2}$ M), the nonlinearity of the metal surface dominates, whereas at higher concentrations, deviation from the charge density model is observed which

has been attributed to $\chi^{(2)}_a$ from the adsorbed pyridine molecules.

These principles have also been applied to the measurement of hydrogen adsorption on polycrystalline silver [55]. The observed changes in the SH response at cathodic potentials for silver in acetonitrile are ascribed to the modification of the nonlinear response of the electrons at the metal surface by the adsorption of a monatomic hydrogen species. A comparison of the calculated surface coverages with those predicted from various models reveals the reaction mechanism for the formation of molecular hydrogen.

In a related study, the electrochemistry occurring at polycrystalline platinum electrodes in sulfuric and perchloric acid solutions has been examined by SHG [56]. Using a Nd:YAG pumped dye laser with the SH light generated at the surface at 289 nm, three different processes in the potential scan were monitored; monolayer oxide formation, double layer charging, and hydrogen atom chemisorption. Figure 7 depicts the cyclic voltammetry and the corresponding SH results for a polycrystalline platinum electrode in 0.5 M sulfuric acid solution. In the ideally polarizable region (0.0 V to +0.5 V), the SH signal increases with increased adsorption of bisulfate and sulfate. Beyond +0.5 V, oxide formation is apparent from the CV, and a decrease in the SH response is also observed. Upon return to the ideally polarizable region, the platinum surface is regenerated, and the SH signal again increases due to anionic chemisorption. A strong SH signal is then observed upon excursion into the region negative of -0.1 V, where chemisorption of hydride species occurs. By comparison of the SH signal with the amount of charge passed during the hydrogen deposition reaction, a linear relationship between the nonlinear susceptibility of the surface and the surface coverage of the adsorbed hydride species is determined.

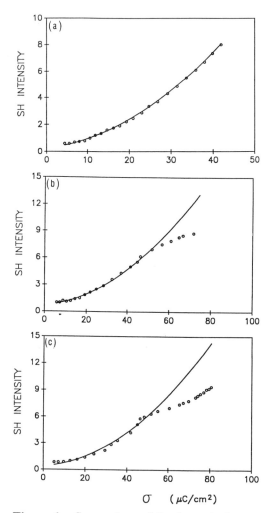

Figure 6. *Comparison of the theoretical expression in equation (5) with the* $\mathbf{I}(\sigma)$ *data for (A) 200 mM NaClO$_4$ with* $\mathbf{a}$ = *0.26,* $\mathbf{b}$ = *4.27 x 10^{-12}, and* $\mathbf{c}$ = *6.14 x 10^{10}; (B) 200 mM NaCl with* $\mathbf{a}$ = *0.656,* $\mathbf{b}$ = *3.09 x 10^{-12}, and* $\mathbf{c}$ = *8.27 x 10^{10}; (C) 200 mM NaBr with* $\mathbf{a}$ = *0.331,* $\mathbf{b}$ = *3.07 x 10^{-12} and,* $\mathbf{c}$ = *7.28 x 10^{10}. (Reprinted from Reference 39.)*

3. Time Resolved Measurements. Time-resolved second harmonic generation has been employed by Corn and coworkers [16], and later by Robinson and Richmond [14,15], to monitor the kinetics of nonfaradaic and faradaic processes induced by the imposition of a fast potential step across the electrode/electrolyte interface. Both groups investigated transient events at Ag electrodes, with the former study on vapor deposited films presumed to be of largely (111) orientation [16,38] and the latter on polycrystalline samples [14]. Corn et al. [16] initially monitored the transient plasmon generated SH signal during reorganization of the double layer following a potential step and then examined the kinetics of deposition of a monolayer of lead on the surface. Similarly, Robinson and Richmond [15] used transient SHG to monitor anion adsorption and desorption in the absence of electron transfer. A detailed examination of the controlled deposition and subsequent removal of one, two, and up to twelve monolayers of thallium on the surface followed. The results of these two studies are described below.

The time dependent changes in the cell current and the charge density on the electrode in response to a potential step are known from chronoamperometry and chronocoulometry, respectively. Corn et al. [16] used the results from these classical electrochemical methods in conjunction with the surface charge density model to predict the time dependent SH signal following a perturbation of the potential. In the absence of faradic processes, the cell current transient decays as a single exponential,

$$i(t) \propto \Delta E \, e^{-t/\tau}, \qquad (7)$$

where ΔE is the amplitude of the voltage change. The time constant τ for establishing the double layer is given by the

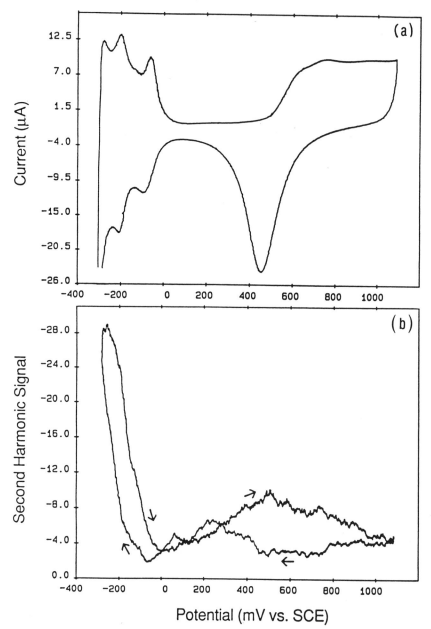

Figure 7. (A) *Cyclic voltammogram for a polycrystalline platinum electrode in a 0.5 M sulfuric acid solution.* (B) *Second harmonic signal (arbitrary units) during the cyclic voltammogram in (**a**). (Reprinted from Reference 56.)*

product of the solution resistance and the double layer capacitance. The surface charge density evolves as

$$\sigma(t) = \sigma_f + (\sigma_i - \sigma_f)\, e^{-t/\tau} \tag{8}$$

where σ_i and σ_f refer to the surface charge density at the initial and final bias potentials, respectively. In the surface charge density model [Eq. (6)], $I(2\omega) \propto \sigma_m^2$ and therefore, $I(2\omega) \propto \sigma(t)^2$. Ignoring the potential dependence of a and b and neglecting c [16], Equation (5) can be recast simply as

$$I_{2\omega} \propto [\sigma_f + (\sigma_i - \sigma_f)\, e^{-t/\tau}]^2. \tag{9}$$

This expression predicts the form of the SH response to a potential step, which causes either charging or discharging of the double layer for comparison with experiment.

The surface charge density model has been tested by Corn and coworkers for a Ag thin film electrode in simple electrolytes using steady state potential dependent [Eq. (5)] [16,38] and time-resolved [Eq. (9)] [16] SH measurements. As previously discussed, surface polaritons were used to generate the SH light, which showed a nominally quadratic dependence on the cell potential, reaching minimum around -750 mV near the PZC for Ag(111) [38]. Corn et al. [16] captured the transient SH response while charging the electrode in Na_2SO_4 between $\sigma_m = 0$ and $\sigma_m < 0$ via a potential step. The open circles in Figure 8 are the SH intensities measured at variable time delays with respect to a voltage step between -750 mV and -1250 mV. Data for the reverse step during cation desorption are also shown [Fig. 8]. These curves can be compared directly with the predictions of the surface charge density model [Eq. (8)]. Figure 8 displays the calculated SH signals from Equation 9 for $\tau = 5$ msec [16]. The quality of fit for the predictions of the surface charge density model to the data is considered below.

Robinson and Richmond [15] investigated the adsorption and desorption of specifically and nonspecifically adsorbed anions on polycrystalline Ag electrodes biased within the limits of the ideally polarizable region. The experiments used the 1.064 μm light from a mode locked picosecond laser as the fundamental beam. The results demonstrated the utility of fast pulsed laser light as a "continuous" monitor of surface dynamics on the millisecond timescale using the time-resolved SHG technique. Figure 9 shows the time dependent SH responses to fast anodic and cathodic potential steps between the PZC and near open circuit (-0.10 V) for polycrystalline Ag in Na_2SO_4. The rates of anion adsorption and desorption, as monitored by the time dependent SH signal, are similar to the respective rates of charging and discharging of the double layer. The transient SH response during adsorption is much slower than estimated for a diffusion controlled flux of the anion to the electrode as predicted for behavior following Fick's Law.

For potential steps with the PZC as one of the limits, as in Figure 9, Equation (9) is simplified, because at this potential the surface charge density is zero by definition. Solving Equation (9) for a cathodic or anodic step to the PZC yields a single exponential decay

$$I(2\omega) \propto \sigma_m^2 e^{-2/\tau} \tag{10}$$

whereas the SH response to the respective reverse steps from the PZC is given by

$$I(2\omega) \propto \sigma_m^2 (1 - 2e^{-t/\tau} + e^{-2t/\tau}) \tag{11}$$

where σ_m is the charge density at the potential other than the PZC. The surface charge density σ_m at -0.10 V is approximately 30-40 $\mu C/cm^2$, and $\tau \approx 14$ msec comes from the single exponential fit to the cell current transients [Eq. (7)]. The calculated fits [Eqs. (10) and (11)] are matched to the SH data at E = -0.10 V.

The surface charge density model recovers the general behavior of the time dependent SH signals in Figures 8 and 9 for both experiments, although the behavior during cation desorption is better described by the model than the reverse process [Fig. 8]. Similarly, the fit is clearly better for anion adsorption than for the desorption [Fig. 9]. Several suggestions have been offered regarding the source of the deviations from the model [16]. Firstly, the capacitance of the system is assumed to be potential independent so that the charge on the electrode varies linearly with potential. This linear dependence does not agree with the results of differential capacitance measurements [39]. Secondly, the large electric field of the laser at the interface leads to potential dependent optical constants [a, b, and c in Eq. (5)] which are neglected in this model. Given these approximations, the authors [16] concluded that the time dependent data are reproduced reasonably well by the surface charge density model.

4. Effects of Under Potential Deposition. Charge transfer processes can occur concurrently with the reorganization of the double layer. Underpotential deposition (UPD) is the stepwise deposition of a foreign metal on an electrode surface at potentials positive of the Nernstian potential for bulk deposition. The UPD process modifies the nonlinear susceptibility of the metal surface. Several SH studies of UPD on polycrystalline electrodes have been reported, and the sensitivity of SHG to the metal-metal interface is apparent. The potential [38] and time

[16] dependencies of Pb deposition on Ag thin film electrodes were studies by Corn and colleagues. Frutak, Miragliotta and Korenowski [57] monitored the potential dependence of Tl UPD on mechanically polished polycrystalline Ag. Robinson and Richmond [14] measured the potential dependence and the transient SH signals during Tl deposition and desorption on electrochemically polished polycrystalline Ag electrodes. UPD of these metals has been well studied on both polycrystalline and single crystal silver electrodes by electrochemical methods [58-60]

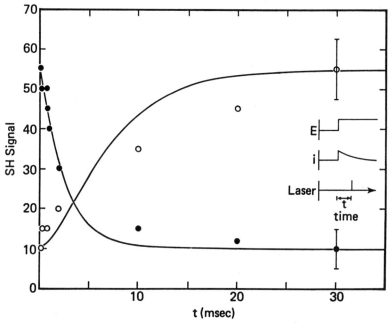

Figure 8. *Transient SH response during cation adsorption and desorption from a silver thin film electrode to a potential step within the IPR. The inset shows the timing of the experiment using 1.064 μm light from a Q-switched Nd:YAG laser incident at the angle meeting the "plasmon angle matching" requirement. The open circles are the SH data measured for a step from -750 to -1250 mV in 0.1 M Na_2SO_4 and the solid circles correspond to the reverse step. The curves are calculated from Equation 9 with τ = 5 msec. (Reprinted from Reference 16.)*

as well as steady state linear optical methods [61-63]. The results of Corn et al. [16] and Robinson and Richmond [14] comprise the first time dependent nonlinear optical measurements of metallic thin film formation in these systems.

Corn et al. [38] observed that the deposition of one monolayer of Pb on a Ag electrode from $PbClO_4$ solution dramatically decreased the SH intensity compared to that from the same electrode in $NaClO_4$ at the identical potential. The SH signal declined with negative potential prior to monolayer deposition. The authors noted that the Pb monolayer changes σ_m and also affects the optical constants in Equation (5). In later work, the time dependent underpotential deposition of a single Pb monolayer was determined via a potential step experiment [16]. The authors submit that three processes contribute to the decay in the SH intensity shown in Figure 10. Up to about 50 msec, the signal falls due to discharging of the double layer (as in Fig. 8) and diffusion of Pb^{+2} ions to the electrode. The longer decay reflects kinetically controlled formation of the metal monolayer.

Robinson and Richmond [14] investigated the electrodeposition of thallium on polycrystalline silver electrodes by time-resolved second harmonic generation. Figure 11 shows the CV recorded for polycrystalline Ag within the underpotential region anodic of bulk thallium deposition (-0.78V). The first three cathodic (A_1 through A_3) peaks are associated with formation of the first thallium monolayer and correspond to respective coverages of approximately $\Theta = 0.33$, $\Theta = 0.68$ and $\Theta = 1$. A polycrystalline electrode is a composite of several crystal orientations separated by grain boundaries. The peaks A_1 through A_3 are believed to arise from deposition at energetically different sites on the electrode surface. This

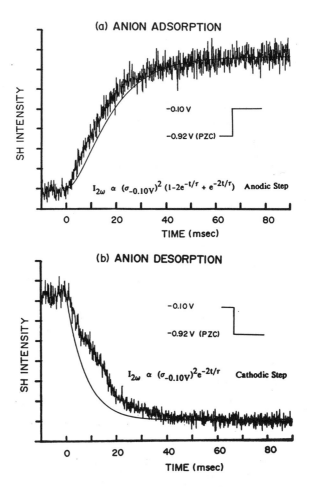

Figure 9. *Transient SH response from a polycrystalline Ag electrode to a potential step within the IPR. 1.064 μm light from a cw mode-locked Nd:YAG laser was focused on the surface. (A) SH response to a step between the PZC and -0.10 V. (B) SH response to the reverse step in 0.25 M Na$_2$SO$_4$. The solid curves are calculated from Equations (10) and (11) for (**a**) and (**b**), respectively, using τ $\simeq$ 14 msec. (Reprinted from Reference 14.)*

structure is not observed on electrodes that are prepared only by mechanical polishing, which yield instead a single broad peak in the underpotential region. The peak labeled B indicates the formation of a second monolayer prior to bulk deposition [14].

The underpotential deposition of thallium significantly alters the nonlinear susceptibility of the interface. Figure 11 displays the potential dependent SH intensity recorded for a scan from -0.10V to -0.76 V where the second monolayer is formed. The SH intensity initially decreases due to the previously noted DC electric field effect. The slope increases abruptly at about -0.43V to -0.45V, in the region where thallium deposition begins (peak A_1 in Figure 11). Deposition at site A_1 is complete at -0.48 V. For smooth electrodes in a simple electrolyte, the minimum in the SH intensity is associated with the zero charge condition (-0.92V for this system) at 45° incidence. Thus, the thallium deposit modifies the nonlinear optical properties of the interface, leading to a minimum at $\Theta \approx 1/3$ ML (-0.48V). As deposition continues up to $\Theta = 1$ ML, the SH intensity rises with a slight change in slope between the deposition at site A_2 ($\Theta \approx 2/3$ ML) and at site A_3 ($\Theta = 1$ ML). Enhancement of 150 to 200 percent in the SH response is observed upon deposition of the second monolayer. The onset of the enhancement corresponds to the beginning of peak B in the CV of Figure 11. The enhancement may be due to a resonance between ω and an electronic transition in bulk Tl, suggesting that the interface takes on the optical properties of bulk Tl at 2 ML coverage. Koos et al. [69] have reported a comparable enhancement at $\Theta = 2$ ML for the Tl/Ag(111) system in SH rotational anisotropy experiments.

Furtak, Miragliotta, and Korenowski [57] investigated Tl UPD on mechanically polished polycrystalline Ag electrodes. In the absence of thallium in the solution, the

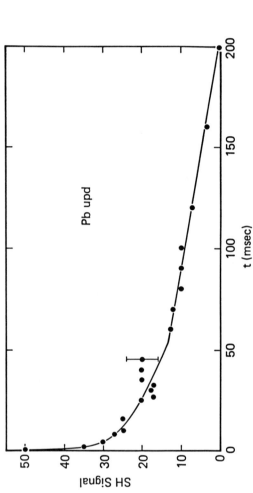

Figure 10. *SH transient response during Pb monolayer formation on a silver thin film electrode as in Figure 8. Potential step from –250 mV to –450 mV in 0.1 M sodium acetate and 5 mM lead acetate. The curve illustrates the three mechanisms discussed in the text. (Reprinted from Reference 16.)*

minimum SH response was observed near -0.40V, almost
500 mV positive of the PZC at 45° incidence. This result is
likely due to plasmon resonance enhanced SHG at the
slightly roughened electrode, although the authors suggest
other sources as well. Surface roughness makes comparison
with the data on electrochemically polished smooth surfaces
difficult.   Their   reported   CV   shows   a   single,   broad

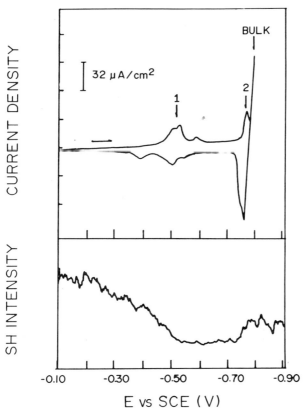

Figure 11. *Cyclic voltammogram for a polycrystalline Ag
electrode during thallium thin film formation and
removal, and corresponding SH intensity during the
cathodic sweep (0.25 M Na_2SO_4, 1 mM Tl_2SO_4,
10 mV/sec sweep rate). Experimental details given in text.
(Reprinted from Reference 14.)*

deposition peak for $\Theta = 1$ and gives no evidence for formation of a second monolayer, although the scan may have ended just anodic of this region. The authors observe a much larger decrease in SH intensity cathodic of -0.0V in the Tl containing solution than in the pure electrolyte. Therefore, they claim that pre-UPD adsorption occurs between -0.2V and -0.5V. Robinson and Richmond [14] report no evidence of this effect.

Robinson and Richmond [14] monitored both the time dependent SH intensity and total cell current in response to a fast potential step between -0.10V and potentials just cathodic of each of the four deposition peaks in the CV [Fig. 11]. Figure 12 displays the time dependent SH signals observed for thallium deposition at sites A_1 through A_3 and site B. Both the optical [Fig. 12] and electrochemical measurements indicate that the first monolayer is formed through sequential, rather than competitive, deposition at three energetically distinct sites on the surface. The second monolayer appears to deposit continuously at one site after the first monolayer is complete [Fig. 12(D)]. The exponential forms of the current transients suggest that activation controlled adsorption is the deposition mechanism. Nucleation and growth by overlapping centers appear to be important only after the adsorption processes are complete, becoming the controlling mechanism in the final stage of deposition of the first monolayer. For deposition at each site, the SH and current transients obey similar rate laws. The SH data suggest consistently faster behavior than the current transients for the first two sites. This result indicates that surface migration of thallium adatoms does not contribute to the kinetics, as this scenario would require that the SH transients decay more slowly than the current transients. Conversely, the SH data suggests filling the third site is slower than the current transient suggests. It is possible that

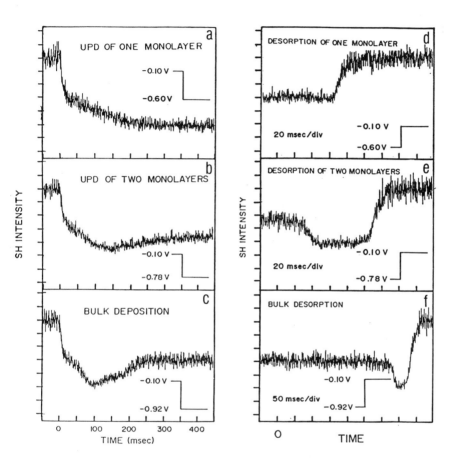

Figure 12. *Transient SH response from a polycrystalline Ag electrode during thallium thin film deposition and removal. Processes occurring during (a) through (f) are listed on the figures. The data are not normalized.*

adatom migration occurs during completion of the first monolayer. The SH data were also analyzed in terms of the Langmuir model for adsorption at equivalent, noninteracting sites. Each adatom is proposed to contribute equally to the coverage dependent interfacial susceptibility such that

$$\chi^{(2)} = A + B\,\Theta/\Theta_s$$

where A is the second order nonlinear susceptibility of the clean surface, B is the adsorbate induced contribution to $\chi^{(2)}$, and Θ_s denotes saturation coverage. The results demonstrate that Langmuir kinetics are not appropriate in this system, even at low coverage.

D. Electrode Surface Symmetry and Order

In general, interfacial chemistry is highly dependent on surface morphology. Unfortunately, direct correlations between surface structure and chemical mechanisms at the electrode/electrolyte interface are difficult to make due to the paucity of in situ surface characterization methods. For this reason, the utility of SHG as a monitor of in situ surface symmetry and order is being explored.

The approach is known as SH rotational anisotropy. A single crystal electrode is rotated about its surface normal, and the modulation of the SH intensity is measured as the angle (ϕ) between the plane of incidence and a given crystal direction changes. A schematic diagram of this experiment is shown in Figure 3. For the experiments reported here, a p-polarized fundamental beam is employed and the p- and s-polarized second harmonic intensities are measured. The rotationally anisotropic nonlinear optical response of a cubic medium has been previously measured in several studies of single crystal semiconductor surfaces [31,66] and a Cu metal substrate [67], in an effort to monitor surface symmetry and reconstruction phenomena at solid/vacuum and solid/air interfaces. Recently, the technique has been extended to the study of the solid/liquid interface as described below.

The nonlinear optical response of a cubic material is dependent on crystal orientation. Anisotropy in the response arises from both surface and bulk sources. At the surface, where the inversion symmetry is broken, the SH response is dipolar and the structural symmetry is reflected in the form of the nonlinear susceptibility tensor, $\chi^{(2)}_{s}$ [Eq. (1)]. In the bulk, the expression for nonlinear polarization is modified for a cubic medium and contains an additional term [28]:

$$\mathbf{P}(2\omega) \propto \varsigma \mathbf{E}(\omega) \nabla \mathbf{E}(\omega). \qquad (12)$$

The coefficient ς, like γ, is an element of a fourth rank tensor, which describes the multipole response of the material. This term is anisotropic with respect to crystal rotation.

The functional form of the induced second harmonic field depends on how the individual surface and bulk tensor elements transform with a rotation about ϕ. The results have been presented in a recent paper by Sipe et al. [68]. The work, which will be described here, involves the (111) crystal face. The expressions for the p- and s-polarized SH intensities with p-polarized input for this crystal orientation are

$$I(2\omega)_{p,p} \propto [a + c \cdot \cos(3\phi)]^2, \quad \text{and} \tag{13}$$

$$I(2\omega)_{p,s} \propto [b \cdot \sin(3\phi)]^2. \tag{14}$$

The topmost atomic layer of a perfectly terminated (111) crystal has 6m symmetry. Since the optical response arises from the bulk as well as the surface, inclusion of successive atomic layers is necessary, and the symmetry is reduced to 3m. Hence, the expressions for the SH intensity explicitly display the appropriate symmetry. For this surface, the angle ϕ is defined as the angle between the $[2\bar{1}\bar{1}]$ direction and the plane of incidence. The constants a, b, and c contain the surface and bulk susceptibility tensor elements, the linear and nonlinear dielectric constants of the material, and appropriate Fresnel factors at ω and 2ω. Three isotropic surface susceptibility tensor elements are contained in a (χ_{zzz}, $\chi_{izi} = \chi_{iiz}$, and χ_{zji}, where i = x, y), whereas the χ_{xxx} element, which is anisotropic with respect to a rotation about the azimuthal axis, is contained in the constants b and c.

The effect of an applied potential is to increase or decrease the observed SH intensity, depending on the phase and magnitude of the $\chi^{(3)}_{ijkj}:E_jE_kE_l$ term relative to the $\chi^{(2)}_{ijk}:E_jE_k$ term in the expression for the induced polarization [$E_l = E_{dc}$, see Eq. (3)]. However, the observed symmetry in the SH intensity as a function of ϕ does not change with an applied static field, since $\chi^{(3)}$ transforms as $\chi^{(2)}$ if the field is along the direction about which the crystal is rotated [69].

1. Native Electrode Surfaces. The results for electrodes held under potential control within the ideally polarizable region are discussed below [69-72]. Figure 13 shows the variation in the p- and s-polarized second harmonic intensity as a Ag(111) electrode in Na_2SO_4 is rotated about its surface normal. Rotational anisotropy from Ag(110) and Ag(100) electrodes under similar conditions has also been observed [69]. The intensity patterns as a function of ϕ [Fig. 13(A)] graphically display the structural symmetry of the crystal surface. In this case, the patterns are consistent with the $3m$ symmetry of a Ag(111) surface. These intensity patterns may be fit to Equations (13) and (14) by taking $|a/c| \propto i$. The anisotropy disappears with electrochemical roughening or the buildup of a thick oxide layer, leaving nonzero p- and s-polarized SH signals that are isotropic with respect to crystal rotation. Recent experiments show that a similar rotational anisotropy has been observed for these silver single crystal electrodes in UHV [73].

The origin of the observed rotational anisotropy for silver single crystals is not readily understood. The contributions of both the free-electron response and interband transitions to the nonlinear polarizability have been recognized since the early work of Bloembergen and colleagues [74]. In the present experiments, the fundamental and second harmonic wavelengths (1.17 eV and 2.34 eV) are well below the energy of silver interband transitions (3.8 eV) [75]. However, rotational anisotropy would not be expected from a purely free-electron model. This seemingly anomalous result may be explained by a dependence of the free-electron polarizability on crystal direction due to the potentials imposed by the ion cores, a deviation from the true free electron-model. It is also possible that bound electrons could contribute through surface states or interband transitions, since the imaginary part of the dielectric constant is not zero even at these wavelengths. There is evidence for surface states close to the Fermi level from photoemission studies at the Ag(111)/vacuum interface [76].

Anisotropy in the nonlinear response as a function of ϕ for a Cu(111) electrode in Na$_2$SO$_4$ [78] and Au(111) [79] has also been observed and is shown in Figures 13(B) and (C). The rotational anisotropy for both copper and gold is more easily understood and has been attributed to the excitation of interband transitions, since the energy of the SH photons (2.3 eV) is large enough to promote d electrons into the sp conduction bands [74]. In contrast to what is observed for silver, only three maxima and minima are observed in the p-polarized SH response for these noble metals. These patterns may be fit by Equation (13) when $|a/c| \geq 1$.

More recently, Georgiadis and Richmond [77] have measured the wavelength dependence of the rotational anisotropy from Ag(111) at various excitation wavelengths throughout the visible region. They find dramatic changes in the anisotropy patterns as well as the magnitude and relative phase of the isotropic and anisotropic coefficients as the incident energy is varied between 640 nm and 532 nm. They attribute these changes to optical resonances between 2ω and interband transitions at the metal surface. The most striking changes occur between 640-610 nm, consistent with the electronic band structure of Ag(111). At 532 nm, where interband states are readily accessed, three maxima and minima occur in the p-polarized output, similar to that found for Cu(111) and Au(111) with 1064 nm excitation.

The dependence of the SH response on bias potential for the (111) faces of silver [69,72,80], copper [78], and gold [79] electrodes has also been examined at 1060 nm. The symmetries of the observed p- and s-polarized rotational patterns do not change as the potential is varied. This is consistent with what is expected for an applied field parallel to the surface normal, about which the electrode is rotated. For Ag(111) in simple aqueous electrolytes, stepping the voltage from a relatively positive potential

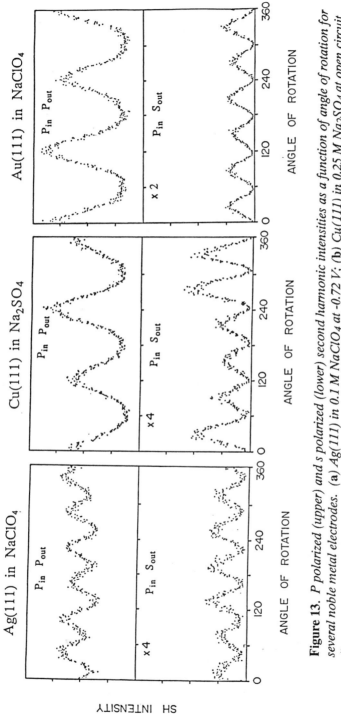

Figure 13. *P polarized (upper) and s polarized (lower) second harmonic intensities as a function of angle of rotation for several noble metal electrodes. (a) Ag(111) in 0.1 M NaClO₄ at -0.72 V; (b) Cu(111) in 0.25 M Na₂SO₄ at open circuit (intensity x 2); and (c) Au(111) in 0.1 M NaClO₄ at -0.4 V (SCE).*

(-0.10 V) to the potential of zero charge (PZC) near -0.76 V decreases the amplitude of the p-polarized SH signal. This decrease occurs on a timescale that is comparable to the discharge of the charge at the surface and is attributed to a change in the contribution of the $\chi^{(3)}_{ijkl}:E_jE_kE_l$ term to the induced polarization. From fitting the observed pattern by Equation (13), the decrease is seen to result from a change in the constant *a*, which contains the isotropic susceptibilities with components parallel to the applied field. There is very little change in the constant *c*, which contains the anisotropic susceptibility χ_{xxx}. Similarly, the s-polarized intensity is not observed to change with potential. In contrast to the Ag(111) results, neither the p-nor the s-polarized SH intensities for Cu(111) change as the potential is varied over the same potential region. This is a result of the fact that the PZC for Cu(111) is near -0.1 V; thus there is not a large positive electric field over this potential region. Au(111) shows an increase in overall intensity with positive sweep for the p-polarized output, whereas the s-output is potential invariant [79].

The potential dependence in the SH rotational anisotropy for Ag(111) has recently been examined for a variety of visible incident wavelengths. At these higher incident energies, a strong potential dependence in the rotational anisotropy is observed [77]. For wavelengths between 610 nm and 532 nm, the potential dependence in both the anisotropic and isotropic coefficients show a variation which is dramatically different than what is obtained with 1064 nm excitation. These results and related optical phase measurement results indicate a potential induced shift in an electronic state at the silver surface is a major factor here.

There is currently considerable controversy over the relative contribution of surface and bulk terms to the overall SH response from crystalline surfaces. The advantage of electrochemical studies for examining these contributions is that any observed potential dependence in the SH response for metals must arise from surface effects, since the applied electric field resides at the surface of the metal. Furthermore, simple and reversible modifications of the surface can be easily performed to change the relative surface and bulk contributions. Experiments that test the effects of potential variation [69,72,80], electrochemical roughening [72], deposition of molecular adsorbates [69], and metallic film formation by underpotential deposition [78] on the rotational anisotropy all demonstrate that surface contributions to the SH response are easily observed and that the SH response is not dominated by bulk contributions. In studies of the Ag(110) surface, the magnitude of the surface to bulk response was found to be ~4.4 under those experimental conditions [69].

2. Effects of Overlayer Deposition. Rotational anisotropy in the second harmonic intensity has also been used to monitor the formation of an underpotentially deposited metal overlayer. Deposition of a monolayer or submonolayer of a foreign metal is controlled by the change in the work function of the surface as the overlayer grows in a stepwise manner [60]. Classical electrochemical techniques have been extensively employed to study these systems [81]. The charge passed in each step has been associated with the deposition of a fractional monolayer or with phase transitions in the overlayer structure [82]. For some metal/metal systems, a second monolayer is deposited prior to bulk deposition. Because of its proven sensitivity to surface structure [67], reconstruction [31,66], and thin film growth [83], SHG is an attractive technique to investigate the processes occurring during lattice formation at the metal/metal interface in solution.

In a series of studies, the rotational anisotropy from the following underpotential deposit systems has been examined: Ag(111)/Pb [69], Ag(111) and Ag(110)/Tl [69], Cu(111)/Tl [78], and Au(111)/Tl [79]. The results for the Ag(111)/Tl system are described below to provide an example of the information which is obtainable from such a study.

Coulometric measurements suggest that the deposition of a monolayer of thallium on the (111) face of silver occurs in three stages [58]. A second full monolayer subsequently deposits prior to bulk deposition. Figure 14 shows the p-polarized SH intensity as a function of ϕ for fractional (A), full (B), and two (C) monolayer coverages. The solid lines are generated by fitting the data to Equation (13). Similar plots of the s-polarized SH intensities have also been measured but are not shown here.

The positions of the maxima and minima in the s-polarized SH intensity patterns (not shown) do not change as a function of coverage, indicating that the polarizability of the interfacial region retains the $3m$ symmetry of the substrate surface. The same results were found to be true for all of the underpotentially deposited overlayers that were studied. Studies of thallium deposition on Ag(111) in UHV suggest that the overlayer is an incommensurate close-packed layer that is rotated from the silver lattice by 5° due to the lattice mismatch [84]. A similar "twist" structure, occurring in domains rotated by 4.5° from the silver lattice, has also been observed for underpotentially deposited lead overlayers in grazing incidence X-ray diffraction studies [50,85]. From the angular dependence of the SH intensity, it is apparent that the $3m$ local site symmetry is preserved even if the long range order is disrupted.

The changing form of the p-polarized SH intensity pattern as thallium is deposited on the silver substrate reflects changes in the isotropic and anisotropic susceptibilities (and hence, the a/c ratio) due to the changing interfacial electronic properties. Insight into how the individual tensor elements change with the deposition and removal of the Tl overlayer is afforded by measuring the SH intensity at a fixed angle ϕ which simplifies the function $I(2\omega) \propto [a + c\cdot\cos(3\phi)]^2$. Figure 15 shows the variation in the p-polarized SH intensity at (A) $\phi = 0°$, (B) $\phi = 30°$, and (C) $\phi = 60°$, as the potential is swept and Tl adatoms are deposited and removed. The arrows indicate the potentials at which peaks corresponding to one and two monolayer deposition are observed in the voltammetry.

The SH intensity shown in Figure 15(B) is proportional to $[a]^2$, which contains the isotropic susceptibilities. The magnitude of a is observed to decrease as the potential is swept to negative values, Tl is deposited, and increases back to its initial value as the Tl overlayer is removed. Changes in a are presumed to reflect changes in the free-electron contribution from the metal/metal interface [67]. The decrease in a as Tl is deposited suggests a localization of the free-electron density by the Tl adatoms which in turn decreases the polarizability of the interface. This decrease must also be attributed, in part, to a decrease in the electric field (the $X^{(3)}:E(\omega)E(\omega)E_{dc}$ contribution) at the interface as the potential is swept toward the PZC.

The SH intensities in Figures 15(A) and (C) are proportional to $[a+c]^2$ and $[a-c]^2$, respectively. The increasing lateral interactions between Tl adatoms as the overlayer approaches one monolayer are reflected in the changing magnitude and phase of c. The c term contains the anisotropic susceptibility tensor element, χ_{xxx}. Concomitant with the deposition of two monolayers is a large enhancement in c, and a phase shift is introduced between a and c. A scan of the s-polarized intensity as a function of potential shows a large enhancement at 2 ML as well. Interband transitions in the wavelength region near 2ω have been calculated and observed for bulk thallium [86-87]. The observation of an enhancement at 2 ML suggests that bulk-like optical properties of the metallic overlayer are reached at 2 ML. At thallium coverages beyond 2 ML, the SH signal does not continue to increase, indicating that the signal arises from the first two atomic layers only. Such an observation is clear evidence of the surface specificity of second harmonic generation.

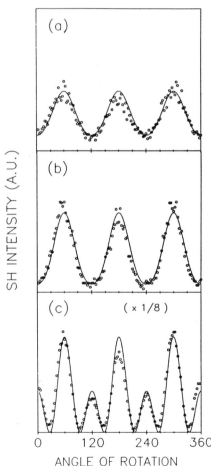

Figure 14. *P polarized second harmonic intensity as a function of angle of rotation for a Ag(111) electrode with various thallium coverages.* (**a**) *0 < Θ < 1 monolayer;* (**b**) *Θ = 1 monolayer; and* (**c**) *Θ = 2 monolayers. (Reprinted from Reference 69.)*

E. Surface Enhanced Second Harmonic Generation

The bulk of this review has addressed studies performed on highly polished surfaces. Another area of research in this field is the study of roughened surfaces wherein an enhanced SH response is observed. As was discovered several years earlier for Raman signals from adsorbates near an electrochemically altered surface [88,89], surface roughening via an electrochemical ORC produces an enhancement of approximately 10^4 in SH signal from silver surfaces cycled in simple electrolytes such as aqueous KCl [3,4]. Similar enhancements have been observed in other optical surface processes including hyper-Raman scattering [90] as well as one and two photon absorption and luminescence [91,92]. The investigations of SHG from roughened surfaces have attempted to elucidate the common features between the SH enhancement mechanisms and those proposed for other surface optical studies.

Studies on bare and solution covered roughened silver surfaces have shown that there are similarities in the enhancement mechanisms for second harmonic generation and other optical processes. There are also some striking differences. For all surface optical processes, the presence of the roughened metal can produce a local field strength at the interface that greatly exceeds that of the applied field [3,4,89]. In general, two primary mechanisms have been advanced to explain the observed enhancements, as described in more detail in the previous chapter [88]. The chemical effect is presumed to arise from an interaction between an adsorbed molecule and the surface when significant perturbation of the eigenfunctions and eigenenergies of the molecule occurs. This effect has been

invoked to explain SERS signals of normally inactive
adsorbate vibrational modes, which are observed at
potentials where the adsorption and surface roughness
features have a combined maximum effect [89]. It has also
been used to explain the SH response from adsorbed
centrosymmetric molecules, since the electric dipole
contribution of the molecule is negligible [93]. However,
the chemical mechanism cannot explain second harmonic
enhancements that have been observed from surfaces in the

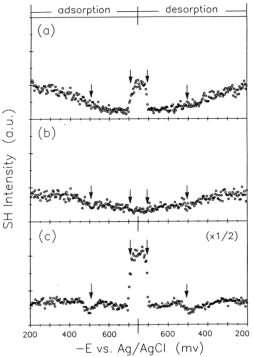

Figure 15. *P polarized second harmonic intensity
from a Ag(111) electrode immersed in Tl_2SO_4, as a
function of potential for various angles, ϕ, of the
electrode crystal axis with respect to the plane of
polarization of incident light.* (**a**) $\phi = 0^\circ$; (**b**) $\phi = 30^\circ$; *and* (**c**) $\phi = 60^\circ$. *The arrows indicate the
potentials at which 1 and 2 monolayers of thallium are
deposited. (Reprinted from Reference 69.)*

absence of the molecular adsorbates. The more appropriate explanation for this phenomenon is the electromagnetic model, which attributes the enhancement to amplification of the incident and reradiated fields by plasmon resonances in the rough substrate [4]. Although considerable discussion has ensued over the past decade regarding the relative importance of these two mechanisms in SERS [89], SHG in the absence of adsorbates offers a means of studying only the electromagnetic or local field enhancement mechanism.

Macroscopic local field enhancements can be very large on roughened surfaces. Nodules and protrusions of hundreds to thousands of angstroms, depending on the degree of roughness or the conditions of deposition, are typical. The fields tend to concentrate at the tips of the protrusions, producing the so-called lightening rod effect [94,95]. In addition, optical fields incident on these protrusions can cause collective oscillations of the localized electrons, which produce a large local field enhancement referred to as the local-plasmon effect [94-95]. The theory of local field enhancements has been developed by a number of authors to treat the various optical processes under consideration [4,89,94,101]. The work of Chen et al. [4] uses a local field correction model to describe the macroscopic local field enhancement for SHG from a roughened metal surface. A collection of noninteracting hemispheres posed on a surface plane represents the surface in this model.

Boyd et al. [96] recently extended the theory of Chen et al. [4] and applied their results to experiments on 16 different materials, ranging from the alkali metals to a semiconductor. The largest enhancements come from good conductors with relatively high electron densities. The poorer conductors such as Pb, Sn, and Ni show less of an enhancement due to the minimal contribution from plasmon resonance effects. The extreme is Ge whose enhancement must all be attributed to the lightening rod effect.

Several investigators have used this surface plasmon enhancement effect to augment weaker SH signals from smooth surfaces. Simon et al. [102] observed an enhancement factor of 30 for SHG from a 560 Å Ag film excited at 6943 Å when prism coupling into the extended surface plasmon of the smooth metal surface was employed. Larger enhancements have been seen by Chen et al. [103] using counterpropagating surface plasmons. As mentioned above, Corn et al. [16,38] used an ATR configuration in electrochemical studies to access surface plasmons from smooth silver electrodes biased within the limits of the double layer charging region, and an enhancement factor of 100 was observed. The parabolic potential dependence in these surface plasmon enhanced experiments is similar to that observed from a roughened surface, rather than that observed in the simpler geometry with a 45° incident angle.

1. Effects of an ORC on the SH Response. The SH signal observed during an oxidation-reduction cycle has been studied extensively for silver in a variety of aqueous electrolytes [4,34,36,37,104-108]. For Ag cycled in KCl, a strong signal is observed in the region where the corresponding current-voltage curve shows that Ag is oxidized to AgCl. This was first reported by Chen et al. [3,4]. An example is shown in Figure 16(A) [104] for this system. Upon bias reversal at +0.5 V, reduction of the halide film occurs, and the SH signal gradually drops. The baseline, however, is observed to increase near -1.0 V after an ORC due to the presence of the roughened surface. A similar second harmonic potential dependence has been reported for Ag in K_2SO_4 [4,37,105,108], KCN [4,108], $KClO_4$ [34,36], and various halide containing solutions [4,93,104,106,107]. Sensitivity to submonolayer film formation has also demonstrated [3,37]. The relative strength of the SH signal from these films is dependent on many factors, including the nonlinear dielectric constant of the film [46], the degree of roughness caused by the ORC [4], resonance enhancement effect [34,46,106], the solubility of the film [141], possible photoinduced changes in the surface [108], and the pH of the solution [40,104,108]. With regards to the latter, it has been shown that for Ag cycled in electrolytes with a pH > 6.0, Ag_2O and AgO can also be formed in this potential region, which can significantly alter the response from silver complexes formed with the primary electrolyte [104,108]. Figures 16(B) and 16(C) demonstrate this behavior in K_2SO_4 at different pH values [104]. In the latter figure, the low nonlinear dielectric properties of the insulating oxide film formed at the higher pH result in a dramatic reduction in SH signal within the oxidation-reduction region. Initial experiments in this area [4] attributed this type of signal reduction to the symmetry of the silver sulfate complexes on the surface, rather than to the presence of oxides.

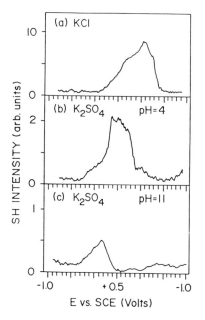

Figure 16. *SH signal from polycrystalline silver cycled in* (**a**) *0.1 M KCl;* (**b**) *0.05 M K_2SO_4 at pH 4; and* (**c**) *0.05 M K_2SO_4 at pH 11. (Reprinted from Reference 34.)*

Oxidatively formed silver complexes were investigated by a combined study using SERS and SHG in an attempt to understand the temporal evolution of the SH intensity associated with electrochemical roughening of a Ag surface and formation of adherent layers of Ag_2SO_4 and AgCN [4,108]. The results of the two techniques correlated well in the oxidation-reduction region when the formation of Ag_2O was avoided. The study also suggested that SHG occurs at the interface between the Ag and the adherent Ag_2SO_4 or AgCN layers and does not arise solely from the films.

The source of the second harmonic generation has been investigated in studies where photoacoustic methods were used to measure the linear optical dielectric properties of the electrode surface at ω and 2ω during an ORC [34,46]. A piezoelectric transducer coupled to the electrochemical cell measured optical absorption by the electrode surface at a fixed wavelength as the potential was varied. The results are shown in Figure 17 for Ag in chloride- and sulfate-containing solutions. For chloride media, the strong optical resonance seen at 532nm [Fig. 17(A)] is concluded to contribute significantly to the large SH response observed during the ORC. In sulfate media, a weaker absorption at 532 nm is observed when Ag_2SO_4 forms on the surface. Luminescence correlating with the optical absorption at 532 nm is also observed in these systems, with the strongest response during AgCl formation [34,46]. In contrast to the optoacoustic signal at 532 nm, the optical absorption at 1.064 μm decreases as the AgCl and Ag_2SO_4 films form [Fig. 17(B)]. The results suggest the absence of optical enhancement at ω for both films. More significantly, they demonstrate the dominance of the optical properties of the film over those of the underlying roughened metal, an issue which is ambiguous at 532 nm. Studies by Marshall and

Korenowski [106] suggest that metal clusters contribute to the luminescence in this Ag/KCl system.

An oxidation-reduction cycle causes irreversible changes in the potential dependence of the SH response when the roughened electrode surface is polarized within the IPR [109]. As shown previously in Figure 3(B), the SH response from the smooth surface reaches a minimum at the PZC and increases with positive sweep. After an ORC, the overall signal increases due to the local field enhancement at the rough surface. The potential dependence in the IPR becomes increasingly parabolic upon repeated cycling, with a strong signal at cathodic potentials and a minimum at approximately 300 mV positive of the PZC. Figure 18 shows the effects of controlled surface roughening on the SH response within the IPR. The optical absorption at ω and 2ω from corresponding photoacoustic measurements is

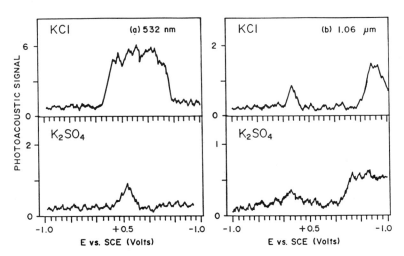

Figure 17. *Photoacoustic signal (arbitrary units) from silver during an ORC in solutions of 0.1 M KCl and 0.05 M K_2SO_4. (**a**) λ = 532 nm; (**b**) λ = 1.064 μm. (Reprinted from Reference 34.)*

also parabolic.   In contrast, a nearly flat and barely detectable response is recorded from the polished surface [34,46].   On roughened surfaces, differential capacitance measurements show only a negligible increase in the amount of ionic adsorption at potentials where adsorption occurs [39].   The authors conclude that the enhanced SH response from the roughened surface biased within the IPR is a reflection of the surface plasmon enhancement mechanisms that were observed in the earlier work of Corn et al. [16] and is not mimicking the change in the degree of surface adsorption as the surface is roughened.   When the surface is roughened, the angle of incidence and subsequent reflection is no longer well-defined.   The SH output is then a computation of different optical geometries from the surface modules and bumps created by the ORC.

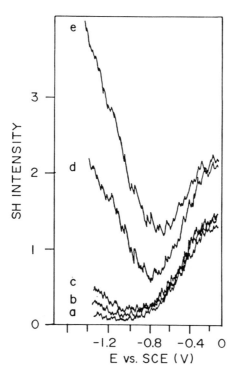

Figure 18. *Effect of slight surface roughening on the potential dependence of the SH intensity from polycrystalline silver in 0.1 M K_2SO_4. Curves (**a-d**) were recorded after oxidation-reduction cycles corresponding to 0, 1, 5, and 12 monolayers of silver. Curve (**e**) was recorded after the addition of 10^{-4} M Ag_2SO_4 to the solution of curve (**d**).*

Second harmonic generation from Cu and Au surfaces · undergoing oxidation has also been reported [36,110]. Biwer et al. [13] studied oxidized Fe electrode surfaces using a picosecond laser. The SHG was correlated with the formation of various Fe(II), Fe(III), and Fe(II-III) oxide complexes in alkaline solutions. Enhancement due to optical resonances with particular forms of the iron oxide film and the SH wavelength is suggested.

2. Molecular Adsorption At Roughened Surfaces. As with SERS, organic adsorbates present during an ORC lead to large enhancements in the SH signal at potentials where surface roughness structures exist [4]. Pyridine is an example of an adsorbate for which this effect occurs. This enhancement is also observed well beyond the completion of electron transfer as indicated by the voltammogram. Figure 19 shows a comparison of these two responses for polycrystalline silver cycled in KCl (A) and KCl with added pyridine (B). Analogous to the enhancement mechanism proposed for SERS, the enhancement may be due to the

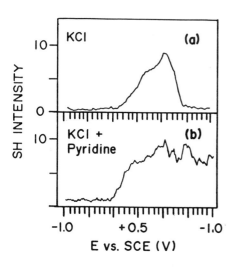

Figure 19. *SH response at 532 nm from a polycrystalline silver electrode cycled in (**a**) 0.1 M KCl; (**b**) 0.1 M KCl and 10^{-4} M pyridine. (Reprinted from Reference 34.)*

interaction of the adatom structures with pyridine molecules [4]. Both the chemical and electromagnetic effects appear to contribute to the enhancement. Photoacoustic measurements using 532 nm light show a nonlinear power dependence of the optical absorption at potentials where an enhanced SH response is observed [46].

III. HYPER-RAMAN SPECTROSCOPY

Another nonlinear optical process which has gained attention in recent years is hyper-Raman scattering. This is a three photon process which involves virtual transitions of two photons from the incident beam of energy $\hbar\omega_i$ and the emitted photon, $\hbar\omega_s = \hbar(2\omega_i - \omega_{vib})$, where ω_{vib} is the molecular vibrational frequency. In contrast to the normal Raman intensity, which is proportional to the incident field intensity $I(\omega_i)$, the hyper-Raman signal is proportional to the square of the incident field and the gradient of the hyperpolarizability with respect to the nuclear displacements [111,112]. The interest in this surface phenomenon arises largely from theoretical predictions that, for molecules having high symmetry, the vibrational selection rules for the second order process are less restrictive than for either Raman scattering or IR absorption. One therefore has the possibility of accessing "silent modes" of the molecule with this method. The major disadvantage of the technique, and the reason that so little work has been done in this area, is the extremely low signal levels. The HRS signal is typically 10^{-5} relative to normal Raman scattering intensities for a laser field of 10^{11} W/cm^2 [113]. The first experimental report of hyper-Raman scattering was made by Terhune in 1965 [114]. Many investigations in gases [115-117], liquids [118], and solids [119] have followed.

Since the onset of interest in SERS for enhancing signal levels from molecular adsorbates on roughened surfaces, spectroscopists have questioned whether similar enhancement mechanisms would make hyper-Raman measurements for surface adsorbates feasible. The complicating factor for surface studies relative to bulk measurements is the smaller number density sampled by the incident beam in the former case. This is a problem which can not be alleviated by merely using higher power densities, due to the possibility of inducing unwanted competing processes such as laser induced desorption, dielectric breakdown, or stimulated Brillouin and stimulated Raman scattering.

The first report of surface enhanced hyper-Raman scattering was made by Murphy et al. in 1982 for SO_3^{2-} molecules adsorbed on Ag powders [120]. Using the 1.064 μm output of a Nd:YAG laser operating at 20 Hz, two peaks at 925 and 616 cm^{-1} were observed, which coincide exactly with the two SO_3^{2-} vibrational peaks in the SERS spectrum. Resonance enhanced hyper-Raman spectroscopy has been the focus of several surface studies by Baranov and coworkers. In these experiments, the vibrational spectra of dye molecules adsorbed on silver colloids have been examined [121].

More pertinent to this review are the recent studies by Van Duyne and coworkers for pyridine on silver [113]. In these studies, a cw mode-locked Nd:YAG laser operating at 82 MHz (60 psec) was used at 1.064 μm to obtain the hyper-Raman spectrum of the adsorbed species. This beam was then subsequently doubled to 532 nm and used to measure the SERS spectrum of pyridine on the same electrode for comparison. Power densities of 4.0 watts and 25mW were used for the hyper-Raman and SERS experiments, respectively. The hyper-Raman intensities were compared to theoretical predictions based on the semiempirical π electron model Hamiltonian of Pairser, Parr [122], and Pople [123]. Figure 20 displays the spectra for pyridine on the electrochemically roughened silver surface obtained by either hyper-Raman [Fig. 20(A)] or Raman [Fig. 20(B)] scattering. The frequencies and number of observed modes for both processes are nearly identical. The differences arise mainly in the relative intensities of the peaks, a factor attributed by the authors to the stronger sensitivity of hyper-Raman scattering to adsorbate orientation. They also concluded that the enhancement observed for the hyper-Raman experiments was higher than predicted by electromagnetic theory and that this difference must be due to a chemical enhancement effect.

Hyper-Raman has the advantage over SHG in measuring vibrational spectroscopy at the interface. However, as with SERS, and in contrast to SHG, exploiting enhancement mechanisms such as surface roughening is crucial to obtaining sufficient signal levels. Further investigation is warranted and could be aided by employing other enhancement schemes including plasmon enhanced hyper-Raman using an ATR configuration.

IV. SUM FREQUENCY GENERATION

Unlike hyper-Raman, sum frequency is more readily applicable to measuring the vibrational spectra of adsorbates on smooth substrates. Sum frequency generation is a three wave mixing phenomenon in which, for vibrational

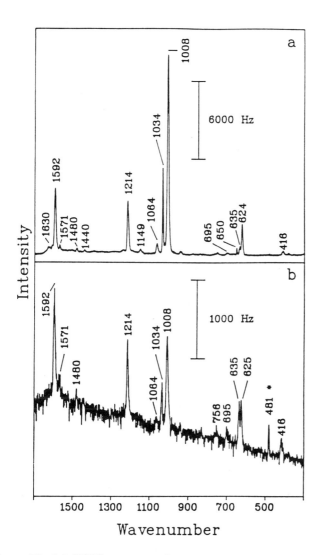

Figure 20. (a) *SERS spectrum of pyridine on spinning Ag electrode, using 25 mW of average power at 532 nm, -0.7 V vs. SCE, scan rate = 1 cm^{-1}/sec, integration time = 1 sec, 3 cm^{-1} slits.* (**b**) *Surface enhanced hyper Raman spectrum of pyridine on spinning Ag electrode, using 4.0 W average power at 1.064 μm mode-locked. Scanning parameters are the same as in (a) above. The starred peak at 481 cm^{-1} indicates a Hg line from stray room light. Note that these spectra are of the same system; one spectrum acquired immediately following the other. (Reprinted from Reference 113.)*

spectroscopic application, an infrared wave at ω_{IR} mixes with a visible wave at ω to yield the SF output at ω_{SF} [124]. When ω_{IR} is resonant with the energy of a vibrational transition, an increase in the SF intensity is expected. The attractive aspect is that this technique makes it possible to obtain IR vibrational spectra via detection of the resonant signal in the visible region. Furthermore, because it is a second order process, it is highly surface specific. The selection rules for SFG are such that the modes must be both IR and Raman active. This, however, is not such a serious restriction, since most modes fit this criterion for an adsorbate on the surface where broken symmetry exists.

As with SHG, SFG has a signal strength that is proportional to the square of the effective surface polarization given in Equation (2) where [125]

$$P_s^{(2)}(\omega = \omega_1 + \omega_2) = \chi_s^{(2)} : E(\omega_1)\, E(\omega_2). \tag{15}$$

As resonance is approached by ω_1, the effective surface nonlinear susceptibility $\chi^{(2)}{}_s$ can be written as

$$\chi_s^{(2)} = \chi_{NR}^{(2)} + \chi_R^{(2)} \ ,$$

$$\text{where } \chi_R^{(2)} = \sum A_\delta \ \Lambda \ (\omega_1 - \omega_\delta + i\Gamma_\delta), \tag{16}$$

$\chi_R^{(2)}$ and $\chi_{NR}^{(2)}$ are resonant and nonresonant parts of $\chi_s^{(2)}$, respectively, ω_δ is the resonance frequency, A_δ is the oscillator strength, and Γ_δ is the damping constant of the δth mode.

A. Experimental Considerations

The experiment requires two coincident laser beams on the surface, a fixed wavelength visible beam, and a second providing tunable infrared radiation for excitation of the adsorbate vibrational mode. The 532 nm doubled fundamental from either a mode-locked picosecond or Q-switched nanosecond laser is generally used as the visible source. This is overlapped on the surface by the tunable IR source in a nearly collinear [125] or counterpropagating [126] geometry relative to the visible beam. The sum frequency signal occurs in a collimated beam and is collected at an angle determined by the k-vector matching at the surface [125]. As noted below, a variety of tunable IR sources have been used, based on the desired spectral region.

B. Spectroscopic Measurements

The first demonstration of the feasibility of this technique was reported in 1987 for coumarin 504 dye molecules on quartz glass [124]. A Nd:YAG laser at 532 nm was coupled to a CO_2 TEA p-polarized laser that was used in an IR, discretely tunable IR source. Several vibrational modes for the adsorbed molecule were measured and compared with IR adsorbance and Raman scattering measurements for coumarin.

SFG measurements have recently been reported for molecules adsorbed at a solid/liquid interface. The system investigated was octadecyltrichlorosilane (OTS) adsorbed at a fused silica substrate in polar (methanol) and nonpolar (hexadecane, CCl_4) solvents [127]. The OTS monolayers were prepared on the substrate by the dipping method and assumed to provide a surface coverage of ≥ 20 Å^2/molecule. The C-H stretching vibrations of the adsorbed OTS molecule were observed using a Nd:YAG-optical parametric oscillator combination. Figure 21 shows the results obtained for the silica/OTS/hexadecane and the silica/OTS/CCl_4 systems. The results for silica/hexadecane in the absence of OTS are also shown. The significance of the latter spectrum is that it demonstrates that bulk contributions from the hexadecane are negligible, an important point since hexadecane has strong C-H adsorption in the infrared, which could conceivably produce a significant resonant bulk response. This is further demonstrated by the similarity in the response from OTS in both CCl_4 and hexadecane. By taking the ratio of the s-stretch intensities of the various polarization combinations, the OTS molecule was determined to be oriented normal to the surface.

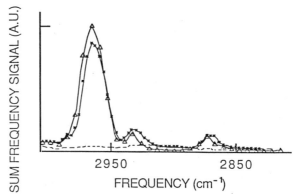

Figure 21. *SFG spectra at different interfaces in the (p_{vis}, p_{IR}) polarization combinations. Dashes: silica-hexadecane interface. Solid squares: silica-OTS-CCl_4 interfaces. Triangles: silica-OTS-hexadecane interface. The dashed and solid lines are guides for the eye. (Reprinted from Reference 127.)*

Similar spectra were also taken for OTS adsorbed at the fused silica surface in methanol [127]. In contrast to the other two solvents, evidence was given for the presence of methanol at the surface in addition to the OTS. Time-resolved adsorption data for OTS at the liquid/silica interface was also reported. The absorption was found to be nearly complete in 10 min.

Since then, several other interfacial studies by SFG have been reported on a solid substrate under ambient conditions, including methanol on glass [125], ocadecyl thiol on gold thin films [126], and stearic acid and cadmium stearate monolayers on silver and germanium substrates [126]. The latter two studies employed a stimulated electronic Raman shifting of visible dye laser pulses in atomic cesium vapor to obtain the tunable IR radiation. Information on relative orientations was obtained in all systems studied.

V. CONCLUSIONS

The general area of surface nonlinear optics holds exceptional promise for future studies of buried interfaces. Many of the techniques are in very early stages of development and warrant further investigation before general applicability can be claimed. Much of the current theoretical and experimental understanding has been derived from measurements at the solid/vacuum or solid/air interface, with further experiments clearly needed at the solid/liquid junction. For second harmonic generation, the ability to derive information in situ about the electronic and structural properties of the electrode looks particularly interesting. Sum frequency generation holds the promise of enabling investigations of surface adsorbate structure without the complication of the bulk contribution. However, the problem of infrared adsorption of the incident beam will continue to be a complicating factor, as in other IR measurements, at the solid/aqueous electrolyte interface. As with SHG, the advantage of being able to study a variety of substrates with nearly unlimited time resolution is particularly appealing.

ACKNOWLEDGMENTS

Appreciation is noted for financial support from the Department of Energy, Basic Energy Sciences (DE-FG06-86ER45273). This review could not have been accomplished without the helpful assistance of Drs. J. Robinson and V. Shannon, and D. Koos.

REFERENCES

1. Shen, Y.R. *The Principles of Nonlinear Optics.* New York: Wiley, 1984.
2. Lee, C.H., Chang, R.K., and Bloembergen, N. *Phys. Rev. Lett.* 18 (1967):167.
3. Chen, C.K., et. al. *Phys. Rev. Lett.* 46 (1981):1010.
4. Chen, C. K., et. al. *Phys. Rev. B.* 27 (1983): 1965 and references therein.
5. Bloembergen, N. and Pershan, P. S. *Phys. Rev.* 128 (1962): 606.
6. Heinz, T.F. Ph.D. Dissertation, University of California, Berkeley, 1982.
7. Mizrahi, V., and Sipe, J. E. *J. Opt. Soc. Am. B.* 5 (1988):660.
8. Corvi, M., and Schaich, W. L. *Phys. Rev. B.* 33 (1986):3688; Weber, M., and Liebsch, A. *Phys. Rev. B.* 35 (1987):7411. Rudnick, J., and Stern, E. A. *Phys. Rev. B.* 4 (1971):4274.
9. For a review of the theory see: Richmond, G. L., Robinson, J. M., and Shannon, V. L. *Prog. in Surf. Sci.* 28 (1988):1.
10. Bloembergen, N., et. al. *Phys. Rev.* 174 (1968):813.
11. Sipe, J. E., Mizrahi, V., and Stegeman, G. I. *Phys. Rev. B* 35 (1987):9091.
12. Second harmonic generation observed in transmission from crystalline calcite, which also possesses a center of inversion, had been previously reported: Terhune, R. W., Maker, P. D., and Savage, C. M. *Phys. Rev. Lett.* 8 (1962):404.
13. Biwer, B.M., et. al., *Surf. Sci.* 176 (1986):377.
14. Robinson, J. M., and Richmond, G. L. *Chem. Phys.* 141(1990):175.

15. Robinson, J. M., and Richmond, G. L. *Electrochem. ACTA* 34 (1989):220.

16. Corn, R. M., et. al. *J. Chem. Phys.* 81 (1984):4127.

17. Shank, C. V., Yen, R., and Hirlimann, C. *Phys. Rev. Lett.* 51 (1983):900.

18. Heinz, T. F., et. al. *Proceedings of the XIV International Quantum Electronics Conference*, Paper THII1. San Francisco, CA June 9-13, 1986.

19. Arjavalingam, G., Heinz, T. F., and Glownia, J. H. *Ultrafast Phenomena V*. ed. G.R. Fleming and A.E. Siegman, 370. Berlin: Springer-Verlag, 1986.

20. Tom, H.W.K. Aumiller, G.D., and Brito-Cruz, C.H. *Phys. Rev. Lett.* 60 (1988):1438.

21. Tom, H.W.K. in "Advances in Laser Science - II", *AIP Conference Proceedings Series* No. 180, ed. W.C. Stwalley, M. Lapp and G.A. Kenney-Wallace. N.Y. AIP 1987.

22. Heinz, T. F., Tom, H.W.K., and Shen, Y. R. *Phys. Rev. A* 28 (1983):1883.

23. Heinz, T. F., et. al. *Phys. Rev. Lett.* 48 (1982):478.

24. Heinz, T. F., et. al. In *Proceedings of the XV International Conference on Quantum Electronics*, Paper W664, Baltimore, MD, 1987.

25. Kemnitz, K., et. al. *Chem. Phys. Lett.* 131 (1986):285.

26. Rasing, Th., et. al. *Phys. Rev. Lett.* 55 (1985):2903.

27. Rasing, Th., et. al. *Phys. Rev. A* 31 (1985):537.

28. Tom, H. W. K. Ph.D. Dissertation, University of California, Berkeley, 1984.

29. Chang, R. K., Ducuing, J., and Bloembergen, N. *Phys. Rev. Lett.* 15 (1965):6.

30. Tom, H. W. K., Heinz, T. F., and Shen, Y. R. *Phys. Rev. Lett.* 51 (1983):1983.

31. Heinz, T. F., Loy, M. M. T., and Thompson, W. A. *Phys. Rev. Lett.* 54 (1985):63.

32. Sipe, J. E. and Stegeman, G. I. In *Surface Polaritons*, ed. V.M. Agranovich and D.L. Mills, New York, 661, North-Holland Publishing Company 1982.

33. Bard, A. J., and Faulkner, L. R. *Electrochemical Methods*. New York: Wiley, 1980.

34. Richmond, G. L., et. al. *J. Opt. Soc. Am. B* 4 (1987):228.

35. Richmond, G. L., *Chem. Phys. Lett.* 110 (1984):571.

36. Richmond, G. L., *Langmuir* 2 (1986):132.

37. Richmond, G. L., *Chem. Phys. Lett.* 106 (1984):26.

38. Corn, R. M., et. al. *Chem. Phys. Lett.* 106 (1984):30.

39. Rojhantalab, H. M. and Richmond, G. L. *J. Phys. Chem.* 93 (1988):3269.

40. Rojhantalab, H. M. and Richmond, G. L., in "Advances in Laser Science - II", *AIP Conference Proceedings* Series No. 180, ed. W.C. Stwalley, M. Lapp, and G.A. Kenney-Wallace New York: AIP 1987.

41. Robinson, J. M., et. al. *Pure and Appl. Chem.* 59 (1987):1263.

42. Wang, C. C. and Duminski, A. N. *Phys. Rev. Lett.* 20 (1968):668.

43. Wang, C. C. *Phys. Rev.* 178 (1969):1457.

44. Miller, R. C. *Appl. Phys. Lett.* 5 (1964):17.

45. Apell, P., preprint.

46. Chu, P., and Richmond, G. L. *J. Electroanal. Chem.* in press.

47. Larkin, D., et. al. *J. Electroanal. Chem.* 138 (1981):401.

48. Rojhantalab, H. M., and Richmond, G. L., Unpublished results.

49. See for example, McIntyre, J.D.E. In *Advances in Electrochemistry and Electrochemical Engineering Vol. 9* ed. R.H. Muller 61. New York: Wiley, 1973.

50. Samant, M. G., et. al. *J. Phys. Chem.* 92 (1988):220.

51. Ho, K.-M., et. al. *J. Electroanal. Chem.* 150 (1983):235.

52. Furtak, T. E., and Lynch, D. W. *Phys. Rev. Lett.* 35 (1975):960.

53. Voss, D. F., et. al. *J. Phys. Chem.* 90 (1986):1834.

54. Weaver, M. J., et. al. *Surf. Sci.* 125 (1983):409.

55. Campbell, D. J., and Corn, R.M. *J. Phys. Chem.* 91 (1987):5668.

56. Campbell, D. J., and Corn, R.M. *J. Phys. Chem.* 92 (1988):5796.

57. Furtak, T. E., Miragliotta, J., and Korenowski, G. M. *Phys. Rev. B* 35 (1987):2569.

58. Bewick, A., and Thomas, B. *J. Electroanal. Chem.* 65 (1975):911.

59. Bewick, A., and Thomas, B. *J. Electroanal. Chem.* 84 (1977):127.

60. See for example, Kolb, D. M. In *Advances in Electrochemistry and Electrochemical Engineering, Vol. II*, ed. H. Gerischer and C.W. Tobias, 125. New York: Wiley, 1978.

61. Takamura, K., Watanabe, F., and Takamura, T. *Electrochim. Acta* 26 (1981):979.

62. Koos, D. A., et. al. In *Proceedings of the 173rd Meeting of the Electrochem. Soc.* Atlanta, GA, May 1988.

63. Kolb, D. M., Przasnyski, M., and Gerischer, H. *Electroanal. Chem. and Interfac. Electrochem.* 54 (1974):25; Gerischer, H., Kolb, D. M., and Przasnyski, M. *Surf. Sci.* 43 (1974):662.

64. Tom, H. W. K., et. al. *Phys. Rev. Lett.* 52 (1984):348.

65. Tom, H. W. K., et. al. *Surf. Sci.* 172 (1986):466.

66. Heinz, T. F., Loy, M. M. T., and Thompson, W. A. *J. Vac. Sci. Technol. B 3* (1985):1467.

67. Tom, H. W. K., and Aumiller G. D. *Phys. Rev. B* 33 (1986):8818.

68. Sipe, J. E., Moss, D. J., and van Driel, H. M. *Phys. Rev. B* 35 (1987):1129.

69. Koos, D. A., Shannon, V. L., and Richmond, G. L. *J. Phys. Chem.* 94 (1990) 2091.
70. Shannon, V. L., Koos, D. A. and Richmond, G. L., *Appl. Opt.* 26 (1987):3579.
71. Shannon, V. L., Koos, D. A. and Richmond, G. L. *J. Chem. Phys.* 87 (1987):1440.
72. Shannon, V. L., Koos, D. A. and Richmond, G. L. *J. Phys. Chem.* 91 (1987):5548.
73. Bradley, R., et. al., *Chem. Phys. Lett.* 168 (1990) 468.
74. Bloembergen, N., Chang, R. K., and Lee, C. H. *Phys. Rev. Lett.* 16 (1966):986.
75. Johnson, P. B., and Christy, R. W. *Phys. Rev. B* 6 (1972):4370.
76. Reihl, B., Schlittler, B. B., and Neff, H. Surf. Sci. 162 (1985):1.
77. Georgiadis, R., et. al. *J. Chem. Phys.* 92 (1990) 4623; Georgiadis, et. al. J. PHys. Chem., in press.
78. Shannon, V. L., et. al. *J. Phys. Chem.* 93 (1989):6434.
79. Koos, D. A. *J. Electrochem. Soc.* 136 (1989):218C.
80. Shannon, V. L., et. al. *Chem. Phys. Lett.* 142 (1987):323.
81. Conway, B. E. *Prog. in Surf. Sci.* 16 (1984):1.
82. Bewick, A., and Thomas, B. *J. Electroanal. Chem.* 85 (1977):329.
83. McGilp, J. F., and Yeh, Y. *Solid State Comm.* 59 (1986):91.
84. Rawlings, K. J., Gibson, M. J., and Dobson, P. J. *J. Phys. D* 11 (1978):2059.
85. Samant, M. G., et. al. Surf. Sci. 193 (1988):L29.
86. Meyers, H. P. *J. Phys. F: Metal Physics* 3 (1978):1078.
87. Liljenvall, H. J., Mathewson, A. G., and Meyers, H. P. *Phil. Mag.* 22 (1970):243.
88. Pemberton, J. previous chapter of this book.

89. For a review see: Chang, R. K., and Furtak, T. E. *Surface Enhanced Raman Scattering* New York: Plenum Press, 1982, and references therein.
90. Murphy, D. V., et. al. *Chem. Phys. Lett.* 85 (1982):43.
91. Harstein, A., Kirtley, J. R., and Tsang, J. C. *Phys. Rev. Lett.* 45 (1980):201.
92. Ritchie, G., and Burstein, E. *Phys. Rev. B* 24 (1981):4843, and references therein.
93. Heinz, T. F., et. al. *Chem. Phys. Lett.* 83 (1981):180.
94. Gersten, J., and Nitzan, A. *J. Chem. Phys.* 73 (1980):3023; *J. Chem. Phys.* 75 (1981):1139.
95. Liao, P. F., and Wokaun, A. *J. Chem. Phys.* 76 (1982):751.
96. Boyd, G. T., et. al. *Phys. Rev. B* 30 (1984):519.
97. Moskovits, M. *Rev. Mod. Phys.* 57 (1985):783.
98. Wokaun, A., et. al., *Phys. Rev. B* 24 (1981):849.
99. Moskovits, M. *J. Chem. Phys.* 69 (1978):4159.
100. Messinger, B. J., et. al., *Phys. Rev. B* 24 (1981):649.
101. Kerker, J., Wang, D. S., and Chew, H. *Appl. Opt.* 19 (1980):4159.
102. Simon, H. J., Mitchell, D. E., and Watson, J. G. *Phys. Rev. Lett.* 33:1531.
103. Chen, C.K., deCastro, A.R.B., and Shen, Y.R. *Opt. Lett.* 4 (1979):393.
104. Richmond, G. L. *Surf. Sci.* 147 (1984):115.
105. Murphy, D. V., et. al. *Surf. Sci.* 124 (1983):529.
106. Marshall, C.D., and Korenowski, G. M. *J. Chem. Phys.* 85 (1986):4172.
107. Marshall, C.D., and Korenowski, G.M. *J. Phys. Chem.* 91 (1987):1289.
108. Chen, T. T., et. al. *Surf. Sci.* 143 (1984):369.
109. Richmond, G. L. *Chem. Phys. Lett.* 113 (1985):359.
110. Richmond, G. L., and Chu, P. *Proceedings of the 189th Nat. Am. Chem. Soc. Meeting.* Miami, Fl, May 1985.

111. French, M. J., and Long, D. A. In *Molecular Spectroscopy* ed. R. F. Barrow. Vol. 4, Ch. 6. London: Chem. Soc., 1976.

112. Andrews, D. L., and Thirunamachandran, T. *J. Chem. Phys.* 68 (1978):2941.

113. Golab, G. T., et. al. *J. Chem. Phys.* 88 (1988):7942.

114. Terhune, R. W., Maker, P. D., and Savage, C. M. *Phys. Rev. Lett.* 14 (1965):681.

115. Ziegler, L. D., and Roebber, J. L. *Chem. Phys. Lett.* 136 (1987):377; Ziegler, L. F., Chung, Y. C., and Zhang, Y. P. *J. Chem. Phys.* 87 (1987):4498.

116. Bersohn, R., Pao, Y. -H., and Frisch, H. L. *J. Chem. Phys.* 45 (1966):3184.

117. Fanconi, B., and Peticolas, W. L. *J. Chem. Phys.* 50 (1969):2244.

118. Schmid, W. J., and Schrotter, H. W. *Chem. Phys. Lett.* 45 (1977):502.

119. Freund, I. *Phys. Rev. Lett.* 19 (1967):1288; Vogt, H., and Neumann, G. *Opt. Commun.* 19 (1967):1288.

120. Murphy, D. V., et. al. *Chem. Phys. Lett.* 85 (1982):43.

121. Baranov, V. V., and Bobovich, Ya. S. *JETP Lett.* 36 (1983):343; Baranov, V. V., Bobvich, Ya. S., and Vasilenko, N. P. *Opt. Spectrosc.* 61 (1986):491 and references therein.

122. Pariser, R., and Parr, R. G. *J. Chem. Phys.* 21 (1953):466.

123. Pople, J. A. *Trans. Faraday Soc.* 49 (1953):1375.

124. Zhu, X. D., Suhr, H., and Shen, Y. R. *Phys. Rev. B* 35 (1987):3047.

125. Hunt, J.H., Guyot-Sionnest, P., and Shen, Y.R. *Chem. Phys. Lett.* 133 (1987):189.

126. Harris, A. L., et. al. *Chem. Phys. Lett.* 141 (1987):350.

127. Guyot-Sionnest, P., et. al. *Chem. Phys. Lett.* 144 (1988):1.

CHAPTER 7

INFRARED SPECTROELECTROCHEMISTRY: A PROBE OF THE MOLECULAR ARCHITECTURE OF THE ELECTROCHEMICAL INTERFACE

Scott M. Stole, Darwin D. Popenoe, and
Marc D. Porter

Ames Laboratory - USDOE and Department of Chemistry
Iowa State University
Ames, Iowa 50011-3020

CONTENTS

I. INTRODUCTION

In recent years, interest in interfacial phenomena has led to the emergence of a vigorous, interdisciplinary area of research [1-6]. Impetus for this emergence derives from several complementary factors. Of particular relevance is the recognition that interfacial phenomena play critical roles in the performance of a variety of technologically significant materials and surface processes, viz. adhesion, corrosion control, tribology (friction and wear), biocompatibility, catalysis, and microelectronics. For instance, the development of strategies to enhance adhesion at the fluoropolymer-metal interface promises to advance the large-scale integration of microelectronic devices. In contrast, schemes to reduce bacterial adhesion are critical to the implantation of complex prosthetic devices, such as joint replacements and artificial hearts.

Equally important is the more basic contribution such studies will make to our understanding of the chemistry and physics of interfaces. For example, to relate a nominally simple macroscopic property such as wetting to a precise microscopic description is enormously difficult at present. More involved interfacial properties and processes are characterized by a correspondingly increased level of complexity. As a consequence, progress in this area of research has demanded and continues to demand a systematic examination of each of the fundamental components that affect the characteristics and hence, the performance of an interface. Specific questions include:

1. What is the chemical identity of the surface species?
2. What are the spatial arrangement, mode of attachment, and packing density of the surface species?
3. How do the above affect the function and long-term performance of the interface?
4. What levels and distributions of surface structures are necessary to achieve the desired performance?

As is apparent, the search for answers to these questions poses one of the most difficult challenges in interfacial science today. Not only is it necessary to develop an integrated approach to construct and to control the architecture of the surface microstructure, but one must also develop the capability to characterize these structures at a molecular level, i.e. composition, spatial orientation, surface coverage, and reactivity. Furthermore, it is important that these characterizations be performed in situ, insuring a direct correlation between the interfacial structure and its performance.

Electrochemistry is yet another area of research that is experiencing the excitement of surface modification [6-13]. These efforts have focused on exploiting the unique opportunities that surface modification provides for manipulating the rate and/or selectivity of heterogeneous electron-transfer processes. As with the aforementioned areas of research, the in situ characterization of the interface is crucial for relating the surface structure to its performance as an electrode for electrocatalysis, as a device for photochemical energy conversion, or as a sensor for chemical analysis. The level of information required from such a characterization includes:

1. The properties of the electrode surface.
2. The composition and structure of the electrical double layer and any adsorbed species.
3. The surface concentration of adsorbed ionic or organic species.
4. The intermolecular and intramolecular interactions between adsorbate, substrate, and electrolytic solution.

Such concerns are not new to electrochemistry or to interfacial science as a whole. A large part of the classical, as well as contemporary, electrochemical literature has focused on delineating the influence of adsorbed ions and molecules on heterogeneous electron-transfer processes [7-14]. For example, it is well known that the electrolysis rates for several cations are accelerated by the presence of trace quantities of adsorbed anions [14]. The question then specifically addresses how the electronic interaction(s) between the solution reactant and the electrode surface are altered by the presence of a non-electroactive adsorbate. Moreover, it has been both the development of sensitive surface analytical techniques and the advent of new approaches to control the molecular architecture at the interface that has rekindled the interest in these traditional and contemporary questions.

As is apparent from the general theme of this monograph, there are a variety of surface analytical techniques that possess the requisite sensitivity to characterize in situ the electrochemical interface. This chapter examines the application of infrared reflection spectroscopy (IRS) as a probe of electrochemical reactions, and of molecular structures and modes of bonding at an electrode surface. Infrared spectroscopy, like other vibrational spectroscopies, provides information regarding the identity or chemical functionality of a species in terms of "group frequencies" that can be directly related to those of known samples. In addition, by the careful application of classical electromagnetic theory, IRS can provide a description of the spatial arrangement (orientation) of an adsorbate. It is also important to note that many of the surface physics techniques are not directly applicable to in situ investigations of the electrochemical interface. These techniques, which include electron energy loss spectroscopy (EELS), X-ray photoelectron spectroscopy (XPS), Auger electron spectroscopy (AES), and low-energy electron diffraction (LEED), require ultra-high vacuum conditions to attain usable electron mean free path lengths. Careful transfer experiments have recently permitted an in vacuo characterization with these techniques [15-17]. However, the integrity of the sample may be compromised as a result of its removal from the electrochemical cell.

To focus our discussion, it is instructive to classify the hybridization of IRS and electrochemical methods into two broad categories. The first consists of those methods that probe an electrochemical process in situ, viz. at the liquid-solid interface. These techniques, which will be designated collectively as infrared spectroelectrochemistry (IR-SEC), represent the principle focus of this chapter. The second classification includes those IRS measurements performed ex situ, i.e. after the electrode has been removed from solution. This latter category conceptually includes spectroscopic methods such as NMR and organic mass spectrometry, techniques applied to bulk samples to characterize the collected products of an electrochemical reaction. We, however, will limit the discussion to the ex situ application of IRS as it is used to probe the electrode surface prior to its immersion or after its removal from an electrochemical cell. In this case, IRS is typically applied in an external (as opposed to internal) reflection mode. Such an approach will provide a basis for an examination of the experimental considerations requisite for the application of IRS as a surface probe as well as facilitate a discussion of its extension to in situ characterizations.

By our definition, IR-SEC refers to those techniques that employ infrared radiation to probe electrochemical events in situ through the intimate coupling of electrochemical and spectroscopic processes. Within this broad definition, a further classification is useful to distinguish between techniques that probe the electrode surface and those that examine processes that transpire in the solution layer immediately adjacent to the electrode-solution interface. Solution studies examine events that take place in the diffusion layer and provide information about the identities of the species generated or consumed by an electrochemical process or by a preceding or subsequent chemical reaction. With these techniques, the electrode acts both as a reaction initiator and as a reflective surface. An example is the monitoring of the products generated from the electrooxidation of solution phase organic species. In contrast, as applied to the characterization of the electrochemical interface, IR-SEC is concerned specifically with probing the events and structures that occur directly at the electrode surface. Such studies may focus on the structural identification of an adsorbed species, relating, for example, this description to the electrocatalytic properties of the electrode material and its interface. The experimental strategies for both types of measurements are essentially identical and exploit the capability of elegant modulation techniques to recover very small infrared absorbances (10^{-5} - 10^{-4}) in the presence of a strongly absorbing aqueous electrolytic solution. Since the sensitivity requirements for solution IR-SEC applications are somewhat less demanding, the discussions of the basic concepts and applications of IR-SEC will focus on the characterization of the electrode surface. Differences between approaches to surface and solution studies will be interjected when appropriate. Accounts of the development of this technique are available [18-23].

The second part of this chapter is a discussion of the basic concepts of classical electromagnetic theory and their relevance to infrared reflection spectroscopy. The third part focuses on the modulation techniques, instrumentation, and SEC cells employed in these measurements. In the fourth part, a few recent examples from this rapidly growing field will be discussed. These examples were selected to illustrate the broad-ranging applicability of these techniques. Therefore, in an effort to maintain a concise presentation, only those topics that are specifically related to the characterization of metal surfaces in an external reflection mode will be included here. For applications that pertain to the use of transmission and internal reflection spectroscopy and to semi-conductor surfaces, the reader is referred to Table 2 (p. 44) and other recent reviews of this topic [18-23].

II. FUNDAMENTALS
AND BACKGROUND

The basis for applying IRS to the characterization of thin films on surfaces was originally developed by Greenler [24-25], and by Francis and Ellison [26]. These efforts defined the dependence of a reflection spectrum on the optical properties of the film and metal substrate, and on the angle of incidence and polarization of the incident light. This section first discusses this dependence by examining the properties of electromagnetic radiation and the boundary conditions that govern its passage from one medium to another. Examples are then given to illustrate the utility of IRS for probing ex situ the composition and spatial arrangement of thin polymeric films and monomolecular assemblies at surfaces with a high (metallic) reflectivity.

A. Propagation of
Electromagnetic Radiation

Electromagnetic radiation in a uniform isotropic medium, as shown in Figure 1, is typically depicted as a plane-polarized wave propagating at a phase velocity equal to c/n, where c is the velocity of light in vacuo, and n is the index of refraction of the medium. The instantaneous magnitude of the oscillating electric field vector $\hat{E}$, which is found from the time-dependent solution of Maxwell's equations, is

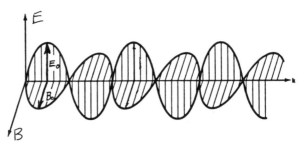

Figure 1. *Plane-polarized electromagnetic wave.*

$$\hat{\mathbf{E}} = E \ ^{\circ} \exp\left[i \left(\omega t - \frac{2\pi n}{\lambda} \mathbf{s} \cdot \mathbf{r} \right) \right],$$ (1)

where $E \ ^{\circ}$ is the maximum amplitude of the wave, λ is the wavelength in vacuo, ω is the angular frequency, $\mathbf{s}$ is a unit vector in the direction of propagation, and $\mathbf{r}$ is a position vector. The wavelength λ is related to the wavenumber, $\bar{v}$, as

$$\bar{v} = 1/\lambda.$$ (2)

The wavelength is also related to the angular frequency ω by $\omega = 2\pi c/\lambda = 2\pi v$, where v is the radiation frequency. Thus, the periodicity of both the electric field and magnetic field are defined in time and space by λ and v. Values of λ, v, and $\bar{v}$, and the equivalent energy in electron volts are given in Table 1 for representative electronic and molecular transitions.

As shown in Equation 1, $\hat{\mathbf{E}}$ is typically treated as a complex-valued function of time and of the spatial coordinates x, y, and z. This figuration is more convenient for mathematical manipulations than the use of a real-valued trigonometric function. An expression similar to Equation 1 can also be written for the magnetic field vector $\hat{\mathbf{H}}$.

TABLE 1. Representative Values for the Energies of Various Molecular and Electronic Excitations.

Transition	$\lambda(\text{Å})$	$v(Hz)$	$\bar{v}(cm^{-1})$	$E(eV)$[a]
Electronic (p $\rightarrow$ p*)	2540	1.8×10^{15}	39370	4.88
Vibrational ($v(C{=}O)$ for carboxylic acid)	57803	5.19×10^{13}	1730	0.214
Rotational (J=1 $\rightarrow$ J=2 for HCl)	2.40×10^{6}	1.25×10^{10}	41.7	5.18×10^{-3}

[a] 1 eV ~ 8065.5 cm^{-1}

In an absorbing medium, the plane wave undergoes an exponential attenuation with increasing propagation distance and is represented as

$$\widehat{\mathbf{E}} = E \,^\circ \exp\left[i\left(\omega t - \frac{2\pi n}{\lambda}\mathbf{s}\cdot\mathbf{r} \right) \right] \exp\left(-\frac{2\pi k}{\lambda}\mathbf{s}\cdot\mathbf{r} \right), \qquad (3)$$

where k is the absorption index and is restricted to $k \geq 0$. If a complex refractive index

$$\widehat{n} = n + ik \qquad (4)$$

is introduced, Equation 3 can be recast to resemble Equation 1, giving

$$\widehat{\mathbf{E}} = E \,^\circ \exp\left[i\left(\omega t - \frac{2\pi \widehat{n}}{\lambda}\mathbf{s}\cdot\mathbf{r} \right) \right]. \qquad (5)$$

Since the refractive index is related to the dielectric constant $\widehat{\varepsilon}$ by

$$\widehat{n} = \sqrt{\mu \widehat{\varepsilon}}, \qquad (6)$$

and the magnetic permeability μ equals unity at optical frequencies, $\widehat{\varepsilon}$ for absorbing materials is complex and can be written as

$$\widehat{\varepsilon} = \widehat{n}^2 = \varepsilon' - i\varepsilon'', \qquad (7)$$

where ε' and ε'' are linked to n and k as

$$\varepsilon' = n^2 - k^2 \qquad (8)$$

$$\varepsilon'' = 2nk. \qquad (9)$$

The intensity and direction of energy flow for a plane wave are given by the Poynting vector **S**:

$$\mathbf{S} = \frac{1}{\mu} \mathbf{E} \times \mathbf{H} . \tag{10}$$

For a discrete optical transition, the attenuation of a propagating wave with intensity I is given by the Lambert law

$$I = I^{\circ} \exp(-\alpha z), \tag{11}$$

where I° is the initial light intensity, α is the absorption coefficient, and z is the distance of penetration into the absorbing medium. The absorption index k is related to α by

$$\alpha = \frac{4\pi k}{\lambda} . \tag{12}$$

The penetration depth, often referred to as the skin depth, of the radiation into the medium is defined as $1/\alpha$, i.e. the distance at which the beam intensity has decreased by 63% of its initial value.

For infrared spectroscopy, the optical properties of each phase are completely defined by a set of optical functions: n and k, or ε' and ε''. Physically, ε' and ε'' are respectively related to the frequency dependent polarizability and the conductivity of the medium. A single complex function, as in either of the following equations, completely defines the optical properties of a homogeneous isotropic medium:

$$\hat{n}(\bar{v}) = n(\bar{v}) + ik(\bar{v}) \tag{13}$$

$$\hat{\varepsilon}(\bar{v}) = \varepsilon'(\bar{v}) + i\varepsilon''(\bar{v}). \tag{14}$$

B. Optical Theory for
Reflection Spectroscopy

In a reflection spectroscopy experiment, electromagnetic radiation interacts with more than one optical medium. In its simplest approximation, such an experiment can be depicted by a stratified medium, with two optically isotropic phases that are separated by a plane boundary, as shown in Figure 2. The entry phase is transparent, whereas the optical functions of the second phase may be complex. The components of both the incident and reflected radiation are defined with respect to the plane of propagation. The E_x and E_z components are in the plane of propagation (p-polarization) and the E_y component is perpendicular to the plane of propagation (s-polarization). The E_x and E_y components are parallel to the interface between the two phases, whereas E_z is perpendicular to this interface. The angle of incidence θ_1 is measured from the surface normal.

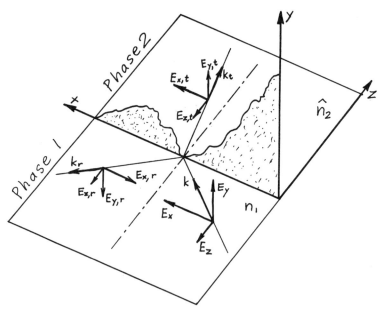

Figure 2. *The electric field vectors for plane-polarized light incident on a phase boundary in a two-phase medium.*

In a three-phase stratified medium, as shown in Figure 3, phase 2 may represent an interfacial structure, consisting, for example, of a polymeric or monomolecular film of thickness, d. An n-phase medium representing a multilayered system, which is exemplified by the Gouy-Chapman model of the electrical double layer, is given is Figure 4. The characteristics of the three- and n-phase media are defined by the optical functions of each phase j as

$$\widehat{n}_j = n_j + ik_j \tag{15}$$

and thicknesses of the intermediate phases d_j.

The Fresnel coefficients quantify the magnitudes of the transmitted and reflected waves emanating from a phase boundary. These coefficients are defined as the ratio of the complex amplitudes of the electric field vectors of the incident wave to that of the reflected or transmitted wave and are a function of the angle of incidence and polarization of the incident beam. Before calculating these coefficients, it is useful to define the refractive coefficient ξ_j for phase j as

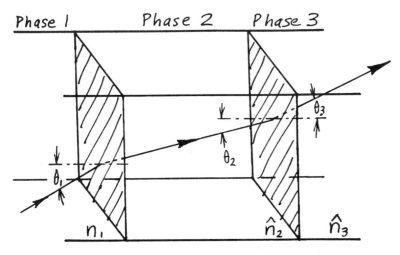

Figure 3. *Radiation incident upon a three-phase medium. Rays for reflected light are omitted for clarity.*

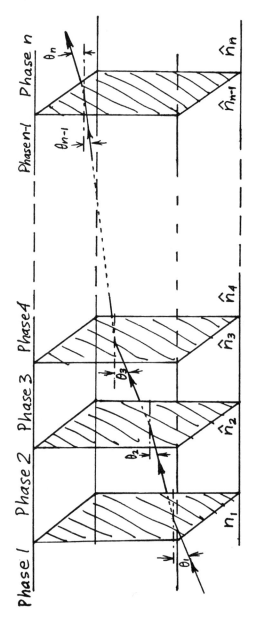

Figure 4. Radiation incident upon an n-phase medium. Rays for reflected light are omitted for clarity.

$$\xi_j = \hat{n}_j \cos\hat{\theta}_j \ . \tag{16}$$

If phase j is absorbing, $\hat{\theta}_j$ is complex. By Snell's law, ξ_j can be related to the angle of incidence and real refractive index of phase 1 as

$$\xi_j = \left(\hat{n}_j^{\,2} - n_1^{\,2} \sin^2\theta_1\right)^{1/2} \ . \tag{17}$$

The complex Fresnel coefficients for reflection r_{jk}, and transmission t_{jk}, at the boundary of phases j and k for radiation polarized parallel and perpendicular to the plane of propagation are then given as

$$r_{\perp jk} = \frac{\xi_j - \xi_k}{\xi_j + \xi_k} \qquad\qquad t_{\perp jk} = \frac{2\xi_j}{\xi_j + \xi_k} \tag{18}$$

$$r_{\| jk} = \frac{\hat{n}_k^2 \xi_j - \hat{n}_j^2 \xi_k}{\hat{n}_k^2 \xi_j + \hat{n}_j^2 \xi_k} \qquad\qquad t_{\| jk} = \frac{2\hat{n}_j \hat{n}_k \xi_j}{\hat{n}_k^2 \xi_j + \hat{n}_j^2 \xi_k} \ . \tag{19}$$

Again, μ for all phases equals unity. These coefficients are derived from Maxwell's equations by applying the continuity requirements of $\hat{E}$ and $\hat{H}$ at the phase boundary.

Plane-polarized light, described by $E_\perp$ and $E_\|$, undergoes a change in amplitude and phase upon reflection at a phase boundary. This change in phase is related to the real and imaginary parts of the Fresnel coefficients by

$$\delta_{jk}^r = \arg(r_{jk}) = \tan^{-1}\left[\frac{\mathrm{Im}(r_{jk})}{\mathrm{Re}(r_{jk})}\right] \ . \tag{20}$$

If the time dependence of the field is $e^{-i\omega t}$, both $\text{Im}(r_{jk})$ and $\text{Re}(r_{jk})$ must be ≥ 0.

From Equations 18 and 19, the reflectivity of each phase boundary, R_{jk}, can be calculated as

$$R_{jk} = |r_{jk}|^2 = r_{jk}\, r_{jk}{}^*,\qquad (21)$$

where $r_{jk}{}^*$ is the complex conjugate of r_{jk}. For the two-phase medium in Figure 3, the reflectivities of the perpendicular and parallel components of the reflected radiation are given as

$$R_{\perp 12} = \left|\frac{\xi_1 - \xi_2}{\xi_1 + \xi_2}\right|^2 \qquad R_{\|12} = \left|\frac{\hat{n}_2^2\xi_1 - \hat{n}_1^2\xi_2}{\hat{n}_2^2\xi_1 + \hat{n}_1^2\xi_2}\right|^2. \qquad (22)$$

For the three-phase medium, r_{123} has

$$r_\perp = \frac{r_{\perp 12} + r_{\perp 23}e^{-2i\beta}}{1 + r_{\perp 12}r_{\perp 23}e^{-2i\beta}} \qquad r_\| = \frac{r_{\|12} + r_{\|23}e^{-2i\beta}}{1 + r_{\|12}r_{\|23}e^{-2i\beta}}, \qquad (23)$$

with $R_{\|,123} = r_{\|,123}\cdot r_{\|,123}{}^*$ and $R_{\perp,123} = r_{\perp,123}\cdot r_{\perp,123}{}^*$. The phase angle term, β, represents the beam attenuation in phase 2 and equals

$$\beta = 2\pi(d/\lambda)\,\xi_2. \qquad (24)$$

Similar expressions, based on matrix manipulations, have been devised for the n-phase optical medium [27-32].

C. Mean-Square Electric Field Strengths at a Reflecting Interface and their Relation to Sensitivity

In a reflection spectroscopy experiment, the sensitivity of the measurement is a strong function of the optical properties of the substrate and the angle of incidence and polarization of the incident light. For an in situ experiment, such as one to examine an electrochemical interface, the sensitivity is further affected by the thickness and optical properties of the solvent and electrolyte [19-23].

In air, the detectability of a thin film is governed to a large extent by the boundary conditions imposed by the free electrons of the substrate. For metal substrates, the electrical conductivity approaches that of its DC value (σ(esu) $\approx 10^{-17}$ s^{-1}) and leads to a high infrared reflectivity (near unity). The dependence of the reflectivity, and hence, the intensity of the mean-square electric field (MSEF) at the surface is elucidated by examining the relation ships between an oscillating $\hat{E}$ and the free conductive electrons in a metal. From the standpoint of physical optics, a reflecting metal surface acts as a collection of charges that are free to move within the metal but are prevented from moving beyond the surface (i.e. outside) of the metal. The incident radiation gives rise to an oscillating electric field vector $\hat{E}$ at the surface, which interacts with the metal as follows: The component of $\hat{E}$ parallel to the surface induces an image dipole in the metal that opposes the incident field [Fig. 5A] whereas the component of $\hat{E}$ perpendicular to the surface induces an image dipole that is aligned with the incident component [Fig. 5B]. The phase change of the reflected wave then results from the orientational difference between the incident electric field and the induced dipole. Figure 6 illustrates the phase shift for light polarized both perpendicular to and parallel to the plane of propagation at a large angle of incidence. For perpendicular-polarized light [Fig. 6A], the incident $\hat{E}$ is parallel to

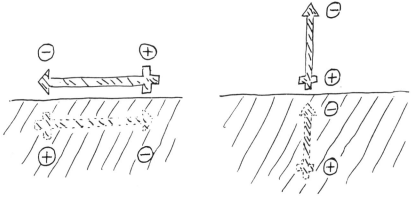

Figure 5. *Orientation of the image dipole in a metal juxtaposed with the external electric field arising from the incident radiation for the component of radiation (A) parallel to, and (B) perpendicular to the metal surface.*

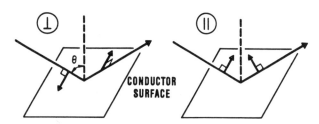

Figure 6. *A representation of the phase change upon reflection for (A) perpendicular-polarized light, and (B) parallel-polarized light . (Reprinted with permission from R.G. Greenler, J. Chem. Phys. 44 (1966): 310.)*

the surface, leading to a phase shift of ~ -180°, as discussed above. This effectively holds for all angles of incidence.

On the other hand, parallel-polarized light at large incident angles has a large portion of its electric field oriented perpendicular to the surface [Fig. 6B]. The resulting induced dipole has a normal component parallel to and reinforcing the normal component of the incident electric field by constructive superposition. Thus, Ê of the reflected light is phase shifted by ~90°. As the angle of incidence increases, the incident and reflected electric field vectors become virtually indistinguishable, corresponding to a phase shift approaching -180°. It should be noted that by convention, when the incident and reflected Ê are antiparallel and equal in magnitude at the surface, the phase change is defined as 0° for parallel-polarized light and -180° for perpendicular-polarized light [33].

Figure 7 shows the phase change δ as a function of angle of incidence for both polarizations. The perpendicular (s-polarized) component is phase shifted by ~180° for all angles of incidence. As a result of the superposition of the incident and reflected $\hat{E}$ vectors, the MSEF at the surface will be effectively zero for this component. If the MSEF is negligibly small, then the absorbance spectrum resulting from interactions between the incident light and a thin film at a metal substrate will be virtually undetectable. On the other hand, the phase shift for the p-polarized (parallel) component of $\hat{E}$ varies from nearly 0° at normal incidence to -180° at grazing incidence. At normal incidence, the MSEF will be small; but as δ approaches 90° for near-grazing angles, the MSEF for the parallel component at the surface increases to almost four times that of the incident radiation. Therefore, the absorbance by a thin film at a metal surface will be at a maximum at grazing angles of incidence with p-polarized light.

Calculations of the electric field intensity due to the super-position of the incident and reflected beams reveal, quantitatively, the effect of many of the experimental parameters upon a reflection spectrum. The boundary conditions imposed by electromagnetic theory define the MSEF of the standing wave at each phase boundary, the value of which is strongly dependent on the optical properties of the substrate, the angle of incidence, and the polarization of the incident light. To foster an understanding of

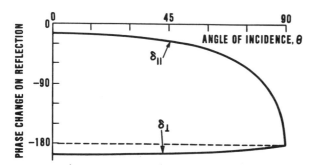

Figure 7. *The phase change upon reflection as a function of angle of incidence for both polarizations of light. (Reprinted with permission from R.G. Greenler, J. Chem. Phys. 44 (1966): 310.)*

the effects of these experimental parameters, it is instructive to examine the MSEF in a two-phase optical medium. Since there is little energy dissipation (absorption) in a thin film such as a monomolecular assembly, the attenuation of the MSEF by the film is relatively small and can be neglected. In other words, for monolayers and thin polymeric films, deductions for a two-phase system accurately represent those for a three-phase system. Values for MSEFs are generally expressed as the ratio of the MSEF in the jth phase, $<E_j^2>$, to that of the incident plane wave in phase 1, $<E_1^{ot2}>$. The following equations define the value of each component of the relative MSEF in the incident phase:

$$\frac{\langle E_{\perp 1}^2 \rangle}{\langle E_{\perp 1}^{ot2} \rangle} = (1 + R_{\perp}) + 2R_{\perp}^{1/2} \cos \left[\delta_{\perp}^r + 4\pi \left(\frac{z}{\lambda} \right) \xi_1 \right] \quad (25)$$

$$\frac{\langle E_{||1x}^2 \rangle}{\langle E_{||1x}^{ot2} \rangle} = \cos^2 \theta_1 \left\{ (1 + R_{||}) - 2R_{||}^{1/2} \cos \left[\delta_{||}^r + 4\pi \left(\frac{z}{\lambda} \right) \xi_1 \right] \right\} \quad (26)$$

$$\frac{\langle E_{||1z}^2 \rangle}{\langle E_{||1z}^{ot2} \rangle} = \sin^2 \theta_1 \left\{ (1 + R_{||}) + 2R_{||}^{1/2} \cos \left[\delta_{||}^r + 4\pi \left(\frac{z}{\lambda} \right) \xi_1 \right] \right\}. \quad (27)$$

A comparison of the results of these calculations using different experimental parameters provides a means to select conditions for high detectability.

A plot of the MSEF at an air/Au interface at 2000 cm^{-1} is shown in Figure 8. As follows from our discussion of boundary conditions, this plot provides insights as to how the high reflectivity of a metal influences the detectability of a surface film. The optical constants for Au were interpolated from a previous study [34]. Figure 8 shows that the MSEF for E_x and E_y are negligibly small (<0.004) for all angles of incidence. In contrast,

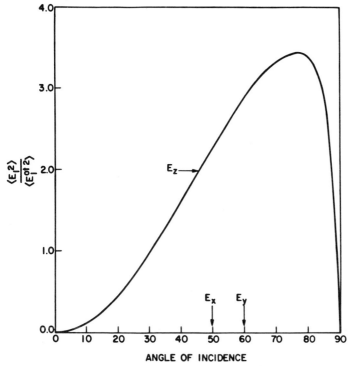

Figure 8. *The mean square electric field at 2000 cm^{-1} as a function of angle of incidence and polarization at the air/Au interface. (Reprinted with permission from M.D. Porter, et al. Anal. Chem. 58 (1986): 2461. Copyright 1986 American Chemical Society.)*

E_z slowly increases with θ_1, reaching a maximum of ~3.4 at 79°. Hence, as noted above, the conditions for high surface detectability at metals are large angles of incidence and p-polarized light.

It should also be noted that the anisotropy of the MSEF at a highly reflecting interface such as air/Au results in the selective excitation of vibrational modes that have a component of their transition dipole normal to the surface. This polarization dependence, commonly referred to as the IR surface selection rule [35], can be exploited to predict the orientation of an adsorbed species (see below). Limitations of such an orientational analysis at materials with a low IR reflectivity have recently been examined [36].

To summarize, for the absorption of light of wavenumber $\bar{\nu}$ by a molecule immobilized at an air-metal interface, three conditions must be met:

1. The molecule must have a nonzero transition dipole moment at $\bar{\nu}$.
2. The magnitude of the MSEF at the interface must be non-zero (with conditions for high detectability at large angles of incidence and p-polarized light).
3. The transition dipole moment must have a component oriented along the surface normal.

D. Optically induced band shape distortions: intuitive considerations

In addition to variations in sensitivity and orientational effects that result from the anisotropy of the MSEF, underlying optical effects can induce distortions in the band shapes and intensities of a reflection spectrum. Therefore, detailing the origin of these effects is necessary before, for example, assigning differences between reflection and transmission spectra to surface-induced changes in the structure or chemical bonding of an organic film. These effects include the reflectivity at the phase 1/phase 2 interface (R_{12}) and the period of the MSEF in phase 2. The effect of R_{12} is a result of the anomalous dispersion of n_2 in the vicinity of an absorption band.

As an example, plots of the real and imaginary parts of the refractive index for the C=O stretch of poly(methyl methacrylate) (PMMA) are shown in Figure 9. For small values of k_2, R_{12} is directly proportional to n_2. Thus the relative contribution of R_{12} to the reflection spectrum of an organic film is greater on the low-energy side of the k_2 maximum. This results in a band with an absorbance maximum that is shifted toward higher energies and has an asymmetric shape. These distortions increase as the thickness of the film increases and the reflectivity of the substrate

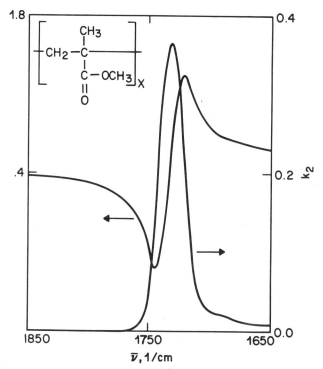

Figure 9. *Complex refractive index for PMMA in the carbonyl stretching region. (Reprinted with permission from M.D. Porter, et al. Anal. Chem. 58 (1986): 2461. Copyright 1986 American Chemical Society.)*

decreases [29,36]. Furthermore, the variation of R_{12} also alters the MSEF in phase 2; that is, the greater R_{12}, the lower the MSEF available to interact with the oscillators in phase 2.

Band shapes and intensities of external reflection spectra are also distorted by the period of the MSEF in phase 2. For small values of k_2, the period of the standing wave in phase 2 is given by

$$x = \frac{1}{(2\bar{v}n_2 \cos \theta_1)},$$ (28)

where x represents the distance between adjacent nodes or antinodes. This equation shows that x is inversely proportional to both $\bar{v}$ and n_2. Thus, as $\bar{v}$ increases, the standing wave contracts (x decreases), concentrating the MSEF in phase 2. In contrast, a decrease in $\overline{v}$ expands the standing wave (x increases); this reduces the MSEF in phase 2.

These considerations indicate that the band shapes and intensities of infrared reflection spectra are a strong function of the relative reflectivity of the substrate and of the thickness and complex refractive index of phase 2. As shown by the examples that follow, the consideration of these optical effects is relevant to the qualitative interpretation of infrared reflection spectra of thin polymer films at all types of reflective surfaces. Furthermore, a quantitative assessment of such effects, based on comparisons of observed and calculated spectra, provides a means to determine the *average* spatial orientation of an organic monomolecular surface structure (see below).

E. Characterization of Polymeric and Monomolecular Films

1. *Band Shape Distortions: PMMA at Glassy Carbon*   The effects of experimental conditions on detectability and on band shape and intensity distortions are shown by the infrared external reflection spectra (IR-ERS) in Figures 10 and 11, which represent the observed and calculated spectra in the carbonyl stretching region for three PMMA films at glassy carbon with average thicknesses of 3270 ± 100, 362 ± 30, and 78 ± 15 Å. Note that *all* inputs into the calculation were experimentally determined. Thin films of PMMA represent an isotropic interfacial structure [38] and therefore illustrate band shape distortions that result *only* from optical effects. Additionally, comparisons between the observed and calculated spectra provide a criterion for assessing the quantitative capabilities of IR-ERS.

Figure 10 shows the observed and calculated spectra for these three films with p-polarized light incident at 60°. As recently re-ported, these conditions provide high detectability at materials with

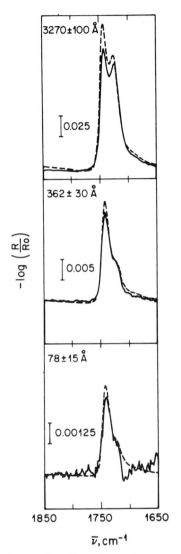

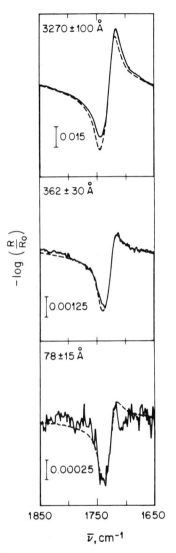

Figure 10. *Experimental (——)
and calculated (- - -) IR-ER spectra for
PMMA films of various thicknesses
at GC: 3270 ± 100 Å; 362 ± 30 Å; and
78 ± 15 Å. The p-polarized light is
incident at 60°. (Reprinted with
permission from M.D. Porter, et al.
Anal. Chem. 58 (1986): 2461.
Copyright 1986 American Chemical
Society.)*

Figure 11. *Experimental (——)
and calculated (- - -) IR-ER spectra for
PMMA films of various thicknesses
at GC: 3270 ± 100 Å; 362 ± 30 Å; and
78 ± 15 Å. The s-polarized light is
incident at 60°. (Reprinted with
permission from M.D. Porter, et al.
Anal. Chem. 58 (1986): 2461.
Copyright 1986 American Chemical
Society.)*

a low IR reflectivity [36]. The ordinate is given as $-\log(R/R_0)$, where R is the reflectance of PMMA/glassy carbon and R_0 is the reflectance of bare glassy carbon (this is the reflection analog of optical absorbance). In all instances, the observed band shapes are dramatically distorted in comparison to those expected for conventional transmission measurements with the polymer dispersed in a KBr matrix. The band shape for the latter measurement is essentially equivalent to that of k_2 in Figure 9. For the observed spectra, absorbance maxima are about 10 cm^{-1} higher in energy than the transmission maximum analog at 1731 cm^{-1}. In fact, the shoulder for the 362 and 78 Å films appears as a distinct peak at 1723 cm^{-1} for the 3270 Å film. As discussed earlier, these band shape distortions result, in part, from the anomalous dispersion of the PMMA refractive index and can be understood qualitatively from the earlier discussion of optical effects and the differences in reflectivities for p- and s-polarized light.

Observed and calculated IR-ERS spectra for the same three films are shown in Figure 11 for an angle of incidence of 60° with s-polarization. These spectra differ dramatically from those in Figure 10. The derivative-like band shapes result from the predominant contribution of the dispersion of n_2. Thus the band shapes strongly resemble the change in n_2. Such distortions, discussed in detail elsewhere [29,36,37], become more pronounced as the thickness of the film increases and are strongly dependent on the angle of incidence and the polarization of the incident light.

2. *Quantitative Aspects of IR-ERS*   A comparison of the observed and calculated band shapes provides a criterion for assessing the quantitative aspects of IR-ERS. Such a comparison represents a verification of the reflection analog of the Beer-Lambert Law. As shown in Figures 10 and 11, the band shapes and intensities for the calculated spectra are predictive of those observed. Observed and calculated peak maxima and minima agree to within 2 cm^{-1}. The integrated absorption strengths for the

observed and calculated spectra agree to better than 93% [36]. These results provide an estimate of the quantitative capabilities of IR-ERS and clearly demonstrate the necessity of considering the inherent differences between ERS and transmission measurements before assigning any band shape and intensity differences to structure or chemical bonding changes of an interfacial structure.

3. *Quantitative Molecular Orientational Analysis* In addition to the characterization of polymeric films, IR-ERS has proven useful for probing the molecular details of ordered monomolecular assemblies at a variety of low surface area materials. The anisotropy of the MSEFs at highly reflective surfaces such as Au provides a means to calculate the average spatial orientation of interfacial surface structures. As described earlier, high surface detectability for IRS is achieved at a grazing angle of incidence with the electric field oriented normal to the surface (p-polarized). In this case, only vibrational modes that have a component of their dipole derivative normal to the surface will interact strongly with the electric field. Because the absorbance of an IR-active vibrational mode is proportional to the square of the scalar product of the incident electric field and the dipole derivative, the average spatial orientation of a given vibrational mode can be calculated as

$$\cos^2 \theta = \frac{A_{\text{obs}}}{3 \, A_{\text{calc}}} \,, \qquad (29)$$

where θ is the angle of orientation of a vibrational mode with respect to the surface normal, and A_{obs} and A_{calc} are the observed and calculated absorbances, respectively, of the vibrational mode [37,39]. Thus, by relating the molecular axis of the adsorbate to the orientation of a vibrational mode, the spatial orientation of the surface structure can be determined. Because the calculated spectra are based on the optical functions of adsorbate precursors, this orientational analysis is applicable only to those vibrational modes that are not strongly perturbed by interactions with the substrate. Modes that are strongly perturbed by interactions with the substrate may undergo changes in force constants and dipole derivatives, invalidating a simple orientational interpretation with Equation (29). More detailed discussions of the limitations of this approach are available [37,39].

4. *Quantitative Characterization of an Organic Monomolecular Assembly at a Metallic Substrate*   A detailed example of the capability of IRS to probe the qualitative and quantitative details of a chemically modified surface is shown in Figures 12 and 13 [40]. These figures show the infrared reflection spectrum of a self-assembled monolayer of arachidic acid [$CH_3(CH_2)_{18}CO_2H$] at a AgO/Ag (native oxide-metal) surface; both contain several structural signatures that are relevant to a molecular-level description of the surface.

The spectrum in Figure 12 provides information concerning bonding between the adsorbate and substrate and the orientation and packing density of the alkyl chains. The absence of a band near 1730 cm^{-1}, together with the presence of an intense band at 1400 cm^{-1} and a weak band at 1514 cm^{-1}, indicates that the reactive chemisorption between the carboxylic acid head group and the AgO/Ag surface converts the acid to a carboxylate salt. Arachidic acid dispersed in a KBr matrix shows an absorption band near 1730 cm^{-1}, attributed to the C=O stretching frequency of the carboxylic acid group, whereas the bands at 1400 cm^{-1} and 1514 cm^{-1} of the monomolecular film are attributed to the symmetric (v_s) and asymmetric (v_a) stretching frequencies of a carboxylate salt, respectively. In addition, the large intensity of v_s with respect to v_a suggests that the carboxylate group exists predominantly as a symmetrically bound bridging ligand.

The spectrum in Figure 12 also provides information about the conformation of the alkyl chains. Studies of crystalline hydrocarbons show that the progressive coupling of the $\omega(CH_2)$ and

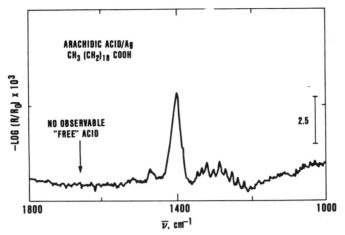

Figure 12. *Infrared external reflection spectrum between 1800 and 1000 cm^{-1} for a spontaneously adsorbed monolayer of arachidic acid on Ag. The p-polarized light is incident at 86°. (Reprinted with permission from N.E. Schlotter, et al. Chem. Phys. Lett. 132 (1986): 93.)*

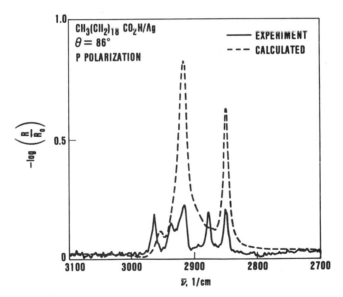

Figure 13. *Observed (———) and calculated (- - -) IR-ER spectra between 3100 and 2700 cm^{-1} for a spontaneously adsorbed monolayer of arachidic acid on Ag. The p-polarized light is incident at 86°. (Reprinted with permission from N.E. Schlotter, et al. Chem. Phys. Lett. 132 (1986): 93.)*

$\gamma(CH_2)$ vibrational modes is a spectroscopic signature of alkyl chains in a fully extended zig-zag conformation [41,42]. Hence, the series of bands between 1350 and 1200 cm^{-1}, which are assigned to the $\omega(CH_2)$ and $\gamma(CH_2)$ modes, indicate that the alkyl chains of the monolayer exhibit this extended conformation and exist in a quasi-crystalline packing environment.

Details of the spatial orientation and packing density of the alkyl chains are provided in Figure 13, which shows an observed and calculated IR-ER spectrum of the monolayer in the C-H stretching region. The bands at 2917 and 2851 cm^{-1} are attributed to $\nu_a(CH_2)$ and $\nu_s(CH_2)$, respectively, and that at 2965 cm^{-1} to $\nu_a(CH_3$, in-plane). The bands at 2938 and 2879 cm^{-1} are assigned to $\nu_s(CH_3)$, which is split as a result of Fermi resonance interactions with a lower energy $\gamma(CH_3)$. These peak positions also indicate that the alkyl chains are in a crystalline environment [41,42].

Evidence regarding the orientation of the alkyl chains can be qualitatively understood by comparing the absorbance of the CH_2 modes (18 CH_2 groups) to that of the $\nu_a(CH_3$, in-plane) mode. Because only those modes that have a component of their transition dipole normal to the surface will be excited by the incident electric field, the near-equivalence of the absorbances indicates that the CH_2 groups are oriented parallel to the surface with a small average tilt. Thus the molecular axes of the alkyl chains exhibit an anisotropic orientation that is near the surface normal. Quantitatively, the orientation of the chains can be calculated by a comparison of the absorbances of the CH_2 modes for the experimental and calculated spectrum with Equation (29). This calculation yields an average tilt of 23°-26° for the molecular axes of the alkyl chains. Such tilts for the alkyl chains are consistent with the symmetric binding of the carboxylate head group to the substrate.

III. EXPERIMENTAL TECHNIQUES AND KEY ISSUES

It has long been recognized that there are two major obstacles to overcome in order to probe electrochemical events with IRS. The first is the strong solvent absorption which can obscure most or all of the measurable optical throughput. The second is the problem of detecting very small absorbances in the presence of the large background (solution) absorbance. The solution for the first obstacle is to use an ultra-thin-layer cell, whereas the second is usually resolved by the application of an optical (polarization) or electrochemical modulation scheme which is coupled with phase-sensitive detection. Examples of thin layer cells [43,44] are shown in Figures 14 and 15. Solution layer thicknesses are ~0.5 - 2.0 μm with aqueous solutions, whereas those in nonaqueous media can be as large as 50 μm. These cells function primarily in an external reflection mode; that is, as shown in Figure 16, the optical beam passes through an IR transparent window, propagates through a thin layer of electrolytic solution, and is

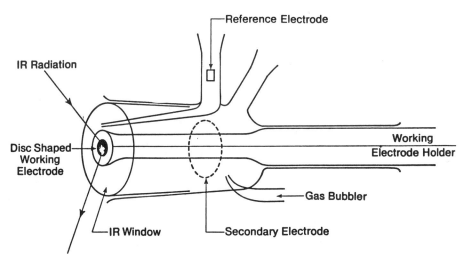

Figure 14. *Schematic diagram of electrochemical infrared cell. Reproduced from Bewick, A., et al. J. Electroanal. Chem., 160 (1984): 47.*

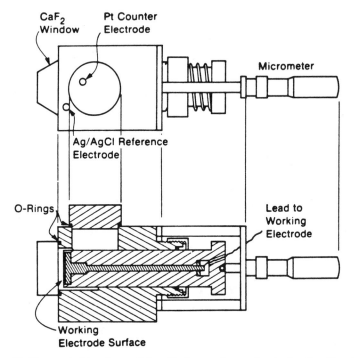

Figure 15. *Top and side views of the thin-layer electrochemical cell with a CaF₂*
window. The side view is shown as a cross-section. (Reprinted with permission
from H. Seki, K. Kunimatsu, W.G. Golden, Appl. Spectrosc. 39 (1985): 137.)

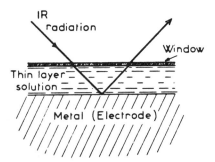

Figure 16. *Schematic diagram for the propagation of light in an external*
reflection spectroscopy measurement. (Reprinted with permission from B. Beden,
C. Lamy, in Spectroelectrochemistry: Theory and Practice, ed.R.J. Gale, New York:
Plenum Press, 1988. 189.)

reflected at the electrode surface. Thus, by coupling the afore-mentioned modulation schemes with the many signal averaging methods readily available by the use of computerized data acquisition and manipulation techniques, it is possible to detect a low analytical signal and separate it from the strong solution absorbance.

In the material that follows in this section, the methodology of IR-SEC is discussed. To start with, a detailed description of the various thin-layer cell designs will be given, including a tabulation of the properties of materials used in their construction. The design and limitations of cells based on internal reflection spectroscopy have been described elsewhere [23]. The discussion of cell designs will be followed by an examination of the two most frequently used modulation techniques employed for the phase-sensitive detection of electrogenerated surface and solution phase species. Other approaches to the in situ applications of IRS to electrochemical problems are essentially variations of electro chemical or polarization modulation techniques and will be dis-cussed when appropriate.

A. Thin-Layer Cells for
Infrared Spectroelectrochemistry

Designs for three-electrode thin-layer SEC cells for external reflection are shown in Figures 14 and 15. In these cells, the solution layer is confined between a flat IR transparent window and a cylindrical electrode. The window is mounted to the cell either with an epoxy resin or with an O-ring seal. The latter method is preferable to eliminate the possible contamination of the electrode and solution from the slow dissolution of the epoxy. The electrode is mounted on a piston constructed either from glass or Kel-F. Electrical connection to the working electrode is made through a channel in the plunger. The electrode surface is usually polished to a specular finish with an alumina slurry. As a final step, the piston is inserted into the cell and polished concurrently to insure that all surfaces are parallel with each other [45,46].

There are two common designs for cell windows, both of which are shown in Figures 14 and 15. The original design used flat windows with IR transparent materials such as silicon, zinc selenide, and calcium fluoride. In much of the early work [43], Si was used to gain access to vibrational modes at the low-energy portion of the mid-IR spectral region. This material is also relatively inert, with a high chemical stability in dilute acidic solutions. However, since Si is not transparent in the visible region, cell alignment and verification of solution filling are problematic. Additionally, the high refractive index of Si produces a high front surface reflection loss. One approach to overcoming these hindrances is to use materials such as CaF_2. This material is transparent in the visible spectral region, has a low refractive index, and is only slightly soluble in acidic solutions. A prismatic window design, as shown in Figure 15, minimizes the reflection losses for high refractive index materials. A listing of various window materials and their chemical properties and optical transparency for IR spectroscopy is given in Table 2. Transmission curves are shown in Figure 17.

An important experimental consequence results from the thin-layer configuration of these cells. This arises from the large uncompensated and nonuniform resistance of the thin solution layer, leading to a relatively long time constant for charging the electrode. Typical time constants are ~5 ms for a solution with 1 M aqueous electrolyte [22]. Thus, distortions of the transient response can be expected in electrochemical modulation experiments that require the flow of large quantities of current.

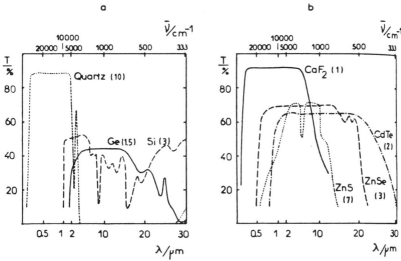

Figure 17. *Plots of transmission (T) versus wavelength in the infrared range for various materials. After ORIEL, Eigenschaften Optischer Materialen, Darmstadt, FRG (1981). Thickness given in millimeters. (Reprinted with permission from B. Beden, C. Lamy, in <u>Spectroelectrochemistry: Theory and Practice</u>, ed.R.J. Gale, New York: Plenum Press, 1988. 189.)*

B. Electrochemical
Modulation Techniques

1. *Electrochemical Modulation Techniques and Dispersive Spectrometers*   The first successful experimental application of infrared reflection spectroscopy to the characterization of the electrochemical interface involved the modulation of the applied voltage at the working electrode [19-23,43]. In this experiment, designated as EMIRS for electrochemically modulated infrared reflectance spectroscopy, the electrode potential undergoes an AC modulation between two potential limits. For measurements with a dispersive instrument, the signal is obtained by scanning slowly and integrating the signal from the monochromator. This approach effectively discriminates against interferences from the bulk electrolytic solution (solvent and supporting electrolyte), allowing the detection of fractional reflectance changes at the 10^{-5} level.

The magnitude of the voltage change may alternate from a few tens to hundreds of millivolts. Modulation rates may vary from a few hertz to tens of hertz, depending on the response characteristics of the spectrometer and the electrochemical system. As a result of the time constant of the thin-layer cell, most applications are limited to a modulation frequency of a few hertz. If the molecular composition or structure at the interface undergoes a change as a result of this modulation, the small AC change in the reflectance signal can be recovered by phase-sensitive detection with a lock-in amplifier. These changes are usually expressed as the difference between two single beam reflectivities, which is ratioed to the reflectivity at one of the applied potentials. The result is a difference spectrum, which is given as

$$\frac{\Delta R}{R} = \frac{R_2(\bar{v}) - R_1(\bar{v})}{R_1(\bar{v})} \quad , \qquad (30)$$

where R_1 and R_2 are the reflectances at applied potentials E_1 and E_2, respectively. The normalization to $R_1(v)$ removes instrument functions such as the instrument energy throughput and detector responsivity, which turns a single beam spectrometer into a pseudo-dual beam spectrometer. For the small values of $\Delta R/R$ often encountered with spectral changes for adsorbates at monolayer surface coverages, this quantity is directly proportional to the more conventional optical absorbance.

The optical layout for an EMIRS spectrometer is shown in Figure 18 [43]. This spectrometer features $f/4$ optics, providing a high energy throughput. The Nernst source is operated at ~2300°C -- above that for normal operation. However, the decrease in source lifetime is offset by increased throughput. A variety of detectors have been used, but liquid N_2 cooled InSb or HgCdTe photoconductive detectors provide the highest optical sensitivity, a key factor in low-throughput measurements. For surface studies, a polarizer selectively passes p-polarized

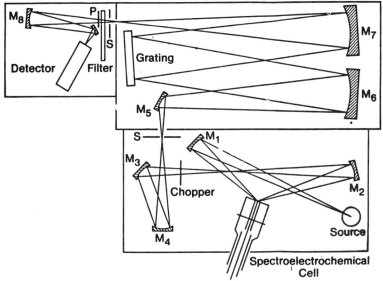

Figure 18. *Schematic diagram of the optics of the EMIRS spectrometer.*
(Reproduced from Bewick, A., et al. J. Electroanal. Chem., 160 (1984): 47.)

radiation. The spectrometer, cell, and detector chambers are purged with dry N_2 to minimize absorption by H_2O and CO_2.

A representative block diagram of the instrumentation used in the EMIRS technique is shown in Figure 19 [22]. The oscillator provides the input waveform to control the frequency and magnitude of the voltage waveform at the electrode. The signal processing, timing sequences, and operation of the monochromator are controlled by computer [43].

2. Electrochemical Modulation Techniques and Fourier Transform Infrared Spectrometers (FT-IRS) It was not long after the development of EMIRS that efforts to exploit the throughput, multiplex, and resolution advantages of FT-IRS were undertaken [44,47]. However, as it applies to studies in electrolytic solutions, the low noise discrimination per scan leads only to a comparable sensitivity with EMIRS. One of the causes of the loss of sensitivity is the limited dynamic range of the A/D converter. Although the amplitude of the centerburst is high, it contains little

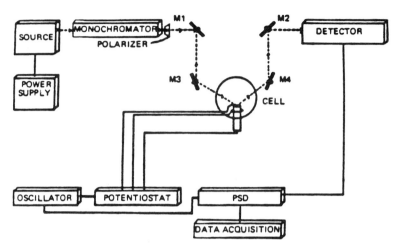

Figure 19. *Block diagram of the instrumentation used for an EMIRS experiment. (Reprinted with permission from Progress in Analytical Spectroscopy, vol. 10, C. Korzenewski and S. Pons, p. 56 Copyright 1987, Pergamon Press.)*

spectral content. Most of the spectroscopic information is located in the wings of the interferogram. As such, the dynamic range of the A/D is limited by the high amplitude of the centerburst, prohibiting the efficient sampling of that part of the interferogram with the most spectral information. Various gain-ranging techniques have been devised to overcome this limitation, and they should be considered in the design of each experiment. In some instances, optical filters that pass only the bandwidth of interest may be useful to enhance sensitivity.

A block diagram of the instrumentation for IR-SEC with a FT-IRS is shown in Figure 20. With the exception of the interferometer, the diagram is equivalent to that in Figure 19 for EMIRS. The basic mode of operation is analogous to that of EMIRS, providing a difference spectrum between two potential limits, E_1 and E_2. When signal averaging over long periods of time, a small number of interferograms are collected successively at the two potential limits. In addition to other advantages [22], "block" co-addition effectively cancels long-term electronic and mechanical drifts and reduces background signals from atmospheric H_2O and CO_2. This approach, which is termed

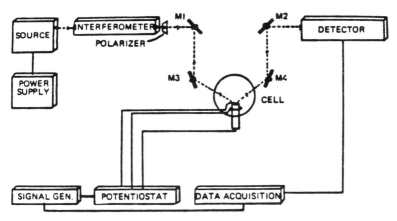

Figure 20. *Block diagram of the instrumentation used for a SNIFTIRS experiment. (Reprinted with permission from Progress in Analytical Spectroscopy, vol. 10, C. Korzenewski and S. Pons, p. 56 Copyright 1987, Pergamon Press.)*

SNIFTIRS for subtractively normalized interfacial Fourier transform infrared spectroscopy, has been used for time-resolved studies [48,49] and for obtaining interfacial spectra in the far IR region [50]. Examples of these and other studies are cited in Table 2.

3. Origins of Band Shapes in Potential Modulation Spectra
Before continuing the discussion of the various modulation techniques, it is worthwhile to examine the underlying factors governing the shapes of the spectral features observed with potential modulation techniques. If it is assumed that E_2 in Equation (30) is more positive than E_1, then many of the most likely band shapes are given in Figure 21 [43]. One possible difference in reflectivity arises from a change in the dielectric function of a metal. This phenomenon, known as the electroreflectance effect, results from the dependence of the number of electrons near the metal surface on the applied potential. Since the reflectivity of metals is governed by the concentration of free electrons near the surface, a change in applied potential induces a change in reflectivity. In the

TABLE 2. Survey of Applications of Infrared
Spectroelectrochemistry.

Chemical Process Observed	Electrode	Type of Modulation	References
Adsorp. of H_2O and D_2O	Pt	Voltage	72,71,88,89,90,73,127
	Au	Voltage	89,127
Adsorp. of H_2	Ag	Voltage	99
	Pt	Voltage	88,97,127
	Rh	Voltage	100,97
Adsorp. of CO, aqueous	Pt	Voltage	77,91,81,116
	Pt	Optical	79,101,80,81,84,85, 98,94,93,121
	Rh	Voltage	91
	Au	Voltage	91
	Pd	Voltage	97,75
Adsorp. of CN^-	Pt	Optical	93,102
	Au	Optical	85,93,102
	Ag	Optical	103,85,93,102,135, 131,130
	Cu	Optical	93,102
Adsorp. of SCN^-	Pt	Voltage	83,137
	Au	Voltage	87
	Ag	Optical	130
	Ag	Voltage	137
Adsorp. of NO	Pt	Optical	81
	Rh	Optical	81
	Au	Optical	81
Diss. adsorp. of CH_3OH	Pt	Voltage	76,77,104,95,97,117, 118,74,104,97,122,124
Diss. adsorp. of C_2H_5OH	Pt	Voltage	120,128
Diss. adsorp. of HCOOH	Pt	Voltage	77,78,92,105,97,122, 132
	Rh	Voltage	119,123

(Continued)

Table 2 (continued)

Chemical Process Observed	Electrode	Type of Modulation	References
Diss. adsorp. of HCHO	Pt	Voltage	106
	Rh	Voltage	106
Mole. adsorp. of HCOOH	Au	Voltage	106
Mole. adsorp. of H_2SO_4	Au	Voltage	87
Reduction of CO_2	Pt	Voltage	107
Anion adsorp. of H_3PO_4	Pt	Voltage	108
	Au	Voltage	86
Anion adsorp. of $CF_3SO_3^-$	Pt	Voltage	109
Adsorp. of CH_3CN	Au	Voltage	73,97,99,110
Adsorp. of difluorobenzene	Pt	Voltage	111
Adsorp. of benzonitrile	Au	Voltage	87
$Fe(CN)_6^{4-/3-}$	Pt	Voltage	87,112,124,140
	Au	Voltage	140
	TiO_2	Voltage	129
Adsorp. of CH_3CN in $LiClO_4$	Pt	Voltage	113,114,83,87
Adsorp. of CH_3CN in TBAF	Pt	Voltage	113,114,81,87
Tetracyanoethylene in CH_3CN	Pt	Voltage	96,83,115,87
Benzophenone in CH_3CN	Pt	Voltage	82,87
Anthracene in CH_3CN	Pt	Voltage	87
2,6-di-t-butyl-4-phenylaniline	Pt	Voltage	83,87
Adsorp. and Orient. of Hydroquinone	Pt	Optical	125,126
Adsorp. and Orient. of HQ sulfonate	Pt	Optical	125
Adsorp. and Orient. of Benzoquinone	Pt	Optical	126
Adsorp. of Azides	Ag	Optical	130
Indole	Pt	Voltage	133

(Continued)

Table 2 (Continued)

Chemical Process Observed	Electrode	Type of Modulation	References
Pyrene	Pt	Voltage	134
Acrylonitrile	Au	Voltage	134
Acetic Acid	Pt	Voltage	136
	Au	Voltage	136
Adsorp. of SO_2	Pt	Voltage	138
Adsorp. of HSO_4^- and SO_4^{2-}	Pt	Optical	139

Portions taken from Reference. 23.

Abbreviations: Diss. adsorp. - dissociative adsorption; Mole. adsorp. - molecular adsorption; Reduct. - reduction; Orient. - orientation

ultraviolet and visible spectral regions, the electroreflectance effect can markedly complicate the interpretation of a difference spectrum. However, the effect usually leads to small structureless shifts in the baseline of a spectrum in the IR region that are negligible [Fig. 21A]. A difference spectrum such as that shown in Figures 21B and 21C may result from an absorption band that is present only at E_1 or E_2. Such changes could be caused by the dependence of the oscillator strength of a vibrational mode, the concentration of a species present in the solution or surface layer, or the orientation of an adsorbate with respect to the surface on the applied potential at the electrode. This latter case arises from the infrared surface selection rule [see Equation (29)]. Bipolar features, similar to those given in Figures 21D and 21E, may be caused by a change in the position or shape of the band as a function of applied potential. Changes in the donation or withdrawal of electron density with applied potential between an adsorbate and an electrode may give rise to this spectral band shape.

Clearly, numerous factors can influence the shape of the observed spectral feature. However, in cases where a more detailed understanding of the origins of a band shape is required, the integration of a potential modulation spectrum should yield a

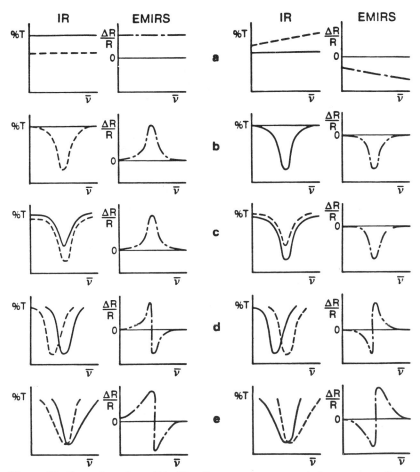

Figure 21. *Examples of possible IR reflectance spectra and the corresponding EMIRS difference spectra. The spectra at the two different potentials are distinguished by the full lines and the dashed lines and the difference spectrum is plotted as a dotted/dashed line. Reproduced from Bewick, A., et al. J. Electroanal. Chem., 160 (1984): 47.*

reasonably interpretable "absolute" spectrum. The application of the polarization modulation technique, described in the next section, also provides an opportunity to resolve such questions.

4. *Polarization Modulation Techniques* An alternative method to obtain an in situ infrared spectrum at the electrochemical interface derives its surface sensitivity from the anisotropy of the MSEF at a metal surface. With this technique [141,47,51], the

polarization of the incident light is modulated between p- and s-polarization with a photoelastic modulator (PEM). For a ZnSe PEM, the modulation rate is 74 kHz. Since only p-polarized light is surface sensitive, the modulation between the two polarizations yields an AC signal due to the species at the electrode surface. This results from the fact that the intensity for p- and s-polarized light will, on the average, be attenuated to the same degree by any randomly oriented gas or liquid phase molecules. With this technique, known as infrared reflection absorption spectroscopy (IRRAS), IR-SEC measurements can be performed without an alteration of the applied potential.

The key instrumental component to the application of this technique is the PEM, the principles of which are well established [51]. The PEM [Fig. 22] is essentially an IR transparent crystal with an isotropic refractive index. The device works by the application of a periodic strain with a piezoelectric transducer along one axis of the crystal and at the frequency of its fundamental longitudinal mode. The strain produces a periodic change in the refractive index of the crystal, resulting in a periodic phase retardation of the incident light with its polarization along the fundamental mode. This effectively rotates the polarization of the incident beam. Thus, by orienting the stressed axis of the PEM 45° from the surface normal and by placing a fixed polarizer

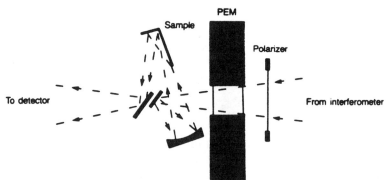

Figure 22. *Optical configuration for polarization-double-modulation FT-IRRAS. The photoelastic modulator and fixed-polarizer assembly modulate the polarization of the light incident on the sample surface. (Reprinted with permission from W.G. Golden, D.D. Saperstein, J. Electron Spectrosc. Relat. Phenom., 30 (1983): 43.)*

in the optical path to pass either s- or p-polarized light, the light incident on the electrode surface can be modulated between both polarizations.

A schematic diagram for signal processing for IRRAS measurements that employ a FT-IRS is given in Figure 23. This electronic configuration splits the signal from the detector preamplifier into two channels which are demodulated separately. One signal passes through the conventional circuitry of the instrument. This signal contains the normal single beam interferogram and equals the sum of the energy throughputs for s- and p-polarized light $(I_p + I_s)$. In the other channel, the signal is demodulated at the PEM frequency and filtered to yield an interferogram that equals $(I_p - I_s)$. After further software manipulation and Fourier transformation, the quotient of $(I_p + I_s)/(I_p - I_s)$ provides a spectrum of the surface species. A block diagram of this instrument is shown in Figure 24. Further details of the basic principles, electrical circuitry, and data manipulation are available [47].

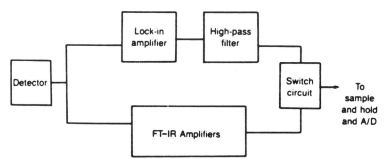

Figure 23. *Schematic of the polarization-double-modulation FT-IRRAS signal processing arrangement. The signal from the detector preamplifier is split into two channels, and each channel is demodulated separately. Reprinted with permission from W.G. Golden, D.D. Saperstein, J. Electron Spectrosc. Relat. Phenom., 30 (1983): 43.)*

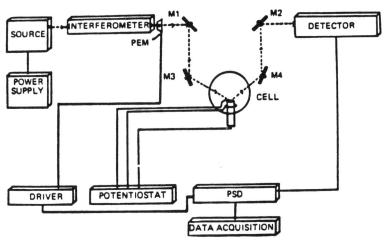

Figure 24. *Block diagram of the instrumentation used for an IRRAS experiment. (Reprinted with permission from Progress in Analytical Spectroscopy, vol. 10, C. Korzenewski and S. Pons, p. 56 Copyright 1987, Pergamon Press.)*

IV. APPLICATIONS

As is apparent from the previous discussions, the development of techniques for the application of IRS to the in situ characterization of the electrochemical interface has provided a means to examine a multitude of traditional as well as contemporary fundamental and practical questions. Selected examples are listed in Table 2. This table is not intended to be exhaustive, but rather to illustrate the broad ranging utility of this rapidly developing research area. Applications range from species adsorbed on the electrode surface to species formed in the thin layer of solution immediately adjacent to the electrode surface, and from aqueous to nonaqueous solvents. In view of the breadth of the applications, and to demonstrate the utility of this technique, the following discussion is restricted to three separate research topics.

The first example discusses the adsorption of the products from the electrocatalytic oxidation of methanol at single and polycrystalline platinum electrodes. This example is of relevance in view of the enormous importance of electrode poisoning by CO adsorption in electrocatalytic processes. The second example deals with the potential dependence of the adsorption of difluorobenzene at a polycrystalline platinum electrode. This example demonstrates the capability of IR-SEC to characterize the nondissociative adsorption of molecular species at an electrode. The last example discusses the application of IR-SEC to the examination of electrochemical processes in nonaqueous solvents. In this latter example, two studies are described. One involves the elucidation of the differences in the reversibility of the reduction of tetracyanoethylene in acetonitrile as a function of the supporting electrolyte. The other examines the structure of the double layer at a platinum electrode as a function of the water content in acetonitrile.

A. Adsorbed Intermediates and Poisons in the Electrocatalytic Oxidation of Methanol at a Platinum Electrode

The immense interest in the electrocatalytic oxidation of small organic hydrocarbons stems from their potential as fuels for energy production. However, the development of such electrochemically based power sources has been greatly inhibited by the poisoning of the electrode surface as a result of the gradual adsorption of intermediates and/or products at active sites for the heterogeneous electron-transfer process. The elucidation of these reaction mechanisms and the identification of these poison(s) are therefore of fundamental and practical importance toward increasing the catalytic activity and long-term stability of electrode materials.

The exact nature of the adsorbed species formed from the electrooxidation of fuel hydrocarbons such as methanol and ethanol has been the subject of extensive controversy since the early 1960s [52-56]. As an example, the structures proposed for adsorbed methanol include CO [52], HCO [53], COH [54], $COOH + HCO$ [55], and $COOH + CO$ [56]. The electrochemical behavior and interpretation become more complex for the longer chain homologs, viz. ethanol [23], as well as for acidic moieties such as formic acid [57], acetic acid [58], and benzoic acid [59].

The inability to identify accurately the structure of the adsorbate has led to the proposal of numerous mechanistic pathways for electrooxidation reactions. Of the previously cited studies, the electrocatalytic oxidation of methanol at a platinum electrode is an excellent example for illustrating the problem solving capability of IR-SEC. The two most commonly proposed intermediates of this reaction are COH [54] and CO [52]. For the COH intermediate, the reaction mechanism is

$$CH_3OH \longrightarrow COH_{(ads)} + 3H_{(ads)} \qquad (31)$$

$$3H_{(ads)} \longrightarrow 3H^+_{(aq)} + 3e^- \text{ (at E>0.4 V vs. SHE)} \qquad (32)$$

$$COH_{(ads)} + H_2O \longrightarrow CO_2 + 3H^+_{(aq)} + 3e^- \qquad (33)$$

where the COH intermediate is adsorbed at three adjacent platinum sites [60]. In contrast, the reaction mechanism that involves adsorbed CO as the principal intermediate [61,62] is written as

$$CH_3OH \longrightarrow CO_{(ads)} + 4H_{(ads)} \qquad (34)$$

$$4H_{(ads)} \longrightarrow 4H^+_{(aq)} + 4e^- \text{ (at E>0.4 V vs. SHE)} \qquad (35)$$

$$CO_{(ads)} + H_2O \longrightarrow CO_2 + 2H^+_{(aq)} + 2e^- \qquad (36)$$

As is apparent, the controversy regarding the structure of the adsorbed intermediate can be readily resolved with IR-SEC.

The earliest attempts at applying IR-SEC to deduce the structure of the adsorbed intermediate of the electrooxidation of methanol at platinum employed EMIRS [63]. From the difference spectrum in Figure 25, linearly bonded =C=O (=C=O linked to one surface atom) was identified as the principle adsorbate with a strong spectral feature at ~2080 cm^{-1}. The presence of a bridge-bonded =C=O (=C=O linked to two surface atoms) was also evident from the spectral feature at ~1860 cm^{-1}.

These observations were confirmed in two subsequent studies, each of which utilized different modulation techniques. The first confirmation employed a variation of the potential modulation technique to construct an "absolute" reflectance spectrum [64]. With this technique, the change in reflectance is monitored at several fixed wavelengths during the imposition of a linear sweep of the electrode potential. Thus, by taking the difference between the reflectance at a given potential and that at a reference potential (a potential where the adsorbed species is absent), an accurate representation of an absorbance spectrum can be reconstructed. Spectra obtained with this approach are shown in Figure 26. The spectrum corresponding to the electrode potential 1.3 V (vs. NHE) exhibits a maximum for $\Delta R/R$ at ~2062 cm^{-1}, which is consistent with a linearly bonded CO intermediate. Studies with an analogous technique, which exploits the multiplex advantage of FT-IRS to examine the time evolution of irreversible electrochemical processes [65], reached similar conclusions regarding the nature of the principal adsorbate [57]. Interestingly, at applied potentials where CO electrooxidation proceeds at a slow rate, this latter study suggested that the linearly bonded CO may act as an adsorbed

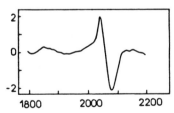

Figure 25. *EMIRS spectrum of CO adsorbed on a Pt electrode in 0.5 M HClO$_4$. CO produced from the chemisorption of 0.25 M CH$_3$OH. (Reprinted with permission from B. Beden, C. Lamy, in <u>Spectroelectrochemistry: Theory and Practice</u>, ed.R.J. Gale, New York: Plenum Press, 1988. 189.)*

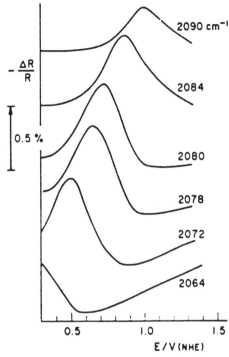

Figure 26. *Change with potential of the IR reflection absorption spectrum of the linearly adsorbed CO species on a Pt electrode. (Reproduced from Kunimatsu, K.; J. Electroanal. Chem., 145 (1983): 219.)*

intermediate (and not as a poison) for methanol oxidation. It is important to recognize, however, that these latter conclusions may be extremely dependent on the modulation rate.

Another confirmation of the nature of the adsorbate for the electrooxidation of methanol employed IRRAS [66]. However, the polarization of the incident light was accomplished with a rotating polarizer as opposed to a photoelastic modulator. These studies examined the relationships between the potential and the time dependence of the formation of the linearly bonded CO from methanol and its effect on electrocatalytic activity. As shown by the infrared spectra in Figure 27, the band intensity for the linearly bonded CO is greatly reduced as the applied potential becomes more negative. This indicates that the formation of the adsorbate becomes more difficult as the initial coverage of adsorbed

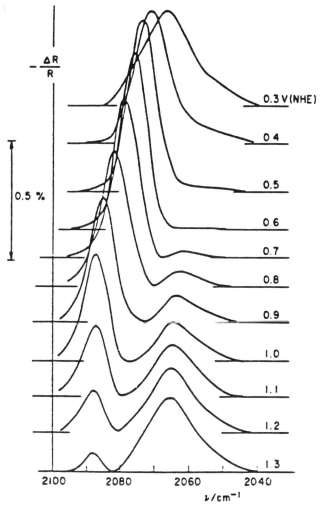

Figure 27. *Potential dependence of the C-O stretching band of the linear CO derived from CH₃OH. (Reproduced from Kunimatsu, K., Kita, H.; J. Electroanal. Chem., 218 (1987): 155.)*

hydrogen increases, which is consistent with the reaction in Equation (34). The dependence of the electrolysis rate on the coverage of the adsorbate [Fig. 28] shows that as CO is oxidatively removed from the surface by the application of an increasingly positive potential, the current for the oxidation of methanol

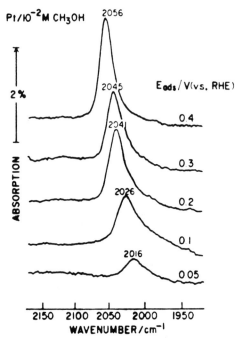

Figure 28. *Potential dependence of the integrated band intensity of the C-O stretching band of the linear CO derived from CH₃OH at 0.4 V in 1 M (1) and 10 mM (2) CH₃OH solutions, respectively. Curve 3 shows the potential dependence of the CH₃OH oxidation current observed after CH₃OH adsorption at 0.4 V in 1 M CH₃OH solution. (Reproduced from Kunimatsu, K., Kita, H.; J. Electroanal. Chem., 218 (1987): 155.)*

increases dramatically. These results point to the role of adsorbed CO as a catalytic poison for the electrooxidation of methanol.

Other studies have examined systematically the structure and distribution of adsorbates as a function of methanol concentration [67] and of the crystalline morphology of the platinum surface [68]. Above methanol concentrations of $\sim 10^{-2}$ M, the predominant form of the adsorbate at polycrystalline platinum is the linearly bonded CO. However, almost equal amounts of both a linearly bonded (2080 cm^{-1}) and bridge-bonded (1860 cm^{-1}) CO were observed at concentrations below $\sim 5 \times 10^{-3}$ M [Fig. 29]. A new band (~ 1700 cm^{-1}), which was tentatively assigned to the carbonyl stretch of a weakly adsorbed aldehyde-like functionality, was also detected. Interestingly, all three species [see Fig. 30]

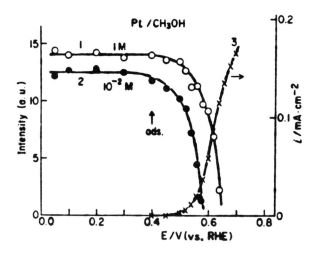

Figure 29. *EMIR spectra of the adsorbed species resulting from the chemisorption at a Pt electrode of 10^{-3} M, 10^{-1} M, and 5 M CH_3OH in 0.5 M $HClO_4$. (Reproduced from B. Beden, et al. J. Electroanal. Chem. 238 (1987): 323.)*

were found to exist at the surface of single crystals of Pt(100), Pt(110), and Pt(111). Further, at Pt(100), these adsorbates were observed over a wide range of methanol concentrations. Together, these results have led to a new interpretation of the mechanism involved in the poisoning of the platinum surface, implicating the importance of lateral interactions between adsorbed CO species.

B. Molecular Adsorption: Difluorobenzene at a Polycrystalline Platinum Electrode

The adsorption of aromatic molecules at electrode surfaces has been a long-standing concern to electrochemists [15]. Such studies have particular relevance to a variety of surface electrochemical processes, including electrocatalysis, chemical and clinical analysis, electroplating, etching, and passivation. Additionally, such studies promise to enhance our basic under

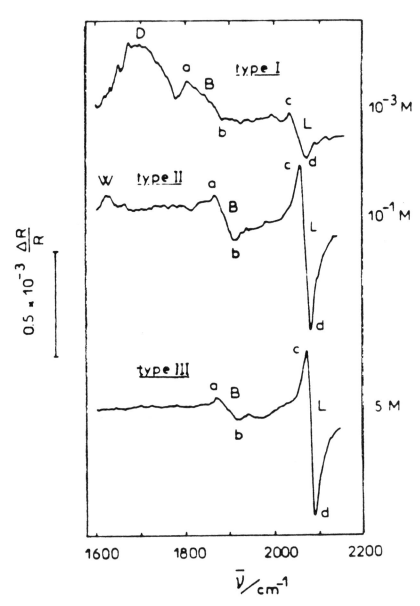

Figure 30. *EMIR spectra of the adsorbed species resulting from the chemisorption of 0.1 M CH$_3$OH in 0.5 M HClO$_4$ at a Pt single-crystal electrode. Exposed face (A) Pt(100); (B) Pt(110); (C) Pt(111). (Reproduced from B. Beden, et al. J. Electroanal. Chem. 238 (1987): 323.)*

standing of surface reaction kinetics, surface acid-base chemistry, and solvation at surfaces.

In many instances, aromatic molecules adsorb at a metal with the ring parallel to the surface, interacting through π-orbitals. Based on analogous structures in organometallic chemistry, this type of bonding most likely occurs through the sigma-donation of electrons in the π-orbitals of the aromatic ring into vacant metal orbitals. Electron density is then returned to the empty π^*-orbitals of the adsorbate via d-π^* back-bonding. Such interactions should induce a decrease in the bond strength of the chemical bonds that are coupled strongly with these molecular orbitals, resulting in a shift of the affected vibrational modes to lower energy. In addition, by variation of the applied potential, the extent of the sigma-donation and d-π^* back bonding can be systematically addressed.

Recently, an extensive series of studies by Hubbard and coworkers has examined the adsorption of a variety of quinone-like moieties at the surface of polycrystalline platinum electrodes as a function of molecular structure, electrolyte, temperature, and pH [15]. These studies, which employed a multiple-injection thin-layer coulometry technique, have suggested a surprisingly intricate dependence of the adsorbate orientation on the solute concentration. For simple quinone-like structures, the orientation changes with increasing solute concentration from that of a closest-packed monolayer with the aromatic ring parallel to the surface to that of a closest-packed layer with the ring along the surface normal. However, although these coulometric measurements provide a detailed macroscopic description of the surface structure in terms of its interfacial concentration, unraveling details of the bonding and structural perturbations of the adsorbate due to its interaction with the electrode requires the application of an in situ molecular-level surface probe.

Pons and Bewick [69] have recently studied the adsorption of p-difluorobenzene and its ortho- and meta-substituted isomers at a polycrystalline platinum electrode with IR-SEC. These experiments, which were performed with the SNIFTIRS version of the potential modulation technique, examined the adsorption as a function of applied potential and solution concentration. For p-difluorobenzene, thirteen of the normal vibrations are infrared active. Those accessible in the mid-infrared region are listed in Table 3, which includes peak positions and symmetry groups. All ten of the B_{1u} and B_{2u} modes undergo a change in their dipole moment in the plane of the aromatic ring, whereas those of the two B_{3u} modes are perpendicular to the plane of the ring. Thus, based on the earlier discussion of the infrared surface selection rule, if the aromatic moiety adsorbs with the plane of the ring parallel (flat) to the surface, only the B_{3u} modes would be evident in an infrared spectrum. In contrast, only the B_{1u} and B_{2u} modes would be observed if the adsorbate adopted an orientation parallel

TABLE 3   Symmetry Groups and Band Assignments for the Infrared Active Modes of p-difluorobenzene.

Symmetry	Vibrational mode	Wavenumber
B_{1u}	C-H stretch	3050 cm^{-1}
B_{1u}	C-H stretch	1511 cm^{-1}
B_{1u}	C-F stretch	1212 cm^{-1}
B_{1u}	C-H bend	1012 cm^{-1}
B_{1u}	C-C bend	737 cm^{-1}
B_{2u}	C-H stretch	3080 cm^{-1}
B_{2u}	C-C stretch	1437 cm^{-1}
B_{2u}	C-C-C stretch	1300 cm^{-1}
B_{2u}	C-H bend	1085 cm^{-1}
B_{2u}	C-F bend	350 cm^{-1}
B_{3u}	C-H umbrella	833 cm^{-1}
B_{3u}	C-C-C bend	509 cm^{-1}
B_{3u}	C-F in phase	186 cm^{-1}

to the surface. For instances where the adsorbate exhibits a random orientation at the surface, all twelve transitions would be observed, with the absorbance of each proportional to its orientation [see Equation (29)].

The difference spectrum for a 0.5 mM solution of p-difluorobenzene in 1.0 M perchloric acid between the potential limits of +0.20 (reference potential) and +0.40 V vs. NHE at platinum is shown in Figure 31. At this solution concentration, combined with the volume of the thin solution layer, the total quantity of p-difluorobenzene is slightly less than that required to form a closest-packed monolayer of the adsorbate in its flat orientation. The bands with positive values of $\Delta R/R$ result from the solution phase species at +0.20 V; those with negative values of $\Delta R/R$ correspond to the adsorbed species at +0.4 V. In Figures 31A - 31C, those bands that have been assigned to B_{1u} and B_{2u} modes have positive values of $\Delta R/R$. In contrast, as shown in Fig. 31D, those modes with B_{3u} symmetry exhibit a bipolar shape.

These observations are consistent with a potential-dependent adsorption process where the aromatic species is adsorbed with its ring parallel to the electrode surface. Thus, the positive values of $\Delta R/R$ (for the B_{1u} and B_{2u} modes) correspond to a decrease in the solution concentration of the aromatic species at +0.4 V relative to that at +0.2 V. As a result of the IR surface selection rules, the bipolar shapes of the B_{3u} bands result from a decrease in the solution concentration of the adsorbate combined with a decrease in the peak frequency of the adsorbed species. In solution, the absorbance maxima for these latter two bands are 833 and 509 cm^{-1}. However, as a result of the electronic interactions of the aromatic species with the metal, the bond order, and hence, the peak frequency of the B_{3u} modes decrease. Similar observations and conclusions were reached in studies of the adsorption of o- and m- difluorobenzene at platinum.

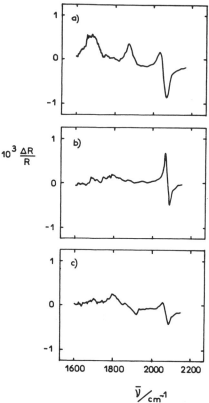

$10^3 \dfrac{\Delta R}{R}$

$\bar{\nu}/_{cm^{-1}}$

Figure 31. *Difference spectrum for p-difluorobenzene at a Pt mirror electrode in 1.0 M perchloric acid solution. Modulation limits are +0.200 V vs. NHE (base potential) and +0.400 V. (A) and (B) are the coaddition of 1600 normalized scans and (C) and (D) are the coaddition of 450 normalized scans. (Reprinted with permission from S. Pons, A. Bewick, Langmuir 1 (1985): 141. Copyright 1985 American Chemical Society.)*

The influence of applied potential on the band shapes for the B_{3u} C-C-C out-of-plane bend of p-difluorobenzene at platinum is shown in Figure 32. This figure shows $\Delta R/R$ spectra at different amplitudes of potential modulation relative to a reference potential of +0.2 V. As is apparent, the negative portion of the bipolar band shifts progressively to lower energies, whereas that attributed to the solution-phase species remains unchanged. These observations indicate an increase in the donation of π-electron density from the adsorbate to the metal, consistent with the above discussion.

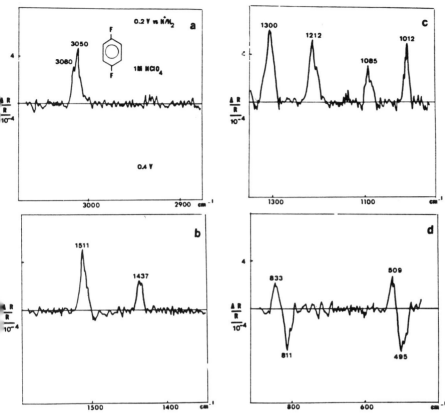

Figure 32. *Difference spectrum of p-difluorobenzene as a function of the magnitude of the modulation potential. (Reprinted with permission from S. Pons, A. Bewick, Langmuir 1 (1985): 141. Copyright 1985 American Chemical Society.)*

This study also examined the effect of the solute concentration (0.08 - 1.4 mM) of p-difluorobenzene on adsorption [Fig. 33]. The two concentration ranges shown, $\Delta R/R$ for the B_{3u} C-C-C out-of-phase bend of both the adsorbed and solution phase species increase as concentration increases. This indicates that the surface coverage of the adsorbate increases as the concentration of the solution phase analog increases. Furthermore (although not shown in this figure), bands for the in-plane (B_{1u} and B_{2u}) vibrational modes appeared at the higher concentrations. These results suggest that as the solution concentration of p-difluoro-benzene increases, the adsorbate reorients from a flat to a skewed or perhaps randomly oriented structure.

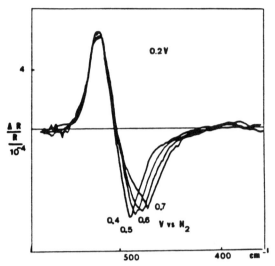

Figure 33. *Difference spectrum of p-difluorobenzene as a function of substrate concentration. ((Reprinted with permission from S. Pons, A. Bewick, Langmuir 1 (1985): 141. Copyright 1985 American Chemical Society.)*

C. Solution and Double Layer Studies

The coupling of potential modulation techniques with FT-IRS has also provided an invaluable tool for the detection of short-lived electrolysis products that accumulate in the diffusion layer [19-23]. Typically, a difference infrared spectrum is obtained by modulating the potential between a base value where only reactants are present and a value where electrolysis products are formed. An interesting example results from the complex electrochemical behavior of organic radical cations and anions, such as that of tetracyanoethylene (TCNE) in aprotic solvents [21]. For the one-electron reduction of TCNE, the radical anion is formed reversibly near 0 V vs. Ag/Ag$^+$ (0.1 M AgNO$_3$) with either n-butyl ammonium tetrafluoroborate (TBAF) or lithium perchlorate as a supporting electrolyte. On the other hand, the reduction of the radical anion to the dianion is quasi-reversible at roughly -0.9 V with (TBAF) as the supporting electrolyte, whereas with lithium perchlorate as the electrolyte, the reduction is more reversible and occurs at about -0.7 V. Factors which may explain these disparate observations include the complexation of the radical anion, conproportionation of the dianion and neutral species, and electrode deactivation caused by the adsorption of electrolysis products.

Infrared difference spectra, obtained by SNIFTIRS, for the one-electron reduction of TCNE in acetonitrile with both TBAF and $LiClO_4$ electrolytes are shown in Figure 34. These spectra were observed regardless of the polarization of the incident light, confirming that all of the bands result from solution phase species. With the anion spectra, both the relative intensity and position of the bands are independent of the electrolyte. The similarity of the infrared spectra for the TCNE radical anion prepared by other means supports the observed electrochemical behavior. The band at 2187 cm^{-1} has been assigned to the B_{1u}, -C≡N stretch, whereas that at 2146 cm^{-1} was attributed to the B_{2u}, -C≡N mode. These bands appear at lower energies than those of the neutral species as a result of the injection of electron density into an unoccupied antibonding orbital.

In contrast to those observed for the TCNE radical anion, the infrared spectra [Fig. 35] for the dianion are markedly different in the two supporting electrolytes. In TBAF, vibrational bands appear at 2141 and 2075 cm^{-1}, whereas in $LiClO_4$ these bands are at 2175 and 2101 cm^{-1}. As discussed for the TCNE radical anion, the decrease in energy for these vibrational modes results from an increase in the electron density in an antibonding orbital. However, the extent of the shift of these bands is less with $LiClO_4$ than with TBAF in solution. Such an observation suggests that ion-pair formation with the more electropositive (and hence polarizing) Li^+, stabilizes the dianion by removal of electron density from the lowest occupied antibonding orbital. Thus, the reduction of the TCNE radical anion proceeds more readily in $LiClO_4$ than in TBAF, in accord with the observed electrochemical response.

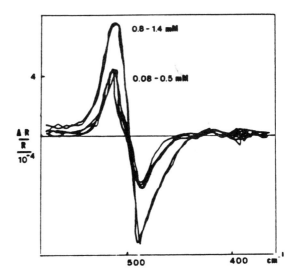

Figure 34. *SNIFTIRS difference spectra for the reduction of TCNE (5 mM) to form the radical anion. Solutions contained acetonitrile and (A) 0.1 M LiClO$_4$ and (B) TBAF as supporting electrolyte. The potential was modulated from 0.5 to -0.5 V (vs. Ag/Ag$^+$) using a Pt electrode. Thin layer thickness ca. 50 μm. (Reprinted with permission from K. Ashley, S. Pons, Chemical Reviews, 88 (1988): 673.)*

D. Double Layer Studies

One of the long-standing questions in electrochemistry is the fundamental nature of the electrical double layer [70]. Contemporary models of the double layer describe the solution side of the electrified interface as an ordered region of ions and solvent molecules. The composition and thickness of the layer depend on the electrode charge, the ionic size, composition, and concentration of the supporting electrolyte, and temperature. These models have been derived from differential capacitance and interfacial surface tension data. However, these techniques provide only a macroscopic description of the double layer. Thus, the development and application of in situ techniques to probe the molecular architecture of the interface are requisite to unraveling the microscopic details of the double layer.

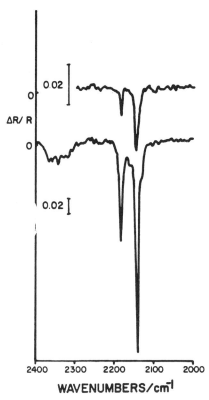

Figure 35. *SNIFTIRS spectra for the reduction of TCNE to TCNE²⁻ in the solution described in figure 34. The potential was modulated from +0.5 to -1.2 V in the solution containing LiClO₄ (A). The potential was modulated from +0.5 to -2.0 V in the spectrum containing TBAF (B). The potential is with reference to Ag/Ag⁺. (Reprinted with permission from K. Ashley, S. Pons, Chemical Reviews, 88 (1988): 673.)*

As listed in Table 2, there have been several recent applications of IR-SEC to the characterization of the electrical double layer. A particularly interesting study has examined the double layer structure in acetonitrile solutions as a function of the composition and concentration of the supporting electrolyte [21]. Spectra obtained with SNIFTIRS at a platinum electrode in anhydrous acetonitrile and 0.1 M TBAF are given in Figure 36. These spectra were obtained by the variation of the size of the potential step while maintaining the same base potential. Bands with positive values for $\Delta R/R$ correspond to species present at the base

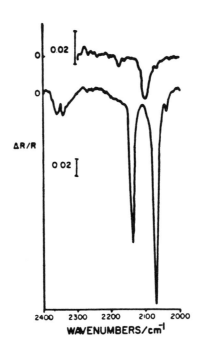

ΔR/R

WAVENUMBERS/cm⁻¹

Figure 36. *SNIFTIRS difference spectrum at a Pt electrode of 0.1 M TBAF in nominally dry acetonitrile. (Reproduced from S. Pons, T. Davidson, A. Bewick, J. Electroanal. Chem. 140 (1982) 211.)*

potential of -0.5 V vs. Ag/Ag⁺ (0.1 M AgNO₃), whereas those with negative values represent the predominant species at the higher potential. These spectra show large changes in four separate regions, each of which increase in magnitude with an increase in applied potential. The band at 1060 cm⁻¹ was assigned to adsorbed TBAF anion. The magnitude of this band increases as a result of the need to balance the increased surface charge on the metal as the applied potential increases. An explanation for increases in the ν(-C≡N) band for adsorbed acetonitrile at 2350 cm⁻¹ with applied potential proceeds in an analogous fashion.

The effects of the addition of 0.1 M H_2O to the TBAF/aceto-nitrile solution give rise to the infrared reflection spectra in Figure 37.   In comparison to Figure 35, two new bands are observed. These bands are attributed to the OH stretching and bending vibrations at ~3350 and ~1650 cm^{-1}, respectively.   The bending vibration exhibits a negative value for $\Delta R/R$, indicating that H_2O is preferentially replaced in the double layer by the TBAF anion as the applied potential becomes more positive.   In contrast, the stretching vibration has a bipolar shape, which is likely a result of the complex dependence of this mode on hydrogen bonding interactions.

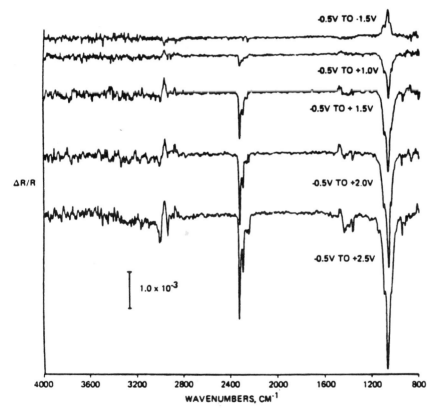

Figure 37. *Same as figure 36 except with 0.1 M water added.   ((Reproduced from S. Pons, T. Davidson, A. Bewick, J. Electroanal. Chem. 140 (1982) 211.)*

V. CONCLUSIONS

We have discussed the development and application of infrared reflection spectroscopy as an in situ probe of the electrochemical interface. This research area has undergone an explosive growth since the pioneering work of Bewick and Pons [71] only seven years ago. As shown in Table 2, applications vary from the characterization of adsorbate orientation at submonolayer concentrations at electrode surfaces to the determination of short-lived radical ions in the diffusion layer, and from aqueous to non-aqueous solvents. Efforts to improve the sensitivity of these measurements will undoubtedly open the way to probe the reaction dynamics [48,49] of a variety of heterogeneous and homogeneous chemical processes. The development of approaches to extend the accessible wavelength range to the far infrared [50] promises to yield information regarding interactions between the adsorbate and metal substrate as well as changes in the vibrational modes of species confined within the electrical double layer. Additionally, the expansion of efforts to examine electrochemical processes at a well-defined single crystal with IR-SEC will enhance the fundamental understanding of mechanisms relevant, for example, to electrocatalysis, providing the requisite information to design materials with a surface texture that is less susceptible to poisoning.

As a last point, it should be noted that by virtue of its high sensitivity, IR-SEC investigations present several experimental complexities. The selection of the appropriate modulation technique and other experimental variables are heavily dependent on the specific chemical system. Thus, the accurate interpretation of the spectral data relies not only on a detailed understanding of underlying principles of these measurements, e.g. classical electromagnetic theory, Fourier transform spectroscopy, and phase-sensitive detection techniques, but also on an extensive a priori understanding of the electrochemical behavior of the system under investigation.

ACKNOWLEDGEMENTS

MDP gratefully acknowledges the support of a Dow Corning Assistant Professorship and a Society of Analytical Chemists of Pittsburgh Starter Grant Award. DDP expresses his gratitude for the support of a BP-America Fellowship. Acknowledgement is also made to the Donors of the Petroleum Research Fund for partial support of this work. Ames Laboratory is operated for the U.S. Department of Energy by Iowa State University under Contract No. W-7405-ENG-82. This work was partially supported by the Office of Basic Energy Sciences, Chemical Science Division.

References

1. Wu, S. *Polymer Interfaces and Adhesion*. New York: Marcel Dekker, 1982.
2. Roberts, G. *Adv. Phys.* 34 (1985): 475.
3. Bowden, F., and Tabor, D. *The Friction and Lubrication of Solids*. London: Oxford Press, 1968, and references therein.
4. Baier, R., et al. *J. Biomed. Mat. Res.* 18 (1984): 337.
5. A. Gristina, *Science* 237 (1987): 1588.
6. Swalen, J., et al. *Langmuir* 3 (1987): 932.
7. Murray, R. W. In Electroanalytical Chemistry, ed. A.J. Bard, vol. 13. New York: Marcel Dekker, 1984.
8. Faulkner, L.R. *Chem. Eng. News* 62 (1984): 28.
9. Fujihira, M. In Topics In Organic Electrochemistry, ed. A.J. Fry and W. Britton. New York: Plenum Press, 1986.
10. Wrighton, M.S. *Science* 231 (1986): 32.
11. Hubbard, A.T. *Acc. Chem.Res.* 13 (1980): 177.
12. Bard, A.J. *J. Chem. Educ.* 60 (1983): 302.
13. Murray, R.W.; Ewing, A.G.; and Durst, R.A. *Anal. Chem.* 59 (1987): 379A.
14. Anson, F.C. *Acc. Chem. Res.* 8 (1975): 400.
15. Hubbard, A.T. *Chem. Rev.* 88 (1988): 633.
16. Bellier, J.; Lecoeur, J.; and Rousseau, A. *J. Electroanal. Chem.* 200 (1986): 55.
17. Peukert, M., and Ibach, H. *Surf. Sci.* 136 (1984): 319.
18. Bewick, A., and Pons, B.S. In *Advances In Infrared and Raman Spectroscopy*, ed. R.J.H. Clark and R.E. Hester, vol. 12, 1-63. London: Wiley Heyden, 1985.
19. Foley, J.K., and Pons, B.S. *Anal. Chem.* 57 (1985): 945A.
20. Pons, B.S., et al. In *Modern Aspects of Electrochemistry*, ed. Bochris, and Conway, No. 17 223, 1986.
21. Ashley, K., and Pons, B.S. *Chem. Rev.* 88 (1988): 673.
22. Korzeniewski, C., and Pons, S. *Prog. Analyt. Spectrosc.* 10 (1987): 1.
23. Beden, B., and Lamy, C. In *Spectroelectrochemistry: Theory and Practice*, ed. R.J. Gale, New York: Plenum Press, 1988. 189.
24. Greenler, R.G. *J. Chem. Phys.* 44 (1966): 310.
25. Greenler, R.G. *J. Chem. Phys.* 50 (1969): 1963.
26. Francis, S.A., and Ellison, A.H. *J. Opt. Soc. Am.* 49 (1959): 131.
27. Hansen, W.N. *J. Opt. Soc. Am.* 58 (1968): 380.
28. McIntyre, J.D.E. In *Advances In Electrochemistry and Electrochemical Engineering*, ed. P. Delahay, and C.W. Tobias, New York: Wiley, 1973.
29. Allara, D.L.; Baca, A.; and Pryde, C.A. *Macromolecules* 11 (1978): 1215.
30. Hansen, W.N. In *Advances In Electrochemistry and Electrochemical Engineering*, ed. P. Delahay, and C.W. Tobias, New York: Wiley, 1973.
31. Heavens, O.S. *Optical Properties of Thin Solid Films*, New York: Dover, 1965.

32. Stern, F. In *Solid State Physics, Advances In Research and Applications,* ed. F. Seitz, and D. Turnbull, vol. 15. New York: Academic Press, 1963.
33. Jenkins, F.A., and White, H.A. *Fundamentals of Optics,* 3rd ed. New York: McGraw Hill, 1957.
34. Weast, R.C., ed. *CRC Handbook of Chemistry and Physics,* Cleveland, OH: CRC Press, 1973.
35. Pearce, H.A., and Sheppard, N., *Surf. Sci.* 59 (1976): 205-17.
36. Porter, M.D., et al. *Anal. Chem.* 58 (1986): 2461.
37. Porter, M.D. *Anal. Chem.* 60 (1984): 63.
38. Schlotter, N.E., and Rabolt, J.F. *J. Phys. Chem.* 88 (1984): 2062.
39. Allara, D.L., and Nuzzo, R. *Langmuir* 1 (1985): 52.
40. Schlotter, N.E., et al. *Chem. Phys. Lett.* 132 (1986): 93.
41. Snyder, R.G.; Hsu, S.L.; and Krimm, S. *Spectrochim. Acta. Part A* 34 (1978): 946.
42. Snyder, R.G.; Strauss, H.L.; and Elliger, C.A. *J. Phys. Chem.* 86 (1982): 5145.
43. Bewick, A., et al. *J. Electroanal. Chem.,* 160 (1984): 47.
44. Seki, H.; Kunimatsu, K.; and Golden, W.G. *Appl. Spectrosc.* 39 (1985): 437.
45. Pons, S.; Davidson, T.; and Bewick, A. *J.Electroanal. Chem.* 63 (1984): 1960.
46. Habib, M.A., and Bockris, J.O'M. *J. Electrochem. Soc.* 132 (1985): 108.
47. Golden, W.G. In *Fourier Transform Infrared Spectroscopy,* ed. J.R. Ferraro, and L.J. Basile, vol. 4. New York: Academic Press, 1985.
48. Yaniger, S.I., and Vidrine, D.W. *Appl. Spectrosc.* 40 (1986): 174.
49. Daschbach, J.; Heisler, D.; and Pons, B.S. *Appl. Spectrosc.* 40 (1986): 489.
50. Li, J., et al. *J. Electroanal. Chem.* 209 (1986):387.
51. Kemp, J.C. *Polarized Light and its Interaction with Modulating Devices, a Methodology Review.* Hillsboro, OR: HINDS International, Inc., 1987.
52. Biegler, T., and Koch, D.F.A. *J. Electrochem. Soc.* 114 (1967): 904.
53. Kamath, V.N., and Lal, H. *J. Electroanal. Chem.,* 19 (1968): 137.
54. Kazarinov, V.E.; Tisyachnaya, Ya.G.; and Andreev, V.N. *Elektrokhimiya.* 8 (1972): 396.
55. Breiter, M. W. *J. Electroanal. Chem.* 15 (1967): 221.
56. Wieckowski, A., and Sobkowski, J. *J. Electroanal. Chem.* 63 (1975): 365.
57. Corrigan, D.S., and Weaver, M.J. *J. Electroanal. Chem.* 241 (1988): 143.
58. Corrigan, D.S., et al. *J. Phys. Chem.* 92 (1988): 1596.
59. Corrigan, D.S., and Weaver, M.J. *Langmuir* 4 (1988): 599.
60. Bagotzky, V.S., and Vassiliev, Y.B. *Electrochim. Acta.* 12 (1967): 1323.
61. Gilman, S. *J. Phys. Chem.* 68 (1964): 70.
62. Biegler, T. *J. Phys. Chem.* 72 (1968): 1571.
63. Beden, B.; Bewick, A.; and Lamy, C. *J. Electroanal. Chem.* 148 (1983): 147.
64. Kunimatsu, K. *J. Electroanal. Chem.* 145 (1983): 219.

65. Corrigan, D.S.; Leung, L.-W.H.; and Weaver, M.J. *Anal. Chem.* 59 (1987): 2252.
66. Kunimatsu, K., and Kita, H. *J. Electroanal. Chem.* 218 (1987): 155.
67. Beden, B., et al. *J. Electroanal. Chem.* 225 (1987): 215.
68. Beden, B., et al. *J. Electroanal. Chem.* 238 (1987): 323.
69. Pons, S., and Bewick, A. *Langmuir* 1 (1985): 141.
70. Bard, A., and Faulkner, L. *Electrochemical Methods: Fundamentals and Applications*, New York: Wiley, 1980.
71. Bewick, A.; Kunimatsu, K.; and Pons, B.S. *Electrochim. Acta* 25 (1980): 465.
72. Bewick, A., and Kunimatsu, K. *Surface Sci.* 101 (1981): 131.
73. Bewick, A., et al. *J. Electroanal. Chem.* 160 (1984): 47.
74. Kunimatsu, K. *J. Electroanal. Chem.* 140 (1982): 205.
75. Kunimatsu, K. *J. Phys. Chem.* 88 (1984): 2195.
76. Beden, B., et al. *J. Electroanal. Chem.* 121 (1981): 343.
77. Bewick, A., et al. 32nd I.S.E. Meeting, Dubrovnik/Cavtat, Yugoslavia (1981):, Extended Abstract A 28, 92.
78. Beden, B.; Bewick, A.; and Lamy, C. *J. Electroanal. Chem.* 148 (1983): 147.
79. Russell, J.W., et al. *J. Phys. Chem.* 86 (1982): 3066.
80. Russell, J.W., et al. *J. Phys. Chem.* 87 (1983): 293.
81. Russell, J.W. Severson, M. 35th I.S.E. Meeting, Berkeley, California (1984):, Extended Abstract A 8-25, 512.
82. Pons, S.; Davidson, T.; and Bewick, A. *J. Electroanal. Chem.* 160 (1984): 63.
83. Pons, S. *J. Electroanal. Chem.* 150 (1983): 495.
84. Golden, W.G.; Kunimatsu, K.; and Seki, H. *J. Phys. Chem.* 88 (1984): 1275.
85. Kunimatsu, K., et al. *Surface Sci.* 158 (1985): 596.
86. Habib, M.A., and Bockris, J. O'M. *J. Electrochem. Soc.* 132 (1985): 108.
87. Bewick, A. Pons, S. In *Advances In Infrared and Raman Spectroscopy*, ed. R.J.H. Clark and R.E. Hester, vol. 12, 1-63. London: Wiley Heyden, 1985.
88. Bewick, A., et al. *J. Electroanal. Chem.* 119 (1981): 175.
89. Bewick, A.; Fleischmann, M.; and Robinson, J. *Dechema Monographie* 90 (1981):1851.
90. Bewick, A., and Russell, J.W. *J. Electroanal. Chem.* 132 (1982): 329.
91. Beden, B., et al. *J. Electroanal. Chem.* 142 (1982): 345.
92. Beden, B. Lamy, C. Bewick, A. *J. Electroanal. Chem.* 150 (1983): 505.
93. Kunimatsu, K., et al. 35th I.S.E. Meeting, Berkeley, California (1984), Extended Abstract A 8-6, 457.
94. Kunimatsu, K., et al. *Langmuir* 2 (1986): 464.
95. K. Kunimatsu, *J. Electroanal. Chem.* 145 (1983): 219.
96. Pons, S.; Davidson, T.; and Bewick, A. *J. Am. Chem. Soc.* 105 (1983): 1802.
97. Bewick, A. *J. Electroanal. Chem.* 150 (1983): 481.
98. Kunimatsu, K., et al. *Langmuir* 1 (1985): 245.
99. Bewick, A., et al. *J. Electron Spectrosc. Relat. Phenom.* 30 (1983): 191.
100. Bewick, A., and Russell, J.W. *J. Electroanal. Chem.* 142 (1982): 337.
101. Russell, J.W., et al. *J. Phys.Chem.* 150 (1983): 495.

102. Seki, H.; Kunimatsu, K.; and Golden, W.G. 35th I.S.E. Meeting, Berkeley, California (1984), Extended Abstract A 9-29, 522.

103. Kunimatsu, K.; Seki, H.; and Golden, W.G. *Chem. Phys. Lett.* 108 (1984): 195.

104. Kunimatsu, K. *J. Electron. Spectroscopy* 30 (1983): 215.

105. Beden, B.; Lamy, C.; and Bewick, A. 33rd I.S.E. Meeting, Lyon, France (1982), Extended Abstract IA 17, 49.

106. Bewick A. In *The Chemistry and Physics of Electroanalysis,* ed. J.D.E. McIntyre, M.J. Weaver, and E.B. Yeager. *Proc. Electrochem. Soc.* 84 (1984): 301.

107. Beden, B., et al. *J. Electroanal. Chem.* 139 (1982): 203.

108. Habib, M.A., and Bockris, J.O'M. *J. Electrochem. Soc.* 130 (1983): 2510.

109. Zelanay, P.; Habib, M.A.; and Bockris, J. O'M. *J. Electrochem. Soc.* 131 (1984): 2464.

110. Bewick, A.; Gibilaro, C.; and Pons, S. Report 1984 TR-39 Order no. AD A14866: 4/6 GAR. Avail. NTIS, From Gov. Rep. Announce Index US, 85-6 (1985) 58.

111. Pons, S., and Bewick, A. *Langmuir* 1 (1985): 141.

112. Pons, S., et al. *J. Electroanal. Chem.* 160 (1984): 369.

113. Davidson, T., et al. *J. Electroanal. Chem.* 125 (1981): 237.

114. Pons, S. Davidson, T. Bewick, A. *J. Electroanal. Chem.* 140 (1982): 211.

115. Pons, S., et al. *J. Phys. Chem.* 88 (1984): 3575.

116. Nakajima, H., et al. *J. Electroanal. Chem.* 201 (1986): 175.

117. Beden, B., et al. *J. Electroanal. Chem.* 225 (1987): 215.

118. Beden, B., et al. *J. Electroanal. Chem.* 238 (1987): 323.

119. Choy de Martinez, M.; Beden, B.; and Lamy, C. 38th I.S.E. Meeting, Maastricht, The Netherlands (September 1987), Extended Abstract 4.66 Volume I, 404.

120. Beden, B., et al. *J. Electroanal. Chem.* 229 (1987): 353.

121. Roe, D.K., et al. *J. Electroanal. Chem.* 216 (1987): 293.

122. Kunimatsu, K., and Kita, H. *J. Electroanal. Chem.* 218 (1987): 155.

123. Hahn, F.; Beden, B.; and Lamy, C. *J. Electroanal. Chem.* 204 (1986): 315.

124. Christiansen, P.A.; Hamnett, A.; and Trevellick, P.R. *J. Electroanal. Chem.* 242 (1988): 23.

125. Chia, V.K.F., et al. *J. Electroanal. Chem.* 163 (1984): 407.

126. Pang, K.P., et al. *J. Phys. Chem.* 88 (1984): 4583.

127. Bewick, A., and Kunimatsu, K. *Surf. Sci.* 101 (1980): 131.

128. Holze, R. *J. Electroanal. Chem.* 246 (1988): 449.

129. Desilvestro, J., et al. *J. Electroanal. Chem.* 246 (1988): 411.

130. Corrigan, D.S., and Weaver, M.J. *J. Phys. Chem.* 90 (1986): 5300.

131. Seki, H.; Kunimatsu, K.; and Golden, W.G. *Appl. Spectrosc.* 39 (1985): 137.

132. Beden, B.; Bewick, A.; and Lamy, C. *J. Electroanal. Chem.* 150 (1983): 505.

133. Bewick, A.; Kunimatsu, K.; and Pons, B.S. *Electrochim Acta* 25 (1980): 465.

134. Korzeniewski, C. Pons, S. *J. Vac. Sci. Technol B* 3 (1985): 1421.

135. Kunimatsu, K.; Seki, H.; and Golden, W.G. *Chem. Phys. Lett.* 108 (1984): 195.

136.   Corrigan, D.S., et al. *J. Phys. Chem.* 92 (1988): 1596.
137.   Foley, J.K.; Pons, S.; and Smith, J.J. *Langmuir* 1 (1985): 697.
138.   Korzeniewski, C.; McKenna, W.; and Pons, S. *J. Electroanal. Chem.* 235 (1987): 361.
139.   Kunimatsu, K., et al. *J. Electroanal. Chem.* 243 (1988): 203.
140.   Blackwood, D.J., and Pons, S. *J. Electroanal. Chem.* 244 (1988): 301.
141.   Golden, W.G.; Dunn, D.S.; and J. Overend *J. Catal.* 71 (1981): 395.

CHAPTER 8

MOSSBAUER SPECTROSCOPY

Daniel A. Scherson

Case Center for Electrochemical Sciences
   and The Department of Chemistry
Case Western Reserve University
Cleveland, OH 44106

CONTENTS

I. INTRODUCTION

Since its discovery over three decades ago, Mossbauer spectroscopy has emerged as a valuable tool in the characterization of materials of interest in biology, chemistry, metallurgy, physics and other fields. Although restricted to only a few elements, this technique has become of rather routine use in the investigation of the electronic and magnetic properties of crystalline and amorphous solid state materials, including polymers and frozen solutions. As evidenced by hundreds of reports in the literature, the analysis of Mossbauer spectra can provide unique information regarding electronic and nuclear spin states, oxidation states, and certain aspects of the local geometry surrounding the active nucleus.

This monograph will provide a brief outline of the principles upon which Mossbauer spectroscopy is based and will illustrate with various examples the advantages and limitations of this technique as a probe of some of the properties of electrochemical interfaces.*

II. THEORETICAL CONSIDERATIONS

The energies associated with nuclear transitions is orders of magnitude larger than those involving vibrational or electronic states. This makes it necessary to account for the effects of mechanical recoil in the emission and absorption of high energy radiation in order to interpret the results of resonance-type measurements.

A. Recoil Energy, Resonance, and Doppler Effect

Consider a gas phase system in which quanta emitted by atoms of mass m in the excited state are used to induce transitions in atoms of the same element in their ground state. For the sake of simplicity, only a single transition with energy ε_o and average lifetime τ will be assumed to be involved.

It may be shown, based on the laws of energy and momentum conservation, that the average magnitude of the energy of the emitted quantum $\varepsilon_o{}'$, will be in general different than ε_o. Three factors contribute to this phenomenon: mechanical recoil, a linear Doppler effect, and a second order Doppler effect, which

---

* This article represents a slightly modified and expanded version of a recent monograph written by the author, which appeared published in *Spectroelectrochemistry: Theory and Practice*, ed. R. J. Gale. New York: Plenum Press, 1988.

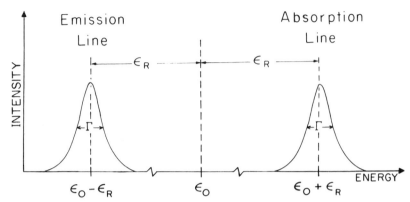

Figure 1. *Effects of recoil on the transition lines associated with the absorption and emission of high energy radiation by isolated atoms. The dashed curve in the center of the figure corresponds to a recoil energy $\varepsilon_R = 0$. For $\varepsilon_R \neq 0$, the separation between the transition energies is $2\varepsilon_R$. No overlap occurs for $2\varepsilon_R > \Gamma$ and thus no resonance absorption would be observed. (Adapted from Figure 2.4 in Reference 2b.)*

account for the motion of the atom prior to the emission. A directly analogous situation will also occur in the case of absorption of radiation by gas atoms in the ground state.

For emitting and absorbing atoms moving with precisely the same velocity, the displacement of the average emission energy with respect to the average absorption energy is given to a good degree of approximation by ε_o^2 / mc^2, a quantity that corresponds to twice the recoil energy ε_R. Hence, for such an ensemble of atoms, the degree of overlap between the emission and absorption bands, which is directly related to the extent of resonance, becomes very small for values of $2\varepsilon_R$ much larger than $\Gamma = h/\tau$, the natural width of the transition band. This is represented pictorially in Figure 1. Such situation would be encountered, for instance, in the case of nuclear transitions involving the ground and first excited states of gas phase ^{57}Fe ($\varepsilon_o = 14.4$ keV), for which $\tau \sim 1.44 \times 10^{-7}$s, and hence $\Gamma \sim 4.56 \times 10^{-9}$ eV.

A collection of gas particles, however, exhibits a statistical distribution of velocities, a factor that will bring about a spread in the emission and absorption energies. The characteristic width of this so-called Doppler broadening is given by $D = 2(\varepsilon_R kT)^{1/2}$, where k is Boltzmann's constant. It follows that the resonance probability will be determined by the relative values of Γ/ε_R and Γ/D.

Two possible means of enhancing resonance absorption for spectroscopic techniques involving such high energy radiation could be envisioned:

1. to raise the temperature of the emitter, and thus increase the Doppler broadening; and
2. to compensate for the recoil energy loss by imparting the emitter an additional momentum either by mechanical means or by relying on a preceding nuclear event.

Although experiments based on these ideas were proven successful in many cases, the general interest in this area prior to 1957 was rather restricted.

In that year, while investigating the nuclear absorption of γ rays emitted by metallic iridium, (^{191}Ir), R. Mossbauer made two observations of far reaching consequences [1]. Specifically, he found that

1. the extent of resonance was found to increase as the temperature decreased, which is in direct contrast with what would be expected based on the arguments put forward above; and
2. the resonance absorption could be totally destroyed if the source of the radiation was moved with respect to the absorber, with velocities on the order of a few cm•s^{-1}.

These findings led Mossbauer to conclude that the phenomenon had to involve nuclear events in which there were no recoil losses both in the emission and absorption of radiation. For this outstanding discovery, Mossbauer was awarded the Nobel prize in 1961.

The following sections will provide a brief introduction to some of the principles upon which Mossbauer spectroscopy is based. The discussion will be restricted to Fe and Sn, as, to date, only these nuclides have been the subject of in situ investigations involving electrochemical systems. More extensive treatments of theoretical and experimental aspects of Mossbauer spectroscopy may be found in a number of excellent specialized books and monographs [2].

B. Phonons, Mossbauer Effect, and Recoilless Fraction

The recoil energy associated with the emission or absorption of radiation by an atom bound to a solid of macroscopic dimensions will be distributed among the available translational and vibrational quantum states. This process may involve

1. a transfer of momentum to the host matrix as a whole, a process that is expected to make a negligible contribution in view of the large mass involved;
2. a site displacement, for which the threshold energy is in the range of 10 to 50 eV; and
3. a thermal excitation of the lattice for lower energies.

If the free-atom recoil energy is of the order of 10 meV, however, and thus of the same magnitude as the separation between the collective vibrational energy levels in a solid or phonons, there is a finite probability that the emission or absorption will occur without exchange of energy between the bound atom and the lattice. In honor of its discoverer, this phenomenon has become known as the Mossbauer effect.

An explicit expression for the fraction of such recoilless or zero- phonon processes, commonly denoted as f, can be derived from the specific model used to represent the solid. The Debye model, for instance, predicts an increase in the magnitude of f when either the γ-ray energy or the temperature decrease, and also when the Debye temperature increases. The latter is a measure of the bond strength between the emitting or absorbing atom and the lattice. It is precisely through a spectral analysis of such recoil-free events that information can be obtained regarding electrical and magnetic interactions involving the nucleus and its environment.

C. Electric Hyperfine Interactions

To a good degree of approximation, the energy associated with the electrostatic interaction of a nucleus and the surrounding charges may be regarded as arising from an electric monopole and an electric quadrupole contributions. The electric monopole interaction gives rise to a shift in the nuclear energy levels of the otherwise isolated atom, whereas the electric quadrupole counterpart lifts the nuclear spin quantum number degeneracy. These contributions serve as a basis for defining two important parameters in Mossbauer spectroscopy, the isomer shift and the quadrupole splitting, which can be related to certain aspects of structure and bonding in a variety of materials.

1. Isomer Shift Within the non-relativistic approximation, only electrons in s-type orbitals have a nonzero probability density at the nucleus and can thus interact with the charge density therein leading to a shift in the energy of the nuclear states. Nuclear excitations are accompanied by changes in the nuclear charge density distribution, and therefore, the actual magnitude of the energy shift is not in general the same for the ground and excited states. In particular, the energy difference between the excited and ground states for a nucleus in the presence, E_s, and in the absence, E_o, of an electric monopole interaction, denoted as ΔE, is given by

$$\Delta E = E_s - E_o = \frac{2}{3} \pi Z e^2 |\psi(0)|^2 [<r^2>_e - <r^2>_g],$$ (1)

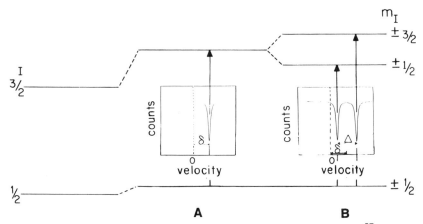

Figure 2. *Effects on the ground and first excited nuclear energy levels of ^{57}Fe due to (A) the isomer shift, and (B) the quadrupole splitting, showing the Mossbauer absorption transitions and the expected spectra. The isomer shift δ is indicated with reference to some arbitrary standard. I and m_I are the nuclear spin and magnetic spin quantum numbers, respectively. (Adapted from Figure 1.5 in Reference 2c.)*

where $e|\psi(0)|^2$ is the electronic charge density at the nucleus; $<r^2>_i$ is the expectation value of the square of the nuclear radius in either the ground ($i = g$) or excited ($i = e$) state; and Ze is the nuclear charge. The term $[<r^2>_e - <r^2>_g]$ involves intrinsic nuclear parameters, whereas $|\psi(0)|^2$ depends on the specific environment surrounding the nuclei and the atom or ion as a whole. Hence, the quantity ΔE in general will vary for different compounds or host lattices. If one of such materials is regarded as the source S and the other as the absorber A, the difference between $(\Delta E)_A$ and $(\Delta E)_S$ defines an experimentally accessible parameter known as the isomer shift δ given explicitly by

$$\delta = (\Delta E)_A - (\Delta E)_S = \frac{2}{5} \pi Z e^2 \{|\psi(0)|_A^2 - |\psi(0)|_S^2\} \cdot (R_e^2 - R_g^2). \qquad (2)$$

The expectation value of the nuclear radius in this equation has been replaced by R, a quantity that represents the radius of a spherically symmetric nucleus with a uniform charge density, in either the excited or ground state. According to Equation (2), δ is a relative quantity and therefore the standard or reference with respect to which the isomer shift is being measured or reported must always be specified. A schematic representation of the nuclear level displacement for ^{57}Fe due to the isomer shift, including the associated Mossbauer spectrum and the corresponding absorption transitions, is shown in Figure 2A.

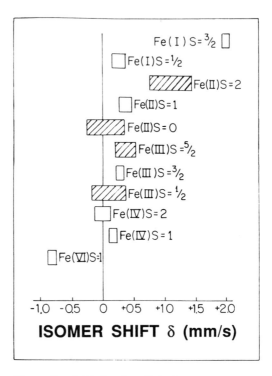

Figure 3. *Oxidation State/Spin Quantum*
State-Isomer Shift correlation diagram for iron in a
variety of compounds. The values of δ are referred
to the α-Fe standard. (Adapted from Figure 3.2 in
Reference 2b.)

The electronic density at the nucleus may be separated into contributions
due to inner core filled orbitals and to partially filled valence orbitals, and thus
δ is expected to be sensitive to the specific nature of the chemical bonds involving
the Mossbauer active species and adjacent atoms in the molecule or lattice.
Furthermore, the value of δ can be modified not only by varying the s-orbital
occupation, but also by a shielding effect associated with orbitals of other types.
The removal of a d-electron from an iron ion, for instance, will lead to a
contraction of the occupied s-orbitals and thus to a shift of δ in the negative
direction. A correlation diagram between the isomer shift and the oxidation state
for the case of iron species is shown in Figure 3.

2. Quadrupole Splitting The interaction between the nuclear quadrupole moment eQ, which is a measure of the extent of deviation of the nuclear charge distribution from spherical symmetry, and the gradient of the electric field associated with the presence of electrons and ions surrounding a specific nucleus may give rise to a lifting of the degeneracy of the nuclear states. This is expected to occur when

1. the charges around the nucleus are distributed in a noncubic symmetry; and
2. $Q \neq 0$, which is true only if the nuclear state spin quantum number I is greater than $1/2$.

The choice of an appropriate coordinate transformation makes it possible to represent the electric field gradient tensor by a matrix with zero off-diagonal elements. In this fashion, the electric field gradient can be specified by two independent quantities: V_{zz}, the diagonal element with the largest absolute value; and $\eta = \{V_{xx} - V_{yy}\}/V_{zz}$, a non-negative quantity known as the asymmetry parameter. V_{zz} and η have contributions due to ions in the lattice, which can be evaluated from molecular or crystal structural parameters, and to the valence electrons, which are amenable to molecular orbital calculations.

In the case of ^{57}Fe, the electric quadrupole interaction will split the first excited state ($I = 3/2$) into two substates without shifting the baricenter of the state giving rise to two absorption lines in the spectra. The energy difference between these states, represented by the distance between the two lines, is called the quadrupole splitting Δ [Fig. 2B]. If the electric field gradient is axially symmetric, for instance, η becomes zero, and $\Delta = eQV_{zz}/2$. Since Q is an intrinsic property of the Mossbauer active nuclide, the differences in the value of Δ may be attributed solely to changes in the electric field gradient tensor, which in turn will be a function of the molecular and electronic structure. An interesting illustration of such phenomena is provided by certain planar organometallic molecules capable of forming axially coordinated adducts. In the case of iron phthalocyanine, a widely studied transition metal macrocycle, the presence of pyridine, imidazole, or picoline in the axial positions results in a decrease in the value of D over the unsubstituted species, the magnitude of which appears to correlate with the strength of the Lewis base character of the ligand [3].

D.   Magnetic Hyperfine Interaction

The nuclear magnetic dipole moment can interact with a magnetic field, inducing a splitting of a nuclear state with spin quantum number I into $2I + 1$, equally spaced, non-degenerate substates. The energies of these substates are given by

SCHERSON

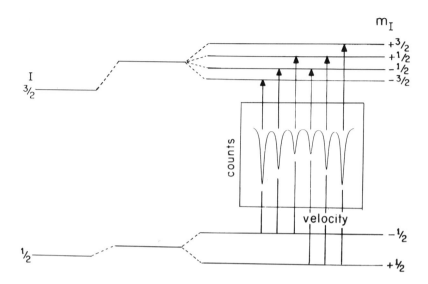

Figure 4. *Effects of the magnetic splitting on the nuclear energy levels of ^{57}Fe, showing the Mossbauer absorption transitions and the resulting spectrum in the absence of quadrupole splitting. The magnitude of the splitting of the lines is proportional to the total magnetic field at the nucleus. (Adapted from Figure 1.6 in Reference 2c.)*

$$E(m_I) = -g_N\beta_N H m_I,$$

(3)

where g_N is the nuclear Lande factor; β_N is the nuclear magneton; H is the strength of the magnetic field; and m_I is the nuclear magnetic spin quantum number. In the case of ^{57}Fe, the magnetic field splits the ground state ($I = 1/2$) and first excited state ($I = 3/2$) into two and four sublevels, respectively. According to the magnetic dipole selection rules, only transitions for which $\Delta I = 1$ and $\Delta m = 0\pm1$ will be allowed, yielding in the case of $V_{zz} = 0$ a symmetric six line spectrum such as that shown in Figure 4. The line intensities of these spectral features are not the same, due to differences in the transition probabilities, which also have different angular distributions. An asymmetry in the magnetically split spectrum will be introduced if $V_{zz} \neq 0$, from which the actual sign of V_{zz} and, thus, the electric field gradient can be determined.

III. EXPERIMENTAL ASPECTS

A detailed description of the principles of operation of conventional Mossbauer spectrometers may be found in a number of excellent monographs [2]. Although some of these concepts will be reviewed here, most attention will be focused on those aspects that are of special importance to the design of in situ experiments.

A. Instrumentation and Modes of Operation

Based on the theoretical formalism outlined in the previous section, the electric and magnetic environments surrounding a specific nucleus modify the energy of the nuclear states. A Mossbauer spectrometer is an instrument that enables the relative velocity of the source and the absorber (sample) to be varied, while simultaneously monitoring the absorption or emission of recoil-free γ rays. This makes it possible to compensate for the minute transition energy differences between a given Mossbauer active nucleus in the source and in the absorber and, thus, to determine the energies at which the resonance conditions are met. In its conventional form, the apparatus consists of a source mounted on a velocity transducer, a detector, and ancillary components that allow a direct correlation between the detector response, expressed most often in terms of the number of counts, and the velocity of the source. Recent advances in microelectronics technology have led to sizable reductions in the size and cost of Mossbauer spectrometers capable of fulfilling essentially all the requirements associated with in situ spectroscopy experiments.

Most Mossbauer spectroscopy measurements are conducted either in the transmission or emission modes. Transmission type experiments involve the use of a source of well-defined characteristics to examine the spectral properties of an unknown absorber, whereas in emission measurements, the source of radiation becomes the sample under investigation, and a known or standard absorber is employed to determine the transition energy differences. In both cases, proportional counters or other kinds of γ-ray detectors are utilized to record the amount of radiation transmitted through the absorber.

An alternate way of acquiring Mossbauer spectra consists in measuring events associated with the deexcitation of nuclei in the sample following the absorption of γ rays. Such a process involves the emission of γ rays, X rays, or electrons, which are most often detected in a back-scattering geometry. The probability associated with different relaxation pathways for ^{57}Fe in the $I = 3/2$ state is shown in Table 1. One of the main advantages of this approach is that the spectral background is small compared to that associated with transmission measurements, as the great majority of measured photons or electrons originate

TABLE 1. Probability of Relaxation Products from Excited ^{57}Fe ($I = 3/2$)	
Type of Emission	*No. Out of 100 Absorptions*
14.4 keV γ-ray	9
6.3 keV X-ray	27
7.3 keV K e$^-$	81
13.6 keV L e$^-$	9
14.3 keV M e$^-$	1
6.4 keV KLL Auger e$^-$	63

from Mossbauer excited nuclei. In addition, it makes it possible to record spectra of materials too thick to be examined in the transmission configuration. It is interesting to note that, due to their small mean free path in a solid, only electrons emitted from the outermost layers of the material may be expected to escape and then be detected. Because of its inherent surface sensitivity, this specific technique, known as conversion electron Mossbauer spectroscopy, may find special use in the study of interfacial phenomena. A comparison of the different backscattering detection techniques is given in Table 2.

Emission Mossbauer spectroscopy is several orders of magnitude more sensitive than conventional transmission mode measurements and thus offers the possibility of detecting species at very low concentrations. Despite this advantage, however, the interpretation of emission data is not always straightforward. Specifically, the emission process in the case of cobalt [Fig. 5], involves the capture of an inner shell electron by the nucleus, generating a highly excited iron nucleus and a hole. The latter can then undergo a series of transitions to valence levels and finally emit an X ray, a process that would preserve the charge state of the original Co nucleus. An alternate channel for deexcitation involves the filling of the core hole by an electron from a higher level, followed by the emission of another electron in order to conserve energy. Such events are referred to as Auger transitions and may yield a variety of charged states for the iron species. The predominant mechanism for deexcitation will be determined primarily by the relative lifetimes of different excited states, which in turn will depend on the properties of the host lattice. These two deexcitation modes, collectively known as after effects, are especially important in materials with rather low electronic conductivity, for which highly ionized states may have long

TABLE 2.   Back-Scattering Detection in Mossbauer Spectroscopy Measurements

Advantages	*Disadvantages*
-Background suppression improves signal to background ratio.	-Restricted solid angle for detection considerably reduces overall sensitivity.
-Equivalent signal to noise ratio can be achieved theoretically in two orders of magnitude less time than in transmission.	
X-Ray	*X-Ray*
-Applicable for measurements in the low temperature range.	-Detector window materials attenuate signal.
-In situ scattering experiments from back of electrode feasible.	-Half absorption length of water for keV radiation only a fraction of mm. Special cell would be required for in situ measurements through front of the electrode.
Conversion Electron	*Conversion Electron*
- Enhanced sensitivity.	- Measurements at low temperature require vacuum chamber. Use of Channeltron, for example, offsets higher sensitivity due to more restricted solid angle for detection.
-Surface specificity.	- Half absorption length of keV electrons by water is of the order of a fraction of a μm.
- Ideally suited for room temperature measurements with gas flow counter.	- Although quasi in situ experiments are feasible, in situ measurements seriously impaired.

enough lifetimes to modify the chemical environment surrounding the Mossbauer active nuclide.

Another mechanism, by which the measured Fe charged state may be different than that of the original parent Co, involves an actual electron transfer reaction in which other host lattice species serve as either donor or acceptor sites. The difficulties in the interpretation of emission Mossbauer spectra introduced

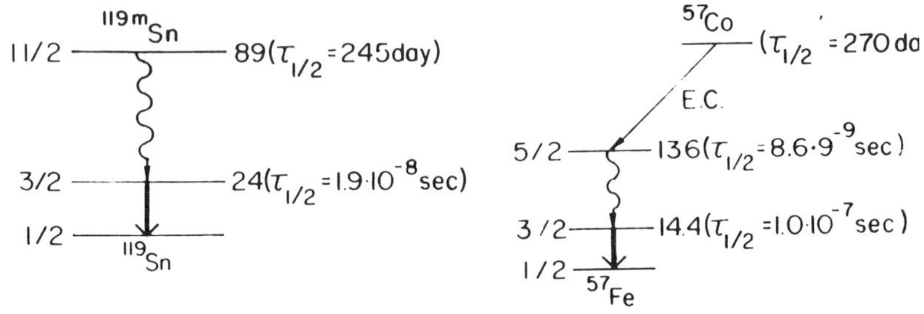

Figure 5. *Decay schemes of* ^{57}*Co and* ^{119m}*Sn. The nuclear transitions associated with Mossbauer spectroscopy measurements are shown by the heavy arrows. Also indicated are the transition lifetimes,* $\tau_{1/2}$ *for the states involved. Internal conversion processes have not been included. Energies are given in keV. E.C. refers to electron capture. (Adapted from Reference 2a.)*

by chemical and after effects could be diminished to some extent by conducting detailed studies of the behavior of known solids.

B. Sources, Data Acquisition, and Data Analysis

The most common type of source for ^{57}Fe Mossbauer spectroscopy consists of elemental ^{57}Co incorporated into a host metal lattice such as rhodium or copper. In the case of ^{119}Sn measurements, ^{119m}Sn-enriched-CaSnO$_3$ or BaSnO$_3$ are used as sources. Schematic diagrams of the radioactive decay schemes for these two isotopes are shown in Figure 5. In addition to these transitions, internal conversion processes may give rise to emission of radiation of other energies. For example, in the case of ^{57}Fe, the $I = 3/2$ state may decay via the ejection of a K shell 7.3 keV electron, and the hole created may be filled by an L shell electron, leading to the emission of either a 6.4 keV electron (Auger process) or X ray in order to conserve energy.

In most applications, the source is moved at constant acceleration between two prescribed velocities in a periodic fashion. This generates a spectrum consisting of mirror images about the minimum or maximum velocity. The data collected in a given cycle are added electronically, usually with a multichannel analyzer, to the cummulative sum of previous cycles, until the signal to noise ratio becomes high enough to perform a reliable data analysis. Prior to an actual experiment, it is customary, and indeed advisable, to record the spectrum of a standard in order to verify the proper operation of the instrument and to calibrate the velocity scale. The separation between the outermost lines of the six-line spectra for metallic iron, which amounts to 10.167 mm•s^{-1}, is most often used for this purpose. Alternatively, the actual velocities can be measured directly by employing interferometric techniques.

The Mossbauer spectral lineshapes in the case of thin absorbers can be represented fairly accurately by Lorenztian-type functions. The values of the isomer shift, quadrupole splitting, linewidth, strength of the effective magnetic field at the nucleus, and other parameters of interest can be determined by a statistical treatment of the data. A number of computer routines have become available, which enable such analyses to be performed in a rather straightforward fashion.

C.   In Situ Mossbauer Spectroscopy [4]

A key factor in the design of electrochemical cells for in situ transmission Mossbauer measurements is to decrease the attenuation of the γ ray beam, so as to reduce the time required for spectra acquisition. This may be accomplished by selecting low absorption materials for windows and electrode supports and by minimizing the amount of electrolyte in the beam path. Radiation in the keV range penetrates rather deeply into matter, and therefore, small amounts of rather high Z elements can be tolerated without seriously compromising the overall cell transmission. As a means of illustration, the half absorption length for 14.4 keV X rays in water is about 3.5 mm, which is about an order of magnitude larger than for 6.4 keV X rays. In the case of aqueous electrolytes, the decrease in intensity of the 14.4 keV γ rays is compensated to a certain extent by the higher absorbance of the 6.4 keV X rays, as it makes the use of an external filter unnecessary.

Highly conducting thin films of gold vapor deposited on Melinex [6] and self-supported thin glassy carbon disks have been used as substrates for in situ transmission MES studies involving electroactive layers. In the case of small particle dispersions, on the other hand, very satisfactory results have been obtained with Teflon-bonded high area carbon electrodes of the type used in fuel cell applications [7]. These electrodes are prepared by adding the dispersion in dry form to an aqueous suspension of emulsified Teflon under ultrasonic agitation. The slurry then is filtered, and the resulting paste is thoroughly homogenized by repeated spreading with a spatula onto a Teflon sheet. After the excess liquid is eliminated, the actual electrode is formed under pressure in a die, and the emulsifier is later removed by heat treatment under an inert atmosphere. The dry, circularly shaped electrode is placed once again in the die, and a current

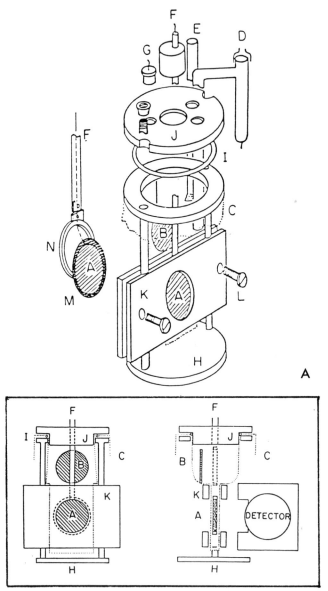

Figure 6. *Spectroelectrochemical cells for in situ Mossbauer measurements. The working electrode in (A) is mounted on a rod that can be moved vertically without disturbing the overall cell operation. During potential changes it is placed in front of the fixed counter electrode in the upper part of the cell and returned to the measuring*

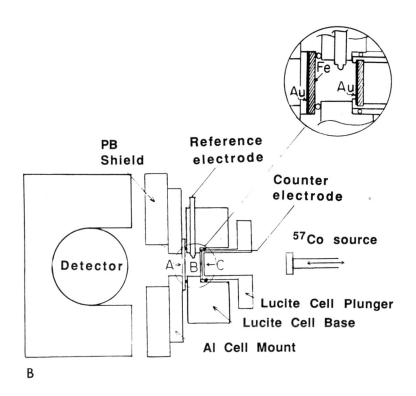

B

area after the current decreases to a small value. A. working electrode; B. counter electrode; C. collapsible cell; D. reference electrode; E. gas bubbler; F. Teflon holder for working electrode; G. stopper with press fitted nickel wire connected to counter electrode; H. aluminum frame; I. Viton O-ring; J. Teflon cell top; K. aluminum plates; L. brass screws; M. nickel screen annulus (current collector); N. Teflon ring for working electrode mounting and mechanical attachment to F through pin (not shown in the figure). (Reproduced from Reference 7). Inset Schematic diagram of the front and side views of electrochemical cell showing sliding mechanism for working electrode and geometrical configuration during Mossbauer measurements. (Adapted from D. Scherson, et al. App. Surf. Sci. 10 (1982):325). The cell in (B) was specifically designed for studies involving passive film formation on iron. The working electrode is fixed, and the counter electrode is mounted on a Lucite plunger. A. passivated Fe working electrode; B. electrolyte; C. Au on Melinex counter electrode (Adapted from Reference 8).

collector, consisting most often of a flexible open metal grid, is attached to one of the faces by compression. A more detailed description of the overall procedure involved in the fabrication of this type of electrode may be found in the original literature [7].

A reduction of the electrolyte volume in the beam path has been most often realized for in situ Mossbauer applications by using a geometry similar to that of conventional spectroelectrochemical thin layer cells. It is customary, in this configuration, to place the counter electrode away from the working electrode to avoid blocking the radiation. This, however, generates a path of high ionic resistance which increases the time response to potential changes. Although this factor may not be important in many applications, it introduces uncertainties in the interpretation of results involving systems in which the rate of change of the potential drop across the interface modifies the nature of the resulting products, such as passive film formation on iron (see section IV.A.2). One way of circumventing this problem is by using a cell with flexible walls made out of a γ ray transparent material such as polyethylene [Fig. 6A] [7]. In this design, the working electrode is placed in front of the counter electrode in the upper part of the cell during changes in polarization to improve the current distribution. After the current reaches a small value, the working electrode is moved downward under potential control and placed in the γ ray beam path. Two aluminum plates of the form shown in the figure are then used to lightly compress the cell walls so as to decrease the amount of solution in the γ ray beam path without blocking the radiation. Alternatively, a semitransparent counter electrode can be placed permanently in front of the working electrode as illustrated in Figure 6B [8].

An area of special interest to the general field of electrocatalysis is the in situ spectroscopic examination of electrodes during actual operation, because considerable insight may be gained into mechanistic aspects of redox processes. At least two in situ Mossbauer experiments of this type, both involving oxygen cathodes, have been reported in the literature [9,10]. A geometry that appears particularly suited for the application of Mossbauer spectroscopy to studies of this type is that of a conventional fuel cell. This device consists of oxygen-fed and hydrogen-fed Teflon bonded high area carbon electrodes placed at a close distance in front of one another. A sheet of Teflon is often attached to the electrode side facing the gas compartment to prevent electrolyte leakage. The feasibility of conducting in situ MES measurements on an operating fuel cell was demonstrated by using a heat treated iron-macrocycle based electrode as the oxygen cathode [10]. This specific fuel cell consisted of two separate sets of elements, which, upon assembly, formed the cathodic and anodic cell compartments. A schematic diagram of the fully assembled fuel cell as well as the geometric arrangement for Mossbauer measurements in the transmission mode is illustrated in Figure 7. Among the many advantages of this configuration are

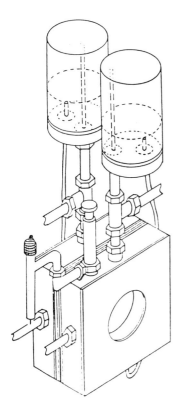

Figure 7. *Diagram of fuel cell and geometric arrangement for in situ Mossbauer measurements in the transmission mode. (Reprinted from Reference 10.)*

a uniform current distribution and the establishment of steady state conditions. The latter is a very important factor, since it might be possible to sustain a finite concentration of reaction intermediates during the measurements and thus provide improved conditions for their detection and study.

D. Quasi In Situ Mossbauer Spectroscopy

In situ spectroelectrochemical techniques may be regarded as a type of methodology in which spectroscopic information about the electrode, the electrode-electrolyte interface, and/or the electrolyte solution is sought under conditions in which the potential across the electrode-electrolyte interface is controlled during the data acquisition. There are some instances, however, in which because of intrinsic physical limitations, experiments cannot be conducted in a conventional in situ fashion. Two techniques that appear to fall in such a category, referred to hereafter as quasi in situ, will be presented in this subsection.

1. Quasi In Situ Conversion Electron Mossbauer Spectroscopy As was mentioned in section III.A., conversion electron Mossbauer spectroscopy, CEMS, provides an advantageous means of studying surface structure because it affords much greater sensitivity than measurements in the transmission mode. Electrons, however, cannot penetrate through detector windows or thick layers of electrolyte, and thus CEMS cannot be readily applied to the in situ study of electrochemical interfaces. Recently, Kordesch et al. [11] developed a quasi in situ technique that makes it possible to detect conversion electrons, using a continuously emersed electrode similar in design to that used by Rath and Kolb in their work function studies [12]. A schematic diagram of the complete electrochemical cell-Mossbauer spectrometer system is shown in Figure 8. The electrode is a disk with its lower half in the solution under potential control and its upper half in the conversion electron detector surrounded by the counting gas. The disk is mounted on a motor that continuously rotates the polarized surface. This carries with it only a very thin layer of solution into the γ-ray beam, returning the previously measured area into the electrolyte. Most counting gases, including Ar, He, and CH_4, are practically inert from an electrochemical standpoint and thus are not expected to interfere with the intrinsic behavior of the interface. Although essentially identical results have been obtained in some cases for spectra recorded in situ both in transmission and by the conversion electron method described above, additional experiments will be required to determine whether this approach consistently reproduces the spectroscopic behavior found under conventional in situ conditions.

2. In Situ Freezing Technique Considerable insight into the nature of a variety of materials can be obtained by a detailed examination of the temperature dependence of the Mossbauer spectral features. Unfortunately, most solutions undergo freezing at rather high temperatures, making it possible to conduct conventional in situ measurements in a wide temperature range only under very special conditions [13]. Certain electrochemical interfaces, however, display rather unique properties that enable some of these limitations to be overcome. Specifically, interfaces of the ideally polarizable type exhibit a behavior that resembles that of an ideal capacitor in the sense that the externally applied potential brings about a charging of the two phases without the passage of current across the interface. Such situation is realized in aqueous solutions, for example, by electrode materials that display high overpotentials for both hydrogen and oxygen evolution in the strict absence of species capable of undergoing electron transfer reactions in the electrolyte.

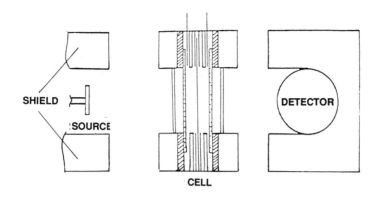

A

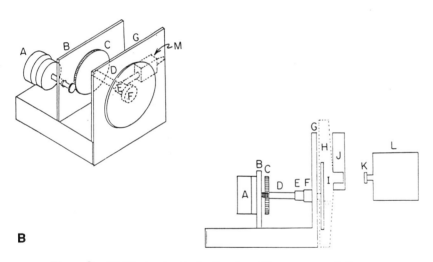

B

Figure 8. *(A) Electrochemical cell and ancillary components for quasi in situ conversion electron Mossbauer measurements. (Reprinted from Reference 11) The counter and reference electrodes are not shown in this figure. (B) Schematic diagram of rotating system. A. motor; B. aluminum support; C. reduction gear; D. phenolic shaft; E. brass contact; F. Teflon bushing; G. aluminum support; H. electrochemical cell; I. working electrode (disk); J. conversion electron counter; K. Mossbauer source; L. Mossbauer Doppler velocity transducer; M. carbon brush assembly.*

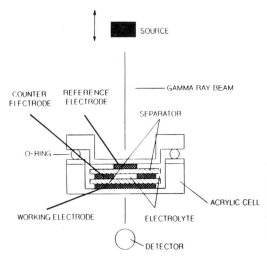

Figure 9. *Schematic diagram of the electrochemical cell for in situ Mossbauer measurements in the in situ freezing mode.*

Under these circumstances, the applied potential may be expected to be preserved even if the external source is removed. Experiments of this kind, involving high area carbon electrodes, have shown that electrodes polarized at voltages of up to a volt, with respect to the open (or rest) potential, undergo shifts of less than a few millivolts over periods of time exceeding several tens of minutes. Such low rates of discharge are not surprising, since the actual surface of thin (ca. 0.5 mm), small cross section electrodes (1 cm^2) may be on the order of 10 to 100 m^2, and the volume of electrolyte (and thus the total amount of oxygen and other impurities in the solution) is very small (<0.2 mL).

Advantage has been taken of this freezing approach in the study of molecules adsorbed at monolayer coverages on high area materials. As will be described later in section IV.E., two such species have been found to display unusually small recoilless fractions at room temperature, even before being placed in contact with the electrolyte. A schematic diagram of a cell used for such in situ freezing studies, involving an iron macrocycle adsorbed on a high area carbon electrode, is shown in Figure 9.

E.   Limitations of the Technique

Besides the fact that the number of Mossbauer active nuclides for that measurements can be conveniently made is rather small, there are other factors that tend to restrict the type of electrochemical systems that can be examined with this spectroscopic technique. In the case of ^{57}Fe in the transmission mode, for instance, the number of scatterers required to obtain adequate statistics in a reasonable period of time (up to several days) is on the order of 10^{17}. Hence, this technique lacks the time resolution of other spectroscopic methods. Also to be considered is the fact that the natural abundance of the Mossbauer active isotopes is 8.58% for ^{119}Sn, and only 2.19% for ^{57}Fe. Therefore, the possibility of conducting transmission Mossbauer measurements in this specific mode, involving species at monolayer coverages on smooth surfaces, even with fully enriched compounds, appears very unlikely.

Emission Mossbauer spectroscopy affords a much more sensitive means of acquiring spectral information, as only 10^{12} atoms are usually required to obtain an adequate signal to noise ratio in a reasonable period of time. Besides the problems associated with the interpretation of emission spectra discussed in the previous section, the appropriate radioactive isotope must be incorporated in the compound of interest. The latter may present challenging synthetic problems, especially when the desired specific activity of the final material is very high. For these reasons most emission experiments demand careful planning.

IV. MODEL SYSTEMS

A number of examples will be provided in this section of in situ Mossbauer spectroscopy as applied to the study of electrochemical phenomena, involving transmission and emission modes, quasi-in situ conversion electron and in situ electrode freezing techniques. It is expected that these examples may serve as a guide for the design of experiments involving a much wider variety of interfacial systems. Except where otherwise indicated, the isomer shifts δ are referred to the α-Fe standard, and δ, the quadrupole splittings Δ, and widths Γ, are given in mm•s^{-1}.

A. Electrochemical Properties of Iron and Its Oxides

A detailed understanding of iron passivation and corrosion is of crucial importance to the development of new iron-based materials and coatings with optimized chemical and structural characteristics to withstand prolonged exposure to a large variety of aggressive gaseous and liquid environments. Because of its specificity, Mossbauer spectroscopy appears to provide an ideal means for studying key aspects of these phenomena. Hence, it is not surprising that most of the literature in the area of in situ application of this technique has been devoted to their investigation.

This subsection has been divided into two parts. The first will present results of two rather recent contributions from which considerable insight has been obtained into the electrochemical behavior of the iron oxyhydroxide system, whereas the second part will address studies of the passive film in borate buffer media.

1. The Iron Oxyhydroxide System   One of the earlier Mossbauer studies of the electrochemical properties of iron was that of Geronov et al. [14] who investigated the spectral changes induced by the charge and discharge of high area iron-carbon polymer bonded electrodes in strongly alkaline media. Despite the fact that the experiments were not conducted under strict potential control, as the circuit was opened during data acquisition, these authors made a number of interesting observations regarding the behavior of iron electrodes in 5 M KOH. In particular, electrodes in the fully charged state (-0.9 V vs. Hg/HgO,OH$^-$) were found to exhibit features associated with metallic iron and Fe(OH)$_2$, whereas two additional peaks, attributed to β-FeOOH, were observed upon discharge of these electrodes under galvanostatic conditions (-0.5 V vs. Hg/HgO,OH$^-$). Similar experiments conducted in the presence of LiOH in the same solution lead to a conversion of the β-FeOOH into bulk magnetite (Fe$_3$O$_4$), as evidenced by the appeareance of the characteristic strong field Zeeman split six-line spectrum.

The first in situ Mossbauer investigation involving the behavior of iron oxides in electrochemical enviroments was the result of a fortuitous incident in which a specimen containing iron phthalocyanine, FePc, dispersed in a high area carbon was accidentally decomposed, during a rather mild heat treatment, to yield a very fine dispersion of a ferric oxide [15]. These studies were aimed at characterizing the interactions of FePc, an effective electrocatalyst for dioxygen reduction [7], with the carbon substrate and their role in the overall catalytic process.

The actual samples were prepared by adding Vulcan XC-72, a high area carbon of about 250 m$^2 \cdot$g^{-1}, to a solution of FePc in pyridine under ultrasonic agitation. The carbon suspension was later transferred to a distillation apparatus and heated until all the excess solvent was removed. The dry dispersion, containing about 10% w/w FePc/XC-72, was then placed into a small crucible and heated in a furnace under a flowing inert gas atmosphere at 280°C so as to eliminate pyridine axially coordinated to the macrocycle. After two hours, the heating was interrupted, and the sample was allowed to cool without disconnecting the stream of inert gas.

Figure 10 shows the cyclic voltammetry of an FePc/XC-72 dispersion, prepared in such fashion, in the form of a thin, porous, Teflon bonded coating electrode in a 1 M NaOH solution. A description of the methodology involved in the preparation of this type of electrode may be found in Reference 14. As can

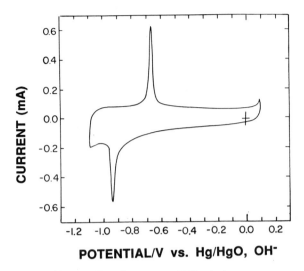

Figure 10. *Cyclic voltammetry of 7% w/w iron phthalocyanine dispersed on Vulcan XC-72 carbon, after a heat treatment at 300°C in a flowing inert atmosphere. The measurement was conducted with the material in the form a thin porous Teflon bonded coating in 1 M NaOH at 25°. Sweep rate: 5 mV/s.*

be clearly seen, the voltammetry of this specimen exhibits two sharply defined peaks separated by about 330 mV. The potentials associated with these features are essentially identical to those found by other workers for the reduction and oxidation of films of iron oxyhydroxide formed on a number of host surfaces, including iron and carbon [16].

A 10% w/w highly enriched ^{57}FePc/XC-72 dispersion, prepared according to the same methodology as that described above, was used in the Mossbauer measurements. The ^{57}FePc was synthesized by heating a mixture of hydrogen-reduced, highly divided metallic ^{57}Fe with dicyanobenzene in an evacuated, sealed ampoule for over a day. It was then extracted with acetone and subsequently purified by vacuum sublimation under reduced pressure. The electrode employed in the in situ Mossbauer measurements was the same as that involved in the operating fuel cell experiments using the in situ spectroelectrochemical cell shown in Figure 6A.

The in situ Mossbauer spectra obtained at 0.0 V is given in Figure 11, Curve A. The parameters associated with this doublet [Table 3] are similar to those reported by various groups for high spin ferric oxyhydroxides [Table 4]. Also,

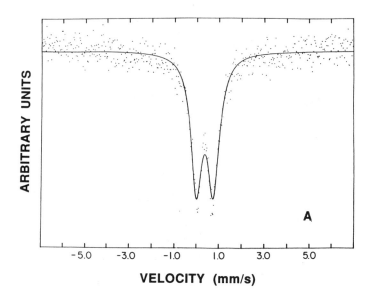

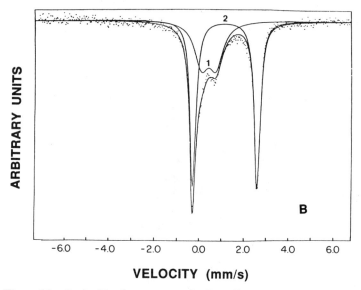

Figure 11.   *In situ Mossbauer spectra for FePc dispersed in Vulcan XC-72 carbon subjected to the same heat treatment specified in the caption Figure 9 obtained at 0.0 V (Curve A), and –1.00 V vs. Hg/HgO,OH⁻ (Curve B). Other conditions given in caption Figure 10.*

TABLE 3.   In Situ Mossbauer Parameters for Small Particles of a Hydrated Ferric Oxyhydroxide, FeOOH(hydrated) Dispersed on High Area Vulcan XC-72 Carbon.[a]

Potential V vs. Hg/HgO,OH⁻	Isomer Shift $\delta/mm \cdot s^{-1}$ vs. α-Fe	Quadrupole Splitting $\Delta/mm \cdot s^{-1}$	Width $\Gamma/mm \cdot s^{-1}$	Figure
0.0	0.37	0.76	0.62	11A
−0.4	0.37	0.74	0.65	—
−0.75	0.37	0.66	0.57	—
−0.85	0.35	0.63	0.60	—
−1.05	1 0.41	0.65	0.77	11B
	2 1.14	2.85	0.32	

[a]*This material was prepared by the heat treatment of iron phthalocyanine dispersed on the carbon in an inert atmosphere at 280°C.*

they appear in agreement with those observed for certain magnetically ordered oxides for which the characteristic six-line spectra collapses into a doublet as the particles become smaller in size. This phenomenon, known as superparamagnetism [2], is attributed to the flipping of the magnetic moment of each microcrystal between easy directions. This occurs in a shorter time than either the Larmor precessional period of the nucleus or the lifetime of the excited 3/2 state of the ^{57}Fe nucleus or both, when the temperature is sufficiently high. Such behavior has been observed, for example, by Hassett et al. [17] for magnetite dispersed in lignosulfonate.

It may be noted that the quadrupole splitting of the heat treated FePc/XC-72 electrode measured ex situ prior to the electrochemical experiments was larger than that found in situ. Smaller values for Δ have been reported for certain ferric hydroxide gels and for small particles of FeOOH [Table 4], and thus the effect observed for this specimen is most probably related to the incorporation of water into the oxide structure. Based on this information, the material observed in situ at this potential will be referred to hereafter as FeOOH(hydrated), without implying any specific stoichiometry.

The in situ spectra obtained at −1.0 V, shown in Figure 11, Curve B yielded a doublet with an isomer shift and quadrupole splitting in excellent agreement with those of crystalline Fe(OH)$_2$ [Table 3]. This provides rather definite evidence that the redox process associated with the voltammetric peaks is given by

$$FeOOH \text{ (hydrated)} + e^- + H^+ \rightarrow Fe(OH)_2 \text{ (crystalline)}. \tag{4}$$

TABLE 4. Ex Situ Mossbauer Parameters of Various Iron Oxides and Oxyhydroxides at Room Temperature.

Specimen	Isomer Shift $\delta/mm \cdot^{-1}$ vs. α-Fe	Quadrupole Splitting $\Delta/mm \cdot s^{-1}$	Width $\Gamma/mm \cdot s^{-1}$	H_{eff} kOe
α-FeOOH (goethite)	0.44	0.16	0.86	367
α-Fe$_2$O$_3$[a] (diam. <10 nm)	0.32	0.98		
β-FeOOH	0.38 (61.4)	0.53	0.26	
	0.39 (38.6)	0.88	0.30	
γ-FeOOH (lepidocrocite)	0.38	0.59	0.27	
α-Fe$_2$O$_3$ (hematite)	0.38	0.24	0.29	523
γ-Fe$_2$O$_3$ (maghemite)	0.43	0.06	0.45	506
Fe$_3$O$_4$	0.39 (49.6)	0.11	0.53	506
nonstoichiometric	0.78 (50.4)	0.28	0.38	465
γ-Fe$_3$O$_4$	0.37 (4.8)[g]	0.59	0.43	
stoichiometric	0.34 (34.4)	0.12	0.29	491
(magnetite)	0.72 (59.8)	0.10	0.31	461
γ-Fe$_3$O$_4$[b] (diam. < 5 nm)	0.37	0.89		
Fe(OH)$_2$[c]	1.18	2.92		
Ferric oxide[d] (small particles)	0.33	0.70		
Ferric oxide[e] (hydrated)	0.35	0.62		
FeOOH[f] (small particles)	0.39	0.62		

Data from S. Music, et al. Croat. Chem. Acta 59 (1986):833, except where otherwise indicated.

[a]*Kundig, W. , et al. Phys. Rev. 142 (1966):327.*
[b]*Aharoni, S. and Litt, M. J. Appl. Phys. 42 (1971):352.*
[c]*Pritchard, A. M. and Mould, B. T. Corros. Sci. 11 (1971):1.*
[d]*Rethwisch, D. G. and Dumesic, J. A. J. Phys. Chem. 90 (1986):1863.*
[e]*Bakare, P. P.; Gupta, M. P.; and Sinha, A. P. B. Indian J. Pure Appl. Phys. 18 (1980):473*
[f]*Vozniuk, P. O. and Dubinin, V. N. Sov. Phys.-Solid State 15 (1973):1265.*
[g] *This feature is due to FeOOH.*

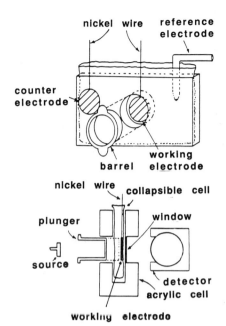

Figure 12. *Electrochemical cell for in situ Mossbauer spectroscopy measurements.*

It may thus be concluded that the specific methodology involved in the dispersion of FePc on high area carbon leads to the thermal decomposition of the macrocycle at temperatures much below those expected for the bulk material, generating small particles of hydrated FeOOH upon exposure to an alkaline solution.

Subsequently, Fierro et al. [18] have reported a series of in situ Mossbauer experiments aimed at investigating the electrochemical behavior of the iron oxyhydroxide system in strongly alkaline media.

A hydrated form of a ferric oxyhydroxide, precipitated by chemical means on a high area carbon, was used in these experiments. This material was prepared by first dissolving a mixture of highly enriched metallic ^{57}Fe and an appropriate amount of natural iron in concentrated nitric acid to achieve about one-third isotope enrichment in the final product. This solution was then added to an ultrasonically agitated water suspension of Shawinigan black, a high area carbon of about 60 $m^2 \cdot g^{-1}$, and the iron subsequently precipitated by the addition of 4 M KOH. A Teflon bonded electrode was prepared with this material, following the same procedure as that described in section III.C., except that no heat treatment was performed to remove the Teflon emulsifier. The ^{57}Fe/XC-72 w/w ratio was in this case 50% and thus much higher than that involved in the heat treated FePc experiments described earlier. The electrochemical cell for the in situ Mossbauer measurements is shown in Figure 12.

The ex situ Mossbauer spectrum for the partially dried electrode yielded a doublet with $\delta = 0.34$ and $\Delta = 0.70$ mm•s^{-1}. A decrease in the value of Δ was found in the in situ spectra of the same electrode immersed in 4 M KOH at -0.3 V vs Hg/HgO,OH$^-$ [Fig. 13, Curve A], in direct analogy with the behavior observed for the heat treated FePc. It is thus conceivable that this material is the same as that found after the thermal decomposition of FePc dispersed on carbon reported by other workers, and that the variations in the value of Δ are simply due to differences in the degree of hydration of the lattice.

No significant changes in the spectra were found when the electrode was polarized sequentially at -0.5 and -0.7 V, by scanning the potential to these values at 10 mV•s^{-1}. This is not surprising since the cyclic voltammetry for an identical, although non-enriched iron/carbon mixture, shown in the inset of Figure 13, indicated no significant faradaic currents over this voltage region for the sweep in the negative direction. In a subsequent measurement at a potential of -0.9 V, the resonant absorption of the doublet underwent a marked drop. This may be due to an increase in the solubility of the oxide and thus in a loss of solid in the electrode and/or to a modification in the recoilless fraction of the solid induced by the hydration of the lattice.

The electrode was then swept further negative to -1.1 V, a potential more negative than the onset of the faradaic current in the voltammogram, yielding after about two hours of measurement, a strong, clearly defined doublet [Fig. 13, Curve B] with parameters in excellent agreement with those of Fe(OH)$_2$ [Table 4]. The potential was then *stepped* to -0.3 V. In contrast to the doublet obtained originally at this voltage, a magnetically split six-line spectrum was obtained in this case [Fig. 14, Curve B]. The Zeeman effect and the value of δ are consistent with those of a magnetically ordered ferric oxide species [Tables 4 and 5]. Unfortunately, the strength of the internal field, H_{eff}, cannot be used as a definite identifying parameter, as the calculated value seems significantly smaller than that expected for a bulk iron oxide, a behavior often attributed to superparamagnetism (vide supra). Furthermore, the asymmetric broadening of the peaks may be ascribed to a distribution of effective magnetic fields, providing evidence for the presence of an ensemble of small particles of varying sizes. From a statistical viewpoint this is accounted for by a Gaussian distribution of Lorentzians, a feature that is built into the computer routine used to fit the data shown in Figure 14, Curve A. It may be noted that Hassett et al. [17] have reported a strikingly similar six-line spectrum for small particles of magnetite dispersed in a lignosulfonate matrix.

In a subsequent measurement, the potential was swept in the negative direction to -1.1 V, yielding once more a Mossbauer spectrum characteristic of

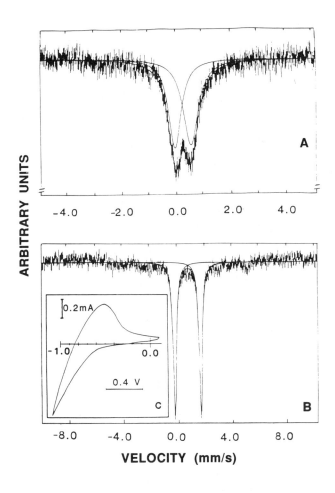

Figure 13. *In situ Mossbauer spectra of a 50% w/w* ^{57}Fe
enriched hydrated ferric oxide precipitated on Schawinigan
black high area carbon in the form of a Teflon bonded electrode
in 4 M KOH at –0.3 V (Curve A) and –1.1 V vs Hg/HgO,OH⁻
(Curve B). Inset: Cyclic voltammogram of the same, although
nonenriched, material in the form of a thin porous Teflon
bonded coating electrode deposited on an ordinary pyrolytic
graphite electrode, in 4 M KOH. Scan rate: 10 mV/s.

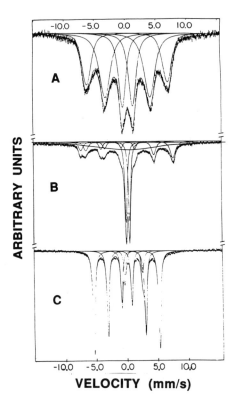

Figure 14. *In situ Mossbauer spectra of the same electrode as in Figure 13 at –0.3 V, after a potential* step *(Curve A), and after a potential* sweep *(Curve B), from –1.1 V. Curve C was obtained at a potential of –1.2 V.*

Fe(OH)$_2$, and later *swept* at 2 mV•s^{-1} rather than *stepped* positive to –0.3 V. As shown in Figure 14, Curve B, the resulting spectrum was different than either that associated with the original material or that obtained after a voltage step. The apparent splitting observed for two of the absorption lines located at negative velocities is typical of magnetite (Fe$_3$O$_4$) in bulk form at room temperature [Table 4]. This is due to the superposition of spectra arising from ferric cations in tetrahedral sites and ferric cations in octahedral sites. The broad background centered at 0.24 mm•s^{-1} may be the result of several effects, including particle size and structural disorder among magnetite crystals, which would distort the Mossbauer spectra. The sharp doublet in the center of the spectrum, as judged by the parameter values given in Table 5, can be attributed to the same hydrated ferric oxyhydroxide observed originally.

The results of these experiments may be explained in terms of differences in the nature of the particles generated by the specific way in which the ferrous oxide is electrochemically oxidized. In particular, a potential step is expected to promote the formation of multitude of nuclei large enough to exhibit a Zeeman

TABLE 5.   In Situ Mossbauer Parameters for Iron Oxides and Oxyhydroxides Dispersed on High Area Schawinigan Black Carbon Electrode

Potential V vs. Hg/HgO,OH⁻	Isomer Shift $\delta/mm \cdot s^{-1}$ vs. α-Fe	Quadrupole Splitting $\Delta/mm \cdot s^{-1}$	Heff kOe	Figure
−0.3 (initial)	0.33(0.34)[a]	0.58(0.70)		13A
−1.1	1.10	2.89		13B
−0.3 (step)	0.37	0.04	406	14A
−0.3 (sweep)	0.33	0.57		14B
	0.28		463	
	0.56	0.15	437	
	0.24			
−1.2	0.00		330	14C
	1.15	2.90		

[a]Values in parenthesis are those obtained for the same electrode dry.

splitting, but on the average smaller than that required to yield a spectra characteristic of bulk magnetite. When the oxidation is performed by sweeping the potential, however, a few magnetite nuclei are generated, which grow to a size sufficiently large to show bulklike behavior.

Considerable insight into the nature of these species could be obtained by examining the temperature dependence of the Mossbauer parameters using the in situ freezing experiments of the type described in section III.D.2.

At the end of these measurements, the electrode was polarized by sweeping the potential to −1.2 V, yielding a six-line spectrum corresponding to metallic iron with some contribution from Fe(OH)₂ [Fig. 14, Curve C]. The potential was then scanned up to −0.3 V, and a spectrum essentially identical to that recorded at −1.2 V was observed. This result clearly indicates that the iron metal particles formed by the electrochemical reduction are large enough for the contributions arising from the pass ivation layer to be too small to be clearly resolved. After scanning the potential several times between −0.3 and −1.2 V, however, the doublet associated with the Fe(OH)₂ disappeared.

2. *The Passive Film of Iron* The structure and properties of the passive film on iron may be regarded as of crucial importance to the further understanding of corrosion inhibition [19]. Despite the efforts of numerous research

groups involving electrochemical and spectroscopic techniques, no consensus has yet been reached regarding such important aspects of the film as the oxidation state of the iron sites, the degree of long-range order, and the extent of hydration. Part of the controversy has centered around the use of ex situ spectroscopic methods for the acquisition of structural and compositional information. In particular, the relevance of the results obtained to the conditions that prevail in actual electrochemical environments has been regarded by many workers as highly questionable, since a) the removal of the electrodes from the electrochemical cell results in a loss of potential control; and b) the exposure of specimens to either air or vacuum and photon, electron, or ion beams may be expected to modify considerably the nature of the film. Because of its high degree of specificity and the possibility of conducting in situ measurements, Mossbauer spectroscopy appears especially suited for the investigation of this particular system. This section will be based principally on the rather recent comprehensive studies of Eldridge, Kordesch and Hoffman [20], which may be regarded as an extension of the pioneering work of O'Grady published in 1980 [21].

Essentially, all in situ Mossbauer studies of the passive film have been performed in borate buffer solutions of pH = 8.4. The choice of this electrolyte has been motivated primarily by the work of Nagayama and Cohen [22], who concluded, based on electrochemical measurements, that the passive layer in this media could be reduced to metallic iron in a reproducible fashion. Except where otherwise noted, all the experiments to be presented in this section were conducted with thin ^{57}Fe enriched film electrodes, vapor deposited on a highly conducting gold on Melinex substrate [6]. Scanning electron micrographs provided evidence that this preparation procedure affords films of a much smoother character than those obtained by electrodeposition from a conventional plating bath. Although some carbon impurities were detected in such vapor deposited iron films, it is highly unlikely that their presence would significantly affect the overall electrochemical characteristics of the pure metal.

The electrochemical cell employed in the experiments is illustrated in Figure 6B. A typical in situ Mossbauer spectrum obtained for an ^{57}Fe film (ca. 11 nm thickness) polarized at -0.4 V vs. α-Pd/H in borate buffer pH = 8.4 is shown in Figure 15, Curve A. The two peaks correspond to the inner components of the sextet characteristic of bulk metallic iron. Upon stepping the potential to 1.3 V, an additional doublet with parameters $\delta = 0.41$ mm$\cdot$s^{-1}, $\Delta = 1.09$ mm$\cdot$s^{-1}, and $\Gamma = 0.83$ mm$\cdot$s^{-1} attributed to the passive film was obtained after about 24 hrs of data acquisition [Fig. 15B]. The electrode polarization was then interrupted, the electrolyte drained, and the film washed with distilled water and stored in a dessicator.

Two significant changes were observed in the ex situ spectra of this dried film [Fig. 15C] compared to those obtained in situ: an increase in the intensity of the passive film features with respect to those of bulk iron, and a decrease in

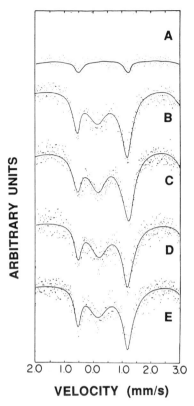

Figure 15. *In situ Mossbauer transmission spectra for 11 nm [57]Fe film in borate buffer (pH = 8.4) at –0.4 V (metallic Fe) (Curve A) and after passivation at +1.3 V vs. α-Pd/H, (Curve B). Curves C and D were obtained ex situ after drying the film, and in situ (+1.3 V) after reintroducing the passive film in the same electrolyte. The spectrum in E was recorded at +1.3 V after two reduction-passivation cycles. See text for additional details.*

the value of Γ [Table 6]. After this measurement was completed, the cell was reassembled and filled with electrolyte, and the same film electrode was polarized at 1.3 V. Although no change was observed in the magnitude of Γ for the passive layer feature as compared to that of the dry film ex situ, the relative peak amplitude was found to be about a third larger than that observed in the original in situ spectra at the same potential [Fig. 15D]. The electrode was then reduced and passivated twice, and a new in situ Mossbauer spectrum was recorded, yielding a spectra [Fig. 15E] almost indistinguishable from that shown in Curve B in the same figure. In particular, the relative passive film/iron substrate resonant absorption contribution, A_{pf}/A_{fe}, was found to be the same as that observed in the original passivated specimen. This indicates that within the sensitivity of this technique, the amount of iron lost in the electrolyte during the whole procedure was negligible and thus that most of the iron in the passive film is reduced back to the metal state. Additional evidence in support of this view was provided by the striking similarities between the conversion electron

TABLE 6. Transmission Mossbauer Data for a ^{57}Fe Film Passivated at +1.3 V vs α-Pd/H in Borate Buffer (pH = 8.4)

Specimen	Isomer Shift $\delta/mm \cdot s^{-1}$ vs. α-Fe	Quadrupole Splitting $\Delta/mm \cdot s^{-1}$	Width $\Gamma/mm \cdot s^{-1}$	Apf/Afe^{a}	Figure
Initial Passivation in situ	0.41	1.09	0.89	0.89	15B
Dry	0.38	1.07	0.75	1.11	15C
Repassivation no reduction in situ	0.40	1.05	0.73	1.04	15D
Two-step cycle repassivations in situ	0.37	1.06	0.79	0.88	15E

^{a}This quantity corresponds to the fraction of total resonant area due to passive film contribution.

Mossbauer spectra of films that had been subjected to a single compared to multiple reduction-passivation cycles.

The dependence of the film characteristics on the rate at which the passivation is performed was investigated also. As shown in Table 7, slow scan rates invariably yield spectra with much larger passive film contribution and substantially lower quadrupole splittings than films formed by a fast sweep or a step. It is interesting to note in this regard that the parameters reported by O'Grady [21] for the passive film measured in situ after multiple reduction-passivation cycles are very similar to those of films obtained by slow scan rates. This provides rather conclusive evidence that the current distribution, which is largely determined by the cell geometry, may play a significant role in controlling certain structural and electronic properties of the film formed on the iron surface.

No spectral differences were found between films formed at 1.3 V and later polarized in sequence at 0.5 and 0.35 V. In contrast, films formed originally at 0.35 V and subsequently stepped to 0.5, 0.9, and 1.3 V exhibited a systematic increase in the relative passive film contribution, a decrease in the isomer shift, and an increase in the quadrupole splitting, to yield at the final potential of 1.3

TABLE 7. In Situ Transmission Mossbauer Data for a ^{57}Fe Film Passivated at +1.3 V vs α-Pd/H in Borate Buffer (pH = 8.4) at Different Scan Rates

Specimen[a]	Isomer Shift δ/mm•s^{-1} vs. α-Fe	Quadrupole Splitting Δ/mm•s^{-1}	Width Γ/mm•s^{-1}	Apf/Afe
stepped	0.38	1.14	0.77	0.84
scanned over 4.5 min	0.40	1.14	0.78	0.87
scanned over 10.25 min	0.40	1.00	0.79	1.30

[a]The potential was always set initially at –0.4 V vs. α-Pd/H.

V parameters very similar to those of films obtained by direct passivation at 1.3 V. It was also found that films formed at lower potentials underwent spectral changes upon drying, an effect that was not observed for films prepared at high potentials. This suggests that the amount of water incorporated in the film decreases as the potential is made more positive.

The Mossbauer parameters for the passive film obtained in quasi in situ conversion electron measurements conducted in the same borate buffer media [Fig. 16] were found to yield good agreement with those obtained in the transmission mode (δ = 0.38, Δ = 1.03). The sharper doublet in Figure 16 corresponds to the inner lines of metallic iron.

Although important information can be obtained by comparing the values of the Mossbauer parameters obtained for the passive film with those of known oxides and oxyhydroxides, extreme care must be exercised in the assignment of spectral features based solely on such data. This is due primarily to modifications in the magnitude of the hyperfine interactions associated with a given material induced by changes in the particle size (vide supra). If such effects are not assumed to play a major role, however, the value of the isomer shift may be regarded as characteristic of a ferric species in high spin, for which δ lies typically in the range between 0.35 and 0.75. Furthermore, the magnitude of Δ is much larger than those of iron oxyhydroxides and crystalline oxides. This would be consistent with the presence of large geometric distortions, such as those expected in noncrystalline lattices, indicating, as originally suggested by O'Grady, that the passive film consists of a highly disordered ferric oxyhydroxide.

An approach that can provide considerable insight into the nature of highly dispersed or amorphous materials, as was briefly mentioned in the previous section, involves a careful examination of the temperature dependence of the

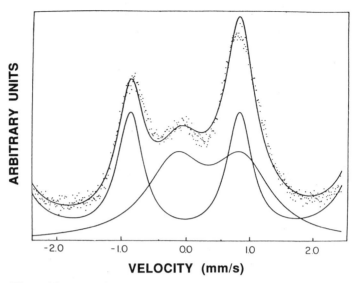

Figure 16. *Quasi in situ conversion electron Mossbauer spectrum of an ^{57}Fe enriched rotating iron film electrode polarized at +1.3 V vs. α-Pd/H in borate buffer (pH = 8.4). The narrow doublet corresponds to the inner lines of metallic Fe, whereas the broader doublet is attributed to the passive film.*

Mossbauer spectra. Unfortunately, the temperature range in which in situ experiments of this type would be feasible is very restricted. Nevertheless, ex situ Mossbauer spectra recorded in the X-ray fluorescence back-scattering detection mode [8] have indicated that the doublet associated with the passive film, prepared in the same fashion as experiments described earlier, essentially disappears at 80 K. Similar experiments, in which the thickness of the enriched iron layer was decreased so as to reduce the contribution due the iron substrate and thus improve the overall resolution, resulted in a broad magnetically split spectra at liquid nitrogen temperature. This was attributed either to the onset of magnetic ordering or a blocking of the superparamagnetic particles. Although none of these explanations appears to be entirely satisfactory, the results provided evidence for the presence of a multiplicity of iron sites in the film, which would be consistent with a highly disordered structure. In situ extended X-ray absorption fine structure EXAFS measurements [23] are expected to provide much needed insight into this specific issue.

B. Mixed Ni-Fe Oxyhydroxides as Electrocatalysts for Oxygen Evolution

The presence of iron in nickel oxyhydroxide electrodes has been found to considerably reduce the overpotential for oxygen evolution in alkaline media associated with the otherwise iron free material [24]. An in situ Mossbauer study of a composite Ni/Fe oxyhydroxide was undertaken in order to gain insight into the nature of the species responsible for the electrocatalytic activity [25]. This specific system appeared particularly interesting, because it offered a unique opportunity for determining whether redox reactions involving the host lattice sites can alter the structural and/or electronic characteristics of other species present in the material.

Thin films of a composite nickel-iron (9:1 Ni/Fe ratio) and iron-free oxyhydroxides were deposited onto Ni foils by electroprecipitation at constant current density from metal nitrate solutions. A comparison of the cyclic voltammetry of such films in 1 M KOH at room temperature [Fig. 17] shows that the incorporation of iron in the lattice shifts the potentials associated formally with

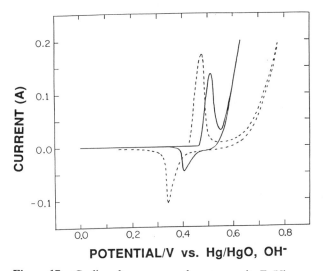

Figure 17. *Cyclic voltammograms for a composite Fe/Ni oxyhydroxide (Fe/Ni 1:9) on a Ni foil substrate in 1 M KOH (solid curve). Scan rate: 10 mV/s. The dashed curve was obtained for an iron-free Ni oxyhydroxyde film under the same experimental conditions.*

the NiOOH/Ni(OH)$_2$ redox processes in the negative direction and decreases considerably the onset potential for oxygen evolution. It may be noted that the oxidation peak is much larger than the reduction counterpart, providing evidence that, within the time scale of the cyclic voltammetry, a fraction of the nickel sites remains in the oxidized state at potentials more negative than the reduction peak.

The in situ Mossbauer experiments were conducted with 90% [57]Fe enriched 9:1 Ni/Fe oxyhydroxide films, which were deposited in the fashion described above onto gold on Melinex supports in a conventional electrochemical cell. Prior to their transfer into the in situ Mossbauer cell, the electrodes were cycled twice between 0 and 0.6 V vs. Hg/HgO,OH$^-$ in 1 M KOH. Two such films were used in the actual Mossbauer measurements in order to reduce the counting time. A description of the in situ Mossbauer cell involved in these experiments may be found in the original literature.

The in situ spectrum obtained at 0.5 V vs. Hg/HgO,OH$^-$ (oxidized state) is shown in Figure 18, Curve A. Following this measurement, the potential was swept to 0.0 V (reduced state), and a new in situ spectrum recorded after the current had dropped to a very small value [Fig. 18, Curve B]. Essentially identical results were obtained when the films were examined first in the reduced and then in the oxidized state.

The spectrum of the oxidized form was successfully fitted with a singlet yielding an isomer shift of 0.22. For the spectrum in the reduced state, a satisfactory fit could be achieved with two singlets, which, when regarded as the components of an asymmetric doublet, yielded $\delta = 0.34$ and $\Delta = 0.43$. In view of the fact that the cyclic voltammetry indicated a slow reduction of the oxidized state, a statistical analysis of the data in Figure 18, Curve B was attempted with a symmetric doublet and a singlet to account for a possible contribution due to the oxidized phase. This approach afforded excellent results, yielding an isomer shift for the singlet very similar to that of the oxidized species in Figure 18, Curve A. Furthermore, the values of δ and Δ for the symmetric doublet were found to be nearly the same as those in the fit involving the asymmetric doublet. These are listed in Table 8.

The isomer shift of 0.32, associated with the reduced state of the composite material, is similar to that reported for various Fe(III) oxyhydroxides and indicates that iron is present in the ferric form. The much smaller quadrupole splitting, however, provides evidence that the crystal environment of such ferric sites is different than that in common forms of ferric oxyhydroxides. The lower value of the isomer shift, observed upon oxidation of the composite film, indicates a partial transfer of electron density away from the Fe(III) sites, which could result indirectly from the oxidation of the Ni(II) sites to yield a highly oxidized iron species. It is interesting to note that recent Raman measurements have provided evidence for the presence of highly symmetrical Ni sites in

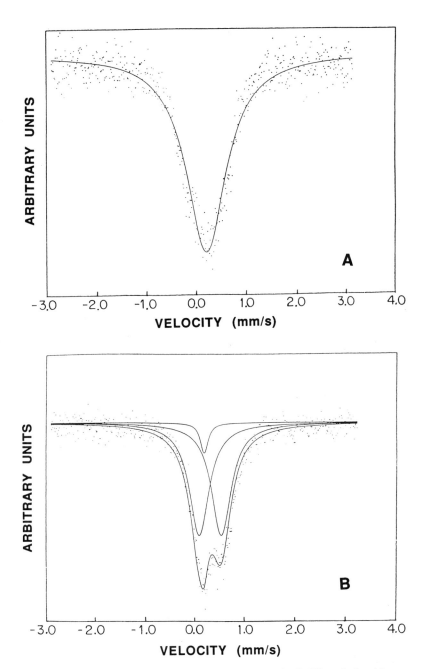

Figure 18. *In situ Mossbauer spectrum of a composite Fe/Ni oxyhydroxide (Fe/Ni 1:9) polarized at 0.5 V (oxidized state) (Curve A) and at 0.0 V vs Hg/HgO,OH⁻ (reduced state) (Curve B) in 1 M KOH.*

TABLE 8.   In Situ Mossbauer Parameters for an Iron-Nickel Mixed
                      Oxyhydroxide in 1 M KOH

Potential V vs. HglHgO,OH⁻	Isomer Shift $\delta/mm \cdot s^{-1}$ vs. α-Fe	Quadrupole Splitting $\Delta/mm \cdot s^{-1}$	Width $\Gamma/mm \cdot s^{-1}$	Figure
0.5	0.22		0.97	18A
0.0	0.32(95)[a]	0.44	0.47	18B
	0.19(5)		0.19	

[a]Values in parenthesis represent the fraction of the total resonant absorption associated
with each peak, assuming a common recoilless fraction for both species.

oxidized nickel hydroxide films [26]. Based on such information, it was postulated that the film structure could be better represented as NiO_2 rather than as
NiOOH. Thus, it seems reasonable that the oxidized composite oxyhydroxide
could contain symmetrical sites that might be occupied by Fe ions. This would
be consistent with the presence of a singlet, rather than a doublet, in the spectra
shown in Figure 18, Curve A. Based on these arguments, Corrigan et al. [25]
concluded that the composite metal oxyhydroxide may be regarded as a single
phase involving distinct iron and nickel sites as opposed to a physical mixture of
$Ni(OH)_2$ and FeOOH particles. This is not surprising since the composite
hydroxide is a better catalyst than either of the individual hydroxides.

In summary, the results of this investigation indicated that the formal
oxidation of the nickel sites in a composite nickel-iron oxyhydroxide modifies
the electronic and structural properties of the ferric sites, yielding a more
d-electron deficient iron species. Although it may be reasonable to suggest that
the electrocatalytic activity of this composite oxide for oxygen evolution may be
related to the presence of such highly oxidized iron sites, additional in situ
spectroscopic measurements such as EXAFS may be necessary in order to
support this view.

C.   Prussian Blue

The addition of ferric ions to an aqueous solution of Fe(II)hexacyanide results
in the formation of a highly colored colloidal precipitate known as Prussian blue
(PB), a material regarded as the oldest coordination compound reported in the
scientific literature [27]. It has recently been found that films of PB deposited on

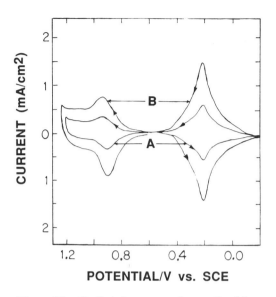

Figure 19. *Cyclic voltammetry of a prussian blue film electrodeposited on a glassy carbon electrode (6 mC/cm^2 PB) at 10 (Curve A) and 20 mV/s (Curve B) in deaerated 1 M KCl (pH = 4.0).*

electronically conducting substrates are capable of undergoing a reversible blue to transparent color transition upon changing the electrode potential between two appropriate values [26]. This is an illustration of what has been referred to as electrochromism, a phenomenon that may find wide application in connection with electronically controlled color display devices.

As shown in Figure 19, the voltammetric behavior of PB films is characterized by the presence of two prominent reversible peaks. The blue to transparent transition occurs in the region between 0.6 and 0.0 V. The nature of the redox processes associated with the electrochromic effect have been investigated using in situ Mossbauer spectroscopy by Itaya and coworkers, [28], in what may be regarded as a classical example of the use of this technique in the study of electrochemical systems.

Films of PB were formed in this case on glassy carbon surfaces by electrodeposition from a mixture of $K_3Fe(CN)_6$ and highly enriched $^{57}FeCl_3$. The in situ experiments were conducted in the same electrolyte as that for the voltammogram of Figure 19, using a cell that is shown schematically in Figure

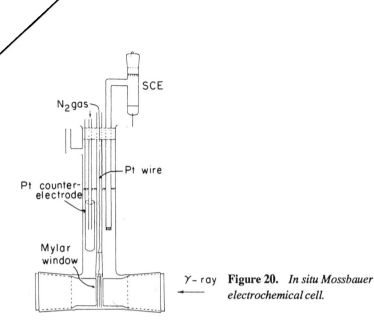

γ- ray **Figure 20.** *In situ Mossbauer electrochemical cell.*

20. The in situ Mossbauer spectra were obtained at a potential of 0.6 V (Prussian blue) and at –0.2 V vs. SCE, which corresponds to the reduced or transparent form of PB. These are given in Figure 21, Curves A and B, respectively. The parameters associated with PB, $\delta = 0.37$ and $\Delta = 0.41$, are characteristic of a Fe^{3+} ion in high spin (Table 9). As noted by these authors, a similar spectrum has been reported by Maer et al. [29] at liquid nitrogen temperature for a precipitate formed by mixing $^{57}Fe(SO_4)_3$ and $K_4Fe(CN)_6$ solutions. For the spectra recorded at –0.2 V, the isomer shift and quadrupole splitting are typical of a ferrous species in high spin. This provides evidence that

1. the redox process responsible for the electrochromic behavior involves a drastic change in the electron density about the iron sites not coordinated to the cyanide ligands, e.g.,

$$Fe_4^{3+}[Fe^{II}(CN)_6]_3 + 4e^- + 4K^+ \rightleftharpoons K_4Fe_4^{2+} + [Fe^{II}(CN)_6]_3; \qquad (5)$$

and

2. no chemical reactions such as ligand exchange between the hydrated ferric ions and $Fe(III)(CN)_6^{3-}$ take place during the electrochemical deposition of thin PB films.

Further work in this area may be required in order to determine the nature of the redox process associated with the additional redox peak at 0.9 V vs. SCE. In addition, it would be of utmost interest to establish whether or not a change

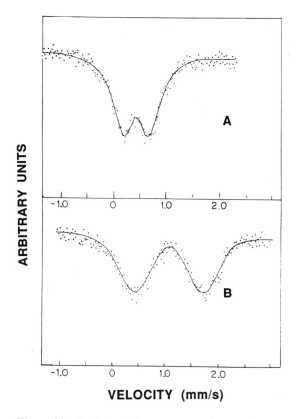

Figure 21. *In situ Mossbauer spectra of a prussian blue film electrodeposited on a glassy carbon electrode in deaerated 1 M KCl (pH = 4.0) at (A) 0.6 V, and (B) –0.2 V vs SCE.*

TABLE 9.   In Situ Mossbauer Parameters for Prussian Blue in 1 M KCl

Potential V vs. SCE	Isomer Shift $\delta/mm \cdot s^{-1}$ vs. α-Fe	Quadrupole Splitting $\Delta/mm \cdot s^{-1}$	Figure
0.6	0.37	0.41	21A
–0.2	1.14	1.31[a]	21B

[a]*This value is listed as 1.13 in the original paper. Inspection of the reported spectra, however, has indicated that it is actually close to 1.31.*

in the oxidation state of one of the sites modifies the electron density at the nucleus of the other redox center, in analogy with the phenomenon observed in the case of the mixed Fe/Ni oxyhydroxides films discussed in the previous section.

D. Transition Metal Macrocycles as Catalysts for the Electrochemical Reduction of Dioxygen

A number of transition metal macrocycles have been shown to promote the rates of oxygen reduction when adsorbed on a variety of carbon surfaces [30]. Attention has been mainly focused on phthalocyanines and porphyrins containing iron and cobalt centers, as their activity in certain cases has been found to be comparable to that of platinum. Essential to the understanding of the mechanism by which these compounds catalyze the reduction of O_2 is the description of the interactions, not only with the reactant but also with the substrate. In situ techniques can provide much of this needed information, and indeed, a number of such methods have been used in connection with this type of system [4c].

1. Iron Phthalocyanine One of the first illustrations of the use of Mossbauer spectroscopy for the in situ investigation of molecules adsorbed on electrode surfaces, involved iron phthalocyanine FePc, adsorbed on high area carbon [7]. It was later found [15], however, that this compound undergoes thermal decomposition at surprisingly low temperature in an inert atmosphere and, thus, the features observed in the early work were not due to individual molecules of FePc adsorbed on the substrate, but rather to small particles of a ferric form of iron oxyhydroxide. Shortly thereafter, Blomquist et al. [9] reported, for the first time, in situ Mossbauer spectra of a fuel cell type electrode containing a polymeric form of iron phthalocyanine, p-FePc, dispersed on a high area carbon. This work was particularly interesting, as the measurements were conducted with the electrode operating as an oxygen cathode in the constant current mode.

A schematic diagram of the cell used in the in situ Mossbauer studies is shown in Figure 22. The key feature in this design is a hollow glass tube, with a plastic window attached to one of its ends, placed very close to the working electrode so as to minimize the absorption of radiation associated with the electrolyte. During the Mossbauer measurements, the electrode was polarized in 2.3 M H_2SO_4 at a constant current density of 10 mA·cm^{-2}, and several hours were required to obtain an acceptable signal to noise ratio. Three in situ spectra were recorded consecutively over a period of about three days, involving in each

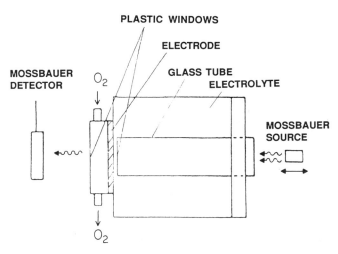

Figure 22. *In situ Mossbauer cell for measurements involving a fuel cell type electrode operating as an oxygen cathode.*

case increasing intervals of time due to losses in the signal strength (vide infra). These are given in Figure 23.

Some difficulties were encountered in the interpretation of the spectra due primarily to two factors:

1. The electrode potential was found to vary in a linear fashion during the measurements [Inset, Fig. 23], and hence, each of the recorded spectra was then an average of the state of the electrode over the specified period of time.
2. Because of the way in which these electrodes were prepared, some of the FePc detected by the Mossbauer may not be in contact with the electrolyte and thus would not contribute to the electrochemical activity.

A satisfactory statistical fit to the data could be obtained, however, with three symmetric doublets, which were attributed to central, peripheral, and oxidized iron sites in the polymer. The associated Mossbauer parameters are listed in Table 10. Based on this information and the results of additional experiments, involving the analytical determination of iron in the electrode and in the electrolyte as a function of the time of operation of the oxygen-fed cathode, it was concluded that

1. the activity of the electrode is directly correlated with the amount of

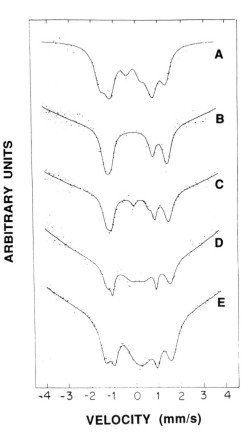

Figure 23. *In situ Mossbauer spectra of a fuel cell type electrode containing apolymeric form of FePc operating as an oxygen cathode in 2.3 M H2SO4. Curves A and E were obtained before and after conducting the actual experiments. The other spectra were acquired between 0–6 h (Curve B); 6–22 h (Curve C); and 22–71 h (Curve D).*

total iron in the electrode, i.e., as the observed potential decreases, increased amounts of iron are found in the electrolyte;

2. the initial loss of resonant absorption area is associated primarily with oxidized sites suggesting that this species undergoes facile dissolution in the electrolyte; and

3. FePc species in which the iron center is formally in the ferrous state are responsible for most of the electrocatalytic activity for O_2 reduction. These sites, however, undergo oxidation during operation, most likely as a result of a build up in the concentration of hydrogen peroxide, generating labile Fe(III) species. This would be consistent with the observed gradual deterioration of the overall performance of the electrode.

TABLE 10. **In Situ Mossbauer Parameters for a Gas Fed Electrode Containing a Polymeric Form of Iron Phthalocyanine Dispersed on High Area Carbon**[a]

Time	Isomer Shift $\delta/mm \cdot s^{-1}$ vs. α-Fe	Quadrupole Splitting $\Delta/mm \cdot s^{-1}$	A(%)	Assignment	Figure
Before[b]	0.27	2.79	40	C	23A
	0.14	1.95	32	P	
	0.33	0.80	28	O	
Between	0.33	2.74	65	C	23B
0–6 h	0.12	1.86	35	P	
Between	0.33	2.77	62	C	23C
6–22	0.12	1.93	29	P	
	0.44	0.75	9	O	
Between	0.32	2.82	49	C	23D
22–71	0.13	1.96	15	P	
	0.30	0.57	36	O	
After[b]	0.37	2.95	40	C	23E
	0.13	1.92	16	P	
	0.32	0.45	44	O	

[a]*The experiments were performed in the constant current mode in 2.3 M H_2SO_4.*
[b]*These refer to measurements conducted before and after polarization.*

2. *Iron tetramethoxyphenyl porphyrin μ-oxo, (FeTMPP)₂O*   The first illustration of the use of Mossbauer spectroscopy as a probe of the redox properties of adsorbed molecules on electrode surfaces was recently reported by Fierro et al. [31]. The μ-oxo form of iron meso-tetrakis methoxy phenyl porphyrin, (FeTMPP)₂O, was selected for this study on the basis of a number of considerations:

1. It is a fairly good electrocatalyst for the reduction of dioxygen in aqueous electrolytes.
2. It displays a well-defined redox peak in a potential region in which the substrate exhibits purely capacitive behavior.
3. It shows good stability when placed in contact with alkaline solutions.

Highly enriched (^{57}FeTMPP)$_2$O was synthesized by the method of Torrens et al. [32] using two milligrams of metallic ^{57}Fe (ca. 99% isotopic purity, DuPont, MA) to prepare anhydrous iron(II) acetate.

The macrocycle was adsorbed from a dichloromethane solution onto Black Pearl, BP, a high area carbon with about 1500 m$^2 \cdot$g^{-1}. This corresponds to a 20% w/w loading and may be shown to be just sufficient to form a monolayer of macrocycle on the carbon, assuming the rings lie flat on the support. The (FeTMPP)$_2$/BP/CH$_2$Cl$_2$ slurry was dried at room temperature. The resulting powder was suspended in a dilute Teflon emulsion under ultrasonic agitation, which was then filtered, dried, and subsequently used to fabricate a thin, disk-shaped Teflon-bonded electrode [33].

The in situ Mossbauer measurements were conducted with a vacuum-tight electrochemical cell designed to fit the end section of the velocity transducer and to minimize attentuation of the γ-ray beam. A flat, ring-shaped macrocyclic-free Teflon-bonded BP carbon electrode, prepared in the same fashion as the working electrode, was employed as the counter electrode, whereas a Hg/HgO,OH⁻ impregnated Teflon-bonded electrode, with a diameter slightly smaller than the orifice of the counter electrode, was utilized as the reference electrode.

All electrodes were stacked in the cell normal to the γ-ray beam in a sandwich type arrangement, separated by cellullose-based films, which served both as electrolyte retainers and electronic insulators. A schematic diagram of the cell is shown in Figure 9.

After assembly, the in situ Mossbauer electrochemical cell was coupled to the end section of the transducer and placed in the bore of the dewar.

A Ranger Scientific MS-900 Mossbauer spectrometer, mounted vertically on a Janis 12CNDT "Supervaritemp" cryostat, was used in the experiments.

The cyclic voltammetry of the electrode in 0.1 M NaOH in a cell open to the atmosphere yielded two well-defined redox peaks with peak potentials at $E_{cath}^P =$ −0.75 V and $E_{anod}^P =$ −0.6 V vs SCE [Fig. 24]. The average peak potential for the redox process compares favorably with those of closely related macrocycles supported on carbon in the same media [34].

The fraction of electrochemically active (^{57}FeTMPP)$_2$O molecules, as determined by a simple integration of the voltammetric peak, was less than a third (ca. 30%) that expected, on the basis of the total number of iron sites in the macrocycle adsorbed originally on the carbon support (vide infra).

The cyclic voltammetry of the working electrode in the in situ Mossbauer cell at room temperature yielded peaks in agreement with those observed in Figure 24.

The (FeTMPP)$_2$O/BP electrode at open circuit under ambient conditions failed to yield any detectable Mossbauer spectra after a collection time of about 24 hr. A similar observation was made earlier for the same macrocycle adsorbed

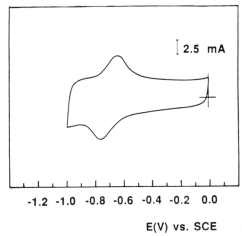

Figure 24. *Cyclic voltammetry of (FeTMPP)2O adsorbed on BP Teflon-bonded electrode in 0.1 M NaOH (see text for details).*

on high area carbon Vulcan XC-72 at room temperature in the form of a dry powder. The solubility of (FeTMPP)2O and closely related porphyrins in aqueous electrolytes is negligibly small, as judged by the fact that no detectable losses of material have been observed upon continuously cycling coatings of the order of a monolayer adsorbed on smooth carbon electrode surfaces. It may thus be concluded that although the effect may be accentuated in the presence of a liquid, the absence of a Mossbauer effect at room temperature appears to be a property intrisic to the adsorbed species and not caused by the dissolution of the macrocycle in the electrolyte.

In an effort to overcome these difficulties, without compromising the in situ character of the measurements, the cell was slowly cooled down to cryogenic temperatures under potential control before any further Mossbauer measurements were attempted. As soon as the electrolyte resistance reached a high enough value, the potentiostat was turned off and the leads were disconnected from the cell.

The Mossbauer spectra obtained at 100 K for the electrode originally polarized at 0.0 V vs Hg/HgO,OH$^-$ [Fig. 25, Curve A], a potential positive to the voltammetric peak, yielded a clearly defined doublet ($\delta_1 = 0.29$; $\Delta_1 = 0.68$). A comparison of the data for the adsorbed material at 0.0 V with that for the same macrocycle in crystalline form indicates a substantial decrease in the magnitude of δ. Since δ in the case of μ-oxo type macrocycles is rather insensitive to temperature, [35], it is unlikely that such difference may be attributed to this factor. A more plausible explanation may be found in structural and electronic modifications induced by interactions of the molecule with the substrate and/or

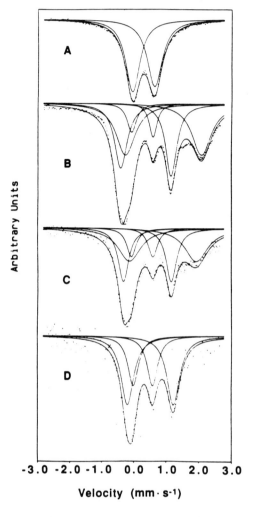

Figure 25. *In situ Mossbauer spectra of a (FeTMPP)₂O/BP electrode in 0.1 M NaOH polarized at 0.0 (Curve A) and −0.9 V vs Hg/HgO,OH⁻ as a function of temperature (Curves B through D).*

the electrolyte, such as axial coordination with hydroxyl ions or functional groups on the carbon.

Marked changes in the spectra were observed upon polarizing the electrode at −0.9 V followed by cooling to 100 K [Fig. 25, Curve B]. This finding is very significant, as it affords yet another proof that the potential control across the interface is indeed preserved upon freezing the cell. A statistical analysis of the spectra revealed the presence of two new symmetric doublets $\delta_2 = 0.91$, $\Delta_2 = 2.35$; $\delta_3 = 0.37$, $\Delta_3 = 1.55$, in addition to the doublet observed at 0.0 V at the

TABLE 11. In Situ Mossbauer Parameters for the Oxidized and Reduced Forms of (FeTMPP)$_2$O Adsorbed on BP High Area Carbon as a Function of Temperature

Potential V vs. Hg/HgO,OH⁻	Temperature (K)	Doublet Number[a]	Isomer Shift δ/mm•s^{-1} vs. α-Fe	Quadrupole Splitting Δ/mm•s^{-1}	Width Γ
Open Circuit (ca. 0.0V)	100	1(100)	0.29	0.68	0.53 0.57
		1(13)	0.25	0.65	0.34 0.29
−0.9	100	2(48)	0.91	2.35	0.72
		3(39)	0.37	1.55	0.42 0.47
		1(17)	0.26	0.66	0.35
−0.9	190	2(47)	0.90	2.06	0.85
		3(35)	0.42	1.48	0.40
		1(38)	0.29	0.59	0.40
−0.9	250				
		4(62)	0.53	1.42	0.48

[a] The numbers in parenthesis represent relative resonant absorption areas.

same temperature. The large differences in the spectra displayed in Figure 25, Curves A and B, indicate that the redox processes involve orbitals with substantial metal contribution. This is agreement with suggestions put forward earlier in the literature, [34], and with theoretical considerations regarding the metal-ring character of the lowest unocuppied molecular orbital of μ-oxo type iron porphyrins [36].

Several additional spectra were recorded as the cell was allowed to warm up. A close inspection of these data indicates an initial increase in the magnitude of Γ_2 at 180 K, accompanied by a slight decrease in Δ_2. No evidence for the presence of doublet 2 was obtained at 250 K. Also to be noted is the monotonic increase in Γ_3 [denoted as doublet 4 in Table 11] from 0.37 to 0.53 at 250 K. At least two explanations can be offered to account for the experimentally observed behavior:

1. the formation of a mixed valence [Fe(II)TMPP-O-Fe(III)TMPP] compound at the more negative potentials; and
2. the presence of adventitious impurities in the cell, most probably hydrated iron oxides, arising either from the carbon itself or from the decomposition of the porphyrin.

Evidence in support of the first of these possibilities is provided by the striking resemblance of the spectral behavior observed with that reported for genuine mixed valence compounds of the type investigated extensively by Hendrickson and coworkers [37]. In that case, two clearly defined doublets could be identified at the lowest temperatures and ascribed to ferrous and ferric sites in the compound. As the temperature is increased, the resonant cross-section of the two features decreases, with the simultaneous emergence of a new doublet with an isomer shift intermediate between that of the two other species. This phenomenon has been attributed to a thermally-induced spin detrapping or, equivalently, to a delocalization of the electrons throughout the iron centers. In direct analogy with the phenomenon described for the porphyrin above, a sizable increase in the width of the ferrous species with a monotonic decrease in the quadrupole splitting was observed (at least for one such mixed valence compound) as the temperature of the specimen was increased.

Although mixed-valence μ-oxo type porphyrins have not as yet been fully characterized, their existence (at least in solution phase) has been proposed, based on cyclic voltammetry measurements in non-aqueous solvents, particularly by Kadish and coworkers [38]. These species do not appear to be stable, undergoing rapid dissociation in the solvents examined. It thus seems plausible that the lack of solubility of (FeTMPP)$_2$O in the alkaline solution (or the interaction of the iron with hydroxyl ions) may help stabilize the mixed-valence μ-oxo type porphyrin and thus prevent its further dissociation.

Additional support for this view is provided by the normalized resonant absorption areas of the peak associated with the original ferric form of (FeTMPP)$_2$O before and after electrochemical reduction. Specifically, the integrated area of doublet 1 in Figure 25, Curve B, divided by the background, represents 30% of that in Curve A, in the same figure. This indicates that 70% of the macrocycle changes oxidation state, a value which is about twice that obtained based strictly on the electrochemical data (vide supra). It thus seems reasonable to assume that the redox process involves a one- rather than a two-electron transfer.

The second explanation put forward above is based on the similarity of the Mossbauer parameters associated with the large quadrupole split doublet (1) with those found in certain partially reduced specimens of small particle size FeOOH [39]. If that were the case ,the, other doublet would correspond to monomeric Fe(II)TMPP, for which the values of δ and Δ closely resemble those of Fe(II)TPP [40].

To further explore this possibility, an attempt was made to recover the adsorbed porphyrin from the electrode after all the in situ experiments had been completed. The extraction was effected with benzene in a Soxhlet, followed by isolation and purification in a silica column. Based on a comparison with a calibrated UV-vis spectra for $(FeTMPP)_2O$ in benzene, all but about one milligram of the original material could be recovered. One possible explanation for the missing fraction (assuming that no macrocycle is lost in the extraction-purification process and that the extraction is completely effective in removing macrocycle that may have become encapsulated in Teflon during the preparation of the electrode) is a reaction within the electrode matrix during the electrochemical experiments. Although porphyrins are believed to be stable in contact with deareated alkaline solutions, hydrogen peroxide can attack macrocycles of this type to yield products, the nature of which have not as yet been unambiguously identified [41]. One possible source of hydrogen peroxide is the reduction of dioxygen in the electrolyte catalyzed by the carbon and/or the macrocycle itself. Although it could be argued that the peroxide-induced decomposition of the macrocycle could give rise to the formation of small particles of FeOOH (which upon reduction would form $Fe(OH)_2$), it seems highly unlikely that the contribution of a minute amount of iron in the sample (10% of the original ^{57}Fe, based on the recovered amount of $(FeTMPP)_2O$) would be associated with such a large fraction of the total resonant absorption area (ca. 48%), as the data in Table 11 indicates. The possibility of impurities in the carbon being responsible for the spectral features can also be dismissed, in view of the fact that the amount of iron in BP obtained from chemical analysis (Galbraith Lab.) is too small (ca. 60 ppm) to be detected in the time scale of the experiments.

In summary, these in situ Mossbauer experiments indicated that:

1. The recoilless fraction of $(FeTMPP)_2O$ (and presumably other macro-cycles) irreversibly adsorbed on high area carbon is too small to enable signals to be detected at room temperature in the presence of the electrolyte.

2. The spectra of $(FeTMPP)_2O$ adsorbed on high area carbon in 0.1 M NaOH at 0.0 V vs Hg/HgO,OH⁻ yielded at 100 K a doublet with parameters in agreement with those of the same compound in bulk form. Two additional doublets were observed at the same temperature when the electrode was polarized at -0.9 V. Two possible explanations have been offered to account for these features: the formation of a mixed-valence μ-oxo iron porphyrin and the reduction of hydrated oxide

impurities generated by the partial decomposition of the macrocycle, with the second doublet being attributed to Fe(II)TMPP. On the basis of the temperature dependence of the Mossbauer peaks and other arguments, it has been concluded that the first of these possibilities appears more likely.
3. The potential across the interface for high area electrodes of the type examined in this investigation is preserved upon freezing the electrolyte.

E. Iron Sulfide

Among the most promising materials for use as cathodes in non-aqueous solvent-based rechargeable lithium batteries [42], pyrite, FeS_2, a naturally occuring iron sulfide, has received special attention. Part of the interest has been motivated by the peculiar behavior displayed by FeS_2/Li cells during discharge. Specifically, plots of the voltage as a function of the extent of discharge [Fig. 26] exhibit, at temperatures between 21 and 30°C, a single plateau, attributed to the reaction

$$4Li + FeS_2 \rightarrow 2Li_2S + Fe \tag{6}$$

At temperatures in the range between 37 and 75°C, however, the discharge curves show a distinct break point at a Li/Fe ratio of about 2. This step-wise process is

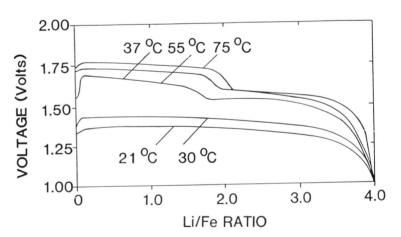

Figure 26. *First discharge plots of FeS2/Li cells obtained at the specified temperatures at a rate of 20h for Li/Fe = 1.*

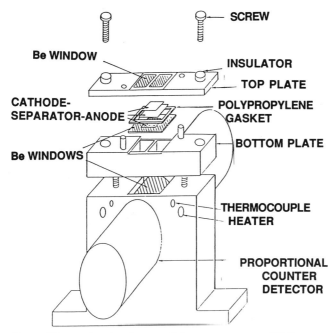

Figure 27. *In situ Mossbauer cell for measurements of FeS$_2$ electrodes in nonaqueous solvents.*

also observed when the discharge current densities are low and has been ascribed to the formation of an intermediate, according to the reaction

$$x\mathrm{Li} + \mathrm{FeS}_2 + x\mathrm{e}^- \rightarrow \text{Intermediate} \qquad (7)$$

It has been postulated that the observed voltage step corresponds to $x = 2$, yielding Fe$_2$LiS$_2$ as the product, a material that is apparently amorphous when prepared at low temperatures.

Various analytical techniques have been employed in order to determine, in an unambiguous fashion, the nature of the discharge intermediates. Very recently, Fong and coworkers [43] developed an in situ Mossbauer cell to identify the products associated with the charging of Li/FeS$_2$ and Li/Li$_2$FeS$_2$ cells [Fig. 27]. In the case of the Li/FeS$_2$ cell, rather clear evidence was obtained for the formation of nonstoichiometric FeS, denoted as FeS$_y$, as judged by the similarities between the Mossbauer spectrum obtained before and after charging [Fig. 28, Curves A and B] and that of a genuine FeS$_y$ specimen [Fig. 28, Curve

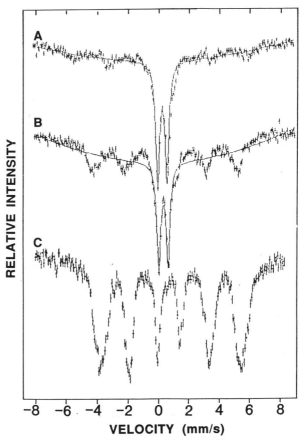

Figure 28. *In situ Mossbauer spectra of a Li/FeS2 cell in 1
M LiAsF6/Propylene carbonate/Ethylene carbonate
electrolyte at 55°C which had been first discharged Li/Fe = 2
and then recharged to 2.45 V (Curve A) and 2.80 V (Curve
B). The central doublet in these curves corresponds to
unreacted FeS2 in the cathode. The spectrum of synthetic
FeSy where y = 1.064 is shown in Curve C.*

C]. The fact that the recharging did not yield the original FeS2 as the product was
cited as the cause of the lack of reversibility of low temperature Li/FeS2 batteries.

The study of the FeS2 electrode in nonaqueous electrolytes has been faced
with rather unexpected complications. In particular, the room temperature Mossbauer spectra of electrodes before and after 50% depth of discharge have been

found to display the same exact features. In fact spectral differences have been observed only at very low temperatures. This would make the use of in situ freezing techniques of the type described in the Experimental Section especially suited for the study of this system.

Preliminary ex situ Mossbauer measurements at 4.5 K [44] have indicated that the material obtained after 50% depth of discharge (or $x = 2$ in the equation above) displays some features which are different than Li_2FeS_2 prepared chemically. This suggests that the discharge process is more complicated than originally anticipated and that it could actually involve more than just a single compound or phase.

F. Tin

Despite the fact that iron has been the subject of the large majority of Mossbauer studies reported in the literature, it is rather interesting to note that the first in situ application of this technique involved tin as the active nuclide. In that work, Cranshaw and Bowles [45] examined the emission spectra of ^{119m}Sn adsorbed on a high area platinum electrode. Although some of the conclusions made by the authors may be open to question, the results obtained clearly indicated that

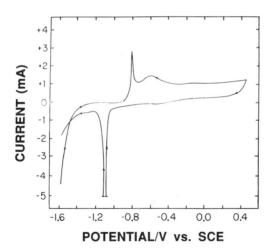

Figure 29. *Cyclic voltammetry of a Sn electrode in borate buffer (pH =8.4). Scan rate: 60 mV/s. Potential is given with respect to the SCE.*

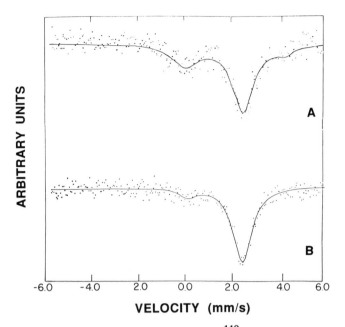

Figure 30. *In situ Mossbauer spectra of a ^{119}Sn enriched Sn electrode electrodeposited on an aluminum substrate in borate buffer (pH = 8.4) at –0.9 V (Curve A) and + 0.2 V vs. SCE (Curve B).*

the tin, in whatever form, was present at the interface and was bound sufficiently strongly to the host lattice to give a Mossbauer spectra. Thus, these types of measurements were indeed feasible.

More recently, Vertes and coworkers [46] have investigated the spectral properties of the passive film on tin in borate buffer media (pH = 8.4) over a wide potential range. A typical voltammetric curve for Sn in this specific electrolyte is shown in Figure 29. At –0.9 V, the transmission Mossbauer spectra of a ^{119}Sn-enriched tin film, electrodeposited on an aluminum substrate [Fig. 30, Curve A], was found to have clear contributions due to β-Sn, δ = 2.5, and SnO$_2$ or Sn(OH)$_4$, δ = 0.03 [Table 12]. The small absorption peak at about 4.2 mm/s was attributed to the high velocity component of a doublet with parameters consistent with those of a Sn(II) species, most probably present in an amorphous form. No Sn(II) species could be detected, however, with in situ measurements obtained at –0.78, –0.75, and +0.2 V, as illustrated for this last potential in the spectrum in Figure 30, Curve B. Based on the electrochemical and spectroscopic

TABLE 12. In Situ Mossbauer Parameters for Tin in Borate Buffer (pH = 8.4)

Potential V vs. SCE	Isomer Shift $\delta/mm \cdot s^{-1}$ vs. CaSnO$_3$
−0.9	0.03
2.50	
4.17[a]	

[a]*This feature has been regarded as the high velocity component of a doublet with an isomer shift of about 2.8 mm•s^{-1}, and quadrupole splitting 2.2 mm•s^{-1}.*

results, these authors concluded that in borate buffer (pH = 8.4), the passive film in the potential region between −1.18 and −0.78 V consists of highly amorphous Sn(OH)$_2$, or hydrated stannous oxide and SnO$_2$, or Sn(OH)$_4$, whereas at much more positive potential only Sn(IV) oxide or hydroxides species are present in the film.

In a separate study, the surface structure of tin layers obtained by the electroless deposition in a strongly alkaline solution was examined by van Noort et al. [47], employing the quasi in situ conversion electron Mossbauer technique introduced originally by Kordesch et al. [11]. The spectrum obtained in the metallation bath with the electrode under rotation, shown in Figure 31A, was best fitted with three singlets. Two of these features could be unambiguously ascribed to β-Sn and SnO$_2$, whereas the third singlet could not be assigned to any known tin compound. This specific peak, however, was not observed when the spectrum was recorded with the same electrode stationary [Fig. 31B], leading these authors to conclude that this species was most probably a tin(II) intermediate in the overall electroless deposition process. A third peak exhibiting the same rotation dependent characteristics, although different Mossbauer parameters, was also detected in experiments involving tin layers prepared by electroless deposition but polarized in a slightly acidic media containing no tin ions.

A series of experiments involving either stationary disks and different solutions or dry electrodes were conducted to determine whether the effects observed could be associated with mechanical motion or the presence of a liquid film on the surface. In all cases examined, however, the spectra remained unchanged, leading these authors to conclude that the third peak was not due to

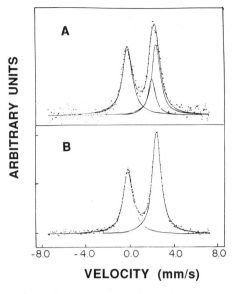

Figure 31. ^{119}Sn *conversion electron Mossbauer spectra of a rotating disk with its lower half in the metallization solution (Curve A). Curve B was obtained with the same disk stationary.*

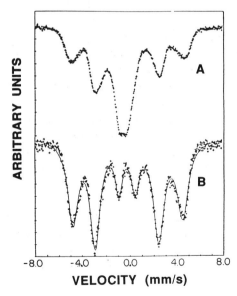

Figure 32. *Emission spectra of ^{57}Fe in cobalt recorded after deposition of a 100–200 Å ^{57}Co layer (Curve A). Curve B shows the spectrum of the same specimen during cathodic polarization at –1.1 V vs. SCE in a deaerated borate buffer solution (pH = 8.5).*

an instrumental artifact but rather to the presence of transient Sn(II) species on the electrode surface.

G.   In Situ Emission Mossbauer

Besides the early study of Bowles and Cranshaw on the interactions of tin with Pt surfaces, referred to in the previous section, the most significant illustrations of the use of in situ Mossbauer in the emission mode appear to be those of Simmons, Leidheiser and coworkers [48], who conducted a rather detailed study of passivation and anodic oxidation of Co surfaces.

The emission Mossbauer spectra of Fe in a rather thick (100–200 Å) cobalt film, deposited by electrochemical means onto a Co specimen before and after polarization at –1.1 V, are shown Figure 32. It should be stressed that even though the original material is Co, the observed spectrum is that of the ^{57}Fe daughter nucleus. The intense lines in Curve A in this figure are attributed to the presence of a layer consisting presumably of cobalt oxihydroxides formed after the film was prepared. The latter undergoes reduction during cathodic polarization at –1.1 V yielding the characteristic six-line spectra of Fe in a Co matrix, as shown in Figure 32, Curve B. Much broader lines were observed in similar experiments involving a film of only 20 to 50 Å thickness, a phenomenon attributed to hyperfine relaxation associated with the presence of small size particles or magnetic dilution effects. The spectra obtained at 0.2, 0.5, and 0.8 V, before and

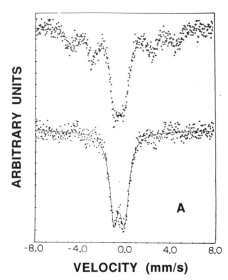

Figure 33. *Emission Mossbauer spectra of* ^{57}*Fe in cobalt polarized at (A) +0.2; (B) +0.5; and (C) +0.8 V vs. SCE in the same electrolyte in caption Figure 32 before (upper spectra) and after (lower spectra) subtracting the contributions due to the unreacted metal.*

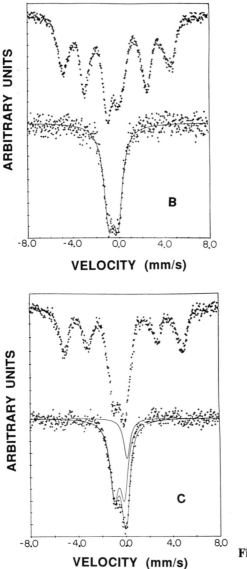

Figure 33. *(continued).*

after subtracting the metal contribution, are given in Figure 33. Based on the analysis of the Mossbauer parameters [Table 13], it was concluded that polarization at increasingly positive potentials leads to spectra consistent with the presence of more oxidized species. It is interesting to note that no Mossbauer signals could be observed when the electrode was polarized at 0.1 V at room

TABLE 13. In Situ Mossbauer Parameters for ^{57}Fe in Anodically Polarized Cobalt Surfaces Doped with ^{57}Co in Borate Buffer pH = 8.5

Potential V vs. SCE	Isomer Shift[a] $\delta/mm\cdot s^{-1}$ vs. α-Fe	Quadrupole Splitting $\Delta/mm\cdot s^{-1}$	Figure
-0.1[b]	-1.15	2.83	33A
	-0.43	0.78	
0.2	-0.39	0.94	
0.5	-0.38	0.81	33B
0.8	-0.39[c]	0.85[c]	33C
	-0.02		

[a]According to the convention, isomer shifts in the emission mode are reported with opposite sign.

[b]Data obtained at liquid nitrogen temperature.

[c]Values constrained during fitting.

temperature. The spectra obtained for this specimen at 77 K, however, indicated species in the +2 and +3 oxidation states. As was pointed out in section III.A., chemical and Auger after effects can generate ^{57}Fe ionic states that may differ from those of the parent ^{57}Co and thus introduce uncertanties in the spectral assigments. Nevertheless, some of these ambiguities could, in principle, be removed by examining the emission Mossbauer spectra of known species.

Acknowledgments

The author would like to express his appreciation to Dr. Cristian Fierro who has been mostly responsible for the implementation of n situ Mossbauer spectroscopy in his laboratory. Support for this work was provided by the Gas Research Institute.

References

1. a. Mossbauer, R. L. Z. Phys. 151 (1958):124.
    b. Mossbauer, R. L. Naturwissenschaften 45 (1958):538.

2. a. Goldanskii, V. I. and Herber, R., Eds. *Chemical Applications of Mossbauer Spectroscopy* New York:Academic Press, 1968.
    b. Guttlich, P.; Link, R.; and Trautwein, A. *Mossbauer Spectroscopy and Transition Metal Chemistry, Inorganic Chemistry Concepts 3*. Berlin: Springer Verlag, 1978.
    c. Dickson, D. P. E. and Berry, F. J., Eds. *Mossbauer Spectroscopy.* Cambridge: Cambridge University Press, 1986.
    d. Gruverman, I. J. Ed. *Mossbauer Effect Methodology*, Vols. I–IX. New York: Plenum Press.

3. Hudson, A., and Whitfield, H. J. *Inorg. Chem.* 6 (1967):1120.

4. For recent reviews see: a. Scherson, D., et al. *J. Electroanal. Chem.* 150 (1983):535.
    b. Vertes, A. and Czako-Nagy, I. *Izv. Khim.* 19 (1986):380.
    c. D. Scherson, In *Spectroelectrochemistry: Theory and Practice,* ed. R. Gale. New York: Plenum Press, 1988.

5. Long, G. J. *Mossbauer Effect Ref. Data J.* 6 (1983):42.

6. Kordesch, M. E., and Hoffman, R. W. *Thin Solid Films* 107 (1983):365.

7. Scherson, D., et al. *J. Phys. Chem.* 87 (1983):932.

8. Eldridge, J., and Hoffman, R. W. *J. Electrochem. Soc.* 136 (1989):955.

9. Blomquist, J., et al. *Electrochim. Acta* 27 (1982):1453.

10. Scherson, D., et al. *J. Electroanal. Chem.* 169 (1984):287.

11. Kordesch, M. E., et al. *J. Electroanal. Chem.* 164 (1984):393.

12. Rath, D. L., and Kolb, D. M. *Surface Sci.* 109 (1981):641.

13. Frese, U., et al. *J. Phys. Chem.* 89 (1985):1059, and references therein.

14. Geronov, Y.; Tomov, T.; and Georgiev, S. *J. Appl. Electrochem.* 5 (1975):351.

15. Scherson, D., et al. *J. Electroanal. Chem.* 184 (1985):419.

16. a. Burke, L. D., and Murphy, O. J. *J. Electroanal. Chem.* 109 (1980):379.
    b. Macagno, V. A.; Vilche, J. R.; and Arvia, A. J. *J. Appl. Electrochem.* 11 (1981):417.

17. Hassett, K. L.; Stecher, L. C.; and Hendrickson, D. N. *Inorg. Chem.* 19 (1980):416.

18. Fierro, C., et al. *J. Phys. Chem.* 91 (1987):6579.

19. For more general references in this topic see:
    a. *Passivity of Metals and Semiconductors*. M. Froment, Ed., Amsterdam: Elsevier, 1983
    b. *Passivity of Metals*, R. P. Frankenthal and J. Kruger, Eds., Princeton: Electrochemical Society, 1978.

20. Eldridge, J.; Kordesch, M. E.; and Hoffman, R. W. *J. Vac. Sci. Technol.* 20 (1982):934.

21. a. O'Grady, W. *J. Electrochem. Soc.* 127 (1980):555.
    b. O'Grady, W. E. and Bockris, J. O'M. *Surface Sci.* 38 (1973):249.

22. Nagayama, M., and Cohen, M. *J. Electrochem. Soc.* 109 (1962):781.

23. Fine, J. M., et al. *J. Vac. Sci. Technol.* 1A (1983):1036.

24. a. Cordoba, S. I., et al. *Electrochim.Acta* 31 (1986):1321

b. Corrigan, D. A. *J. Electrochem. Soc.* 134 (1987):377.

25. Corrigan, D., et al. Submitted to *J. Phys. Chem.* (1987)

26. Desilvestro, J.; Corrigan, D. A.; and Weaver, M. J. *J. Phys. Chem.* 90 (1986):6408.

27. For a review on the electrochemical and other physicochemical properties of thin films of Prussian blue and related polynuclear transition metal cyanides see: Itaya, K.; Uchida, I.; and Neff, V. *Acc. Chem. Res.* 19 (1986):162.

28. Itaya, K., et al. *J. Phys. Chem.* 86 (1982):2415.

29. Maer Jr., K., *J. Am. Chem. Soc.* 90 (1968):3201.

30. For a review see: a. van der Brink, F.; Barendrecht, E.; and Visscher, W. *J. Royal Neth. Chem.* 99 (1980)253.

b. Tarasevich, M. R., and Radyushkina, K. A. *Russ. Chem. Rev.* 49 (1980):718.

31. Fierro, C.; Mohan, M.; and Scherson, D. Submitted to *Langmuir* (1989).

32. Torrens, M. A.; Straub, D. K.; and Epstein, L. M. *J. Am. Chem. Soc.* 94 (1972):4160.

33. Tanaka, A. A., et al. *J. Phys. Chem.* 91 (1987):3799.

34. Shigehara, R., and Anson, F. *J. Phys. Chem.* 86 (1981):2776.

35. Collman, J. P., et al. *J. Am. Chem. Soc.* 97 (1975):2627.

36. Tatsumi, K. and Hoffmann, R. *J. Am. Chem. Soc.* 103 (1981):3328.

37. See for example:
a. Kaneko, Y. et al. *Inorg. Chem.* 28 (1989):1067.
b. Mashuta, M. S., et al. *J. Am. Chem. Soc.* 111 (1989):2745, and references therein.

38. Kadish, K. M., et al. *J. Am. Chem. Soc.* 97 (1975):282.

39. Pritchard, A. M., and Mould, B. T. *Corrosion Science* 11 (1971):1.

40. Collman, J. P.; Hoard, J. L.; and Epstein, L. M. *J. Am. Chem. Soc.* 97 (1975):2676.

41. Forshey, P., et al. In *Adv. Chem. Ser.* No. 201, ed. K. M. Kadish, 1506. Washington: American Chemical Society, 1982.

42. Clark, M., *Lithium Batteries*, ed. J. Gabano. New York: Academic Press, 1983.

43. Fong, R.; Jones, C. H. W.; and Dahn, J. R. *J. Power Sources* 26 (1989):333.

44. Leger, V. Z., et al. Electrochemical Society Meeting, Hollywood, Florida 1989. Abstract # 74.

45. Bowles, B. J., and Cranshaw, T. E. *Phys. Lett.* 17 (1965):258.

46. a. Vertes, A., et al. *J. Electrochem. Soc.* 125 (1978):1946.
b. Varsanyi, M. L., et al. *Electrochim. Acta* 30 (1985):529.

47. van Noort, H. M.; Meenderink, B. C. M.; and Molenaar, A. *J. Electrochem. Soc.* 133 (1986):263.

48. Simmons, G. W.; Kellerman, E.; and Leidheiser, Jr. H. *J. Electrochem. Soc.* 123 (1976):1276. Simmons, G. W., and Leidheiser, H. In *Mossbauer Effect Methodology* ed. I. J. Gruverman and C. Seidel, Vol. 10. New York: Plenum Press, 1976.

CHAPTER 9

RADIOACTIVE LABELING: TOWARD CHARACTERIZATION OF WELL-DEFINED ELECTRODES

Piotr Zelenay

Department of Chemistry
Warsaw University
02-089 Warsaw, Poland

Andrzej Wieckowski

Department of Chemistry
University of Illinois
Urbana, IL 61801

CONTENTS

479

I. INTRODUCTION

Methods of surface electrochemistry extend beyond the in situ techniques that are covered in this volume. A demarcation line is usually drawn between the ex situ and the in situ methods, but, in addition to the methodological aspects, some basic issues are at stake when such a division is discussed. One such issue is the detailed relevance of UHV methods in the characterization of the solid/liquid interface vs. barely surmountable obstacles of in situ spectroscopies in probing surface species with no solution interference. Rapid and spectacular progress in molecular-level surface electrochemistry was initiated in laboratories [1-5] which combined ultra-high vacuum (UHV) surface science techniques [6] with electrochemical methods of electrode surface characterization. Access via "UHV-electrochemistry" to powerful surface sensitive probes, such as low energy electron diffraction (LEED), Auger electron spectroscopy (AES), temperature programmed desorption (TPD), electron energy loss spectroscopy (EELS), photoelectron spectroscopies (PES), or vacuum scanning tunneling microscopy (STM), has offered a leading edge over solution techniques of nonelectrochemical electrode characterization. Only very recently merging of these two methodological lines has begun due to new in situ methods and procedures. A variant of a radio-electrochemical technique [7], combining radioactive labeling and electrochemical surface characterization (radio-electrochemistry), was developed in Urbana to *bridge* the vacuum work with in situ investigations of single crystal electrodes. Such parallel in situ and ex situ research is dedicated to providing complementary information and to unraveling dynamic (kinetics, steady-state) effects that are not accessible to the UHV-electrochemistry procedures. Since molecule-specific, absolute measurements of surface concentrations (Γ) are offered by radio-electrochemistry [8,9], it can provide back-up results for new solution methods of surface analysis that have not yet been cross-tested by an independent technique. A separate and distinctive advantage provided by radiochemistry is its capability of following surface diffusion in an averaged or space-resolved regime. Since only preliminary measurements were performed in our laboratory regarding this option for research, it will not be covered in this chapter.

II. OPPORTUNITIES OF "RADIOCHEMISTRY FOR ELECTROCHEMISTRY" (DETAILED)

A common-sense hierarchy can be imposed on a set of questions addressed to chemistry of the solid-liquid, electrified interface. One would like to know *what* the interfacial components are, especially those that are adsorbed on the electrode, *how many* molecules are adsorbed per cm^2 of the surface (i.e. surface concentration Γ), and how surface concentrations depend on the *variables of electrochemical research*: E, c, t, T, as well as the substrate material, surface crystallography, and isotopic composition of either the solvent or surface reagent, or both. Obviously, the Γ vs. t measurements allow the determination of system kinetics, whereas the Γ vs. c measurements give access to interfacial thermodynamics (for reversible processes). There is probably no better method than radio-electrochemistry with which to address these questions for a broad class of electrodes, adsorbates, and electrochemical environments [8,9]. By performing surface characterization in situ, radio-electrochemistry contributes to a comprehensive understanding of the interface, and provides a *well-documented, chemical background* for spectroscopic and diffraction analyses. If the analogy can be called upon [7a], the method developed in our laboratory promises to fulfill a similar function in in situ research, as Auger surface analysis has in the UHV, surface-related sciences.

Regarding the contribution of radiochemistry at single crystal, well-defined electrodes, relationships between packing densities and the types of unit cells can be obtained, and the crystallographic elements may be logged in an interfacial thermodynamic analysis at reactive (catalytic) surfaces. As mentioned earlier, surface diffusion can be studied and correlated with system crystallography. Measurements with the unstable isotope of *hydrogen* (tritium), while proved feasible, await to be fully explored.

III. WELL-DEFINED, SINGLE-CRYSTAL ELECTRODES

We will describe below a radiochemical technique developed [7] to conduct measurements of adsorption at morphologically uniform, as well as ordered, single- crystal, i.e., *well-defined* electrodes [1].

The application of well-defined surfaces to electrochemical systems allows unique resolution regarding surface-related electrode processes and, by emphasizing structural components in electrochemical reactivity, may lead to progress in heterogeneous electrocatalysis [1,2]. Furthermore, new knowledge is being accumulated regarding the organization of the compact interface at substrates which display two-dimensional periodicity and long-range order [10]. Data provided by the radiochemical method of surface analysis are adding a new dimension to these investigations [7b,11,12]. In general, since processes unresolvable on disordered substrates may become resolved on well-defined electrodes, fundamental electrochemical research should be focused on such well-characterized materials.

Pursuing this strategy, the earlier routine in "radiochemistry for electrochemistry" to investigate ill-defined, predominantly porous electrodes [9] has been redirected toward the characterization of well-defined systems [11,12]. Therefore, the critical element of research developed at Urbana was the method of electrode preparation. Regarding single crystals of platinum, the quenching method developed by Clavilier [13,14] has had a decisive impact on the in situ community of electrochemists and spectroscopists. It continues to offer a convenient opportunity for the application of techniques that only require small and regenerable electrodes. Disadvantages of this method for larger samples have been discussed [15-17]. An alternative technique was developed and tested in our laboratories, with the aid of surface electron spectroscopies [17,18]. Along these lines, we previously reported on the behavior of clean, but *disordered* surfaces of Pt(111) and Pt(100) [19,20]. When such surfaces were subjected to annealing in an iodine-containing argon atmosphere, the disorder/order transition was clearly identified and the lack of C-containing impurities was confirmed by Auger. Since electrochemical oxidation of chemisorbed iodine left on the surface after the annealing causes the system to disorder [20-23], a cleaning method had to be developed that would not result in the displacement of the surface platinum atoms. We found that a quantitative removal of iodine could be obtained by rinsing the I-covered surface with aqueous electrolyte saturated with carbon monoxide [17,18]. This step is followed by anodic stripping of adsorbed carbon monoxide in CO-free electrolyte in a potential range where the crystallographic nature of the electrode is retained. Parallel research by other groups has shown that iodine desorption also occurs in a negative going potential excursion in basic

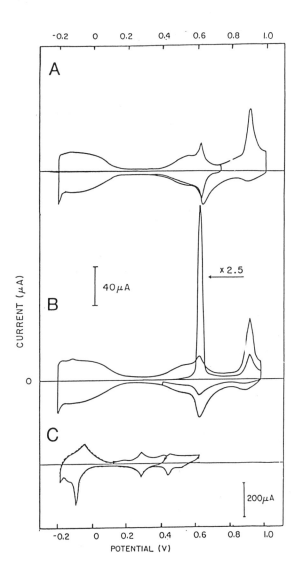

Figure 1. *(A) Cyclic current-potential curves for a Pt(111) electrode. (B) Electrooxidation of chemisorbed carbon monoxide on the Pt(111) electrode [18]. (C) Cyclic voltammograms of ordered Rh(111) electrode. Scan rate: 50 mV s⁻¹. All potentials given vs. Ag/AgCl, reference [Cl⁻] = 1 M. Reproduced from Ref. 18 by permission of Elsevier Science Publishers.*

solutions not containing CO [23,24]. By either of these two approaches, one can preserve the well-ordered character of platinum surfaces and execute in situ radiochemical research that conforms to the state-of-the art requirements of surface science. The application of the I/CO method to IR investigations of the well-defined Pt(111) electrode has recently been reported [25].

The voltammetry of the Pt(111) surface obtained by I/CO replacement in our UHV-electrochemistry instrument is shown in Figure 1A [18[. The Pt(111)($\sqrt{7}$ x $\sqrt{7}$)θ_I = 0.43 surface was transformed to the Pt(111)($\sqrt{3}$ x 3)θ_{CO} = 0.70 [26] through the I-CO replacement procedure outlined above. The stripping peak of the electrosorbed CO is shown in Figure 1B [18,27]. Either of the two voltammetric profiles can be used as an in situ mode of assessing surface cleanliness and order.

Figure 1C shows the voltammetric profile of a clean Rh(111) electrode prepared by the I-CO method [28]. Independent verification of this voltammogram has recently been reported [29]. This and similar studies promise to evolve into in situ research focused on single-crystal surfaces of rhodium, which is a metal of contrasting electronic properties to platinum, but which shares with platinum its strong catalytic appeal [28].

IV. RADIOCHEMICAL INSTRUMENT

Disc-shaped, single-crystal or polycrystalline electrodes are used for the radiochemical [7,11,12] and accompanying ultra-high vacuum measurements [18]. A sketch of the apparatus, including electrode/detector assembly [Fig. 2A] and experimental set-up [Fig. 2B] is shown in Figure 2. Glass scintillator detection of nuclear radiation is used and recommended [30] for the measurements. We plan to space-resolve packets of photons produced upon inelastic collisions of energized electrons (β) with the scintillating solid and to use them for imaging two-dimensional diffusion of adsorbed products at single-crystal electrodes. For the measurements reported in this review, the averaged output of the glass scintillator was used. The dark-current corrected counts generated from the electrode surface (surface counts) are linearly processed by a radiometric, essentially photon-counting, device, which records amplitudes proportional to surface concentrations of β-labeled adsorbates. To implement such measurements, an open/squeeze procedure is employed [demonstrated in Fig. 2A] [7].

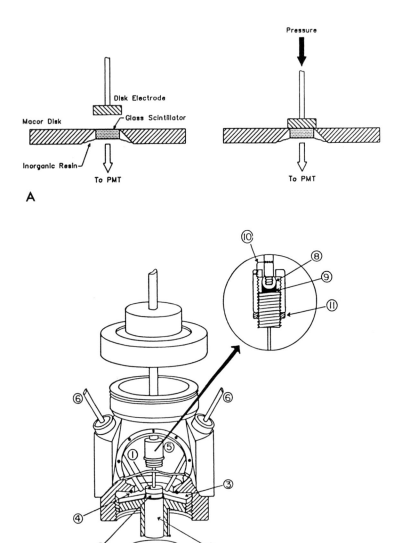

Figure 2. *(A) Diagram of the electrode in the raised position for adsorption (left) and the "squeezed" position for adsorbate measurement (right). (B) Diagram of the Teflon cell: (1) platinum electrode; (2) glass scintillator; (3) Macor ceramic disk cell bottom; (4) Teflon O-ring; (5) flexible elbow (see insert); (6) cell ports (six); (7) light pipe; (8) stainless steel sphere; (9) concave Teflon spacer; (10) platinum wire for electrical contact; (11) lock nut [7a]. Reproduced from Ref. 7a by permission of the American Chemical Society.*

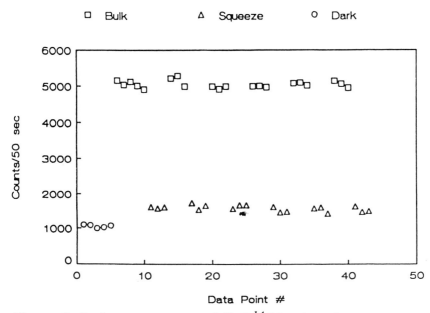

Figure 3. *Dark count uncorrected NaH $^{14}CO_3$ data showing squeeze reproducibility. After five dark counts and five bulk counts were recorded, squeeze and bulk measurements were alternated after recording three data points in each position.*

In an open mode, the electrode surface is at a distance of a millimeter (or more) from the detector surface, and no counts are recorded from the radioactive source at the surface. In contrast, bulk counts are taken in this semi-infinite mode of measurement and are used for system calibration. With smooth electrodes, the bulk counts are significantly higher than the anticipated surface counts, and the radiochemical method is not surface-specific unless the bulk concentration of the labeled reactant is held in the micromolar or submillimolar range. To allow the use of higher concentrations, the radioactive background (solution) is squeezed out from between the two surfaces by bringing them to a realistically attainable close proximity. The limit of such an approach defined in our laboratory is 1 μm, whereas a routinely employed distance is between 1 and 2 μm. A dedicated and systematically implemented polishing procedure was developed and reported in Reference 7a. It guarantees a reproducible output between the bulk and squeeze stages [demonstrated in Fig. 3].

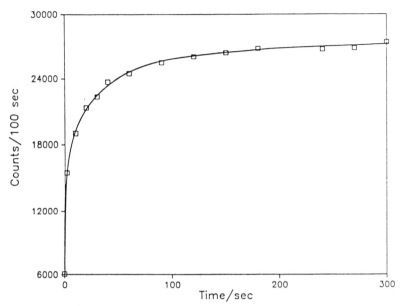

Figure 4. *[^{14}C] Formic acid adsorption from 1 mM solution onto polycrystalline platinum at 0.0 V [7a]. Reproduced from Ref. 7a by permission of the American Chemical Society.*

With a 3 micrometer gap thickness, the ratio of the surface counts to gap (background) counts can be deduced from the data shown in Figure 4. At 1 mM concentration of formic acid and at a surface concentration of 6×10^{14} molecules cm^{-2}, the ratio is equal to 4. This ratio decreases with an increase in the bulk concentration of the adsorbate and increases with a decrease in the gap thickness. Thus, the precision of radiochemical measurements is rapidly reduced when the bulk concentration is higher than 5 mM but can be remedied by narrowing the interplanar distance (gap) below 1 μm. Progress in such a direction, although not impossible, is not straightforward and requires more advanced methods of polishing than used so far in our laboratory.

V. CALCULATION OF SURFACE CONCENTRATION FROM COUNT DATA

Surface concentration and related quantities, such as coverage and packing density (a number of molecules per surface site), can be calculated through the application of the rules which govern absorption of "white" energized electrons in condensed media [8,9]. The semi-infinite Equations (1) give a relationship between the bulk counts (N_{b-c}) and solution parameters under "open" conditions (Fig. 2A):

$$N_{b-c} = k/2 \;\; 3.7 \times 10^{10} \, S \, a_1 \int_0^\infty \exp(-\mu x) \, dx =$$
$$k/2 \;\; 3.7 \times 10^{10} \, S \, a_1 \, \mu^{-1} \tag{1}$$

where:

k = the counting efficiency (counts per disintegrations). Division by 2 indicates 2π counting geometry (in the absence of backscattering, only 50% of nuclear particles can be detected)

3.7×10^{10} = the conversion factor from curies (Ci) to disintegrations per sec;

S = the geometric area of the detector (cm^2);

a_1 = specific activity of solution (Ci cm^{-3});

μ = linear coefficient of absorption of β^- radiation in solution phase (cm^{-1});

x = the thickness of solution layer (cm).

The surface-counts corrected for the gap-counts are given by Equation (2):

$$N_{s-c} = k/2 \;\; 3.7 \times 10^{10} \, \Gamma \, S \, R \, a_2 \, N^{-1} f_b \exp(-\mu x) \tag{2}$$

where:

Γ = surface concentration (molecules cm^{-2});

R = roughness factor;

a_2 = the specific activity of the adsorbate (Ci $mole^{-1}$);

N = Avogadro's constant (6.02×10^{23} molecules $mole^{-1}$);

f_b = backscattering correction.

A combination of the two equations gives the final formula through which the surface concentrations are calculated:

$$\Gamma = \frac{N_{s-c}}{N_{b-c}} \frac{N\ 10^{-3}c}{\mu R\ f_b\ \exp(-\mu x)} \tag{3}$$

where 10^{-3} is the scaling factor for converting liter to cm^3.

Absolute surface concentration measurements can be made, provided that values of all the parameters of the RHS of Equation (3) are either known or can be measured with sufficient precision and accuracy. In particular, it is convenient to be able to measure the counting rate in the squeeze position, where no adsorbate is present at the surface. The measurements of, and correction for, the gap counts can then be carried out in a straightforward manner. Since oxidized or hydrogen covered surfaces can be used for adsorbate-free measurements, such experimental option is usually available for the radio-electrochemistry. If not, specific activities can be controlled via liquid-scintillation counting, and radioactive solutions containing nonadsorbing species can easily be used for counting efficiency measurements.

Backscattering correction is known from nuclear [31] and Auger [32] spectroscopy-related work, and, for high density materials such as platinum and gold, is equal to 1.86. The absorption coefficient for β^- radiation in the supporting electrolyte is obtained using the formula derived by Lerch [33] and experimental data published by Suttle and Libby [34].

VI. RADIOCHEMICAL RESEARCH WITH ELECTRODE SURFACES

Four types of surface radiochemical measurements have been chosen as specific topics for this article. We begin with reporting on our work with well-defined, single-crystal electrodes and on investigations of reversible chemisorption on the Pt(111) surface [ll,l2,35]. Next, a comparative analysis of adsorption of N-containing molecules on a platinum and gold electrode is presented [36-42], and this is followed by a report on adsorption of sulfate (bisulfate) anions on smooth gold electrodes [43,44] and on copper adatoms. Finally, our earlier data on tritiated water adsorbed on platinum from DMSO solutions are brought to focus [45].

A. Radio-Electrochemistry On Well-Defined Electrodes

Once the prospects for radiochemical investigations with well-characterized substrates became defined [17], reversible chemisorption processes on Pt(111) have become an object of our research. The fundamental reason behind this choice was the need to better understand the voltammetry in aqueous acidic media of several noble metal electrodes displaying (111) crystallographic orientation [13-16,28,46-48], with platinum receiving our initial attention [7,ll,l2,l8]. Such voltammograms have been shown to respond to changes in the electrochemical environment in a manner not anticipated from the earlier and well-documented measurements on polycrystalline substrates. The change corresponds to the transition from perchloric and hydrofluoric acid solutions to electrolytes containing surface interacting anions and/or their protonated Brönsted components. Consequently, it was proposed that adsorption of such anions (e.g. sulfate) on the surface was a driving force in the voltammetric response [16]. A direct charge transfer between the anions and the electrode was postulated [16] and contrasted with the original interpretation, which required adsorption of high-energy hydrogen in the double layer region of the electrode potentials [13]. An extensive discussion of this issue is available [7b,l0]. Our recent contribution to this area will be presented below.

Cyclic voltammograms of the Pt(111) electrode in 0.1 M perchloric acid electrolyte are shown in Figure 5 (solid lines). The voltammetric curves taken in 0.1 M $HClO_4$ with sulfuric acid,

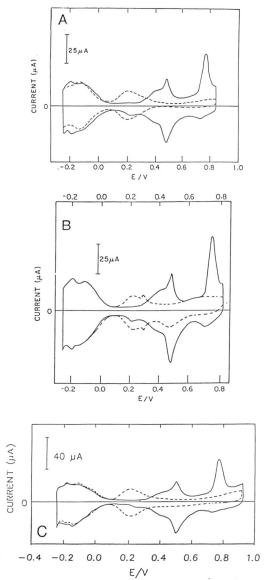

Figure 5. *The effect of addition to 0.1 M HClO₄ of 0.5 mM: (A) acetic acid [11], (B) sulfuric acid [12], and (C) phosphoric acid on the voltammetry of the Pt(111) electrode. Scan rate: 50 mV s⁻¹. Potentials are given vs. the Ag/AgCl reference. Solid lines represent the data obtained in pure 0.1 M HClO₄, and the dashed lines, those obtained in the same electrolyte containing the additives. Reproduced from Refs. 11 and 12 by permission of Elsevier Science Publishers.*

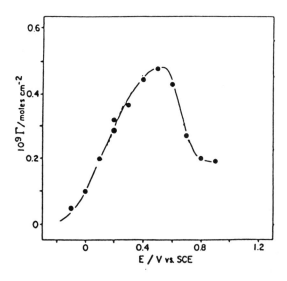

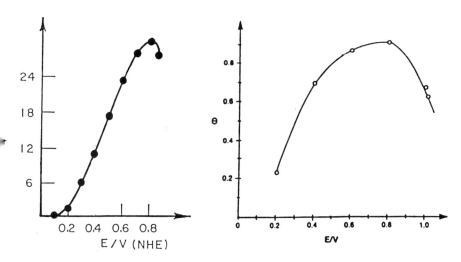

Figure 6. *Potential dependence of adsorption of (A) acetic acid [35]. The bulk concentration was 1 mM in 1 M HClO4. (B) Sulfate anions (expressed as amount of charge per cm²,* Ref. 49). *The concentration of H2SO4 in 1 M perchloric acid was 10 mM. (C) Phosphoric acid, c = 6.2 x 10⁻² M in 1 M HClO4 (NHE) [51]. Smooth [35] and rough [49,51] polycrystalline Pt electrodes were used for the investigations. Reproduced from Ref. 49 by permission of Plenum Publishing Corp., and Refs. 35 and 51 by permission of the American Chemical Society.*

acetic acid, and phosphoric acid present in the electrolyte are shown in Figures 5A, 5B and 5C, respectively (dashed lines). The voltammetric current-potential profiles taken in the electrolyte containing the additives significantly differ from that obtained in perchloric acid. In particular, the surface redox behavior observed in the potential range from 0.3 to 0.6 V in the clean electrolyte is shifted approximately 200 mV in the negative direction upon addition of 0.5 mM of the studied compounds. Moreover, the sharp oxidation peak at 0.8 V in clean $HClO_4$ is either eliminated or strongly suppressed due to such an addition. Assuming that the differences in the electrochemical behavior are due to the interactions between the anions and the electrode surface, one would anticipate a similar, if not identical, adsorption behavior for the three species under consideration. Indeed, such behavior would not be unreasonable, given the earlier radiochemical and spectroscopic results with the three systems studied on polycrystalline platinum [9,11,35,43,44,49-51]. Consistent, reversible patterns of adsorption were observed, and peaked-type, surface concentration vs. electrode potential curves were recorded [Figs. 6 A-C].

What should be strongly brought into focus is that basically different species are adsorbed. Molecular adsorption of undissociated acids was identified in the cases of acetic [35,50] and phosphoric [51] acid, whereas evidence was presented that adsorption of sulfuric acid is anionic [44]. Despite this difference, the reported radiochemical measurements with polycrystalline electrodes indicate that the effects of the electric field on adsorption are practically identical. There is no readily available explanation to account for this behavior, unless one assumes that undissociated acid molecules are highly polarized in an adsorbed state. The strong surface dipoles can mimic adsorbed anionic forms, especially if the surface anions are to a certain extent neutralized through a partial charge transfer process [52]. However, we found that the anticipated differences in the mode of adsorption between these species can be resolved on single-crystal, well-defined electrodes. The surface concentration vs. electrode potential plots for a Pt(lll) electrode in $HClO_4$ electrolyte containing acetic acid and sulfuric acid are shown in Figures 7A and 7B, respectively. A monotonic increase in the Γ vs. E plot observed for adsorption of sulfate anions [Fig. 7B] should be contrasted with a phase transition type of response in the case of acetic acid adsorption [Fig. 7A]. Furthermore, the threshold of the "anomalous" voltammetric features [13] in the double layer

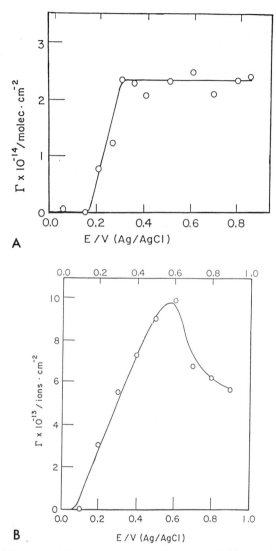

Figure 7. *The potential dependence of adsorption of (A) acetic acid [11[, and (B) sulfuric acid [12] on Pt(111) (vs. Ag/AgCl). Bulk concentration was 0.5 mM in both studies. Reproduced from Ref. 11 and 12 by permission of Elsevier Science Publishers.*

region [Fig. 5] *coincides with the onset of adsorption* in the two systems studied (the radiochemical data with phosphoric acid are not yet available). An identification of this correlation is a major contribution of the radiochemical research to progress in the understanding of the Pt(lll) voltammetry in popular supporting electrolytes. Likewise, our data demonstrate that very similar voltammetric features of this electrode in solutions containing acetic and sulfuric acid are neither associated with equally similar Γ vs. E plots nor with comparable surface concentrations [Fig. 7].

Our explanation of the data presented above has been that Clavilier's original assumption regarding the high-energy hydrogen [l3] is correct and that the position of the "anomalous" wave of hydrogen adsorption/desorption processes is modified due to anionic or molecular *coadsorption* [7b,12]. A strong argument supporting this assumption is that ca. 1/3 of a monolayer, which is not accounted for by the hydrogen adsorbed in the normal (most negative) potential range, can be added from the charge on the positive side of the potential of zero charge (p.z.c.) of the Pt(lll) electrode [53]. Likewise, a good correspondence was found between the onset of the anomalous voltammetric features and the shape of the Γ vs. E plot, as discussed before. However, the electro-reflectance data of McIntyre et al. [54] do not support the assumption that the H_{ads}/H^+ redox couple may account for the anomalous behavior. In electrolytes containing nonadsorbing anions, it was concluded that reversible adsorption and desorption of OH is the major factor, as proposed earlier by some other workers [16,46]. A new concept, which would remedy the lack of completion of the hydrogen monolayer in the "normal" potential region, requires an assumption that relatively stable water clusters block the surface sites for free access to adsorbed hydrogen precursors. In a full scope, Wagner and Ross [l0] allow for formation of a hydrogen bonding network through interfacial components with the simultaneous appearance of long-range order effects. They also propose that the chemisorbed anions become incorporated in the hydrogen bonded structures in an appropriate potential range, and play a significant role in suppressing surface oxidation processes. If correct, this elegant mechanism, with support from low temperature surface science [55-57], would dramatically change our concepts of the structure of the compact double layer at solid electrodes. From the standpoint of radiochemical research, the notion regarding the suppression of the surface oxidation would have to be reconciled with the surface/bulk mobility of sulfate anions, demonstrated in Figure 8. Since the anions belong to the compact surface structures, their mobility tends to indicate that the whole structure has some degree of freedom for exchange with

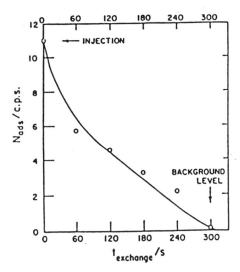

Figure 8. *Exchange of labeled HSO$_4^-$ ions adsorbed on a Pt(111) electrode by non-labeled H$_2$SO$_4$ added to the solution phase at the moment indicated by the arrow. E = 0.6 V vs. Ag/AgCl [12]. Reproduced from Ref. 12 by permission of Elsevier Science Publishers.*

solution components and, most probably, for surface diffusion. The blocking mechanism must therefore be electronic rather than structural. The nature of this mechanism has yet to be worked out.

A common feature between the concepts developed by Wagner and Ross [10] and by us [35,50] is the assumption of interfacial water to be immobilized on the surface, at least in part, due to combined chemical and electrical effects. A consensus between radiochemical, spectroscopic, and electrochemical research seems also to have been reached regarding the crucial role of the reversible chemisorption in the organization of the ordered interface. The initial and mass-transfer independent donation of electronic density from the electron-rich adsorbed products changes the p.z.c. of the electrode and either destabilizes chemisorption of high-energy hydrogen or allows for a not yet clearly identified pseudocapacitive process to occur. The discussion of these aspects will intensify when new data at well-defined electrodes becomes available. It will further accelerate with the advent of the in situ spectroscopies of electrochemical surface science, displaying better sensitivity and signal-to-noise ratio with respect to interfering solution background and/or absorbance.

B. Bonding Through Nitrogen in Surface Electrochemistry

Sexton and Hughes, who studied adsorption of acetonitrile on Pt(111) from the *gas phase*, found that most of the surface product adsorbed at 100 K desorbed to vacuum at 210 K [58]. However, part of the product was stable on the surface up to 340 K, where a second desorption maximum was observed. Equivalent measurements in electrochemistry consisted of exposure of a clean platinum surface to CH_3CN containing electrolyte, flushing the cell and electrode with clean supporting electrolyte (without air contact and potential change) and checking the surface by an appropriate surface sensitive technique [36-42]. Conway et al., using voltammetry [36], Szklarczyk and Sobkowski, using radio-electrochemistry [38], and Hubbard et al., using voltammetry [37a], single-crystal electrodes, and Auger spectroscopy [37b], showed that a strongly bonded, N-containing residue survives rinsing and evacuation [37b]. It was found in some of the studies that approximately 1/3 of the initial coverage is adsorbed in a weakly bonded configuration [36,38] and either desorbs upon rinsing or exchanges with unlabeled acetonitrile from solution [38]. Therefore, it appears that a qualitatively similar pattern of behavior emerges from the vacuum and solution investigations.

Indeed, the results are surprisingly similar, given the fact that a well-defined Pt(111) surface was used for the vacuum work [58], whereas a porous, polycrystalline platinum electrode was used in the radiochemical measurements [38]. After processing electron energy loss spectroscopy data, Sexton and Hughes concluded that the weakly bonded product (desorption at 210 K) was

$$
\begin{array}{c}
CH_3 \\
\diagdown \\
C\!\!=\!\!=\!\!=\!\!=\!\!N \\
\diagup \qquad \diagdown \\
Pt \qquad\qquad Pt
\end{array}
$$

which was designated as $\eta^2(C,N)$ acetonitrile. The strongly bonded state was proposed to be molecular acetonitrile adsorbed on step sites. The abundance of steps and other surface imperfections on the ill-defined platinum was probably such that the proportions between the strongly and weakly bonded forms were reversed between the two studies. Parallel radiochemical and ultra-high vacuum work with well-defined electrodes and acetonitrile will most likely bring this proportion to a rational common denominator.

The quoted radiochemical work [38] showed that strongly bonded molecular acetonitrile is adsorbed associatively in a narrow potential range from +0.45 to +0.75 V (NHE). Below +0.45 V, as shown by voltammetry, a one-electron reduction process takes place, with simultaneous uptake of 1 proton, to generate a species identified as

$$
\begin{array}{c}
H_3C \\
\diagdown \cdot \\
C - \ddot{N} - H \\
| \quad | \\
Pt \quad Pt
\end{array}
$$

Further reduction takes place below +0.15 V (NHE) and causes a complete desorption of this product at the hydrogen evolution edge. Above +1.0 V, the oxidation of molecular acetonitrile begins, and the surface is essentially free of the organic residue at +1.4 V.

The data summarized in Table 1 and the radiochemical results in Figures 9 and 10 show that trends derived from the behavior in vacuum can provide good guidelines in the electrochemical surface reactivity of N-containing compounds at a platinum electrode. Hydrogen cyanide desorbs to vacuum at 373 K [59-61], and molecular pyridine desorbs at 260 K, although full desorption is not achieved until the threshold of its decomposition at 370 K [62] [Table 1]. Electrochemical stability among the three N-containing products, as measured through potentials of the corresponding reduction, varies accordingly [Table 1]. That is, the products of cyanide and pyridine are stable with respect to electroreduction down to H_2 evolution. The stability mirrors their stronger bonding to platinum with reference to acetonitrile (complete desorption between 210-340 K). Interestingly, electrosorbed pyridine is surface-redox inactive [42], as are acetonitrile,

TABLE 1. Comparison of the Stability of Four N-containing Compounds Adsorbed on Platinum in Vacuum and in Solution.   The Diagnostic Tests are the Desorption/ Decomposition Temperatures in Vacuum and the Reduction Potential in Electrolytic Solutions.

	Molecular Desorption Peaks (K)		*First Decomposition Peak (K)*	*Potential[a] of Desorption (V vs NHE)*
	1st	2nd		
CH$_3$CN	210	340	n.o.[b]	0.20
HCN	420	n.o.	420	stable[c]
Pyridine	260	tail[d]	370	stable
DMF[e]	n.f.[f]	n.f.	n.f.	0.15

[a]*With respect to hydrogen electrode in 0.5 M H$_2$SO$_4$.*

[b]*Not observed.*

[c]*Pronounced reductive desorption was not observed even at the threshold of hydrogen evolution in the studied electrolyte.*

[d]*Desorption tail was observed beginning with the first desorption peak extending to 370 K.*

[e]*N,N-Dimethylformamide.*

[f]*Not found.*

cyanides and ferrocyanides [38,39]. The comparison of the voltammetric behavior between pyridine and HCN on polycrystalline Pt is shown in Figure 11.

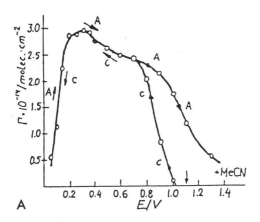

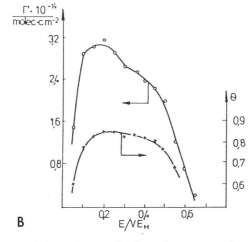

Figure 9. *Potential dependence of adsorption on rough polycrystalline Pt of (A) acetonitrile (the direction of potential excursion is indicated in arrows) [38]. (B) Dimethylformamide [65] (crosses refer to potential dependence of surface coverage). Bulk concentration was 10 mM; rough polycrystalline Pt electrodes were used in both studies. Potentials are given vs. hydrogen electrode in 0.5 M H_2SO_4. Reproduced from Refs. 38 and 65 by permission of Pergamon Journals, Ltd.*

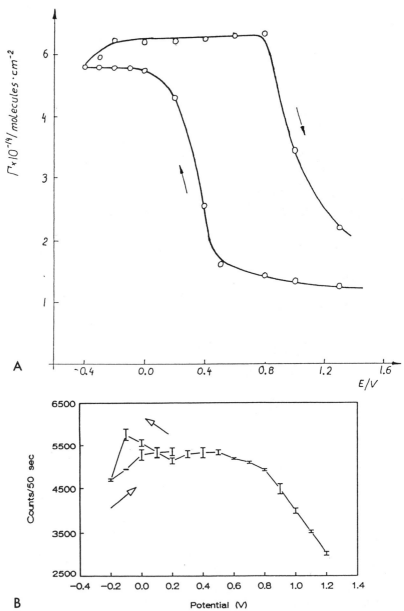

Figure 10. *Potential dependence of adsorption of (A) sodium cyanide from neutral media on rough Pt [39] and (B) pyridine from 0.1 M HClO4 [42] on smooth Pt. Reproduced from Ref. 39 by permission of Elsevier Science Publishers.*

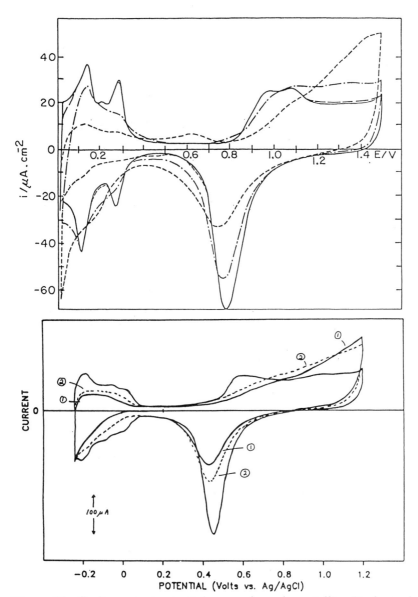

Figure 11. *Cyclic current-potential curves for polycrystalline Pt electrodes in clean supporting acidic electrolytes after chemisorption (and cell flushing) of (A) hydrogen cyanide [39] and (B) pyridine [42]. Scan rate: 50 mV s⁻¹. The rough polycrystalline Pt (potentials are vs. NHE) and smooth Pt electrodes (vs. Ag/AgCl) were used for HCN and pyridine studies, respectively. Dotted line represents the 1st scan, the thin solid - the 2nd, and the dashed line the nth scan, practically overlapping with the stable profile. Reproduced from Ref. 39 by permission of Elsevier Science Publishers.*

Chemisorption of cyanides and ferro/ferricyanides on platinum, first identified by radioactive labeling [39] and later confirmed by IR spectroscopy [63] and LEED/Auger [64], provides a basis for a comparative analysis of results obtained by solution and ultra-high vacuum-electrochemistry techniques. Both vacuum and solution results are the same regarding the nature of adsorption (i.e., chemisorption) and generally agree on the packing densities of the N-containing products. More recent work by Horanyi and Rizmayer [40] described the interactions between cations and chemisorbed cyanides by the radioactive labeling. The authors confirmed the UHV measurements by Hubbard's group as to the following details [9]:

1. CN$^-$ species preserve their charge upon chemisorption on Pt.
2. An exchange takes place between cations attached to the chemisorbed CN$^-$ and those in the solution phase, without loss of the adsorbed organic material.
3. Ca^{2+} are bonded to the CN adlattice more strongly than Na$^+$ and can displace the latter cations from their original position in the compact interface.

However, quantitative agreement between the solution and vacuum work is poor. The packing density of adsorbed cyanides was 0.81 ± 0.1 at Pt(111) vs. 0.14 on rough polycrystalline Pt [radiochemistry, Reference 40]. Correspondingly, the ratio of the packing density of CN$^-$ to that of Ca^{2+} was approximately 10:1 on Pt(111) and 2:1 on the polycrystalline surface. These factors indicate strong structural factors involved in the composition of the compact interface and underscore again the need for transition from polycrystalline to well-defined electrodes in in situ surface-electrochemistry.

The research reviewed in this section exhibits a common pattern in electrosorption of acetonitrile, cyanides, and pyridine. That is, a potential range was found where the chemisorption was associative, and the adsorbate electrooxidation took place in the potential range where the platinum surface itself was electrooxidized [Fig. 11] [Table 1].

Adsorption of N,N-dimethylformamide displays rather different behavior, as evidenced by voltammetry [Fig. 12] [Table 1] and radiochemistry [65]. Two products were identified, one oxidized in the double layer potential range and another at more positive potentials. The reaction scheme proposed to account for these observations is:

$$\begin{array}{c} O \\ \backslash\backslash \\ C - N \\ / \quad \backslash \\ H \quad CH_3 \end{array} \begin{array}{c} CH_3 \\ / \end{array} \quad + \quad 5\,Pt \xrightarrow{H_2O} Pt - \text{"formyl part"}$$

$$+ \quad Pt - \text{"amide part"} \; + \; 1.5\,e \; + \; 1.5\,H^+$$

with the N-containing part desorbing in the hydrogen potential range [Table 1]. As before, the electrooxidation of the amide part coincides with the oxidation of platinum, but the formyl part mimics carbon monoxide electrooxidation [66, and references therein]. Such behavior is consistent with the recently developed [50a] and reviewed [9] classification of adsorption processes on platinum. The classification categorizes electrochemical adsorption processes into three main groups: surface coordination (1st group), processes leading to formation of CO-type products (2nd group), and reversible chemisorption (3rd group). Consequently, the products coordinating platinum through the nitrogen terminal belong to the first group, the N-complexing products belong to the first group (with several other homologic series of compounds capable of coordination to the d-electron metal surfaces), and the CO-type adsorbates belong to the second group. The systematization goals notwithstanding, the radiochemical analysis of interactive routes of N-compounds with platinum has its distinctive significance in determining surface rules for electrochemistry in highly polar organic solvents [38,67].

Another molecule that contains nitrogen and has been studied by surface scientists and electrochemists is pyridine [7a,37,41,62,68-75]. The relevant issues are its molecular reorientation on metal surfaces, the comparison between surface interactions of pyridine with various metals, and the comparison between the gas-phase and electrochemical behavior. Described below will be our radiochemical and electrochemical research intended to illuminate contrasting features in adsorption of pyridine on polycrystalline gold and platinum electrodes [7a,33,73-75].

On both smooth metals, fast adsorption of pyridine was found, but resulting kinetics were not systematically followed.

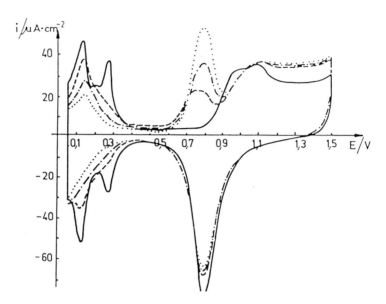

Figure 12. *The cyclic voltammetric curves for a rough polycrystalline Pt electrode in 0.5 M H₂SO₄ in the absence (—) and in the presence of DMF in the bulk of solution. $c_{DMF} = 5 \times 10^{-3}$ M (---), $c_{DMF} = 10^{-2}$ M (—) $c_{DMF} = 0.1$ M (····), sweep rate, S = 40 mV s^{-1} [65]. Potentials are given vs. hydrogen electrode in 0.5 M H₂SO₄. Reproduced from Ref. 65 by permission of Pergamon Journals, Ltd.*

The variables employed in our work were the electrode potential and the bulk concentration of pyridine in the supporting electrolytes, which were 0.1 M perchloric acid in the studies on platinum and 0.05 M potassium perchlorate with gold. The concentration of pyridine was not higher than 1 mM. With gold electrodes, we attempted to measure pyridine adsorption from acidic solutions, but surface-counts were small and irreproducible. At the present moment we can conclude that if any surface accumulation is occuring, it is probably at the level of 1% of a monolayer or smaller. More products can be adsorbed from concentrated solutions but, as shown in section IV, such an adsorption can not be studied by radio-electrochemistry at smooth electrode surfaces.

The voltammetric characterization of a platinum electrode covered by pyridine was shown in Figure 11B. The corresponding data for gold are presented in Figure 13. In the

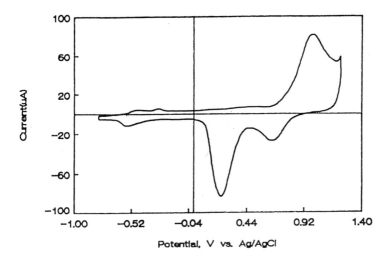

Figure 13. *Cyclic voltammograms of smooth polycrystalline gold in 0.05 M KClO₄ alone (dashed line) and containing 5 x 10⁻⁴ M pyridine (solid line). Sweep rate 50 mV s⁻¹ [42].*

oxidation region, the current-potential curve deviates from the one observed with the clean electrode surface studied in the same supporting electrolyte. This indicates that desorption of pyridine takes place along with the gold electrooxidation. Since much less pronounced oxygen suppression is associated with pyridine adsorption on gold than on platinum [Fig. 11B], one can conclude that the process of desorption is facilitated in the former case. This initial voltammetric study confirms a realistic expectation that bonding of pyridine is stronger at platinum than at gold.

Surface concentration - electrode potential relationships for pyridine adsorption on platinum and gold are presented in Figures 10B and 14, respectively. Significant differences have been found between the two systems. Pyridine desorbs from gold at sufficiently negative potentials [Fig. 14]. In this negative range, good agreement was found with the earlier data obtained by the use of chronocoulometry [73]. Contrary to the behavior of pyridine on gold, no significant desorption was found on platinum [Fig. 10B], even at the hydrogen evolution edge. This reemphasizes the very high affinity of pyridine towards platinum, as discussed above (section VI.B).

ZELENAY, WIECKOWSKI

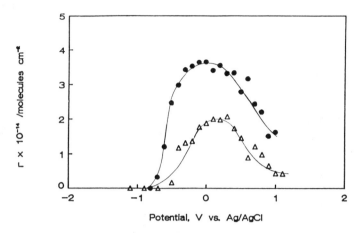

Figure 14. *Potential dependence of adsorption of pyridine on a smooth Au electrode from 0.05 M KClO₄. (▲) 10⁻⁴ M, (O) 5 x 10⁻⁴ M, and (●) 10⁻³ M. Reproduced from Ref. 39 by permission of Elsevier Science Publishers.*

For gold electrodes and upon positive going electrode polarization, the decrease in pyridine surface concentration was observed above 0.05 V. The desorption commences before the beginning of electrooxidation of gold and is complete at approximately 1.2 V. Although pyridine oxidatively desorbs from platinum, full desorption is not attained even at potentials approaching the oxygen evolution edge. To clean the platinum surface, several negative/positive going voltammetric scans had to be applied in perchloric acid supporting electrolyte. Regardless of the metal used, adsorption of pyridine on the walls of the glass-Teflon cell was extensive, as evidenced from difficulties that we experienced with system decontamination between individual runs.

A comparison between surface/bulk concentration profiles is informative regarding the modes of attachment of the surface pyridine to the two studied surfaces [Fig. 15]. The Γ vs. E output for platinum is practically flat when an incremental dosing is applied [Fig. 15, squares]. Within this dosing sequence, the bulk concentration of pyridine was systematically increased, and the surface concentration was monitored radiochemically at each point. Figuratively speaking, except for the first data point at 10^{-6} M, the bulk pyridine "sees" the surface covered by adsorbed products from the earlier run. The pattern of adsorption here was different than that shown in Figure 15, squares, when a clean

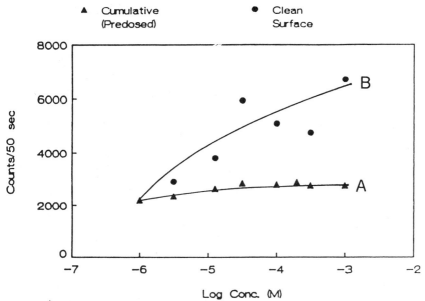

Figure 15. *The concentration dependence of pyridine adsorption on polycrystalline Pt at 0.2 V. (▲) packing density observed for a clean electrode at each concentration; (●) packing density observed for an electrode that was predosed with 10⁻⁶ M pyridine. Cumulative additions were made to this initial concentration to reach higher ones. Also shown are the theoretical packing densities for vertical (Δ) and horizontal (□) pyridine expected for a coverage of 0.73. See text and ref. 42.*

platinum surface was used for each of the adsorption measure-ments. The results obtained within this program are shown in Figure 15, triangles; a systematic increase in surface concentration is seen with a tendency to stabilize at the end of the series. The comparison between these two data sets gives evidence to a "predosing effect" earlier observed by Hubbard and Soriaga in their studies of quinones [75]. Their interpretation for quinones also seems to apply to the orientation of adsorbed pyridine on the polycrystalline surface used for this work. That is, the flat orientation prevails at low bulk concentration, while at high coverages, the vertical orientation allows the pyridine molecules to be more tightly packed on the surface.

The change in the orientation indicates a significant modification in the mode of attachment of pyridine to the surface. In the most extreme case, the π-type surface complex, with the pyridine molecular plane parallel to the surface (the η^6 notation in the current nomenclature), gives way to a nitrogen bonded, vertical arrangement. The geometric configurations to be assumed by chemisorbed pyridine are actually more numerous, as illustrated in Figure 16 [69]. As known from the gas-phase studies, the η^6 geometry (J), and the configuration denoted as II in Figure 16, are characteristic of low temperature adsorption (~100 K). The tilting occurs as a result of higher pyridine dosing of the surface. At room temperature, pyridine adsorption on platinum has been shown to be strongly dependent on the crystallographic orientation of the surface. On Pt(lll), only one pyridine geometry has been found which corresponds to the α-pyridyl state [III in Figure 16] [62,69]. On Pt(ll0), the low exposure of the surface to gas-phase pyridine causes the η^6 adsorption [70]. At high coverages, the bonding through nitrogen becomes a significant component via geometries II and IV of Figure 16 [70]. Since the uptake of electrosorbed pyridine depends on its bulk concentration, at least in the mode of measurements represented by Figure 15, Curve B, we conclude

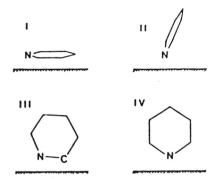

Figure 16. *Illustration of some possible geometries for pyridine coordination to a surface (I) parallel; (II) with the C2 axis inclined at an angle to the surface; (III) ring plane perpendicular to the surface, coordination through N and C2, α-pyridyl; (IV) ring plane perpendicular, coordination through N only [69].*

that pyridine adsorption on the polycrystalline substrate mimics, at least formally, the gas-phase behavior for the Pt(ll0) [33]. The in situ work on pyridine electrosorption on different crystallographic planes of platinum is in high demand to assess the degree of similarity of this process with adsorption from the gas phase on the crystallographically normalized substrates.

The surface/bulk concentration profiles, i.e., adsorption isotherms, at a smooth gold electrode taken at several potentials are shown in Figure 17. The system behaves reversibly (see below) and the surface concentrations are insensitive to the dosing sequence. Thermodynamic examination of the isotherms may prove difficult since, as shown by chronocoulometry, molecular reorientation is involved at certain coverages [41,73]. Even without this complicating factor, the lateral interactions between adsorbed molecules can not be decoupled from the intrinsic heterogeneity of the polycrystalline substrates. This calls for work on single crystals so as to reduce the number of variables and to explore the crystallographic effects in the 2-D interactions at metal electrodes.

The test for adsorption reversibility is provided by radio-electrochemistry by following the exchange between the adsorbed, radio-labeled material with unlabeled molecules added in excess to

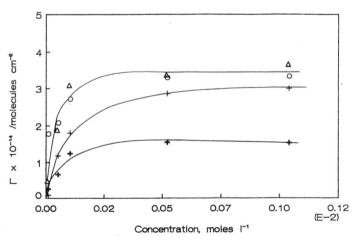

Figure 17. *Adsorption isotherms of pyridine on gold taken at several electrode potentials: (+) -0.4 V, (Δ) 0.0 V, (O) 0.3 V and (+) 0.9 V vs. Ag/AgCl.*

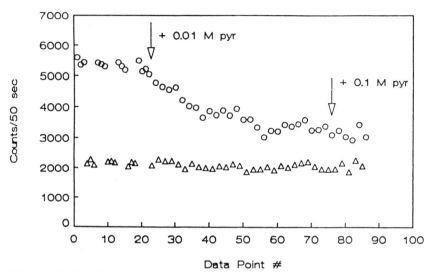

Figure 18. *Exchange experiment at a polycrystalline platinum electrode. The surface was dosed with 1 mM [14C] pyridine followed by rinsing with clean electrolyte. Arrows indicate where unlabeled pyridine was added. The total time elapsed is about 2.5 hr (0) squeeze, (Δ) bulk data [42].*

the bulk of solution (and present in the interfacial region). For gold, a pattern of behavior for reversibly chemisorbed anions [Fig. 8] was observed. For platinum, on the contrary, no exchange between the surface and solution material was found as long as the potential was kept in the double-layer range. If the electrode potential was changed to the hydrogen range, a slow displacement of the labeled by unlabeled material was activated [Fig. 18]. The sluggishness of the response nicely underscores the strength of the surface chemical bond between pyridine and platinum.

C. Adsorption of Anions on Gold and Copper Adatoms

The interest in heterogeneous catalysis and electrocatalysis by bimetallic substrates has motivated many researchers to study various metal composites at the fundamental level [76-81]. Since submonolayer coverages can be obtained through the metal underpotential deposition process (UPD), electrochemistry provides a straightforward way of preparing bimetallic electrodes [78-80]. Studies of reaction rates with such surfaces has attracted much attention [76,80]. Likewise, following the response in surface interactions of anions in the process of metal deposition, i.e., upon change from substrate metal to metal deposit [82-87], is a promising avenue of research, which we are actively pursuing. Such studies are informative regarding the nature of change in the interfacial (electrocatalytic) environment in the course of the electrolysis. The research with radio-labeled ions has already contributed to the progress in this area, as reviewed recently [9] and earlier [43].

The well-known system of copper underpotential deposition on gold was chosen as a candidate for the study depicted above [4,78,79,88]. We have investigated adsorption of sulfate/bisulfate anions from 0.1 M perchloric acid and 0.05 M potassium perchlorate electrolyte on the smooth, polycrystalline Au. The radiochemical results by Horanyi et al., using a porous gold electrode [82,83], showed enhanced anion adsorption on the UPD copper, as well as on silver and cadmium [Fig. 19]. Porous gold is an ill-characterized surface. The application of morphologically uniform, smooth Au electrodes (thoroughly examined by the voltammetry) is bringing the radiochemical research closer to the investigations of well-defined substrates [89]. In contrast to the earlier studies, correlated electrochemistry-radiochemistry measurements have been conducted and will be discussed below.

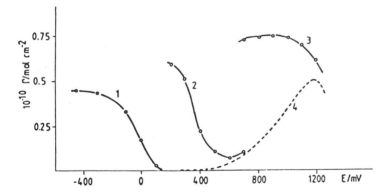

Figure 19. *Effect of the underpotential deposition of (1) Cd^{2+}, (2) Cu^{2+} and (3) Ag^+ on the potential dependence of the adsorption of HSO_4^- ions. Curve 4 (---) corresponds to the potential dependence without any addition; $c_{sul\ acid} = 4 \times 10^{-4}$ M, $c_{Me} = 8 \times 10^{-4}$ M. A porous gold electrode was used for these studies [82]. Reproduced from Refs. 3 and 82 by permission of Elsevier Science Publishers.*

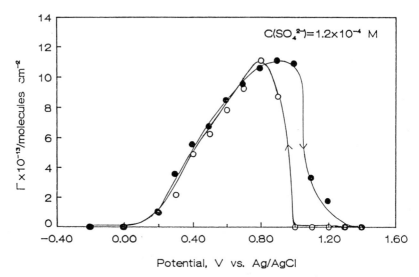

Figure 20. *Potential dependence of adsorption of sulfate/bisulfate anions on smooth gold electrode. Filled symbols and an arrow in the "down" direction indicate a positive going potential excursion. Open circles and an arrow "up" correspond to a negative going polarization. No adsorption was found below 0.0 V.*

The surface concentration - electrode potential profiles for adsorption of sulfate from 0.1 M HClO₄ are shown in Figure 20, and the corresponding voltammograms are illustrated in Figure 21. Adsorption of sulfate/bisulfate anions was measured after 15 sec of waiting at each potential in the "up" position of the electrode [Fig. 2A]. Longer waiting periods resulted in slow desorption, to be discussed elsewhere. The comparison between the radiochemistry and voltammetry clearly delineates a fundamental relationship between the structure of the compact double layer and the state of the electrode surface with respect to surface redox processes. That is, due to the reversibility of the surface oxidation/reduction process [Fig. 20], the adsorption depends on the direction of the potential excursion during the measurement. On the positive going sweep, the clean metal sites are open to anionic adsorption to a more positive potential limit than during the reverse run. Adsorption is thus retarded in the negative going program, which results in the hysteresis in the Γ vs. E plot seen in Figure 21.

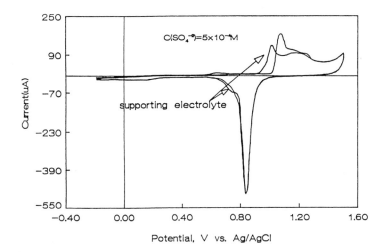

Figure 21. *Cyclic current-potential curves for a smooth Au electrode in 0.1 M HClO₄ electrolyte (dotted line) and in the same solution containing 10^{-3} M sulfuric acid (solid line).*

The data obtained when copper adatoms were electrodeposited onto the surface, beginning with the UPD, are shown in Figures 22 and 23. Since no adsorption took place on clean gold below 0.3 V [Fig. 20], the anionic adsorption at potentials more negative than 0.3 V [Fig. 22] is unambiguously associated with copper deposition on the gold electrode. Consequently, the threshold of such an enhanced adsorption, as determined by radiochemistry, coincides with the onset of the UPD current. The second shallow adsorption maximum in the -0.1 to -0.2 V range correlates very well with the end of the copper underpotential deposition. This maximum is followed by a steady but slow increase in the surface count-rates along the bulk deposition. A third maximum was observed in the neutral media (see below). Regarding the acidic electrolyte, one should notice a shoulder on the Γ vs E branch in the potential range of 0.0 to 0.2 V. We conclude that adsorbed anions respond to two stages of the underpotential deposition process marked on the voltammogram shown in Figure 23. On the negative branch of the respective current-potential plots, the two maxima are present, one at 0.23 and another at 0.05 V. Evidently, the shoulder in Figure 22 is due to the feature represented by the 0.05 V UPD transition.

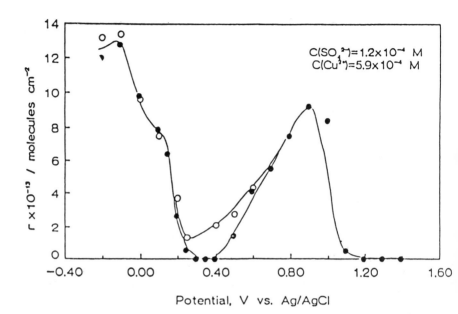

Figure 22. *Potential dependence of adsorption of sulfate/bisulfate anions on smooth Au electrode in solution containing copper cations. The supporting electrolyte was 0.1 M HClO₄. Filled circles represent a positive going and the open circles a negative going polarization, respectively.*

Regarding the radiochemical component of our work, the data qualitatively correspond to those reported earlier by Horanyi et al. [82,83]. As expected, the resolution is better with the smooth than with the porous surfaces (cf. the data in Figures 19 and 22). An extrapolation of this observation promises significant progress in the radiochemical measurements with single-crystal electrodes of this metal, as mentioned above.

The data obtained in neutral media follow the pattern from above rather closely. In Figure 24, the Γ vs. E profile obtained in potassium perchlorate electrolyte containing copper cations is shown. The third, most negative peak is due to sulfate adsorption on a copper film of several monolayers thickness. This behavior was unexpected from adsorption studies of sulfate on clean (porous) copper [83], and was not observed in the former studies of the copper UPD from aqueous solutions [82]. (On the clean copper, a monotonic decrease in the sulfate coverage was observed at electrode potentials more negative than 0.2 V (RHE) [Fig. 25] [83]). The processes that are unlikely to account for this

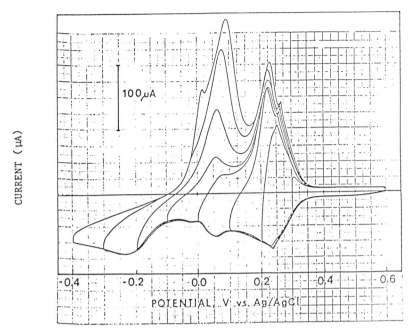

Figure 23. *Cyclic current-potential curves for a smooth Au electrode in 0.1 M HClO₄ with 0.5 mM Cu²⁺. The scan rate was 50 mV s⁻¹. "Window opening" curves were taken in 100 mV intervals.*

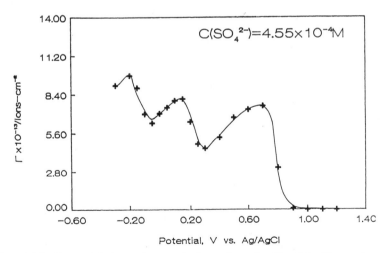

Figure 24. *Potential dependence of adsorption of sulfate/bisulfate anions on a smooth Au electrode in solution containing copper cations. The supporting electrolyte was 0.05 M KClO₄ (negative going polarization).*

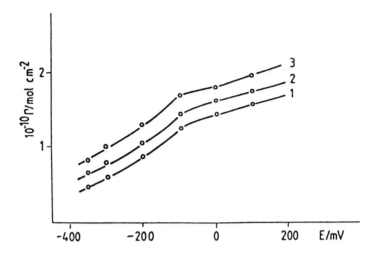

Figure 25. *Potential dependence of the adsorption of HSO_4^- ions on a porous (copperized) copper electrode at different H_2SO_4 concentrations in 1 M $HClO_4$. (1) 4×10^{-4}, (2) 8×10^{-4}, (3) 2.4×10^{-3} M H_2SO_4 (Γ values are referred to the real surface area). Potentials are given vs. NHE [83]. Reproduced from Figs. 3 and 83 by permission of Elsevier Science Publishers.*

behavior are the beta electron flux attenuation (the type of electrode-detector arrangement) and sulfate incorporation into the deposit (film uniformity). Thus, a mechanistic interpretation is justified. Since adding copper to gold in the UPD region produces a copperized electrode of a monolayer thickness, such a newly created surface will tend to accept anions in a way analogous to the behavior of clean copper [Fig. 25] [83]. In addition to this basic chemical principle, and due to partial, rather than integral charge transfer between the Cu^{2+} cations and the substrate [82], the surface charge distribution diverges from the one intrinsic to the clean gold electrode. This creates a new surface electrochemistry and new bonding propensity for the anions. The balance between the electrostatic and chemical components is difficult to assess. As already discussed by others [82], the purely electrostatic attraction can be excluded, since perchloric acid is adsorbed extremely weakly, even at much higher bulk concentration, than sulfate. To track the "nature of the surface chemical bond" [90] between the anions and the electronically unsaturated metal sites is a challenge for spectroscopic surface analysis.

The appearance of the third, most cathodic peak [Fig. 24] can be related to potassium cations being present in the neutral electrolyte, as well as to the opening of the UPD to a broader potential range without hydrogen evolution interference. The simultaneous adsorption of anions and cations, predominantly on platinum, was extensively studied by Frumkin et al. [9], Kazararinov et al. [92], and Horanyi et al. [43, and references therein] and has recently been reviewed [9]. At sufficiently negative potentials it appears [Fig. 24] that copper electrodeposition on gold is accompanied by adsorption of potassium cations and, consequently, by an excessive adsorption of sulfate. The ultimate descent of the Γ vs. E branch in the most negative potential range is most likely due to hydrogen adsorption process, which changes the character of the interface and the pattern of its reactivity.

As demonstrated above, the electrochemical component of our research provides a crucial voltammetric characterization, and the surface count rates correctly identify the facts regarding the organization of the compact interface at the morphologically uniform surfaces. Tracking the cationic counterpart would characterize the interface even more fully [43]. Using solutions of different pH will allow us to decouple protonated Brönsted bases from less or nonprotonated anions or molecules in adsorption. Despite the expectations that the single-crystal work will offer even better insight, the data analyzed above provide material to reflect upon the variety of processes and structures in the interfacial region. Adsorption of generally neutral organic species (surface poisons and reactive intermediates) takes place in this highly charged and surface-active ionic environment. Spectroscopic studies of such molecules do reflect this variety of field discontinuities and surface effects. Without information of the type reviewed above, the interpretation of in situ spectroscopic data may be incomplete or ambiguous. As in gas-phase surface science, a multitechnique approach is prerequisite for successful system characterization. The broad arsenal of techniques described in this volume indicates that the in situ analysis of electrode surfaces may be approaching the state-of-the-art performance in surface science, regarding surface composition and structure.

D.   Radio-Electrochemistry of Surface Hydrogen

The instrument for radiochemical measurements with tritium-labeled adsorbates is shown in Figure 26 [30]. A glass scintillator similar to the one described earlier [Fig. 2] is employed, and the electrode material is vacuum deposited on the glass substrate. Both surface counts and bulk counts are simultaneously recorded, but the bulk counts are negligible (or acceptable) up to the bulk concentration of 10 mM when using smooth surface electrodes [9]. Since the energy of the electrons emitted from tritium is an order of magnitude lower than that from C-14, an excessive attenuation of the electron flux in the electrode material must be avoided, which is achieved by applying metal films of 1,000 Å, or thinner. If one attempts to apply the instrument of Figure 2 to the

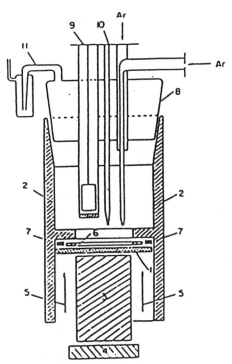

Figure 26. *The instrument reported in ref. 30. (1) Electrode, (2) Teflon frame, (3) light pipe, (4) photomultiplier, (5) tightening, (6) Teflon gasket, (7) rubber gasket, (8) Kel-F sealed glass (Pyrex) ground joint, (9) counterelectrode (closed by fritted disk), (10) reference hydrogen electrode (Luggin capillary), (11) bubbler, Ar, inlets of argon. Reproduced from Ref. 30 by permission of The Electrochemical Society, Inc.*

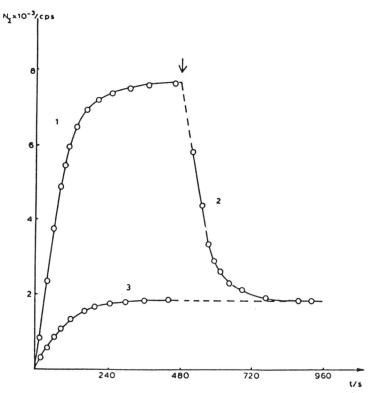

Figure 27. *The total counting rates ($N_\Sigma = N_{ads} + N_{backg}$) vs. time plots obtained in two different experimental procedures. In the first one (curves 1 and 2) 0.025 cm^3 of HTO was added to the DMSO-based electrolyte (curve 1) followed by the addition of 0.5 cm^3 of H$_2$O (the addition indicated by vertical arrow, curve 2). In the second procedure 0.5 cm^3 of H$_2$O was added to the supporting electrolyte followed by the addition of 0.025 cm^3 of HTO to give the same final specific activity as in the previous case. Note that the same final level of N_Σ is obtained. The background level, N_{backg}, was ca. 10^3 cps (counts per second) [93]. Reproduced from Ref. 93 by permission of Elsevier Science Publishers.*

detection of T-labeled adsorbates, the gap thickness would have to be below 1 μm. As already discussed in this chapter, submicron gaps have not yet been achieved. In the thin film arrangement [Fig. 26], only polycrystalline substrates have been studied to date. The possibility of using epitaxially deposited metallic overlayers on ordered scintillating materials for the measurement is an interesting direction of the evolution of this method.

The methodological advantage of the tritium variant of the radioactive labeling vs. the C-14 component is counterbalanced, in part, by the high mobility of tritium in molecular structures. Due to a tritium surface-solution exchange, the surface counts from tritium can either be lost, or can be diminished to an unmeasurable level. Fortunately, in many interesting systems, tritium is strongly bonded to the surface through its parent molecule, and its rate of escape is either negligible or can be controlled. In the latter instance, a track record of radiochemical rate of escape is one of the research options in attempting to measure the distribution and destiny of the interfacial hydrogen.

An example of a successful study with T-labeled molecules is given below. Adsorption of water (H_2O) was studied on platinum from $DMSO/KClO_4$ supporting electrolyte [93]. As checked independently, the exchange of hydrogens between DMSO chemisorbed on platinum and water molecules did not occur. After addition of tritiated water to the electrolyte, a strong count rate from the surface was observed [Fig. 27]. This signal was relatively potential independent, and the chemisorbed DMSO was not perturbed by the water content, as shown by voltammetry. Adding light (deuterated) H_2O to 20 ml of electrolyte in micromolar quantities resulted in a sharp drop in surface counts [Fig. 27]. Since the dilution effects can be neglected, this pattern of response shows that the measurements are surface-specific. We concluded that adsorption of water was reversible and took place in the second monolayer of the interface. Indeed, the Temkin isotherm was identified when the surface/bulk concentration profiles were linearized through appropriate relationships.

VII. CONCLUSIONS

Radioactive labeling belongs to the group of nuclear methods of surface electrochemistry [94]. In addition to radioactive labeling, the methods include Mössbauer spectroscopy, neutron scattering and NMR. Mössbauer spectroscopy has already been proven to be an extremely useful technique, especially in corrosion research. The remaining two methods await further use in surface electrochemical studies. From among these four methods, radioactive labeling provides the sensitivity required for characterization of smooth electrode surfaces. Cross-analysis of the data obtained in several radiochemical laboratories identifies the relationships needed to develop a unified theory of the compact electrochemical interface and surface reactivity at metal electrodes [9]. Bringing a part of this existing information to the readers' attention was one of the objectives of this review. The principal goal was to show the future potential of in situ research at single crystal electrodes by radio-electrochemistry. As concluded above, superior properties of well-defined electrodes should convince researchers to use them more broadly in their laboratories. Fortunately, such a trend is clearly seen in this volume.

Acknowledgments

Helpful comments by Elizabeth K. Krauskopf and Lesa M. Rice-Jackson regarding this manuscript are greatly appreciated. The anion interactions with gold were studied in collaboration with Dr. Joseph Gordon's group, IBM (San Jose).

The authors acknowledge financial support by Dow Chemical U.S.A., and by the Air Force Office of Scientific Research (AFOSR-89-0368). Glenna Wilsky's assistance with the manuscript preparation is highly appreciated.

References

1. Hubbard, A. T. *Acc. Chem. Res.* 13 (1980): 177.
2. Yeager, E. *J. Electrochem. Soc.* 128 (1981): 160c.
3. Ross, P. N. and Wagner, F. T. *Adv. in Electrochem. and Electrochem. Eng.* 13 (1984): 69.
4. Kolb, D. M. *Z. phys. Chemie NF* 154 (1987): 179.
5. Hubbard, A. T. *Chem. Rev.* 88 (1988): 633.
6. Somorjai, G. A. *Chemistry in Two Dimensions: Surfaces.* Ithaca, NY: 1981, Cornell University Press.
7. a. Krauskopf, E. K.; Chan, K.; and A. Wieckowski *J. Phys. Chem.* 91 (1987): 2327.
   b. Wieckowski, A. In M. Soriaga, ed. ACS Symposium Series, "Molecular Phenomena at Electrode Surfaces" *Electrochemical Surface Sci.*, Vol. 17: 245.
8. Kazarinov, V. E. and Andreev, V. N. In *Comprehensive Treatise of Electrochemistry,* ed. E. Yeager, et al., Vol. 9. New York: 1984, Plenum.
9. Wieckowski, A. In "In Situ Surface Electrochemistry: Radioactive Labeling" *Modern Aspects of Electrochemistry,* ed. J. O'M. Bockris, B. E. Conway, and R. E. White, Vol 21. New York: 1990, Plenum.
10. Wagner, F. T. and Ross, P. N., *J. Electroanal. Chem.* 250 (1988): 31.
11. Rice, L. M.; Krauskopf, E. K.; and Wieckowski, A. *J. Electroanal. Chem.* 239 (1988): 413.
12. Krauskopf, E. K.; Rice, L. M.; and Wieckowski, A. *J. Electroanal. Chem.* 244 (1988): 347.
13. Clavilier, J. *J. Electroanal. Chem.* 107 (1980): 211.
14. Clavilier, J.; Feliu, J. M.; and Aldaz, A. *J. Electroanal. Chem.* 243 (1988): 419.
15. Aberdam, D. et al. *Surf. Sci.* 171 (1986): 303.
16. Al Jaaf-Golze, K.; Kolb, D. M.; and Scherson, D. *J. Electroanal. Chem.* 200 (1986): 353.
17. Zurawski, D. et al. *J. Electroanal. Chem.* 230 (1987): 221.
18. Wasberg, M. et al. *J. Electroanal. Chem.* 256 (1988): 51.
19. Wieckowski, A. et al. *Inorg. Chem.* 23 (1984): 565.
20. Wieckowski, A. et al. *Surf. Sci.* 146 (1984): 115.
21. Hubbard, A. T. et al. *J. Electroanal. Chem.* 150 (1983): 165.
22. Stickney, J. L. et al. *Surf. Sci.* 130 (1983): 326.
23. Lu, F. et al. *J. Electroanal. Chem.* 222 (1987): 305.
24. Mebrahtu, T. et al. *J. Electroanal. Chem.* 219 (1987): 327.
25. Leung, L-H. W.; Wieckowski, A.; and Weaver, M. J. *J. Phys. Chem.* 92 (1988): 6985.
26. Ertl, G.; Neumann, M.; and Streit, K. M. *Surf. Sci.* 64 (1977): 393.
27. Palaikis, L. et al. *Surf. Sci.* 199 (1988): 183.
28. a. Hourani, M. and Wieckowski, A. *J. Electroanal. Chem.* 227 (1987): 259.
   b. Hourani, M. and Wieckowski, A. *J. Electroanal. Chem.* 244 (1988): 147.
29. Weaver, M. Private communication, 1988.
30. Wieckowski, A. *J. Electrochem. Soc.* 122 (1975): 252.
31. Zumwalt, L. R. In "Absolute Beta Counting Using End-Window Geiger-Müller Counters and Experimental Data on Beta Particle Scattering," AECV-567. Oak Ridge, TN: U.S. Atomic Energy Commission, Technical Information Service.
32. Ichimura, S.; Shimizu, R.; and Ikuta, T. *Surf. Sci.* 115 (1982): 259.
33. Lerch, P. *Helv. Phys. Acta* 26 (1953): 663.

34. Suttle, A. D. and Libby, W. F. *Anal. Chem.* 6 (1955): 921.
35. Corrigan, D. S. et al. *J. Phys. Chem.* 92 (1988): 1596.
36. a. Angerstein-Kozlowska, H.; MacDougall, B.; and Conway, B. E.
       J. Electroanal. Chem. 39 (1972): 287.
    b. MacDougall, B.; Conway, B. E.; and Kozlowska, H. *J. Electroanal. Chem.*
       32 (1971): App. 15.
    c. Conway, B. E.; MacDougall, B.; and Kozlowska, H. *Trans. Faraday Soc.* 68
       (1972): 1566.
37. a. Lane, R. F. and Hubbard, A. T. *J. Phys. Chem.* 8 (1977): 734.
    b. Garwood, G. A. and Hubbard, A. T. *Surf. Sci.* 118 (1982): 223.
38. Szklarczyk, M. and Sobkowski, J. *Electrochim. Acta* 25 (1980): 1597.
39. Wieckowski, A. and Szklarczyk, M. *J. Electroanal. Chem.* 142 (1982): 157.
40. Horanyi, G. and Rizmayer, E. M. *J. Electroanal. Chem.* 215 (1986): 369.
41. Stolberg, L.; Lipkowski, J.; and Irish, D. E. *J. Electroanal. Chem.* 238 (1987):
    333.
42. a. Krauskopf, E. K.; Rice-Jackson, L. M. and Wieckowski, A. *Langmuir* 6
       (1990): 970.
    b. Zelenay, P.; Rice-Jackson, L. M. and Wieckowski, A. *Langmuir* 6 (1990):
       974.
43. Horanyi, G. *Electrochim. Acta* 25 (1980): 43.
44. Kunimatsu, K. et al. *J. Electroanal. Chem.* 243 (1988): 203.
45. Wieckowski, A. *J. Electroanal. Chem.* 135 (1982): 285.
46. Wagner, F. T. and Ross, P. N. Jr. *J. Electroanal. Chem.* 150 (1983): 141.
47. Markovic, N. et al. *J. Electroanal. Chem.* 214 (1986): 555.
48. Zei, M. S. et al. *J. Electroanal. Chem.* 229 (1987): 99.
49. Sveshnikova, D. A.; Kazarinov, V. E.; and Petrii, O. A. *Elektrokhimiya* 13
    (1977): 1505.
50. a. Wieckowski, A. *Electrochim. Acta* 26 (1981): 1121.
    b. Wieckowski, A. et al. *Electrochim. Acta,* 26 (1981): 1111.
51. Zelenay, P.; Habib, M. A.; and Bockris, J. O'M. *Langmuir* 2 (1986): 393.
52. a. Schultze, J. W. and Koppitz, F. D. *Electrochim. Acta* 21 (1976): 327.
    b. Koppitz, F. D. and Schultze, J. W. *Electrochim. Acta* 21 (1976): 337.
53. Wagner, F. T. and Moylan, P. E. Extended Abstract 528. Presented at The
    Electrochemical Society Spring Meeting, Atlanta, GA, May, 1988.
54. McIntyre, J. D. E. et al. In Situ Spectroreflectance Studies of Adsorption on
    Flame-Annealed Pt(lll) Electrode Surfaces, presented at the 194th National Meeting
    of ACS, New Orleans, LA, August 30-September 4, 1987.
55. Thiel, P. and Madey, T. *Surf. Sci. Rep.* 7 (1988): 211.
56. Firment, L. and Somorjai, G. A. *Surf. Sci.* 55 (1976): 413.
57. Fisher, G. B. and Gland, J. L. *Surf. Sci.* 94 (1980): 446.
58. a. Sexton, B. A. and Avery, N. R. *Surf. Sci.* 129 (1983): 21.
    b. Sexton, B. A. and Hughes, A. E. *Surf. Sci.* 140 (1984): 227.
59. Bridge, M. ; Marbrow, R. A. and Lambert, R. M. Letter to the Editor, *Surf. Sci.*
    57 (1976): 415.
60. Bridge, M. E. and Lambert, R. M. *J. Catal.* 46 (1977): 143.
61. Hagans, P. L. et al. *Surf. Sci.* 203 (1988) 1.
62. a. Johnson, A. L. et al. *J. Phys. Chem.* 89 (1985): 4071.
    b. Grassian, V. H. and Muetterties, E. L. *J. Phys. Chem.* 90 (1986): 5900.
63. Pons, S. et al. *J. Electroanal. Chem.* 160 (1984): 369.
64. Baltruschat, H. *J. Electroanal. Chem.* 234 (1987): 229.
65. Szklarczyk, M. and Sobkowski, J. *J. Electrochim. Acta* 26 (1981): 345.
66. Palaikis, L. et al. *Surf. Sci.* 199 (1988): 183.

67. Sobkowski, J. and Szklarczyk, M. *Electrochim. Acta* 25 (1980): 383.
68. Gland, J. L. and Somorjai, G. A. *Surf. Sci.* 38 (1973): 157.
69. Connolly, M. et al. *Surf. Sci.* 185 (1987): 559.
70. Surman, M. et al. *Surf. Sci.* 179 (1987): 243.
71. Hamelin, A. *J. Electroanal. Chem.* 144 (1983): 365.
72. Baltruschat, H.; Rach, E.; and Heitbaum, J. *J. Electroanal. Chem.* 194 (1985): 109.
73. Stolberg, L. et al. *J. Electroanal. Chem.* 207 (1986): 213.
74. A collaborative project between the University of Guelph, Canada and the University of Illinois. To be published.
75. a. Soriaga, M. P. and Hubbard, A. T. *J. Am. Chem. Soc.* 104 (1982): 2735.
    b. Soriaga, M. P. and Hubbard, A. T. *J. Phys. Chem.* 88 (1984): 1089.
76. A discussion of recent progress in surface chemistry and catalytic properties of bimetallic and alloy surfaces is offered in *Langmuir* 5 (1988): 1075. Presented are papers from the Symposium on Bimetallic Surface Chemistry and Catalysis (preface by B. E. Koel and C. T. Campbell), which was held as part of the 194th National Meeting of the ACS, New Orleans, LA, September 1-3, 1987.
77. Sinfelt, J. H. *Bimetallic Catalysts*, New York: Wiley, 1983.
78. Kolb, D. M. *Advances in Electrochemistry and Electrochemical Engineering*, ed. H. Gerischer and C. W. Tobias, Vol. 11. New York: Wiley, 1978.
79. Adzic, R. R. *Advances in Electrochemistry and Electrochemical Engineering*, eds. H. Gerischer and C. W. Tobias, Vol. 13. New York: Wiley, 1984.
80. Kokkinidis, G. *J. Electroanal. Chem.* 201 (1986): 217.
81. Goodman, D. W. *Ann. Rev. Phys. Chem.* 37 (1986): 425.
82. Horanyi, G.; Rizmayer, E. M.; and Joo, P. *J. Electroanal. Chem.* 152 (1983): 211.
83. Horanyi, G.; Rizmayer, E. M.; and Joo, P. *J. Electroanal. Chem.* 154 (1983): 281.
84. Horanyi, G.; Rizmayer, E. M.; and Konya, J.*J. Electroanal. Chem..* 176 (1984): 339.
85. Horanyi, G. and Rizmayer, E. M. *J. Electroanal. Chem.* 176 (1984): 349.
86. Horanyi, G. and Rizmayer, E. M. *J. Electroanal. Chem.* 21 (1986): 187.
87. Horanyi, G. and Vertes, A. *J. Electroanal. Chem.* 205 (1986): 259.
88. Beckmann, H. O. et al. *Symp. Faraday Soc.* 12 (1978): 51.
89. Scherson, D. A. and Kolb, D. M. *J. Electroanal. Chem.* 176 (1984): 353.
90. Rhodin, T. N. and Ertl, G. *The Nature of the Surface Chemical Bond.* New York: North Holland, 1979.
91. a. Frumkin, A. N. et al. *Elektrokhimiya 8* (1972): 599.
    b. Frumkin, A. N. and Petrii, O. A. *Electrochim. Acta* 20 (1975): 347.
92. a. Kolotyrkin, T. Ya.; Petrii, O. A.; and Kazarinov, V. E. *Elektrokhimiya* 10 (1974): 1352.
    b. Kazarinov, V. E. and Andreev, V. N. *Elektrokhimiya* 11 (1974): 1482.
93. Wieckowski, A.; Szklarczyk, M.; and Sobkowski, J. *J. Electroanal. Chem.* 113 (1980) 79.
94. "Nuclear Methods in Surface Electrochemistry," symposium organized as part of the 177th Meeting of the Electrochemical Society, Montreal, Canada, May 6-11, 1990 (D. Scherson and A. Wieckowski, organizers).

CHAPTER 10

THE QUARTZ CRYSTAL MICROBALANCE AS AN IN SITU TOOL IN ELECTROCHEMISTRY

Daniel A. Buttry

Department of Chemistry
University of Wyoming
Laramie, WY 82071-3838

CONTENTS

CHAPTER 10

THE QUARTZ CRYSTAL MICROBALANCE AS AN IN SITU TOOL IN ELECTROCHEMISTRY

Daniel A. Buttry
Department of Chemistry
University of Wyoming
Laramie, WY 82071-3838

I. INTRODUCTION

By the very nature of the phenomena studied, electrochemistry deals extensively with interfacial processes. Both in application and in fundamental studies, knowledge of the types and amounts of various species that exist at the electrode/electrolyte interface is essential to a molecular level understanding of the relationship between structure and function in electrochemical phenomena. Consequently, many different types of experimental techniques have been applied towards this end. Improvements in the sensitivity of such techniques have pushed the detection limits for interfacial species to monolayer and even submonolayer levels. This Chapter describes the use of the quartz crystal microbalance (QCM) to measure minute mass changes at electrode surfaces, in situ, during electrochemical processes. It will be seen that, in favorable cases, these mass changes reveal changes in the populations of interfacial species that are associated in some way with the electrochemical processes. Rather than present an exhaustive review of the area, this Chapter will focus on the considerations regarding application of the QCM to studies of mass changes at electrode surfaces during redox events and will present some representative examples illustrating what can be achieved with the method.

The QCM has been used by the vacuum community for

some time for the determination of the mass of films deposited in evaporative depositions. A large literature exists on this topic, which has been exhaustively reviewed [1]. In related work, the QCM and other such devices have been employed for the determination of the materials properties of polymeric samples of various types [2]. Also, the QCM has seen use in detection schemes in analytical methods such as gas and liquid chromatography and particle detection, to name a few [3]. The considerations which pertain to these areas also come into play in the application of the QCM to electrochemical problems, so it will be fruitful to examine them in more detail in the context of the electrochemical experiment.

The use of the QCM to study mass changes at surfaces that are of electrochemical origin was pioneered by Mieure and Jones [4,5] and Nomura and coworkers [6-17]. Mieure and Jones [4,5] were able to determine the mass of a variety of metallic deposits produced during electrodeposition by applying a cathodic current to the crystal electrode for a given time, removing the crystal from the cell, washing and drying the crystal, and measuring the change in the resonant frequency of the crystal in air. This procedure formed the basis for analytical determinations of several metals, most notably cadmium, with detection limits in the submicromolar range. Nomura and Iijima [8] were the first to demonstrate the use of the QCM as an in situ tool for measuring mass changes at the QCM electrodes during the electrochemical experiment, thus demonstrating that proper design of the oscillator circuitry allowed for stable oscillation of the QCM in a liquid. (Prior to this time it had been commonly believed that the QCM could not be used in liquids due to excessive viscous loading.) They were able to detect silver ions in solution at submicromolar concentrations by the decrease in the QCM resonant frequency caused by electrodeposition on it.

Bruckenstein and Swathirajan [18] were the first to study monolayer deposits on the QCM. They produced underpotential deposits (UPD) of silver on the QCM and made ex situ mass determinations of these in investigations of electrosorption valency. Bruckenstein and Shay then reported on the first in situ mass determination of a monolayer system, studying oxide formation on Au electrodes [19]. They also published an important contribution on the experimental aspects of the use of the QCM in electrochemical studies [20].

In 1984, Kaufman, Kanazawa, and Street published the first account of the use of the QCM to study ion transport during redox processes in thin polymer films [21]. Soon thereafter, the IBM group reported on the mass determination of a UPD deposit of Pb on a Au electrode [22]. This publication also presented the oscillator and potentiostat circuits originally designed by Kanazawa and since used by the IBM group. This group has continued to apply the QCM to problems in the areas of monolayer adsorption and deposition and mass changes during redox in thin films on electrodes.

Here at the University of Wyoming, the QCM has been applied to the in situ measurement of transport of ionic species [23-25] and solvent [25] in thin films of redox and conducting polymers, measurement of submonolayer to multilayer mass changes at electrodes during electrochemically induced adsorption/desorption processes of surfactants bearing redox head groups [26,27], determination of deposition and dissolution mechanisms for electrochromic films [28], and analytical assays for enzyme substrates using enzymes immobilized on the QCM [29]. Some selected examples will be discussed below to illustrate the types of effects that can be observed using the QCM in electrochemical studies. In general, in electrochemical applications it is the ability to simultaneously determine both the electrochemical parameters of the system and the effective mass of the electrode which makes the technique so attractive, so the in situ use of the device will be the main focus here.

II. EXPERIMENTAL METHODS

A. Instrumentation and Materials

The physical basis of operation of the QCM originates in the converse piezoelectric effect, in which the application of an electric field across a piezoelectric material induces a deformation of the material [1]. If this electric field is applied at the proper frequency (determined by the geometry and properties of the sample), then the piezoelectric material may be induced to oscillate in a mechanically resonant mode. For the QCM, these conditions correspond to the creation of a standing acoustic shear wave within the quartz crystal. This situation is schematically depicted in Figure 1. For the so-called fundamental mode (the one shown in the figure), the node of this standing wave is at the midpoint between the two faces of the QCM disk and the antinodes at the two faces of the disk.

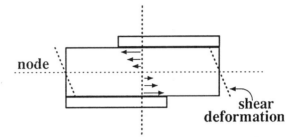

Figure 1. Edge view of QCM crystal showing the node of the acoustic wave passing through the center of the disk and the deformation of the crystal caused by the shear motion. The thickness and shear deformation have been greatly exaggerated for clarity. The vertical dashed line passes through the center of the QCM electrode pad. The sizes of the arrows represent approximate magnitudes of the shear deformation within the bulk of the disk.

The higher frequency odd harmonics may also be excited. For these, the antinodes are also at the faces of the disk, and the number of nodes within the bulk of the disk is equal to the harmonic number.

For the QCM, the electric field is usually applied using two electrodes that are vapor deposited onto the two faces of the quartz disk. These electrodes are shown in Figures 1 and 2. Figure 2 gives both an edge and top view of a QCM disk. These electrodes actually become a part of the composite resonator by virtue of their attachment to the disk, so that mass changes that occur at the surface of these electrodes are sensed by the resonator. Thus, in its simplest configuration, the electrochemical/QCM (EQCM) experiment involves the

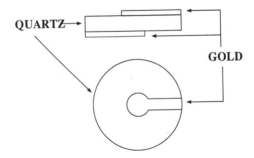

Figure 2. Schematic top and edge views of a QCM crystal with vapor deposited gold electrodes.

application of a high frequency, alternating electric field (usually in the 4-15 megahertz (MHz) region, depending on the mode to be excited and the geometry of the quartz crystal) to excite the quartz crystal into its resonant oscillation, the use of electrochemical techniques to induce redox processes at one of the disk electrodes, and the simultaneous detection of both the electrochemical variables (e.g., current, potential, charge) and the oscillation frequency of the quartz disk.

For use in the determination of mass changes in thin films, quartz is by far the most commonly used piezoelectric material. This is because of its favorable mechanical properties (low frictional resistance to the propagation of acoustic waves and high shear modulus) and the fact that it may be easily synthesized in pure, crystalline form with a low defect density. Quartz crystals for QCM applications are generally cut into disks or rectangular wafers with the angle of the cut defining the direction of propagation of the acoustic wave. AT-cut crystals are commonly used in QCM applications [1]. These crystals oscillate in a pure shear mode with the direction of motion of the crystal being exactly coplanar with the face of the crystal disk, as shown in Figure 1. In principle, operation at the frequencies of the first and higher odd harmonics is possible, but limitations at higher frequencies usually arise due to the complexity of the electronics.

Quartz crystals may be obtained from commercial sources with a variety of surface characteristics. A common surface finish is obtained by mechanical polishing. This yields a surface which is optically rough (frosty). Such roughness may aid in adhesion of the vapor deposited electrodes on the crystal, but can cause complications in the determination of absolute frequency changes for transfer of crystals from air into liquids (vide infra). Another type of crystal surface finish is obtained by chemical etching methods. This yields an optically smooth surface which is highly reflective with the faces parallel to within at least one micron. This treatment is frequently referred to as an overtone polish, because operation with acceptable frequency stability at the higher frequency odd harmonics of the crystal (the odd overtones) requires crystals that are less rough than can be obtained from simple mechanical polishing. In addition to surface treatment, crystals can also be obtained in a variety of sizes and geometries. In our laboratories, 1 inch diameter, overtone polished, AT-cut quartz crystals with resonant frequencies near 5 MHz are routinely used (Valpey-Fisher Corporation, Hopkinton, Massachusetts).

BUTTRY

As mentioned above, crystals may be operated at the fundamental resonant frequency or at the higher odd harmonics. The fundamental frequency of AT-cut quartz crystals is reciprocally related to the thickness of the crystal. For example, a 5 MHz crystal is ca. 330 microns thick while a 15 MHz crystal is only ca. 110 microns thick. The mass sensitivity increases as the square of the fundamental frequency of the crystal [30] and linearly with the harmonic number for a crystal with a given fundamental frequency [22] (see Equation # (1)), so the operation of the crystals at higher frequencies, either by driving the crystals at higher harmonics or using thinner crystals, would seem to be desirable, judging from the criterion of increased mass sensitivity. However, the manipulation of crystals having thicknesses much less than 200 microns is experimentally challenging. These single crystal quartz disks are extremely brittle so that even small stresses can cause cracking, resulting in a high rate of breakage for the thinner crystals. Also, the complexity of the oscillator circuitry for operation at higher harmonics is greater. Operation at high frequencies is further complicated by problems arising from viscous loading by the solution. Thus, the maximum frequency of operation, and therefore, the maximum mass sensitivity, is determined by a combination of considerations including cost, the sophistication of available electronics expertise and equipment, and the types of samples which will be investigated (e.g. for thick films, greater mass sensitivity may not be as important as the ability of the crystal/oscillator system to continue operation under large mass loading). Our research group has opted for the use of 5 MHz crystals operated in the fundamental mode as a compromise between the need for good mass sensitivity and ease of use.

In electrochemical applications of the QCM, the electrodes that are used to apply the alternating electric field that induces the oscillation are usually vapor deposited onto the two faces of the disk in such a way that the area defined by the center of the disk is the only region of the crystal which is sandwiched between the electrodes [see Fig. 2]. In this way, the shear motion is confined to the center of the disk so that the structures used to mount the crystal to the electrochemical cell do not unduly influence the resonant frequency of the device. These electrodes may be composed of virtually any type of metal or other good conductor. In nearly all of our investigations, gold electrodes have been used, because gold is easily deposited by thermal vacuum deposition methods, and it is a well characterized, widely used noble metal electrode with a wide potential window for electrochemical experiments. A thin layer of Cr or Si (ca. 10-50 Å) is used to promote adhesion between the gold electrode and the underlying quartz substrate. Use of excessive amounts of these adhesion promoters produces spurious electrochemical results due to their diffusion through the gold to the electrode surface. On the other hand, use of less than the necessary amount of these materials can result in poor adhesion of the electrodes to the quartz surface. This is disastrous because of the consequent instability in the oscillation frequency due to the delamination of the electrode. Thus, one must take special care that the electrodes have good adhesion, especially when monolayer or submonolayer mass changes are to be observed.

As is always true for precise correlation of electrochemical charges with surface populations, one must be cognizant of the influence of surface roughness on the measurement. The charge for the formation and removal of a monolayer of Au oxide provides a convenient measure of this [19]. Also, since electrochemistry can occur both on the circular disk and the rectangular strip that extends to the edge of the quartz crystal, account must be taken of the difference between the piezoelectrically and electrochemically active areas of the deposited Au layer [23,24].

The QCM crystals may be mounted in the electrochemical cell in a variety of ways. Use of adhesives to attach the crystal to an appropriately sized hole in the cell has been reported [20]. Another option is to construct electrochemical cells having glass o-ring vacuum joints to mount the crystals. In this case the QCM crystal is sandwiched between two o-rings in the joint. This provides an easy method of exposing only one of the QCM electrodes to the solution (which is usually the desired procedure) and also allows for simple replacement of the crystal. Cells may also be fabricated of Teflon, polypropylene, Kel-F, or other polymeric materials in which o-ring mountings may be machined.

A schematic of an EQCM instrument is shown in Figure 3. This schematic shows that one of the two QCM electrodes is simultaneously used to provide the alternating electric field that excites the device into mechanical resonance and as the working electrode in the electrochemical experiment. In the configuration used by us, the QCM working electrode is at true ground (as opposed to the virtual ground at the summing junction of an operational amplifier) in both the potentiostat

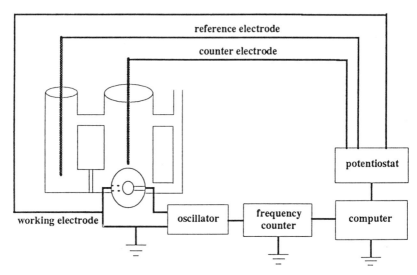

Figure 3. Schematic of the EQCM apparatus.

and the oscillator circuit [22]. Other designs have also been used [20]. The oscillator circuit [22] is a broadband oscillator that seeks to operate at the resonant frequency of the crystal. Thus, the oscillator tracks the resonant frequency of the QCM during the electrochemically induced mass changes. This frequency is measured with a commercial frequency counter that is connected either to an analog recorder or a computer capable of reading the signal type provided by the frequency counter (e.g., analog, RS-232, BCD, IEEE-488, etc.). Computerization of the instrument, while not absolutely necessary, provides several advantages over conventional methods, including facile control of the electrochemical waveform, the ability to signal average, and access to a wide variety of powerful data manipulation procedures.

The oscillator circuit used in our labs has been described [22]. Construction of this circuit requires careful attention to placement of the components and ground planes. A schematic of the circuit board is available from the author on request. The circuit may be powered using either a power supply or batteries, with the latter generally causing less noise, but not being suitable for measurements of long term frequency changes due to drift in the output voltage of the batteries and consequent drift in the oscillation frequency of the QCM. Any frequency counter with some sort of output signal for the frequency may be used. Typically, both analog and IEEE-488 interfaces are available. The speed of the frequency measurement is a function of the accuracy with which the measurement is to be known and is generally not a negligible quantity. In many commercial frequency counters, resolution of 1 Hz in the measurement of a frequency of 5 MHz requires a 1 second measurement time. Increasing the resolution by a factor of 10 causes a corresponding increase in the measurement time by a factor of 10, and vice versa. We use a Philips PM 6654 series frequency counter, which uses a clever phase matching technique that allows for more rapid frequency measurements than the traditional approaches. For example, a frequency of 5 MHz can be measured with a resolution of 1 Hz in just 6 milliseconds with this counter.

The potentiostat is of the Wenking style [22]. A data acquisition and control board (Data Translation 2801-A) provides the interface to an IBM PC, IBM AT, or 80386 based PC. Analog ramp generators are used for cyclic voltammetric and other electrochemical experiments requiring true analog ramps. As is nearly always the case when several instruments are interconnected, grounding presents a problem in the EQCM. The typical problems and their solutions are well discussed in the book by Morrison [31]. Shielding is of the utmost importance for noise-free operation of the QCM. This is because the usual frequencies of oscillation are the same as those of short-wave radio transmitters. Placement of the entire instrument inside a Faraday cage may, in some cases, be necessary, although placing the oscillator board inside a metal box will usually reduce the noise to acceptable levels.

B. Procedures

Crystals may be used repeatedly if facilities for deposition of the electrodes are available. Proper cleaning of the crystals and use of highly pure materials will ensure the best reproducibility, especially in investigations of adsorption/desorption processes and other surface phenomena. The usual methods for cleaning glass parts may be used for cleaning the crystals, with the exception of basic solutions containing alcoholic solvents, which will cause etching. Electrical connection to the QCM electrodes may be made using conducting paint.

The vacuum o-ring joint allows the crystal to be mounted to

the electrochemical cell in such a way that one of the crystal electrodes may be kept outside of the solution. This must be done for two reasons. The first is that immersion of the second electrode usually causes loss of oscillation due to capacitive shunting of the two electrodes through the solution [20]. With some oscillator circuits, however, oscillation may be maintained in this condition [13]. In this case, a second problem arises due to the potential difference between the two crystal electrodes (which must be present to induce oscillation), which causes spurious, uncontrolled electrochemical processes to occur. These will generally cause mass changes for at least one of the QCM electrodes, due to deposition, dissolution, or formation of gas bubbles on the electrode surface. Gas bubbles cause very large, erratic frequency changes due to the change in the viscous loading of the crystal from the solution.

Temperature control is absolutely necessary for certain types of experiments with the QCM. The temperature dependence of the oscillation frequency of QCM's has been discussed [1]. In fact, crystals may be cut specifically to give large or small temperature coefficients at specific temperatures. For AT-cut crystals the temperature dependence of the oscillation frequency near room temperature is weak, being usually less than one part per million (i.e., 5 Hz per degree for a 5 MHz crystal). However, as will be discussed below, the density and viscosity of the solution influence the QCM resonant frequency. Thus, since these quantities change as functions of temperature, so does the QCM oscillation frequency when it is immersed in a liquid. We have measured this effect [32] and find temperature coefficients of between 15 and 50 Hz per degree. The poor reproducibility is undoubtedly due to stress from the mounting, which changes uncontrollably with temperature. Therefore, measurement of long term frequency changes requires control of the temperature to at least 0.1 degree. Fortunately, many different commercial temperature controllers are available that allow for control to within 0.01 degree. Temperature control is generally not required for measurement of short term frequency changes, such as those, that occur on the time scale of a typical cyclic voltammetric (CV) experiment. In this type of EQCM experiment, one is generally concerned only with the changes in the resonant frequency that occur during the scan, not with the absolute value of the resonant frequency.

In the measurement of very small frequency changes due to surface processes at electrodes, it is usually necessary to use

signal averaging techniques.   When the experiment is
performed under computer control, it is necessary that the event
may be reproducibly initiated and data captured at the same
times relative to the initiation event.   Simple averaging then
provides for elimination of much of the noise in the experiment.
Another useful procedure for noise reduction is Fourier
filtering. However, care must be taken in applying such
methods because of the possibility of data corruption. The noise
levels which prevail in our instrument (after proper attention to
grounding) are on the order of 0.05 Hz for the short term noise
for the average of ten CV/EQCM scans at a scan rate of 50
mV/s. For reference, a monolayer of Pb atoms has a mass of ca.
0.33 $\mu g/cm^2$, which will give a frequency change of ca. 19 Hz
[22].   Thus, submonolayer mass measurements are easily
accessible with the EQCM.

III.   FREQUENCY-MASS CORRELATIONS AND THE INFLUENCE OF THE DEPOSIT PROPERTIES ON THE MEASURED FREQUENCY CHANGE

It has been stated above that mass changes at electrode surfaces
may be obtained from the change in the resonant frequency of
the EQCM that occurs during the electrochemical process.
However, several conditions must prevail to allow for the
quantitative correlation of frequency changes with mass
changes.   In addition, the considerations that relate to this
quantitative comparison are much more stringent for thick films
on electrodes than for monolayer adsorbates, due to the
increased possibility of influence by the viscoelastic properties
of the deposit on the resonant frequency of the EQCM.   We
first consider the relationship between frequency and mass for
the simple case of a thin, rigid (i.e., perfectly elastic) film,
which does not attenuate the acoustic shear wave (i.e., having a
viscosity effectively equal to zero).
   The first quantitative treatment that gave the relationship
between mass changes and frequency changes was by
Sauerbrey [33], whose pioneering work eventually lead to the
following equations:

$$\Delta f = -f_o^2\, m\, /\, N\, \rho = -2f_o^2\, m\, /\, n\, (\rho\, \mu)^{1/2} \qquad , \qquad (1)$$

in which Δf is the frequency change induced by the gain or loss of mass; f_o is the resonant frequency of the QCM composite resonator prior to the addition or removal of mass (in units of Hz); m is the mass per unit area of the deposit (in units of g cm^{-2}); N is the frequency constant of the quartz crystal used (N=0.167 x 10^6 Hz cm for 5 MHz AT-cut quartz); n is the harmonic number of the oscillation; ρ is the density of quartz (ρ = 2.648 g cm^{-3}); and μ is the shear modulus of quartz (μ = 2.947 x 10^{11} g cm^{-1} s^{-2}). The frequency constant for the quartz crystals, N, is thus seen to contain information about the materials properties of the quartz (i.e., its shear modulus). The negative sign in the equation indicates that <u>addition</u> of mass to the resonator results in a <u>decrease</u> in its resonant frequency and vice versa. This equation is perhaps more frequently written as

$$\Delta f = -C_f m \quad , \tag{2}$$

in which C_f is a constant containing all of the above material properties and the resonant frequency of the QCM resonator prior to the mass change. For a 5 MHz crystal such as those used in our labs, the value of C_f is 56.6 Hz cm^2 μg^{-1}. Thus, for a mass change of one μg deposited uniformly over an area of one cm^2, the corresponding frequency change that would be measured would be -56.6 Hz. For our crystals, the piezoelectrically active area which is sandwiched between the two gold electrodes is 0.28 cm^2, so that a mass change of 0.28 μg distributed uniformly over this area would cause a frequency change of -56.6 Hz. This points to the fact that it is the areal density of the deposit, not its absolute mass, that determines the magnitude of Δf.

For very small mass loadings (i.e., less than 2% change in the resonant frequency due to the mass change) this linear relationship very accurately describes the frequency change which occurs when mass is deposited or removed. When larger changes occur, the situation becomes considerably more complicated, because the above equation is implicitly based on the assumption that all of the mass is present at the antinode of the standing wave, so that the deposited mass does not experience any shear deformation. In this case, the properties of the deposit are not important in the determination of m from Δf. This situation will be referred to as the thin film limit. When this is not the case (i.e., when the deposit is thick enough to experience shear deformation), then the properties of the deposit do become of importance for the determination of m from Δf. This effect was first quantitated by Miller and Bolef

[34] and later simplified by Lu and Lewis [35] for the case of a material in which no loss occurs (i.e., the viscosity is identically zero). This treatment explicitly accounts for the difference between the acoustic impedances of the quartz substrate and the deposited mass, where the acoustic impedance of a material, $Z=(\rho \mu)^{1/2}=\rho v$, where ρ is the density, μ is the shear modulus, and v is the speed of sound in the material. This so called Z-match treatment provides for a better measure of the true mass change for frequency changes of up to 40 % of the original resonant frequency [36]. Its use requires a knowledge of μ_f and ρ_f for the deposited material, quantities that may be known for metallic deposits, but will frequently be unknown for other electrochemically generated films. The equation in the form derived by Lu and Lewis is shown below:

$$\tan (\pi f_c / f_o) = - (\rho_f v_f / \rho_q v_q) \tan (\pi f_c / f_f) , \qquad (3)$$

where f_c is the resonant frequency of the composite resonator formed by the quartz crystal and the deposited film; f_o is the resonant frequency of the QCM prior to the deposition (i.e., $\Delta f = f_c - f_o$); and $f_f = v_f / 2 t_f = \mu_f^{1/2} / 2 t_f \rho_f^{1/2}$ is a quantity that can be thought of as the resonant frequency that the free standing deposited film would have. Here v_f is the velocity of the acoustic wave in the deposit, and t_f is its thickness. For deposits having large thicknesses or acoustic impedances very different from that of the quartz crystal, this Z-match approach provides a much more accurate measure of the deposit thickness. However, in the thin film limit, this equation approaches the Sauerbrey equation given above.

The use of the Z-match approach is usually unnecessary when studying the deposition of nonpolymeric deposits such as metals or metal oxides (i.e., materials with very large shear moduli), because the deposit thickness must be very large before these considerations come into play. For example, if a 5 MHz crystal were used to measure Cu deposition, then the deposit would have to cause a frequency change on the order of 1 MHz (i.e., $f_c = 4$ MHz) for the thickness calculated from the Sauerbrey equation to be in error by 10%. This would be a deposit approximately 20 μm thick. However, due to the load on the oscillator circuitry caused by the large losses in the solution, it is difficult to operate with such thick deposits.

The situation becomes essentially intractable for deposition of multiple films onto a given QCM when these films are thick enough to diverge from the thin film limit. Thus, in electrochemical studies in which films are deposited onto an underlying electrode (usually gold in our case), it is best to remain within the thin film region by keeping the total frequency change to less than 2 % of the original resonant frequency. These considerations also indicate that the use of thin films for the QCM electrodes is most desirable, so that the entire thickness of this electrode is at the antinode of the shear wave.

The treatments described above do not take into account the possibility of viscous loss within the deposited film. This is perfectly acceptable for deposition of metals or crystalline or polycrystalline inorganic materials, which, in general, have very small viscosities and relatively large shear moduli. However, for the case of organic polymer films, it is certainly possible that significant amounts of viscous loss can occur within the film, especially under conditions of extensive solvent swelling [2]. This loss occurs because shear waves cannot be sustained in viscous media and are therefore attenuated as they travel through such a material. This phenomenon has been used to advantage by polymer chemists for many years to study the viscoelastic properties of polymer solutions, an area that is exhaustively and elegantly treated in the classic text by Ferry [2].

In addition to the influence of the film properties on the resonant frequency of the QCM, the shear wave damping that occurs in the solution itself causes large changes in resonant frequency when the QCM is transferred from air into the solution. This effect has been quantitatively investigated by Kanazawa and coworkers [37a] who arrived at the following relation for the frequency change induced by the transfer:

$$\Delta f = -f_o^{3/2} (\eta_s \rho_s / \pi \mu_q \rho_q)^{1/2} , \qquad (4)$$

in which η_s is the solution viscosity and ρ_s is the density of the solution. This equation shows that the frequency change induced by immersion in a solution is related to the density (i.e., the effective mass of the solution that is being moved along with the QCM surface) and the viscosity (a measure of loss of the shear wave amplitude by momentum transfer to the solution). Similar arguments apply to the case of viscous films on the QCM. Note that this equation does not apply to the general case of deposition of a viscoelastic film, in which case both the shear modulus and the viscosity of the film need to be taken into account. Kanazawa has recently described the general case for such films [37b]. This treatment is an elegant, physically based approach, which allows one to calculate the frequency shift for deposition of a film (Δf) given values for η_f, μ_f, t_f (the film thickness), η_s, and ρ_s. Kanazawa's master equation connects these six parameters, so that a knowledge of any five allows one to calculate the sixth. Unfortunately, there are usually several unknown quantities in such a situation, these being η_f, μ_f, and d_f, with Δf as the experimentally observed quantity.

The properties of many, but not all, deposits of interest to the electrochemical community are such that the Sauerbrey equation may be used. Thus, for metallic deposits or oxide film growth, for example, one generally expects that Equation (1) will hold, due to the large shear moduli and small viscosities of such materials. Of course, other considerations (such as, deposit roughness, porosity, etc.) can also complicate the interpretation of the frequency change. Some of these will be discussed below. For polymeric films, it is especially important to consider the possibility of shear wave attenuation within the film, and, therefore, deviation from the thin film limit. This is due to the generally lower values for μ and larger values for η observed for such materials [2]. These values are known to be frequency dependent, with μ increasing and η decreasing with increasing frequency, a tendency that leads towards rigid film behavior. However, the absolute values of μ and η depend very much on factors such as the extent of swelling and the glass transition temperature. Thus, it is best to employ some skepticism as to the applicability of Equation (2) to such systems until some experimental evidence in support of its validity is obtained.

Several approaches to the verification of rigid film behavior are possible, with the most desirable often determined by the available equipment and the type of process being studied. Perhaps the simplest method when studying depositions is to verify that when the deposit thickness is increased, the frequency change due to deposition increases in a corresponding manner. Thus, if the deposit is redox active or can be electrochemically stripped off in a control experiment, then one can determine the relationship between the electrochemical charge and Δf. This approach has been used in a study of the redox properties of poly(aniline) films using the EQCM [23]. Similarly, if deposit thickness may be independently determined, then it can be ascertained whether or not this quantity is proportional to Δf. Although such information does not provide completely unambiguous evidence of rigid film behavior, due to the possibility of compensating effects, it is certainly a useful additional piece of evidence to take into consideration.

Another possible method for verifying that the viscoelastic properties of the deposit do not influence the oscillation frequency of the QCM is to measure the impedance (or conductance) spectrum of the crystal before and after the deposition. It has been shown that the width of the resonant peak in the conductance spectrum of the composite resonator is related to the viscous loss due to materials present at the crystal surface [38]. If this width changes significantly during the deposition (aside from the broadening due to the attenuation of the shear wave by the solution), then the deposit is undoubtedly contributing to shear wave attenuation with corresponding frequency changes not due directly to mass changes. This approach to verification of thin film behavior has been used only once [23], but it should become more widespread due to the sensitivity of the width of the conductance peak to such viscous losses and the ability to very accurately measure this quantity with a network or impedance analyzer.

Another consideration relating to the quantitative correlation of frequency with mass measurements is the uniformity of the deposit. It is well known that the mass sensitivity of the QCM is not constant across the face of the QCM disk. Rather, the mass sensitivity is given by an apparently Gaussian function with a maximum at the center of the disk shaped QCM electrode and a minimum near to its edge [39,40]. The cause for this situation is schematically shown in Figure 4, in which the velocity vectors are shown for that time during the oscillation at which the velocity of the surface of the crystal is at its maximum. The center of the crystal is seen to be moving more than the region near to the electrode edges. For plano-convex, crystals (i.e., having one face planar and the other very slightly convex) the sensitivity falls to essentially zero at the edge of the QCM electrode [39], whereas for crystals having both faces planar, the sensitivity does not fall to zero until nearly a millimeter radially away from the edge of the QCM electrode [39,40]. The details of the radial mass sensitivity also depend on the geometry of the QCM electrodes [39]. The value of C_f quoted above for use in the Sauerbrey equation is for a planar crystal with disks of equal size. The value which will prevail for other configurations depends on the details of their

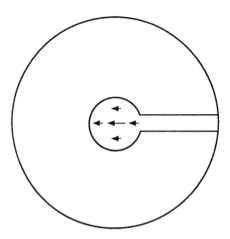

Figure 4. Top view of a QCM disk. The arrows represent the relative sizes of the velocity vectors for different regions of the gold electrode pad at the instant of maximum velocity of the surface.

geometries. The important point to note is that for the use of such equations, one requires assurance that the deposit is uniformly distributed across the face of the QCM electrode. For cast or spin-coated polymeric films or for vacuum deposited films this will generally not be a problem, but for electrochemically deposited films, one must take into consideration edge effects in the current density distribution across the QCM electrode.

Finally, electrode roughness has been shown to greatly influence the oscillation frequency of the QCM in solution [41-44]. This occurs due to trapping of solution within the dips and depressions of the surface and its consequent measurement as "attached" mass. This effect must be taken into account whenever the electrochemical process being investigated can cause a change in the surface roughness.

IV. SELECTED EXAMPLES OF THE APPLICATION OF THE EQCM TO ELECTROCHEMICAL SYSTEMS

A. Underpotential Deposits

Bruckenstein and Swathirajan were the first to apply the QCM to the measurement of masses of underpotential deposits [18], providing direct mass measurements of Ag and Pb UPD monolayers on Au electrodes. As pointed out above, these were not in situ experiments. Rather, the UPD monolayers were deposited on the QCM crystal, which was subsequently removed from the solution, washed, dried, and subjected to a measurement of its resonant frequency. This frequency was used with the Sauerbrey equation to determine the mass of the UPD layer. They found fairly close agreement between the coverages determined by rotating ring-disk (Ag), rotating disk (Pb), and the QCM methods. Possible sources of error in the QCM measurement were identified to be (a) adsorption and/or desorption of impurities from the solution; (b) presence of solvent on the surface during the frequency measurement (i.e., not removed during the drying step); and (c) experimental artifacts related to the method of connection to the crystal electrodes [18].

The first in situ use of the EQCM to measure monolayer UPD deposits was by the IBM group [22]. This study reported the application of the technique to Pb UPD deposits on Au electrodes. The electrosorption valency γ was obtained in this case. In agreement with previous results obtained by a variety of methods, a value of 2.0 was found. This study importantly demonstrated the in situ capabilities of the EQCM for measurement of monolayer mass changes. It is worth pointing out that these data were obtained without the benefit of signal averaging, implying that monolayer mass changes from single events may be measured.

Continuing on the study of UPD processes with the EQCM, Deakin and Melroy [45] reported on a detailed study of the values of γ for several metals, these being Pb, Bi, Cu, and Cd, on Au electrodes. They presented a simple way to obtain γ from the slope of the plot of mass versus electrochemical charge. This slope may be interpreted as the mass deposited per electron and is given by $M/F\gamma$, where M is the molar mass of the UPD ion and F is the Faraday. The slope of such a plot thus provides a sensitive measure of γ at any potential. These authors found that for the case of Pb on Au, γ deviated significantly from 2 at the current peaks in the UPD process. This was attributed either to changes in γ or variations in the charging current due to shifts in the potential of zero charge on the UPD adlayer with respect to that on bare Au.

For the case of Bi on Au, there were dramatic deviations of γ from the expected value of 3. The UPD of Bi on polycrystalline Au shows three major current peaks at ca. 0.3, 0.2, and 0.15 V versus SSCE. The value of γ for the first two peaks was found to be 2.7. Additional charge was passed at the third peak, but only a very slight mass <u>loss</u> was observed there. The most likely interpretation of this is that the third UPD peak is caused by the further reduction of the Bi adsorbate layer, to give the value expected for completely discharged Bi (i.e., from 2.7 to 3.0). The slight mass loss may be due to desorption of weakly adsorbed anions as a consequence of this discharge.

The last two systems studied by these authors were Cu and Cd on Au. In the case of Cu, the value of γ was found to be 1.4 during stripping of the UPD layer at a potential of 0.25 V versus SSCE. This is in agreement with work done in other groups, albeit in different electrolyte systems [46]. The results for Cd on Au were not very conclusive, due to passage of additional Faradaic currents from proton reduction in the acidic media used for the UPD experiments and due to formation of a Cd/Au alloy. However, the authors provided an estimate of γ for Cd on Au of between 1.6 and 2.0.

Deakin, Li, and Melroy also recently published on a study of the mass changes that occurred during adsorption of iodide and bromide ions on Au electrodes [47]. Although this is not strictly a UPD system, the results did indicate that γ can also be obtained for such systems. Values of γ of 1.0 and 0.4 were found for iodide and bromide adsorption, respectively. An important point to be made from this study is that electrolyte adsorption can produce significant responses in the EQCM frequency changes. Thus, such adsorption processes must always be considered in the interpretation of mass changes for other monolayer processes. Another notable finding of this study is that through the use of signal averaging, it is possible to observe mass changes of less than 20 ng cm^{-2}.

These studies have demonstrated that the EQCM may be successfully used for monolayer mass measurements. A number of considerations implicit to the interpretations of these data relate to the precise conditions that prevail at the surface of the EQCM. For example, questions which have yet to be addressed in sufficient detail to allow for generalizations to be made are: How many layers of solvent are rigidly "attached" to the electrode surface? To what extent does this change when the electrode surface is altered, as it is in the adsorption of a UPD or other adlayer? When a surface is charged, to what extent do the counterionic charges present in the solution near the surface influence the resonant frequency of the EQCM? The further application of the EQCM method to monolayer systems will undoubtedly bring more attention to such questions.

B. Mass Transport During Redox Processes in Polymer Films on Electrodes

A number of groups have contributed to this area of research. These investigations have been driven by the need to understand how ion and solvent transport relate to the kinetics and thermodynamics of charge propagation in such films and how these processes are associated with the unique waveshapes frequently observed for such films. In addition, it is possible to use the EQCM to measure important quantities relating to film deposition and dissolution, such as current efficiency and growth kinetics.

The primary events that occur in the redox cycling of films of this type are ion transport and solvent transport. The movement of ionic species is driven by the requirement to maintain electroneutrality within the bulk of the film. The considerations which can be used to understand such processes are the same as those applied to the behavior of ion exchangers, an area with a large literature of its own. The excellent book by Helfferich presents a most lucid account of these [48]. Solvent transport is a consequence of the difference in the thermodynamic activity of the solvent inside and outside of the film. The large changes in charge density in these films (i.e., the creation or elimination of charged sites) by redox processes should, in general, cause dramatic changes in solvent activity, leading to the expectation of relatively large fluxes of solvent, the direction of which depends on the details of the system under study. A recent account of a useful theoretical framework for describing the phenomena of ion and solvent transport during redox processes in thin polymer films on electrodes has been presented by Bruckenstein and Hillman [49]. The ability of the EQCM to monitor the mass changes that accompany the redox processes in these types of films makes it an ideal tool for investigating the extent to which ion and solvent transport influence their electrochemical behavior. The application of the EQCM to several such systems will be described below, but first it will be fruitful to examine the general considerations relating to correlation of mass and electron fluxes in such systems.

In the thin film limit, in which the EQCM senses only mass changes and not changes in the material properties of the thin films, the total frequency change that can occur during the oxidation or reduction of the film (Δf_t) is given by the following simple equation:

$$\Delta f_t = \Delta f_c + \Delta f_a + \Delta f_s \quad , \tag{5}$$

where Δf_c is the frequency change caused by the transport of cationic species; Δf_a is that caused by transport of anionic species; and Δf_s is that caused by transport of solvent. In general, none of these need be equal to zero, but cases may be found in which some of them are. The connection between the electrochemical charge and the EQCM frequency change is given by the following equation:

$$Q = (10^{-6} F C_f^{-1}) \, \Delta f_t \, MW^{-1} \quad , \tag{6}$$

where the first three terms provide for the proper unit conversions between charge and mass, F is the Faraday constant, and MW is the effective mass of the species undergoing transport. This equation is best used to calculate MW from Q and Δf_t (the two experimental observables) by rearrangement. Then, MW is used to provide insight into the identities of the species that undergo transport during the redox event. Consider the oxidation of a vinyl polymer containing initially neutral, pendent redox groups that can be reversibly oxidized to a cationic state. (The poly(vinylferrocene) (PVF) system is a good example [24]). For such a system, the simplest possible case would involve the oxidation of the pendent redox groups with no transport of cations (i.e., $\Delta f_c = 0$) or of solvent (i.e., $\Delta f_s = 0$). In this case, the entire frequency change would be attributable to the insertion of anionic species required to effect charge compensation within the cationic film created during oxidation. Thus, MW will be exactly equal to the molar mass of the anion of the supporting electrolyte. Significant disagreement between MW and this molar mass is a sure indication that Δf_c and/or Δf_s are not equal to zero. For example, if MW were less than the molar mass of the anion, this might indicate that some compensating transport process occurs during the oxidation so that while anion insertion occurs to increase the total mass of the film, so does this other process occur to decrease the total mass of the film. Examples of candidate processes are the loss of solvent from the film during oxidation and the loss of cationic species from the film during oxidation. Thus, the least ambiguous results are obtained for those cases in which ion transport is unidirectional (i.e., the transport number (t) of one of the ionic species is very near to 1).

The next case to consider is that in which the transport number for one of the ionic species is near to 1, but solvent transport also occurs. For simplicity, consider the case in which t for the anion is near to one (i.e., $t_a = 1$ and therefore $t_c = 0$). In this case, MW may be higher than that value predicted from the molar mass of the anion if solvent transport occurs in the same direction (i.e., solvent accompanies the anions as they enter and leave the film). On the other hand, if MW is lower than the predicted value, this is probably due to opposing directions of transport for the anions and solvent. For this case, in the absence of definitive proof that $t_c = 0$, it is difficult to say anything quantitative about the results. However, if the contribution from the solvent transport is large enough, then it is sometimes possible to use the different masses of isotopically substituted solvents to deconvolute the contributions to Δf_t made by the ionic species and the solvent. Here one is relying on the possibility of changing Δf_s by some amount which is predictable from the known masses of the two isotopic forms of the solvent. For example, in aqueous solutions, substitution of D_2O for H_2O should lead to an increase in Δf_s by exactly 10% due to the 10% larger mass of D_2O with respect to H_2O.

The last case to be considered is the most complicated, in that contributions to Δf_t arise from all of the possible sources. The transport numbers of the ionic species are all less than 1 here, so that the fractional contributions to charge compensation are not known with certainty a priori. This situation usually arises when the exclusion of the co-ion from the interior of the film (for example, exclusion of the cations from the supporting electrolyte from the interior of a PVF film in the ferricenium state) by Donnan exclusion [51] breaks down, usually due to very high concentrations of supporting electrolyte, highly swollen films, or films with very small charge densities. When Donnan exclusion breaks down, the possibility of sorption (i.e., the incorporation of neutral pairs of cations and anions from the supporting electrolyte [50]) needs to be considered. Sorption has the effect of removing the direct connection between the electrochemical charge and the number of ionic species that enter or leave the film because neutral pairs of cations and anions can enter or leave the film with no corresponding reduction or oxidation process. When mass changes occur that are not coupled to the injection or removal of electrons from the film, then one cannot take advantage of the equations presented above, which relate Δf_t to Q, so the possibility of quantitative analysis of the data is greatly diminished. A way out of this situation is to vary the identity of one of the ionic species in the supporting electrolyte, such as changing from $HClO_4$ to HBF_4, so that the contribution to Δf_t from Δf_a changes by an amount which might be predictable from the molar masses of the two different anions. This approach, however, is fraught with difficulties because the behavior of polyelectrolyte systems is extremely sensitive to the nature of the counterionic species that are present, so that even small changes in ionic radius or solvation can have a profound influence on such properties as solvent swelling, counterion binding, and so forth. Thus, this third case of what might be called mixed transport is virtually intractable in the quantitative sense and will not be considered further.

The application of the EQCM to the study of solvent and ion transport in thin redox polymer films is best demonstrated by describing its use on a particular system. As an example, we describe some very recent EQCM studies from our group of a polymer film containing viologen redox groups incorporated as part of the backbone of the polymer chains. As shown in Figure 5, the redox chemistry of these moieties is relatively straightforward. They can be reduced reversibly in two discrete,

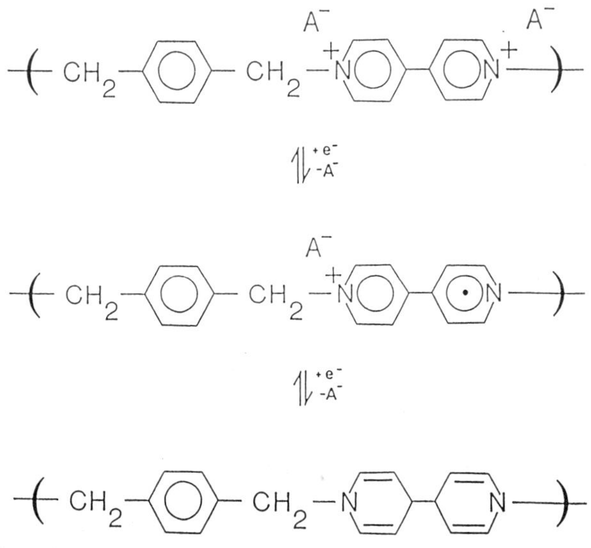

Figure 5. The redox states of poly(xylylviologen).

one electron steps, first to a cation radical state, then to the
neutral, doubly reduced state. The requirements for the
maintenance of charge neutrality within the film change
considerably during these redox events. The fully oxidized
form requires two anions per monomer unit, the cation radical
requires one anion per unit, and the fully reduced form requires
none. When the electrochemistry is carried out in aqueous
solutions, the films are stable if the anion of the supporting
electrolyte is ClO_4^-, BF_4^-, or PF_6^-. When one of these anions is
not present in the solution, the films rapidly dissolve, resulting
in reduction of the electrochemical response of the viologen
centers.

Figure 6A shows the voltammetry of a film of poly(xylyl-

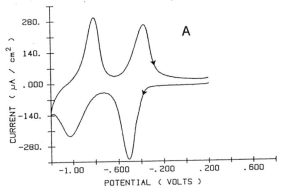

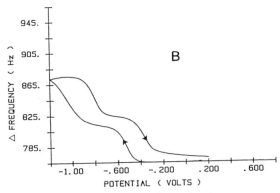

Figure 6. (A) The CV of poly(xylylviologen) showing the two waves for the two
redox couples of the polymer. (B) EQCM curves showing the frequency changes
observed during the redox events in (A). The scan rate is 50 mV s^{-1}. Supporting
electrolyte is 0.3 M NaClO$_4$.

viologen) (PXV) in an aqueous solution of $NaClO_4$. Figure 6B shows the EQCM frequency change observed during this scan. The salient feature of the curves is that the frequency increases during the reduction processes of both waves and decreases during the subsequent oxidations. The increase in frequency indicates that mass is lost during the reduction and regained during the oxidation. This is most likely due to anion expulsion during reduction and their recapture during oxidation. In this case, the anion is ClO_4^-. Comparison of Δf_t with the cathodic charge passed under the first reductive wave reveals that *MW* is 140 g mol^{-1}, larger than the molar mass of ClO_4^- which is 99.5 g mol^{-1}. The response is virtually identical when cations other than Na^+ are used as supporting electrolyte, strongly suggesting that the response is dominated by anion transport. The values of Δf_t for films with different thicknesses (measured in the dry state by ellipsometry) scale linearly with the film thickness, a good indication that equation 1 is applicable to this system. That the value of *MW* is larger than the molar mass of ClO_4^- indicates that some amount of solvent is transported out of the film during the expulsion of the anions. The data suggest a molar ratio of expelled anions to expelled water molecules of roughly 1 to 2, respectively.

A particularly useful way in which to present the data from such an experiment derives from a consideration of the detailed relationship between the mass and electrochemical parameters. Recall that the current *i* is a measure of the instantaneous flux of electrons at the electrode surface, and that its integral with respect to time (or potential during a voltammetric experiment performed at a constant scan rate), the charge *Q* is a measure of the total number of electrons that has been consumed or produced by the redox process. On the other hand, the frequency change during such a scan is also a measure of this same total number of electrons to the extent that there is a direct connection between the mass change and the charge. Thus, a plot of frequency versus charge provides a way to gauge this connection. The slope of this plot may be interpreted to be the effective mass change per electron passed, which may not necessarily be constant throughout the scan. Figure 7 shows such a plot for the data in Figure 6. It is worth noting in this context that computerization of the experiment greatly aids in these types of data manipulations. This type of data treatment was first discussed by Deakin and Melroy [45].

The gross features of the plot in Figure 7 suggest that there is an essentially linear relationship between mass and charge

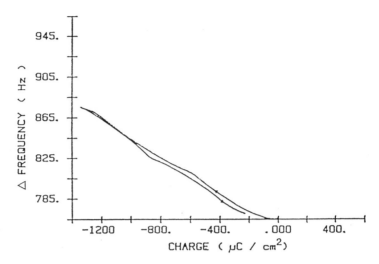

Figure 7. A plot of Δ*f* versus *Q* for the data in Figure 6.

for this experiment. The slope, obtained by a linear-least-squares regression of the data for the first reduction wave, gives a mass per electron (i.e., *MW*) of 140 g mol^{-1} for the first reduction. Note that this result is no different than the treatment described in Equation (6), although this method should be much more accurate and also allows one to obtain *MW* from *df/dQ* as a function of *Q*. There are more subtle features in the plot, such as inflection points between the waves and at the beginning and end of the scan, but these are likely due to residual charge from double layer and background processes, which were not subtracted from the observed *Q* before plotting. Substitution of PF$_6^-$ for ClO$_4^-$ in the supporting electrolyte changes *MW* to a value of 165 g mol^{-1}, independent of the identity of the cation. Thus, the effective mass of the migrating species increases, as expected for substitution of this heavier (molar mass = 145 g mol^{-1}) anion. Significant solvent transport is also indicated here, although the molar ratio of anions to water molecules is closer to 1 to 1, respectively. The transport of slightly less water for PF$_6^-$ than for ClO$_4^-$ seen here is quite similar to behavior for the poly(vinylferrocene) system previously studied by this method [24]). (It should be pointed out here that there is no need for the number of water molecules that accompanies the ionic species during the redox event to be an integral multiple of the number of ions [49].) Thus, this viologen system is characterized by charge compensation processes dominated by anion transport with small amounts of solvent.

At this point, we undertake to describe briefly the major results of some of the research that has been published for the application of the EQCM to redox processes in polymer films. In one of the earliest applications of the EQCM to mass changes in conducting polymer films, Kaufman, Kanazawa, and Street reported the determination of ion transport during redox cycling of the conducting polymer, poly(pyrrole) [21]. They found that the redox induced transition from the insulating state to the conducting state via oxidation of the material was accompanied by the insertion of the anionic species of the supporting electrolyte. On reduction to reattain the insulating state, the behavior depended strongly on the identity of the supporting electrolyte. For example, in LiClO$_4$ electrolyte this reduction was accompanied by *cation* insertion (rather than anion expulsion), to leave a film containing both the ClO$_4^-$ that had been originally inserted during oxidation as well as Li$^+$, a situation presumably caused by the relatively higher mobility of Li$^+$ than of ClO$_4^-$ in the films. When the tosylate anion was used for the supporting electrolyte, the oxidation (to the conducting state) and the reduction (to the insulating state) were accompanied by anion insertion and expulsion, respectively. No cation insertion on reduction was observed in this case. This is consistent with the argument that the effects in the ClO$_4^-$ case are due to highly specific ion pairing between the cationic sites of the oxidized polymer and the ClO$_4^-$. In this work, the quantitative comparison between the mass changes and the electrochemical charges was not made, so correlation of the numbers of ions undergoing transport with the numbers of electrons being delivered to or removed from the films was not considered in great detail.

Our research group at the University of Wyoming has published a number of accounts of the measurement of ion and solvent transport in polymer films using the EQCM. The first system to be studied was the redox polymer poly(vinylferro-cene) (PVF) [24], which can be reversibly oxidized to the ferricenium state and reduced back to the ferrocene state. Figure 8 shows the results of CV/EQCM experiments for a PVF film in 0.1 M KPF$_6$ and in 0.1 M NaClO$_4$ + 0.1 M HClO$_4$ [24]. In plate a, the CV (Curve A) and EQCM frequency data (Curve B) are shown for the experiment done in 0.1 M KPF$_6$. In the CV, an oxidation wave is observed at 0.48 V in the positive scan, and the corresponding reduction is observed at 0.23 V in the negative scan. These data are typical for PVF in this supporting electrolyte. Curve B shows that a marked mass gain

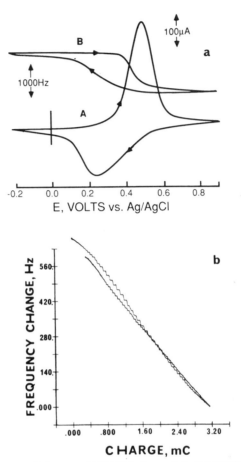

Figure 8. (a) (A) of PVF on a gold EQCM electrode in 0.1 M KPF$_6$. Scan rate = 10 mV s^{-1}. (B) Frequency curve obtained simultaneously with (A). (b) Plot of frequency versus charge for a scan from 0.0 to 0.6 V and back for a PVF film in 0.1 M NaClO$_4$ + 0.1 M HClO$_4$. The film was thinner than that in (a). Scan rate = 25mV s^{-1}

occurs concurrent with the anodic wave in the positive scan, whereas loss occurs during the corresponding cathodic wave in the negative scan. The total charge for oxidation of the film was 12.8×10^{-3} C cm^{-2}, which should result in a mass change of 1.92×10^{-5} g cm^{-2} if charge compensation is achieved solely by anion (PF$_6^-$) insertion during oxidation. Equation (2) predicts that a frequency change of 1093 Hz would be observed for such a case. The observed value was 1100 Hz, providing strong support for the interpretation suggested above. If each and every electron removed from the film during oxidation causes insertion of one anion (and vice versa), then there should be a one to one correspondence between the charge and mass change. The linearity of the plot of frequency change versus charge in plate b (obtained for a film in supporting electrolyte containing ClO_4^-) demonstrates this fact. The value of MW obtained from the slope of the plot using Equation (6) is ca. 2 % larger than predicted for transport of only ClO_4^-. It was suggested that this may be due to very small amounts of solvent incorporation for the ClO_4^- system in comparison to the PF_6^- system [24].

Dramatically different behavior has more recently been observed for other anions. For example, in solutions containing NO_3^-, the oxidation and subsequent anion insertion is accompanied by a significant amount of solvent transport into the film. It has proven possible with this system to take advantage of the different masses of D_2O and H_2O, as in the experiment described above, to verify the contribution of solvent transport to the net mass change of the film during redox in this medium [52]. A third class of behavior for PVF films is that previously reported for the case of Cl^- containing electrolytes [24] in which oxidation leads to delamination or dissolution of the film from the surface of the EQCM. As seen in Figure 9, the loss of material from the surface causes a dramatic increase in the resonant frequency of the EQCM, by an amount which closely corresponds to that expected for such a process (i.e., the predicted mass change for loss of all of the film is very near to the observed value). On the return (negative) scan, some of this material is redeposited onto the EQCM electrode surface with a functional dependence on time characteristic of diffusion processes (i.e. the mass regain is roughly linear with the square root of time). The multiple peaks in the CV of PVF under these conditions appear at the same potentials at which the loss and recapture of the polymer film occur, as judged by the positions of the abrupt frequency changes [24]. This type of behavior is seen for a wide range of anions (Cl^-, HSO_4^-, $H_2PO_4^-$, etc.) and follows trends that derive from the aqueous solubilities of salts of a variety of organic cationic species [52].

The mass changes due to ion and solvent transport during redox processes in the conducting polymer poly(aniline) were also studied by our group [23]. The experiment involves switching the polymer between its insulating and conducting states by oxidation or reduction and measuring the mass changes that are a consequence of this switching. The interest

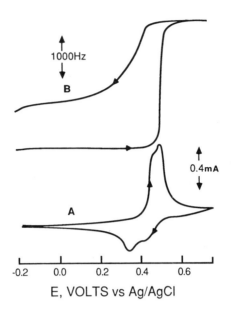

Figure 9. (A) CV of PVF on a gold EQCM electrode in 1.0 M NaCl. Scan rate = 50 mV s^{-1} (B) Frequency curve obtained simultaneously with (A).

in such systems is to ascertain whether the transport of ionic species or solvent limits in any way the overall rate of the switching process. Based on this information, it may be possible to design strategies that increase the switching rate by manipulating these transport processes. The fully reduced state of the polymer is its insulating state, and oxidation produces the conducting state (if the pH is not too high (i.e., not greater than 3)). In this system, the general finding was that during switching from the insulating to the conducting state, anion insertion is mostly responsible for maintaining electroneutrality within the film. However, proton expulsion was also found to make a significant contribution, especially in strongly acidic solutions (pH < 1). The extent of proton transport was found to be a function of the degree of protonation of the reduced form of the polymer. Thus, by measuring the transport numbers of the anion and the proton as a function of pH, it was possible to obtain the pK$_a$ for the reduced form of the polymer. In addition, it was found that conditions of low pH favored faster switching rates, indicating that when the transport number for H$^+$ is increased, so is the switching rate. As an extension of this work we have shown recently [53] that when poly(aniline) is electropolymerized within a polyanionic Nafion matrix, the counterions of the anionic fixed sites of the Nafion component provide a source of protons that may be rapidly expelled during the switching process. These composite films exhibit slightly faster switching rates than normal poly(aniline) films. Thus, the insight provided by the EQCM into how ion transport influences the switching rate has allowed for the development of strategies designed to enhance this property.

In a recent contribution from our laboratory, the extent of solvent transport during redox cycling of the Fe sites in thin films of nickel ferrocyanide (the nickel analog of Prussian blue) was determined [25]. This system has been thoroughly investigated by Bocarsly and coworkers [54], who have focused on the unique dependence of its redox potential on the size of the cation in the supporting electrolyte. This size dependence has been speculated to be due to the zeolitic nature of the nickel ferrocyanide lattice, with solvation effects suspected of playing a major role in the energetics of ion insertion and expulsion [55]. Thus, knowledge of the extent of solvent transport during redox cycling of the Fe sites in this material is of paramount importance to understanding the origin of its size selectivity.

The determination of the amount of solvent transport was accomplished by obtaining the different values of Δf_t when the experiment was done in D_2O as compared to H_2O, as described above. In this system, the lattice of the zeolitic material has a net negative charge, so that cations from the supporting electrolyte reside within the octahedral vacancies of the lattice to maintain charge, neutrality. Oxidation of the Fe sites from Fe(II) to Fe(III) leads to expulsion of one half of these cations and a consequent influx of water to fill the void volume left behind. Thus, Δf_t for oxidation is comprised of two contributions, Δf_c, which is positive (indicating mass loss), and Δf_s, which is negative (indicating mass gain). The contribution from Δf_s was shown to increase by exactly 10% upon substitution of D_2O for H_2O, as expected for such a situation. This measurement represents the first completely unambiguous determination of solvent transport during a redox process in a thin film on an electrode and demonstrates the potential power of the EQCM technique for such measurements.

These few examples have been selected to give an appreciation for the types of information that are available from the EQCM technique. It is especially significant that the correlation of mass changes in the deposit with various electrochemical parameters (such as switching rate, current efficiency, etc.) can provide guidance for the improvement of specific properties. Thus, while the information provided by the EQCM is not molecularly specific, as, for example, in vibrational spectroscopies, in favorable cases it does provide additional, _quantitative_, data to which any model of the experimental system must answer. It also provides a way to observe solvent transport directly, something which still eludes other methods.

V.   CONCLUSIONS

As is true of all instrumental techniques, the QCM has both desirable and undesirable attributes in terms of its application to electrochemical problems. Among the desirable attributes are its relative simplicity and moderate cost. A fully computerized system can be assembled for under $10,000, which is a very reasonable price for the ability to detect mass changes with monolayer sensitivity, especially with an in situ measurement. The linear relationship of the frequency change to the mass change makes the method simple and, therefore, attractive. That the mass sensitivity is solely determined by the physics of the device and does not require calibration, is an especially significant advantage of this method over others. The method suffers from the possible sensitivity of the measurement to the material properties of the deposit, especially for polymer films. Unfortunately, it is not always simple to determine when such effects are important. However, it should be possible to quantitatively model the composite resonator composed of the electrode, film, and solution, so that such effects may be dealt with in a satisfactory way. A significant disadvantage of the method, in comparison to other methods for determining interfacial populations, is a lack of molecular specificity (the only observable is the mass change). This entails the use of various "tricks" to deconvolute the contributions of the various species to the net mass change, such as using isotopically labeled solvents or ions and using series of supporting electrolytes with ions of different, but known, molar masses. Another undesirable attribute is the need to use thin film electrodes and the possibility of overloading the device, thereby causing a cessation of the oscillation. These factors mitigate against certain experimental configurations and the use of some types of electrode materials.

The use of QCM methods in electrochemical science has just begun in the past few years. It has already proven itself a powerful and extremely useful addition to the repertoire of techniques available to the modern electrochemist, both for the study of monolayer and submonolayer processes at solid electrodes and for monitoring mass changes from a variety of causes in thin films. The combination of ease of use and moderate cost should lead to its more widespread use in the electrochemical community.

A. Acknowledgments

We gratefully thank the Office of Naval Research for supporting our efforts in the application of the QCM to electrochemistry.

B. References

1. See, for example, *Applications of the Piezoelectric Quartz Crystal Microbalance. Methods and Phenomena.* Vol. 7 ed. C. Lu and A. Czanderna. New York: Elsevier, 1984.
2. See, for example, Ferry, J.D. *Viscoelastic Properties of Polymers.* New York: Wiley, 1961.
3. Alder, J.F., and McCallum, J.J. *Analyst* 108 (1983):1169.
4. Mieure, J.P., and Jones, J.L. *Talanta* 16 (1969):149.
5. Jones, J.L., and Mieure, J.P. *Anal. Chem.* 41 (1969):484.
6. Nomura, T., and Hattori, O. *Anal. Chim. Acta* 115 (1980):323.
7. Nomura, T. *Anal. Chim. Acta* 124 (1981):81.
8. Nomura, T., and Iijima, M. *Anal. Chim. Acta* 131 (1981):97.
9. Nomura, T., and Okuhara, M. *Anal. Chim. Acta* 142 (1982):281.
10. Nomura, T., and Mimatsu, T. *Anal. Chim. Acta* 143 (1982):237.
11. Nomura, T., and Maruyama, M. *Anal. Chim. Acta* 147 (1983):365.
12. Nomura, T., and Nagamune, T. *Anal. Chim. Acta* 155 (1983):231.
13. Nomura, T., and Tsuge, K. *Anal. Chim. Acta* 169 (1985):257.
14. Nomura, T., and Ando, M. *Anal. Chim. Acta* 172 (1985):353.
15. Nomura, T.; Watanabe, M.; and West, T.S. *Anal. Chim. Acta* 175 (1985):107.
16. Nomura, T.; Okuhara, T.; and Hasegawa, T. *Anal. Chim. Acta* 182 (1986):261.
17. Nomura, T., and Sakai, M. *Anal. Chim. Acta* 183 (1986):301.
18. Bruckenstein, S., and Swathirajan, S. *Electrochim. Acta* 30 (1985):851.
19. Bruckenstein, S., and Shay, M. *J. Electroanal. Chem.* 188 (1985):131.
20. Bruckenstein, S., and Shay, M. *Electrochim. Acta* 30 (1985):1295.
21. Kaufman, J. H.; Kanazawa, K.; and Street, G. B. *Phys. Rev. Lett.* 53 (1984):2461.
22. Melroy, O., et al. *Langmuir* 2 (1986):697.
23. Orata, D., and Buttry, D.A. *J. Am. Chem. Soc.* 109

(1987):3574.
24. Varineau, P.T., and Buttry, D.A. *J. Phys. Chem.* 91 (1987):1292.
25. Lasky, S.J., and Buttry, D.A. *J. Am. Chem. Soc.* 110 (1988):6258.
26. Buttry, D.A.; Nordyke, L.; and Donohue, J.J. *Proceedings of the Second Chemically Modified Surfaces Symposium*, ed. W. Collins and D. Leyden. New York: Gordon and Breach, 1988.
27. Donohue, J.J., and Buttry, D.A. *Langmuir* 5 (1989):671.
28. Ostrom, G.S., and Buttry, D.A. *J. Electroanal. Chem.* 256 (1988):411.
29. Lasky, S.J., and Buttry, D.A. *Chemical Sensors and Microinstrumentation*, ed. R.W. Murray et al. ACS Symposium Series No. 403, Chap. 16, p. 237, Washington, D.C.: American Chemical Society, 1989.
30. Reference 1, page 31.
31. See, for example, Morrison, R. *Grounding and Shielding Techniques in Instrumentation*, 3rd edition. New York: Wiley Interscience, 1987.
32. Donohue, J.J., and Buttry, D.A. Unpublished data.
33. Sauerbrey, G.Z. *Phys.* 155 (1959):206.
34. Miller, J.G., and Bolef, D.I. *J. Appl. Phys.* 39 (1968):5815.
35. Lu, C., and Lewis, O. *J. Appl. Phys.* 43 (1972):4385.
36. Lu, C. *J. Vac. Sci. Tech.* 12 (1975):578.
37. A. Kanazawa, K.K., and Gordon, J.G. *Anal. Chem.* 57 (1985):1770. B. Kanazawa, K.K., preprint.
38. O' Donnell, M.; Busse, L.; and Miller, J.G. In *Methods of Experimental Physics*, ed. L. Marton, and C. Marton, Vol. 19:29. New York: Academic Press, 1981.
39. Pulkner, H.K, et al. *Thin Solid Films* 32 (1976):27.
40. Ullevig, D.M., Evans, J.F., and Albrecht, M.G. *Anal. Chem.* 54 (1982):2341.
41. Schumacher, R., Mueller, A. and Stoeckel, W. *J. Electroanal. Chem.* 219 (1987):311.
42. Benje, M., et al. *Ber. Bunsen Phys. Chem.* 90 (1986):435.
43. Schumacher, R., Borges, G., and Kanazawa, K. *Surf. Sci.* 163 (1985):L621.
44. Schumacher, R., Gordon, J.G., and Melroy, O. *J. Electroanal. Chem.* 216 (1987):127.
45. Deakin, M.R., and Melroy, O. *J. Electroanal. Chem.* 239 (1988):321.
46. Zei, M.S., et al. *Ber. Bunsen Phys. Chem.* 91 (1987):349

47. Deakin, M., and Melroy, O. *J. Electroanal. Chem.* 243 (1988):343.
48. Helfferich, F. *Ion Exchange*, New York: McGraw-Hill, 1962.
49. Bruckenstein, S., and Hillman, A.R. *J. Phys. Chem.* 92 (1988):4837.
50. Reference 48, page 133.
51. Reference 48, page 135.
52. Varineau, P.T., and Buttry, D.A.   Manuscript in preparation.
53. Orata, D.O., and Buttry, D.A. *J. Electroanal. Chem.* 257 (1988):71.
54. See: Humphrey, B.D.; Sinha, S., and Bocarsly, A.B. *J. Phys. Chem.* 91, (1987):586, and references therein.
55. Humphrey, B.D.; Sinha, S.; and Bocarsly, A.B. *J. Phys. Chem.* 88 (1984):736.

INDEX